Understanding College Algebra

Fifth Edition

Michael L. Levitan

Villanova University

Dr. Tracy Wang

Curry College

BVT
PUBLISHING

Custom Publishing Division

Requests for permission to make copies of any part of this work should be mailed to Permissions Department, BVT Publishing, LLC, P.O. Box 492831, Redding, CA 96049-2831.

MANAGING EDITOR: Traci Sartain

PROJECT EDITOR: Paul Bedard

TEXT AND COVER PRINTING: Lightning Source

TYPESETTING: Rhonda Minnema

Printed in the United States of America

Understanding College Algebra, Fifth Edition

ISBN: 978-1-59602-611-7

To All Curry College Students

Contents

Chapter 3 ▪ Functions   147

Chapter 4 ▪ Polynomial Functions   233

Chapter 5 ▪ Rational, Exponential, and Logarithmic Functions   297

Chapter 6 ■ Systems of Equations and Inequalities   391

Preface

This fifth edition of *Understanding College Algebra* maintains our objective of providing a textbook designed for use *by the student*. The book is written in a supportive style and includes abundant pedagogic tools to encourage the student to read the text with care, follow the numerous examples, and tackle the exercises. The skills and confidence the student acquires will enable him or her to succeed in more advanced mathematics courses (calculus in particular) that are required in the study of engineering, the natural sciences, business, and management.

New to This Edition

This edition increases emphasis on incorporating graphing calculators as powerful problem-solving and visualization tools, without sacrificing the emphasis of the author on traditional approaches. New exercises, as well as attention-grabbing chapter openings and projects, have been added to help instructors and students make connections between algebra and the real world.

- More than 80 new exercises, many of which incorporate updated features of graphing calculators, including several *Mathematics in Writing* questions to encourage critical thinking.

- An expanded chapter opening for each chapter, which will motivate the topics discussed in the chapter. The openers include useful references to reliable mathematics and mathematics-related websites. A significant feature of these openers is the emphasis on how mathematics is being used to design and understand our world and our future, particularly in the area of technology. The intent is for the students to make connections and see the applicability of the subject.

- New chapter projects for each chapter, related to the chapter opening material, which will give the instructor a focus and show students how the topics in the chapter can be used in the real world. These projects include applications in computer graphics, biology, computer networks, and many other areas of scientific and mathematical interest. The project can be used by instructors to bring the ideas of the chapter into sharper focus, and to continue the motivation provided by the chapter openers.

- Updated graphing calculator sections which give students new options for problem-solving while continuing to emphasize "classic" approaches. These include more graphics captured directly from calculator screens. The use of calculators to solve systems of equations, perform matrix operations, visualize solutions to inequalities, quickly generate sequences and partial sums, and much more, will give instructors and students more options, and help integrate this vital teaching tool wherever it is reasonable to do so.

Increased Use of Technology

Because many students now have access to graphing calculators, the new graphing calculator material gives instructors a flexible approach for incorporating this technology into their course design. This material, written by Paul Bedard of St. Clair Community College, provides basic and advanced instructions, as well as numerous exercises. Each *Graphing Calculator Alert* section instructs students how to use their graphing calculator effectively. Each *Power User's Corner* section illustrates the special features of the graphing calculator in more advanced calculations. More than 350 exercises, marked with a special icon, give students a chance to practice using their calculators to explore essential algebra concepts graphically.

Pedagogic Tools

Useful features from earlier editions have been retained and enhanced.

- Concepts are introduced gradually, supported by fully worked examples, figures and realistic applications to help students build problem-solving skills.

- Many algebraic procedures are described with the aid of a "split screen" that displays, side by side, both the steps of an algorithm and a worked-out example.

- Numerous applied problems from a variety of fields, written by Marilyn Belkin of Villanova University, Nina Edelman of Spring Garden College, and John Santomas of Villanova University.

- A *Progress Check* following many worked-out examples provides an exercise with its answer, enabling the student to test his or her understanding of the material just explained.

- *Warnings* reinforce good mathematical habits by pointing out incorrect practices most commonly found in homework and exams.

- Numerous vignettes have been included throughout the book. These are independent of the text, yet are often related to the mathematical concepts discussed near where the vignettes appear. They are intended to provide some additional interesting material for the student and instructor.

- To help students check their understanding of the concepts, each chapter concludes with a list of terms and symbols and a list of key ideas for review. In addition, the *Chapter Review Exercises* and *Review Tests* give students a chance to practice what they have learned. The *Cumulative Review Exercises* at the end of every third chapter provide additional review practice.

Exercises

 Abundant, carefully graded exercises provide practice in the mechanical and conceptual aspects of algebra. Exercises requiring the use of a calculator or graphing calculator are indicated by the calculator icons shown to the left. Although some exercises require student skills in graphing as well as graphing calculators, the latter may be disregarded, if desired. Answers to selected odd-numbered exercises, review exercises, review tests and cumulative exercises appear in an appendix at the back of the book. Worked-out solutions to selected review exercises appear in a separate appendix at the back of the book. The solved *Review Exercises* reassure students that they have mastered the concepts in preparation for the *Review Tests*.

Supplementary Material

Students using *Understanding College Algebra,* fourth edition, may purchase the *Study Guide and Student Solutions Manual* by Cheryl Roberts of Northern Virginia Community College. It includes complete solutions to the odd-numbered exercises, to the graphing calculator exercises, and to every exercise in the *Chapter Reviews, Progress Checks,* and *Cumulative Review Exercises.* In addition, each chapter of this manual begins with ten additional *Practice Exercises* and ends with a *Chapter Test* containing 20–25 exercises. Solutions to the *Practice Exercises* and answers to the *Chapter Tests* are also included.

Instructors who adopt this text may receive, free of charge, the following items:

- The *Instructor's Resource Manual with Transparency Masters,* by Mohan Tikoo of Southeast Missouri State University, includes chapter-by-chapter lecture notes annotated with references to the appropriate *Algebra and Trigonometry* transparency masters. These lecture notes also contain advice for integrating graphing calculators into the course. In addition, this manual contains approximately 2500 test questions, including graphing calculator test questions, referenced by chapter and section to the text. The 100 transparency masters show the most essential figures from the text for use in classroom lectures.

- The *Instructor's Solutions Manual,* by Cheryl Roberts of Northern Virginia Community College, contains complete solutions to every exercise in the text.

—Michael Levitan,
Villanova University

Acknowledgments

The author and publisher wish to acknowledge the many helpful suggestions from faculty at a variety of institutions who have used the earlier editions of this book. these suggestions have strongly influenced the preparation of this edition. We look forward to continuing to receive comments and suggestions from faculty and students.

We also benefited greatly from the considered opinions of the following mathematicians who read parts or all of the initial draft of the revision:

Daniel D. Anderson	University of Iowa
Paul R. Boltz	Harrisburg Area Community College
Kate Danforth	Corning County College
Iris B. Fetta	Clemson University
Dean Franzen	University of Northern Iowa
Henry Hosek, Jr.	Purdue University–Calumet
Richard Katz	California State University–Los Angeles
Gary S. Kersting	Sacramento City College
Lynne Kotrous	Central Community College–Platte Campus
Jean Lane	Union County College–Cranford
Kurt Lewandowski	Clackamas Community College
Stanley M. Lukawecki	Clemson University
Melissa Richardson	Anne Arundel Community College
Marilyn Schiermeier	North Carolina State University
George L. Szoke	University of Akron
Mohan Tikoo	Southeast Missouri State University
Jan Vandever	South Dakota State University
Carroll Wells	Western Kentucky University
Bostwick F. Wyman	University of Ohio

The accuracy of the solutions to the worked examples and of the answers to the *Progress Checks* and *Exercises* have been verified independently by Sudhir Goel of Valdosta State College, Norma James of New Mexico State University, Ann Ostberg of Central Community College–Platte Campus, and Paul Bedard, St. Cloud Community College. The exercises and answers were checked again independently by

Hugo Sun	California State University–Fresno
Lynne Kotrous	Central Community College–Platte Campus
John Khalilian	University of Alabama–Tuscaloosa
Kerry Wyckoff	Brigham Young University

Although we trust that this process has increased the accuracy of the answer section as much as possible, all errors are our responsibility and we would appreciate hearing about them.

We want to thank Sue Boshers for typing portions of this manuscript. We also wish to express our appreciation to Paul Bedard, Project Editor, and Traci Sartain, Project Coordinator.

Furthermore, there is no doubt that Marjorie Woodall cheerfully and carefully prepared the index under some very demanding conditions.

Finally, we want to thank Mary Davis, our erudite grammarian, who had many helpful suggestions for the language and punctuation of this text.

—*Michael Levitan,*
Villanova University

To the Students

This book was written for you, and it gives you every possible chance to succeed. We would like to have you think of mathematics as a challenging game—but not as a spectator sport. This leads to our primary rule: *Read this textbook with a pencil and paper handy.* We illustrate every new idea or technique with fully worked-out examples. As you read the text, carefully follow the examples and then do the *Progress Check* boxes. The key to success in a math course is working problems, and the Progress Checks are there to provide immediate practice with the material you have just covered.

Your instructor will assign homework from the extensive selection of exercises that follows each section in the book. By doing many problems, you will develop the necessary skills in algebra, and your confidence will grow. Because algebraic techniques and concepts build on previous results, you cannot afford to skip any of the work.

To help prevent or eliminate improper habits and to help you avoid the errors that we see each term as we grade papers, we have interspersed *Warning* text throughout the book. These point out common errors and emphasize the correct methods to be used.

The material on calculators and graphing calculators will help you do your homework rapidly and with greater accuracy. It will also enable you to solve realistic problems, when the numbers involved are not always "nice."

There is important review material at the end of each chapter. The *Terms and Symbols* should all be familiar by the time you reach them. If your understanding of a term or symbol is hazy, use this section to find the place in text where it is introduced, then go back and review the material.

It is possible to become so involved with the details of techniques that you lose track of the broader concepts. The list of *Key Ideas for Review* at the end of each chapter will help you focus on the principal ideas.

The *Review Exercises* at the end of each chapter can be used as part of your preparation for examinations. If you get stuck on an exercise, see if there is a similar example worked out in the text. Alternatively, there may be a similar exercise in the *Review Exercises* numbered in **bold**. This indicates that a worked-out solution appears in the back of the book. You are then ready to try the *Review Test*. You will soon pinpoint weak spots and you can go back for further review and more exercises in those areas.

We believe that the eventual payoff of studying mathematics is an improved ability to tackle practical problems in your field of interest. To that end, this book places special emphasis on word problems, which so often trouble students. Algebra is the bridge to all other fields of mathematics, and the mastery of algebra is well worth your effort.

—*Michael Levitan,*
Villanova University

List of Graphing Calculator Topics

The graphing calculator material has been designed to give you a flexible approach to using this technology in your course. The *Graphing Calculator Alert* sections instruct students on using a graphing calculator effectively. The *Power User's Corner* sections illustrate the special features of the graphing calculator in more advanced calculations. The lists below show the locations of these two types of boxes and the topics they cover. The *Instructor's Manual* lists the exercises requiring the use of a graphing calculator and those for which it is optional.

Graphing Calculator Alert Topics

Section	Topic
2.2	Formulas
2.3	Quadratic Formula
2.5	Inequalities
3.1	Viewing Rectangles and Plotting Points
3.1	Function Graphs
3.1	Circle
3.3	Piecewise-Defined Function
3.3	Turning Points
3.4	Slope of a Line
3.4	Vertical Lines
4.2	Function Graphs
4.5	Complex Numbers
6.2	Evaluating e^x
6.3	Evaluating e^x with $\ln x$
7.1	Solving Equations with Zoom-In

Graphing Calculator Power User's Corner Topics

Section	Topic
3.5	Graphing Inverse Functions
4.2	Graphing Polynomial Functions
4.6	Analyzing Roots
4.7	Approximating Roots
5.1	Graphing Rational Functions
5.2	Graphing Circles
5.3	Graphing Parabolas
5.4	Graphing Ellipses and Hyperbolas
5.5	Graphing General Conic Sections
7.5	Solving Systems of Inequalities
8.1	Reduced Row Echelon Form
9.1	Partial Sums

CHAPTER 1

The Foundations of Algebra

http://mathworld
.wolfram.com
/Polynomial.html

Suppose you asked a friend of yours, who is a physics major, "How long does it take for a rock to reach the ground after being thrown into the air?" She will tell you that an object thrown straight up with a velocity of 20 meters per second would reach the ground in a little more than 4 seconds, if air resistance was not a factor. This is true, however, only on the Earth! What if we were on another planet, or even a large moon like Ganymede? An object thrown straight up from the surface of Ganymede, with the same initial velocity of 20 m/s, would take almost 20 seconds to reach the ground. (Check out the Chapter Project.)

If you asked your friend how she arrived at these conclusions, she could use words like *algebraic expression*, *factoring*, and *polynomial*. Before you read this chapter, explore one of these words at http://mathworld.wolfram.com/Polynomial.html. This site can help you discover the meanings of many other terms as well.

Many problems that each of us encounters in the real world require the use and understanding of mathematics. Often, the methods used to solve these problems share certain characteristics, and it is both helpful and important to focus on these similarities. Algebra is one branch of mathematics that enables us to learn basic problem-solving techniques applicable to a large variety of circumstances.

For example, if one starts with 2 apples and gets 3 more apples, how many apples does one have? If the travel time between Philadelphia and New York was 2 hours in the morning and 3 hours in the afternoon, how much time was spent traveling? The solution to the first problem is

$$2 \text{ apples} + 3 \text{ apples} = 5 \text{ apples}$$

The solution to the second problem is

$$2 \text{ hours} + 3 \text{ hours} = 5 \text{ hours}$$

Algebra focuses on the fact that

$$2x + 3x = 5x$$

It does not matter what meaning one gives to the symbol x.

Although this level of abstraction can create some difficulty, it is the nature of algebra that permits us to distill the essentials of problem solving into such rudimentary formulas. In the examples noted above, we used the *counting* or *natural numbers* as the number system needed to describe the problems. This number system is generally the first that one learns as a child. One can create other formulas for more general number systems.

We shall begin our presentation with a discussion of the *real number system* and its associated properties. We note a correspondence between the real numbers and the points on a real number line, and give a graphical presentation of this correspondence. The remainder of this chapter is devoted to a review of some fundamentals of algebra: the meaning and use of variables, algebraic expressions and polynomial forms, scientific notation, factoring, operations with algebraic fractions, and an introduction to the *complex number system*.

1.1   The Real Number System

Sets

We will need to use the notation and terminology of sets from time to time. A **set** is simply a collection of objects or numbers that are called the **elements** or **members** of the set. The elements of a set are written within braces so that the notation

$$A = \{4, 5, 6\}$$

tells us that the set A consists of the numbers 4, 5 and 6. The set

$$B = \{\text{Exxon, Ford, Zenith}\}$$

consists of the names of these three corporations. We also write $4 \in A$, which we read as "4 is a member of the set A." Similarly, Ford $\in B$ is read as "Ford is a member of the set B," and Chrysler $\notin B$ is read as "Chrysler is not a member of the set B."

If every element of a set A is also a member of a set B, then A is a **subset** of B. For example, the set of all robins is a subset of the set of all birds.

Example 1   Set Notation and Properties

The set C consists of the names of all coins whose denominations are less than 50 cents. We may write C in set notation as follows:

$$C = \{\text{penny, nickel, dime, quarter}\}$$

We see that dime $\in C$, but half dollar $\notin C$. Further, the set $H = \{\text{nickel, dime}\}$ is a subset of C.

✔ Progress Check

The set V consists of the vowels in this particular sentence.

a. Write V in set notation.

b. Is the letter k a member of V?

c. Is the letter u a member of V?

d. List the subsets of V having four elements.

Answers

a. V = {a, e, i, o, u}   b. No   c. Yes

d. {a, e, i, o}, {e, i, o, u}, {a, i, o, u}, {a, e, o, u}, {a, e, i, u}

The Set of Real Numbers

Since much of our work in algebra deals with the real numbers, we begin with a review of the composition of these numbers.

The numbers 1, 2, 3, . . . , used for counting, form the set of **natural numbers**. If we had only these numbers to use to show the profit earned by a company, we would have no way to indicate that the company had no profit or had a loss. To indicate no profit we introduce 0, and for losses we need to introduce negative numbers. The numbers

$$\ldots, -2, -1, 0, 1, 2, \ldots$$

form the set of **integers**. Thus, every natural number is an integer, and the set of natural numbers is seen to be a subset of the set of integers.

When we try to divide two apples equally among four people we find no number in the set of integers that expresses how many apples each person should get. We need to introduce the set of **rational numbers**, which are numbers that can be written as a ratio of two integers,

$$\frac{p}{q}, \quad \text{with } q \text{ not equal to zero}$$

Examples of rational numbers are

$$0 \quad \frac{2}{3} \quad -4 \quad \frac{7}{5} \quad \frac{-3}{4}$$

By writing an integer n in the form $\frac{n}{1}$, we see that every integer is a rational number. The decimal number 1.3 is also a rational number, since $1.3 = \frac{13}{10}$.

We have now seen three fundamental sets of numbers: the set of natural numbers, the set of integers, and the set of rational numbers. Each successive set includes the previous set or sets, and each is more complicated than the one before. However, the set of rational numbers is still inadequate for sophisticated uses of mathematics, since there exist numbers that are not rational, that is, numbers that cannot be written as the ratio of two integers. These are called **irrational numbers**. It can be shown that the number a that satisfies $a \cdot a = 2$ is such a number. The number π, which is the ratio of the circumference of a circle to its diameter, is also such a number.

The decimal form of a rational number always forms a repeating pattern, such as

$$\frac{1}{2} = 0.5000\ldots$$

$$\frac{13}{10} = 1.3000\ldots$$

$$\frac{1}{3} = 0.333\ldots$$

$$\frac{-2}{11} = -0.181818\ldots$$

(*Note:* The three dots, known as ellipses, following the numbers in each of the examples above means that the pattern continues in the same manner forever.)

The decimal form of an irrational number *never* forms a repeating pattern. The rational and irrational numbers together form the set of **real numbers**. (See Figure 1.)

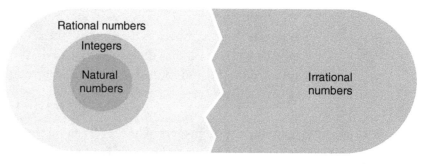

Figure 1   The Set of Real Numbers

Calculator Alert

(1) Rational Numbers

A calculator display shows only a finite number of digits, which is often an approximation of the exact answer. Use your calculator to convert the rational numbers $\frac{1}{2}$, $\frac{13}{10}$, $\frac{1}{3}$, and $\frac{-2}{11}$ to decimal form and note how these representations differ from those shown above.

$$1 \div 2 = 0.5$$

$$13 \div 10 = 1.3$$

$$1 \div 3 = 0.3333333333$$

$$-2 \div 11 = -0.1818181818$$

Which representations are exact and which are approximate?

(2) Irrational Numbers

Most calculators provide a rational decimal *approximation* to irrational numbers. For example, ten-digit approximations to $\sqrt{2}$ and π are

$$\sqrt{2} = 1.414213562$$

$$\pi = 3.141592654$$

The System of Real Numbers

The system of real numbers consists of the set of real numbers together with the operations of addition and multiplication; in addition, this system satisfies the properties listed in Table 1, where a, b and c denote real numbers.

Example 2   Properties of Real Numbers

Specify the property in Table 1 illustrated by each of the following statements.

a. $2 + 3 = 3 + 2$

b. $(2 \cdot 3) \cdot 4 = 2 \cdot (3 \cdot 4)$

c. $2 \cdot \dfrac{1}{2} = 1$

d. $2(3 + 5) = 2 \cdot 3 + 2 \cdot 5$

Solution

a. commutative under addition

c. multiplicative inverse

b. associative law under multiplication

d. distributive law

Table 1 Properties of Real Numbers

Example	Algebraic Expression	Property
$3 + 4$ is a real number.	$a + b$ is a real number.	**Closure under addition** The sum of two real numbers is a real number.
$2 \cdot 5$ is a real number.	$a \cdot b$ is a real number.	**Closure under multiplication** The product of two real numbers is a real number.
$4 + 8 = 8 + 4$	$a + b = b + a$	**Commutative under addition** We may add real numbers in any order.
$3(5) = 5(3)$	$a(b) = b(a)$	**Commutative under multiplication** We may multiply real numbers in any order.
$(2 + 5) + 3 = 2 + (5 + 3)$	$(a + b) + c = a + (b + c)$	**Associative under addition** We may group the addition of real numbers in any order.
$(2 \cdot 5)3 = 2(5 \cdot 3)$	$(ab)c = a(bc)$	**Associative under multiplication** We may group the multiplication of real numbers in any order.
$4 + 0 = 4$	$a + 0 = a$	**Additive identity** The sum of the unique real number 0 and any real number leaves that number unchanged.
$3(1) = 3$	$a(1) = a$	**Multiplicative identity** The product of the unique real number 1 and any real number leaves that number unchanged.
$5 + (-5) = 0$	$a + (-a) = 0$	**Additive inverse** The number $-a$ is called the **negative, opposite,** or **additive inverse** of a. If $-a$ is added to a, the result is the additive identity 0.
$7\left(\dfrac{1}{7}\right) = 1$	If $a \neq 0$, $a\left(\dfrac{1}{a}\right) = 1$	**Multiplicative inverse** The number $\frac{1}{a}$ is called the **reciprocal,** or **multiplicative inverse,** of a. If $\frac{1}{a}$ is multiplied by a, the result is the multiplicative identity 1.
$2(5 + 3) = (2 \cdot 5) + (2 \cdot 3)$ $(4 + 7)2 = (4 \cdot 2) + (7 \cdot 2)$	$a(b + c) = ab + ac$ $(a + b)c = ac + bc$	**Distributive laws** If one number multiplies the sum of two numbers, we may add the two numbers first and then perform the multiplication or we may multiply each pair and then add the two products.

Equality

When we say that two numbers are **equal,** we mean that they represent the same value. Thus, when we write

$$a = b$$

(read "a equals b"), we mean that a and b represent the same number. For example, $2 + 5$ and $4 + 3$ are different ways of writing the number 7, so we can write

$$2 + 5 = 4 + 3$$

Equality satisfies four basic properties shown in Table 2, where a, b and c are any real numbers.

Example 3   Properties of Equality
Specify the property in Table 2 illustrated by each of the following statements.

a. If $5a - 2 = b$, then $b = 5a - 2$.

b. If $a = b$ and $b = 5$, then $a = 5$.

c. If $a = b$, then $3a + 6 = 3b + 6$.

Solution
a. symmetric property   b. transitive property   c. substitution property

Additional Properties

Using the properties of real numbers, the properties of equalities, and rules of logic, we can derive many other properties of the real numbers, as shown in Table 3, where a, b, and c are any real numbers.

Table 2   Properties of Equality

Example	Algebraic Expression	Property
$3 = 3$	$a = a$	Reflexive property
If $\frac{6}{3} = 2$ then $2 = \frac{6}{3}$.	If $a = b$ then $b = a$.	Symmetric property
If $\frac{6}{3} = 2$ and $2 = \frac{8}{4}$, then $\frac{6}{3} = \frac{8}{4}$	If $a = b$ and $b = c$, then $a = c$.	Transitive property
If $\frac{6}{3} = 2$, then we may replace $\frac{6}{3}$ by 2 or we may replace 2 by $\frac{6}{3}$.	If $a = b$, then we may replace a by b or we may replace b by a.	Substitution property

Table 3   Additional Properties of Real Numbers

Example	Algebraic Expression	Property
If $\frac{6}{3} = 2$ then $\frac{6}{3} + 4 = 2 + 4$ $\frac{6}{3}(5) = 2(5)$	If $a = b$, then $a + c = b + c$ $ac = bc$	The same number may be added to both sides of an equation. Both sides of an equation may be multiplied by the same number.
If $\frac{6}{3} + 4 = 2 + 4$ then $\frac{6}{3} = 2$.	If $a + c = b + c$ then $a = b$.	Cancellation law of addition
If $\frac{6}{3}(5) = 2(5)$ then $\frac{6}{3} = 2$.	If $ac = bc$ with $c \neq 0$ then $a = b$.	Cancellation law of multiplication
$2(0) = 0(2) = 0$ $2(3) = 0$ is impossible.	$a(0) = 0(a) = 0$ If $ab = 0$ then $a = 0$ or $b = 0$.	The product of two real numbers can be zero only if one of them is zero. The real numbers a and b are said to be **factors** of the product ab.
$-(-3) = 3$	$-(-a) = a$	Rules of signs
$(-2)(3) = (2)(-3) = -6$	$(-a)(b) = (a)(-b) = -(ab)$	
$(-1)(3) = -3$	$(-1)(a) = -a$	
$(-2)(-3) = 6$	$(-a)(-b) = ab$	
$(-2) + (-3) = -(2 + 3) = -5$	$(-a) + (-b) = -(a + b)$	

We next introduce the operations of subtraction and division. If a and b are real numbers, the *difference* between a and b, denoted by $a - b$, is defined by

$$a - b = a + (-b)$$

and the operation is called *subtraction*. Thus,

$$6 - 2 = 6 + (-2) = 4 \qquad 2 - 2 = 0 \qquad 0 - 8 = -8$$

We can show that the distributive laws hold for subtraction, that is,

$$a(b - c) = ab - ac$$
$$(a - b)c = ac - bc$$

Calculator Alert

In addition to a key for subtraction, most calculators have a key to represent negative numbers. This key may be labeled $\boxed{+/-}$, $\boxed{(-)}$, or $\boxed{\text{CHS}}$. We write –6, for example, to represent the keystrokes necessary to enter a negative number into your calculator. You must select the keystrokes that are appropriate for your calculator.

If a and b are real numbers and $b \neq 0$, then the *quotient* of a and b, denoted $\frac{a}{b}$ or a/b, is defined by

$$\frac{a}{b} = a \cdot \frac{1}{b}$$

and the operation is called *division*. We also write $\frac{a}{b}$ as $a \div b$ and speak of the *fraction a over b*. The numbers a and b are called the *numerator* and *denominator* of the fraction $\frac{a}{b}$, respectively. Observe that we have not defined division by zero, since 0 has no reciprocal.

In Table 4, a, b, c and d are real numbers with $b \neq 0$, $c \neq 0$, and $d \neq 0$.

✔ Progress Check

Perform the indicated operations.

a. $\dfrac{3}{5} + \dfrac{1}{4}$ b. $\dfrac{5}{2} \cdot \dfrac{4}{15}$ c. $\dfrac{2}{3} + \dfrac{3}{7}$

Answers

a. $\dfrac{17}{20}$ b. $\dfrac{2}{3}$ c. $\dfrac{23}{21}$

Table 4 Additional Properties of Real Numbers

Example	Algebraic Expression	Property
$\dfrac{6}{10} = \dfrac{2 \cdot 3}{2 \cdot 5} = \dfrac{3}{5}$	$\dfrac{ac}{bc} = \dfrac{a}{b}$	Rules of fractions
$\dfrac{2}{3} \cdot \dfrac{5}{7} = \dfrac{10}{21}$	$\dfrac{a}{b} \cdot \dfrac{c}{d} = \dfrac{ac}{bd}$	
$\dfrac{4}{6} = \dfrac{2}{3}$ since $4 \cdot 3 = 6 \cdot 2$	$\dfrac{a}{b} = \dfrac{c}{d}$ if $ad = bc$	
$\dfrac{2}{9} + \dfrac{5}{9} = \dfrac{7}{9}$	$\dfrac{a}{b} + \dfrac{c}{b} = \dfrac{a+c}{b}$	
$\dfrac{\frac{2}{9}}{\frac{5}{9}} = \dfrac{\frac{2}{9}}{\frac{5}{9}} \cdot \dfrac{(9)}{(9)} = \dfrac{2}{5}$	$\dfrac{\frac{a}{d}}{\frac{b}{d}} = \dfrac{\frac{a}{d}}{\frac{b}{d}} \cdot \dfrac{(d)}{(d)} = \dfrac{a}{b}$	
$\dfrac{2}{3} + \dfrac{5}{4} = \dfrac{2}{3} \cdot \dfrac{(4)}{(4)} + \dfrac{5}{4} \cdot \dfrac{(3)}{(3)}$	$\dfrac{a}{b} + \dfrac{c}{d} = \dfrac{a}{b} \cdot \dfrac{(d)}{(d)} + \dfrac{c}{d} \cdot \dfrac{(b)}{(b)}$	
$\qquad = \dfrac{8}{12} + \dfrac{15}{12} = \dfrac{23}{12}$	$\qquad = \dfrac{ad + cb}{bd}$	
$\dfrac{\frac{2}{3}}{\frac{5}{7}} = \dfrac{\frac{2}{3}}{\frac{5}{7}} \cdot \dfrac{(3 \cdot 7)}{(3 \cdot 7)} = \dfrac{2(7)}{5(3)} = \dfrac{14}{15}$	$\dfrac{\frac{a}{b}}{\frac{c}{d}} = \dfrac{\frac{a}{b}}{\frac{c}{d}} \cdot \dfrac{(bd)}{(bd)} = \dfrac{ad}{cb}$	

Exercise Set 1.1

In Exercises 1–8, write each set by listing its elements within braces.

1. The set of natural numbers from 3 to 7, inclusive.

2. The set of integers between −4 and 2.

3. The set of integers between −10 and −8.

4. The set of natural numbers from −9 to 3, inclusive.

5. The subset of the set $S = \{-3, -2, -1, 0, 1, 2\}$ consisting of the positive integers in S.

6. The subset of the set $S = \{-\frac{2}{3}, -1.1, 3.7, 4.8\}$ consisting of the negative rational numbers in S.

7. The subset of all $x \in S$, $S = \{1, 3, 6, 7, 10\}$, such that x is an odd integer.

8. The subset of all $x \in S$, $S = \{2, 5, 8, 9, 10\}$ such that x is an even integer.

In Exercises 9–22, determine whether the given statement is true (T) or false (F).

9. −14 is a natural number.

10. $-\frac{4}{5}$ is a rational number.

11. $\frac{\pi}{3}$ is a rational number.

12. $\frac{1.75}{18.6}$ is an irrational number.

13. −1207 is an integer.

14. 0.75 is an irrational number.

15. $\frac{4}{5}$ is a real number.

16. 3 is a rational number.

17. 2π is a real number.

18. The sum of two rational numbers is always a rational number.

19. The sum of two irrational numbers is always an irrational number.

20. The product of two rational numbers is always a rational number.

21. The product of two irrational numbers is always an irrational number.

22. The difference of two irrational numbers is always an irrational number.

In Exercises 23–36, the letters represent real numbers. Identify the property or properties of real numbers that justify each statement.

23. $a + x = x + a$

24. $(xy)z = x(yz)$

25. $xyz + xy = xy(z + 1)$ is a real number

26. $x + y$

27. $(a + b) + 3 = a + (b + 3)$

28. $5 + (x + y) = (x + y) + 5$

29. cx is a real number.

30. $(a + 5) + b = (a + b) + 5$

31. $uv = vu$

32. $x + 0 = x$

33. $a(bc) = c(ab)$

34. $xy - xy = 0$

35. $5 \cdot \dfrac{1}{5} = 1$

36. $xy \cdot 1 = xy$

In Exercises 37–40, find a counterexample, that is, find real values for which the statement is false.

37. $a - b = b - a$

38. $\dfrac{a}{b} = \dfrac{b}{a}$

39. $a(b + c) = ab + c$

40. $(a + b)(c + d) = ac + bd$

In Exercises 41–44, indicate the property or properties of equality that justify the statement.

41. If $3x = 5$, then $5 = 3x$.

42. If $x + y = 7$ and $y = 5$, then $x + 5 = 7$.

43. If $2y = z$ and $z = x + 2$, then $2y = x + 2$.

44. If $x + 2y + 3z = r + s$ and $r = x + 1$, then $x + 2y + 3z = x + 1 + s$.

In Exercises 45–49, a, b and c are real numbers. Use the properties of real numbers and the properties of equality to prove each statement.

45. If $-a = -b$, then $ac = bc$.

46. If $a = b$ and $c \neq 0$, then $\dfrac{a}{c} = \dfrac{b}{c}$.

47. If $a - c = b - c$, then $a = b$.

48. $a(b - c) = ab - ac$

49. Prove that the real number 0 does not have a reciprocal. (*Hint*: Assume $b = \frac{1}{0}$ is the reciprocal of 0. Supply a reason for each of the following steps.

$$1 = 0 \cdot \frac{1}{0}$$
$$= 0 \cdot b$$
$$= 0$$

Since this conclusion is impossible, the original assumption must be false.)

50. Give three examples for each of the following:

   a. a real number that is not a rational number

   b. a rational number that is not an integer

   c. an integer that is not a natural number

51. Give three examples for each of the following:

   a. two rational numbers that are not integers whose sum is an integer

   b. two irrational numbers whose sum is a rational number

52. Find a subset of the reals that is closed with respect to addition and multiplication but not with respect to subtraction and division.

 53. Perform the indicated operations. Verify your answers using your calculator.

   a. $(-8) + 13$

   b. $(-8) + (-13)$

   c. $8 - (-13)$

   d. $(-5)(3) - (-12)$

   e. $\left(\dfrac{8}{9} + 3\right) + \left(\dfrac{-5}{9}\right)$

   f. $\dfrac{\frac{-5}{3}}{2}$

   g. $\dfrac{\frac{5}{8}}{\frac{1}{2}}$

   h. $\dfrac{\frac{-2}{3}}{\frac{-4}{3}}$

   i. $\left(\dfrac{3}{4}\right)\left(\dfrac{21}{37}\right) + \left(\dfrac{3}{4}\right)\left(\dfrac{16}{37}\right)$

   j. $\dfrac{\frac{1}{3} - \left(\frac{-1}{4}\right)}{\frac{7}{8} - \frac{3}{16}}$

   k. $\dfrac{\left(\frac{3}{5}\right)\left(\frac{1}{7}\right)}{\frac{1}{2} + \frac{1}{3}}$

   l. $\dfrac{2}{5}\left(\dfrac{3}{2} \cdot \dfrac{4}{7}\right)$

54. What is the meaning attached to each of the following?

a. $\dfrac{6}{0}$

b. $\dfrac{0}{6}$

c. $\dfrac{6}{6}$

d. $\dfrac{0}{\frac{1}{2}}$

e. $\dfrac{0}{0}$

55. Use your calculator to convert the following fractions to (repeating) decimals. Look for a pattern that repeats.

a. $\dfrac{1}{4}$ b. $-\dfrac{3}{5}$ c. $\dfrac{10}{13}$ d. $\dfrac{2}{7}$

e. Does your calculator round off the final digit of an approximation, or does your calculator "drop off" the extra digits? To answer this question, evaluate $2 \div 3$ to see if your calculator displays 0.6666666666 or 0.6666666667.

56. A proportion is a statement of equality between two ratios. Solve the following proportions for x.

a. $\dfrac{7}{8} = \dfrac{x}{12}$

b. $\dfrac{7}{x} = \dfrac{11}{3}$

57. On a map of Pennsylvania, 1 inch represents 10 miles. Find the distance represented by 3.5 inches.

58. A car travels 93 miles on 6 gallons of gasoline. How far can it travel on 10 gallons of gasoline?

59. A board 10 feet long is cut into two pieces, the lengths of which are in the ratio of 2 : 3. Find the lengths of the pieces.

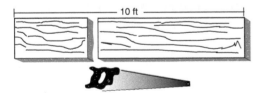

60. An alloy is $\frac{3}{8}$ copper, $\frac{5}{12}$ zinc, and the balance lead. How much lead is there in 282 pounds of alloy?

 61. Which is the better value: 1 pound 3 ounces of beans for 49 cents or 13 ounces for 35 cents?

 62. A piece of property is valued at $28,500. What is the real estate tax at $75.30 per $1000.00 evaluation?

63. A woman's take-home pay is $210.00 after deducting 18% withholding tax. What is her pay before the deduction?

64. List the set of possible ways of getting a total of 7 when tossing two standard dice.

Applications 1.1

1. The enrollment at Curry College was increased by 4.2% over the last year's enrollment of 1679. Find the increase in enrollment and the current enrollment.

2. The estimated population in Boston was increased from 559,034 in 2005 to 654,169 in 2009. Find the percent of increase.

3. As of March 25, 2001, the Total Public Debt Outstanding of the United States of America was $14.26 trillion and was 97.3% of calendar year 2010's annual gross domestic product (GDP). Find 2010's GDP.

4. A daily cost C of renting a car is $29.99 plus $0.20 per mile traveled. If m is the number of miles traveled, then $C = 29.99 + 0.20m$. If you paid $61.79 for a one day rental, how many miles did you travel?

Use the following information for problems #5–#8.

1 all-beef frank: +50 calories
1 slice of bread: +68 calories

Run (1 minute): –15 calories
Swim (1 minute): –13 calories

5. If a person eats 3 beef franks and runs for 10 minutes, what is the caloric gain or loss? State your answer in a complete sentence.

6. If a person eats 5 slices of bread and runs for 15 minutes, what is the caloric gain or loss? State your answer in a complete sentence.

7. If a person eats 4 beef franks and swims for 7 minutes, what is the caloric gain or loss? State your answer in a complete sentence.

8. If a person eats 2 beef franks in 4 slices of bread and then runs for 22 minutes, what is the caloric gain or loss? State your answer in a complete sentence.

1.2   The Real Number Line

There is a simple and very useful geometric interpretation of the real number system. Draw a horizontal line. Pick a point on this line, label it with the number 0, and call it the **origin**. Designate the side to the right of the origin as the *positive direction* and the side to the left as the *negative direction*.

Next, select a unit for measuring distance. With each positive integer n, we associate the point that is n units to the right of the origin. With each negative number $-n$, we associate the point that is n units to the left of the origin. Rational numbers, such as $\frac{3}{4}$ and $-\frac{5}{2}$, are associated with the corresponding points by dividing the intervals between integers into equal subintervals. Irrational numbers, such as $\sqrt{2}$ and π, can be written in decimal form. The corresponding points can be found by approximating these decimal forms to any desired degree of accuracy. Thus, the set of real numbers is identified with all possible points on this line. There is a real number for every point on the line; there is a point on the line for every real number. The line is called the **real number line**, and the number associated with a point is called its *coordinate*. We can now show some points on this line.

Negative direction •—•—•—|—|—•—•—•—•—•—→ Positive direction
$-\frac{5}{2}$ $\frac{3}{4}$ $\sqrt{2}$ π
-3 -2 -1 0 1 2 3

The numbers to the right of zero are called *positive;* the numbers to the left of zero are called *negative*. The positive numbers and zero together are called the **nonnegative numbers**.

We will frequently use the real number line to help picture the results of algebraic computations. For this purpose, we are only concerned with relative locations on the line. For example, it is adequate to show π slightly to the right of 3 since π is approximately 3.14.

Example 1   Real Number Line
Draw a real number line and plot the following points: $-\frac{3}{2}, 2, \frac{13}{4}$.

Solution

Inequalities

If a and b are real numbers, we can compare their positions on the real number line by using the relations *less than, greater than, less than or equal to,* and *greater than or equal to,* as shown in Table 5.

Table 5   Inequalities

Symbol	Meaning
<	Less than
>	Greater than
≤	Less than or equal to
≥	Greater than or equal to

Table 6 describes both algebraic and geometric interpretations of the inequality symbols, where a and b are real numbers.

Expressions involving inequality symbols, such as $a < b$ and $a \geq b$, are called **inequalities**. We often combine these expressions so that $a \leq b < c$ means both $a \leq b$ and $b < c$. (*Note:* $a < c$ is also true.) For example, $-5 \leq x < 2$ is equivalent to $-5 \leq x$ and $x < 2$. Equivalently, x is between -5 and 2, including -5 and excluding 2.

✔ Progress Check

Verify that the following inequalities are true by using either the "Equivalent Statement" or the "Geometric Statement" of Table 6.

a. $-1 < 3$ b. $2 \leq 2$

c. $-2.7 < -1.2$ d. $-4 < -2 < 0$

e. $-\dfrac{7}{2} < \dfrac{7}{2} < 7$

Table 6   Inequalities

Algebraic Expression	Meaning	Equivalent Statement	Geometric Statement
$a > 0$	a is greater than 0.	a is positive.	a lies to the right of the origin.
$a < 0$	a is less than 0.	a is negative.	a lies to the left of the origin.
$a > b$	a is greater than b.	$a - b$ is positive.	a lies to the right of b.
$a < b$	a is less than b.	$a - b$ is negative.	a lies to the left of b.
$a \geq b$	a is greater than or equal to b.	$a - b$ is positive or zero.	a lies to the right of b or coincides with b.
$a \leq b$	a is less than or equal to b.	$a - b$ is negative or zero.	a lies to the left of b or coincides with b.

Table 7   Properties of Inequalities

Example	Algebraic Expression	Property
Either 2 < 3 , 2 > 3, or 2 = 3.	Either $a < b$, $a > b$, or $a = b$.	Trichotomy property
Since 2 < 3 and 3 < 5, then 2 < 5.	If $a < b$ and $b < c$ then $a < c$.	Transitive property
Since 2 < 5, then 2 + 4 < 5 + 4 or 6 < 9.	If $a < b$ then $a + c < b + c$.	The sense of an inequality is preserved if any constant is added to both sides.
Since 2 < 3 and 4 > 0, then 2(4) < 3(4) or 8 < 12.	If $a < b$ and $c > 0$, then $ac < bc$.	The sense of an inequality is preserved if it is multiplied by a positive constant.
Since 2 < 3 and −4 < 0, then 2(−4) > 3(−4) or −8 > −12.	If $a < b$ and $c < 0$, then $ac > bc$.	The sense of an inequality is reversed if it is multiplied by a negative constant.

The real numbers satisfy the properties of inequalities shown in Table 7, where a, b and c are real numbers.

Example 2   Properties of Inequalities

a. Since −2 < 4 and 4 < 5, then −2 < 5.

b. Since −2 < 5, −2 + 3 < 5 + 3, or 1 < 8.

c. Since 3 < 4, 3 + (−5) < 4 + (−5), or −2 < −1.

d. Since 2 < 5, 2(3) < 5(3), or 6 < 15.

e. Since −3 < 2, (−3)(−2) > 2(−2), or 6 > −4.

Absolute Value

Suppose we are interested in the *distances* between the origin and the points labeled 4 and −4 on the real number line. Each of these points is four units from the origin, that is, the *distance is independent of the direction* and is nonnegative. (See Figure 2.) Furthermore, the distance between 4 and −4 is 8 units.

When we are interested in the magnitude of a number a, and do not care about the direction or sign, we use the concept of **absolute value**, which we write as $|a|$. The formal definition of absolute value is stated as follows.

$$|a| = \begin{cases} a & \text{if } a \geq 0 \\ -a & \text{if } a < 0 \end{cases}$$

Since distance is independent of direction and is always nonnegative, we can view $|a|$ as the distance from the origin to either point a or point $-a$ on the real number line.

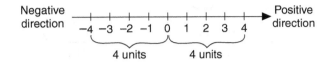

Figure 2   Distance on the Real Number Line

Example 3   Absolute Value and Distance

a. $|4| = 4$ $|-4| = 4$ $|0| = 0$

b. The distance on the real number line between the point labeled 3.4 and the origin is $|3.4| = 3.4$. Similarly, the distance between point −2.3 and the origin is $|-2.3| = 2.3$.

In working with the notation of absolute value, it is important to perform the operations within the bars first. Here are some examples.

Example 4   Absolute Value

a. $|5 - 2| = |3| = 3$

b. $|2 - 5| = |-3| = 3$

c. $|3 - 5| - |8 - 6| = |-2| - |2| = 2 - 2 = 0$

d. $\dfrac{|4 - 7|}{-6} = \dfrac{|-3|}{-6} = \dfrac{3}{-6} = -\dfrac{1}{2}$

Graphing Calculator Alert

Your calculator may have an absolute value key, usually labeled $\boxed{\text{ABS}}$. If you have a graphing calculator, it is important to use parentheses when you use this key.

Examples: a. ABS(5 − 2)

b. ABS(2 − 5)

c. ABS(3 − 5) − ABS(8 − 6)

d. ABS(4 − 7) ÷ (−6)

Table 8 describes the properties of absolute value where *a* and *b* are real numbers.

We began by showing a use for absolute value in denoting distance from the origin without regard to direction. We conclude by demonstrating the use of absolute value to denote the distance between *any* two points *a* and *b* on the real number line. In Figure 3, the distance between the points labeled 2 and 5 is 3 units and can be obtained by evaluating either $|5 - 2|$ or $|2 - 5|$. Similarly, the distance between the points labeled −1 and 4 is given by either $|4 - (-1)| = 5$ or $|-1 - 4| = 5$.

Table 8   Basic Properties of Absolute Value

Example	Algebraic Expression	Property
$\lvert -2 \rvert \geq 0$	$\lvert a \rvert \geq 0$	Absolute value is always nonnegative.
$\lvert 3 \rvert = \lvert -3 \rvert = 3$	$\lvert a \rvert = \lvert -a \rvert$	The absolute values of a number and its negative are the same.
$\lvert 2 - 5 \rvert = \lvert -3 \rvert = 3$ $\lvert 5 - 2 \rvert = \lvert 3 \rvert = 3$	$\lvert a - b \rvert = \lvert b - a \rvert$	The absolute value of the difference of two numbers is always the same, irrespective of the order of subtraction.
$\lvert (-2)(3) \rvert = \lvert -2 \rvert \lvert 3 \rvert = 6$	$\lvert ab \rvert = \lvert a \rvert \lvert b \rvert$	The absolute value of a product is the product of the absolute values.

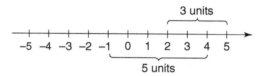

Figure 3   Distance on the Real Number Line

Using the notation $\overline{AB}$ to denote the distance between the points A and B, we provide the following definition.

Distance on the Real Number Line
The **distance** $\overline{AB}$ between points A and B on the real number line, whose coordinates are a and b, respectively, is given by

$$\overline{AB} = \lvert b - a \rvert$$

The third property of absolute value from Table 8 tells us that $\overline{AB} = \lvert b - a \rvert = \lvert a - b \rvert$. Viewed another way, this property states that the distance between any two points on the real number line is independent of the direction.

Example 5   Distance on the Real Number Line
Let points A, B and C have coordinates -4, -1 and 3, respectively, on the real number line. Find the following distances.

a. $\overline{AB}$ b. $\overline{CB}$ c. $\overline{OB}$, where O is the origin

Solution
Using the definition, we have

a. $\overline{AB} = \lvert -1 - (-4) \rvert = \lvert -1 + 4 \rvert = \lvert 3 \rvert = 3$

b. $\overline{CB} = \lvert -1 - 3 \rvert = \lvert -4 \rvert = 4$

c. $\overline{OB} = \lvert -1 - 0 \rvert = \lvert -1 \rvert = 1$

✔ **Progress Check**

The points P, Q and R on the real number line have coordinates –6, 4 and 6, respectively. Find the following distances.

a. $\overline{PR}$ b. $\overline{QP}$ c. $\overline{PQ}$

Answers

a. 12   b. 10   c. 10

Exercise Set 1.2

1. Draw a real number line and plot the following points.

    a. 4   b. –2

    c. $\dfrac{5}{2}$ d. –3.5

    e. 0

2. Draw a real number line and plot the following points.

    a. –5   b. 4

    c. –3.5   d. $\dfrac{7}{2}$

    e. –4

3. Give the real numbers associated with the points A, B, C, D, O and E on the real number line below.

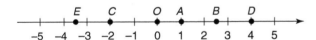

4. Represent the following by real numbers.

    a. a profit of $10

    b. a loss of $20

    c. a temperature of 20°F above zero

    d. a temperature of 5°F below zero

In Exercises 5–10, indicate which of the two given numbers appears first, viewed from left to right, on the real number line.

5. 4, 6   6. $\dfrac{1}{2}$, 0

7. $-2, \dfrac{3}{4}$ 8. 0, –4

9. $-5, -\dfrac{2}{3}$ 10. 4, –5

In Exercises 11–14, indicate the set of numbers on a real number line.

11. The natural numbers less than 8.

12. The natural numbers greater than 4 and less than 10.

13. The integers that are greater than 2 and less than 7.

14. The integers that are greater than –5 and less than or equal to 1.

In Exercises 15–24, express the statement as an inequality.

15. 10 is greater than 9.99.

16. –6 is less than –2.

17. a is nonnegative.

18. b is negative.

19. x is positive.

20. a is strictly between 3 and 7.

21. a is strictly between $\dfrac{1}{2}$ and $\dfrac{1}{4}$.

22. b is less than or equal to –4.

23. b is greater than or equal to 5.

24. x is negative.

In Exercises 25–30, give a property of inequalities that justifies the statement.

25. Since $-3 < 1$, then $-1 < 3$.

26. Since $-5 < -1$ and $-1 < 4$, then $-5 < 4$.

27. Since $14 > 9$, then $-14 < -9$.

28. Since $5 > 3$, then $5 \neq 3$.

29. Since $-1 < 6$, then $-3 < 18$.

30. Since $6 > -1$, then 7 is a positive number.

In Exercises 31–44, find the value of the expression. Verify your answer using your calculator.

31. $|2|$

32. $\left|-\dfrac{2}{3}\right|$

33. $|1.5|$

34. $|-0.8|$

35. $-|2|$

36. $-\left|-\dfrac{2}{5}\right|$

37. $|2-3|$

38. $|2-2|$

39. $|2-(-2)|$

40. $|2|+|-3|$

41. $\dfrac{|14-8|}{|-3|}$

42. $\dfrac{|2-12|}{|1-6|}$

43. $\dfrac{|3|-|2|}{|3|+|2|}$

44. $\dfrac{|3-2|}{|3+2|}$

In Exercises 45–50, the coordinates of points A and B are given. Find $\overline{AB}$.

45. $2, 5$

46. $-3, 6$

47. $-3, -1$

48. $-4, \dfrac{11}{2}$

49. $-\dfrac{4}{5}, \dfrac{4}{5}$

50. $2, 2$

51. For what values of x and y is $|x+y| = |x| + |y|$?

52. For what values of x and y is $|x+y| < |x| + |y|$?

53. Find the set of integers whose distance from 3 is less than or equal to 5.

54. List the set of integers x such that
    a. $-2 < x < 3$
    b. $0 < x < 5$
    c. $-1 < 2x < 10$

55. For the inequality $-1 < 5$, state the resulting inequality when the following operations are performed on both sides.
    a. add 2
    b. subtract 5
    c. multiply by 2
    d. multiply by -5
    e. divide by -1
    f. divide by 2
    g. square

56. A computer sales representative receives $400 monthly plus a 10% commission on sales. How much must she sell in a month for her income to be at least $600 for that month?

In Exercises 57–62, use the coordinates given in Exercises 45–50 to find the midpoint of the interval.

63. For what values of x does each of the following hold?
    a. $|3-x| = 3-x$ b. $|5x-2| = -(5x-2)$

64. Evaluate $\dfrac{|x-3|}{x-3}$ for $x = -2, -1, 0, 1, 2$. Make a conjecture about the value of this expression for all values of x.

Applications 1.2

1. For the set of integers whose distance from 10 is less than or equal of 7. Sketch your answer(s).

2. The highest point on Earth is Mount Everest, 8.85 kilometers above sea level. the lowest point is the marianas Trench in the Pacific, 10.91 kilometers below sea level. What is the distance between these two extremes?

3. Here are the temperature changes by the hour in Boston:

1 PM	2 PM	4 PM	5 PM	6 PM
+10	+7	+1	-3	-5

If the temperature was initially 45 degrees, what was it at 6:00 PM? What was the total temperature change from 1:00 PM to 6:00 PM? What was the net temperature change from 1:00 PM to 6:00 PM?

4. In the last 54 years the highest measured temperature in Boston for December was 24 degrees Celsius, most recently registered on December 7, 1998, while the typical high temperature is 5. The lowest documented temperature for Boston for the past 54 years in December was -27, most recently registered on December 30, 1933, and the typical low is -2. Find the difference between these extremes.

5. Joe's pizzeria is located on the tenth floor of a building. He got on the elevator and he went three floors up, four down, five up, and then seven floors down. What floor is Joe on now?

6. The price of the DELL Inc. stock at the beginning of a day was $15.47. Here are the changes in price during the day from 10 AM to 4 PM in every hour: +0.12, +0.89, +0.17, -0.24, -1.25, +0.02, -0.05. What was the price of the stock at the end of the day? If you are a "day trader", did you lose money? Explain your answer.

1.3 Algebraic Expressions; Polynomials

A **variable** is a symbol to which we can assign values. For example, in Section 1.1 we defined a rational number as one that can be written as $\frac{p}{q}$, where p and q are integers and q is not zero. The symbols p and q are variables, since we can assign values to them. A variable can be restricted to a particular number system (for example, p and q must be integers) or to a subset of a number system.

If we invest P dollars at an annual interest rate of 6%, then we will earn $0.06P$ dollars interest per year, and we will have $P + 0.06P$ dollars at the end of the year. We call $P + 0.06P$ an **algebraic expression**. Note that an algebraic expression involves **variables** (in this case P), **constants** (such as 0.06), and **algebraic operations** (such as $+, -, \times, \div$). Virtually everything we do in algebra involves algebraic expressions.

An algebraic expression takes on a **value** when we assign a specific number to each variable in the expression. Thus, the expression

$$\frac{3m + 4n}{m + n}$$

is **evaluated** when $m = 3$ and $n = 2$ by substitution of these values for m and n:

$$\frac{3(3) + 4(2)}{3 + 2} = \frac{9 + 8}{5} = \frac{17}{5}$$

We often need to write algebraic expressions in which a variable multiplies itself repeatedly. We use the notation of exponents to indicate such repeated multiplication. Thus,

$$a^1 = a \qquad a^2 = a \cdot a \qquad a^n = \underbrace{a \cdot a \cdot \cdots \cdot a}_{n \text{ factors}}$$

where n is a natural number and a is a real number. We call a the **base** and n the **exponent** and say that a^n is the nth **power** of a. When $n = 1$, we simply write a rather than a^1.

It is convenient to define a^0 for all real numbers $a \neq 0$ as $a^0 = 1$. We will provide motivation for this seemingly arbitrary definition in Section 1.7.

Example 1   Multiplication with Natural Number Exponents

Write without using exponents.

a. $\left(\dfrac{1}{2}\right)^3$ b. $2x^3$

c. $(2x)^3$ d. $-3x^2y^3$

Solution

a. $\left(\dfrac{1}{2}\right)^3 = \dfrac{1}{2} \cdot \dfrac{1}{2} \cdot \dfrac{1}{2} = \dfrac{1}{8}$ b. $2x^3 = 2 \cdot x \cdot x \cdot x$

c. $(2x)^3 = 2x \cdot 2x \cdot 2x = 8 \cdot x \cdot x \cdot x$ d. $-3x^2y^3 = -3 \cdot x \cdot x \cdot y \cdot y \cdot y$

Warning

Note the difference between

$$(-3)^2 = (-3)(-3) = 9$$

and

$$-3^2 = -(3 \cdot 3) = -9$$

Calculator Alert

Your calculator evaluates exponents using a special key, which may be labeled $\boxed{x^y}$, $\boxed{y^x}$, or $\boxed{\wedge}$.

Example: $(1 \div 2)\boxed{x^y}3 = 0.125$

or $(1 \div 2)\boxed{y^x}3 = 0.125$

or $(1 \div 2)\boxed{\wedge}3 = 0.125$

We will use $\boxed{x^y}$ or $\boxed{\wedge}$ to indicate the exponentiation key in this text.

In addition to the exponentiation key, your calculator probably has a special key labeled $\boxed{x^2}$.

Examples: $(-3)\boxed{x^2} = 9$

$-3\boxed{x^2} = -9$

Later in this chapter we will need an important rule of exponents. Observe that if m and n are natural numbers and a is any real number, then

$$a^m \cdot a^n = \underbrace{a \cdot a \cdot \cdots \cdot a}_{m \text{ factors}} \underbrace{a \cdot a \cdot \cdots \cdot a}_{n \text{ factors}}$$

Since there are a total of $m + n$ factors on the right side, we conclude that

$$a^m a^n = a^{m+n}$$

Example 2   Multiplication with Natural Number Exponents

Multiply.

a. $x^2 \cdot x^3$

b. $(3x)(4x^4)$

Solution

a. $x^2 \cdot x^3 = x^{2+3} = x^5$

b. $(3x)(4x^4) = 3 \cdot 4 \cdot x \cdot x^4 = 12x^{1+4} = 12x^5$

✔ Progress Check

Multiply.

a. $x^5 \cdot x^2$ b. $(2x^6)(-2x^4)$

Answers

a. x^7 b. $-4x^{10}$

Polynomials

A polynomial is an algebraic expression of a certain form. Polynomials play an important role in the study of algebra, since many word problems translate into equations or inequalities that involve polynomials. We first study the manipulative and mechanical aspects of polynomials. This knowledge will serve as background for dealing with their applications in later chapters.

Let x denote a variable and let n be a constant, nonnegative integer. The expression ax^n, where a is a constant real number, is called a **monomial in x**. A **polynomial in x** is an expression that is a sum of monomials and has the general form

$$P = a_n x^n + a_{n-1} x^{n-1} + \cdots + a_1 x + a_0, \qquad a_n \neq 0 \tag{1}$$

Each of the monomials in Equation (1) is called a **term** of P, and $a_0, a_1, \ldots, a_n$ are constant real numbers that are called the **coefficients** of the terms of P. Note that a polynomial may consist of just one term; that is, a monomial is considered to be a polynomial.

Example 3   Polynomial Expressions

a. The following expressions are polynomials in x:

$$3x^4 + 2x + 5 \qquad 2x^3 + 5x^2 - 2x + 1 \qquad \frac{3}{2}x^3$$

Notice that we write $2x^3 + 5x^2 + (-2)x + 1$ as $2x^3 + 5x^2 - 2x + 1$.

b. The following expressions are not polynomials in x:

$$2x^{1/2} + 5 \qquad 3 - \frac{4}{x} \qquad \frac{2x - 1}{x - 2}$$

Remember that each term of a polynomial in x must be of the form ax^n, where a is a real number and n is a nonnegative integer.

The **degree of a monomial in x** is the exponent of x. Thus, the degree of $5x^3$ is 3. A monomial in which the exponent of x is 0 is called a **constant term** and is said to be of *degree zero*. The nonzero coefficient a_n of the term in P with highest degree is called the **leading coefficient** of P, and we say that P is a **polynomial of degree n**. The polynomial whose coefficients are all zero is called the **zero polynomial**. It is denoted by 0 and is said to have no degree.

Example 4   Vocabulary of Polynomials

Given the polynomial

$$P = 2x^4 - 3x^2 + \frac{4}{3}x - 1$$

The terms of P are

$$2x^4, \quad 0x^3, \quad -3x^2, \quad \frac{4}{3}x, \quad -1$$

The coefficients of the terms are

$$2, \quad 0, \quad -3, \quad \frac{4}{3}, \quad -1$$

The degree of P is 4 and the leading coefficient is 2.

A *monomial in the variables x and y* is an expression of the form $ax^m y^n$, where a is a constant and m and n are constant, nonnegative integers. The number a is called the **coefficient** of the monomial. The *degree of a monomial in x and y* is the sum of the exponents of x and y. Thus, the degree of $2x^3 y^2$ is $3 + 2 = 5$. A *polynomial in x and y* is an expression that is a sum of monomials. The *degree of a polynomial in x and y* is the degree of the highest degree monomial with nonzero coefficient.

Example 5   Degree of Polynomials

The following are polynomials in x and y:

$$2x^2 y + y^2 - 3xy + 1 \qquad \text{Degree is 3.}$$
$$xy \qquad \text{Degree is 2.}$$
$$3x^4 + xy - y^2 \qquad \text{Degree is 4.}$$

Operations with Polynomials

If P and Q are polynomials in x, then the terms ax^r in P and bx^r in Q are said to be **like terms**, that is, like terms have the same exponent in x. For example, given

$$P = 4x^2 + 4x - 1$$

and

$$Q = 3x^3 - 2x^2 + 4$$

then the like terms are $0x^3$ and $3x^3$, $4x^2$ and $-2x^2$, $4x$ and $0x$, -1 and 4.

We define equality of polynomials in the following way.

Two polynomials are equal if all like terms are equal.

Example 6   Equality of Polynomials
Find A, B, C and D if

$$Ax^3 + (A + B)x^2 + Cx + (C - D) = -2x^3 + x + 3$$

Solution
Equating the coefficients of the terms, we have

$$A = -2 \qquad A + B = 0 \qquad C = 1 \qquad C - D = 3$$
$$B = 2 \qquad\qquad\qquad\qquad D = -2$$

If P and Q are polynomials in x, the *sum $P + Q$* is obtained by forming the sums of all pairs of like terms. The sum of ax^r in P and bx^r in Q is $(a + b)x^r$. Similarly, the *difference $P - Q$* is obtained by forming the differences, $(a - b)x^r$, of like terms.

Example 7   Addition and Subtraction of Polynomials
a. Add $2x^3 + 2x^2 - 3$ and $x^3 - x^2 + x + 2$.

b. Subtract $2x^3 + x^2 - x + 1$ from $3x^3 - 2x^2 + 2x$.

Solution
a. Adding the coefficients of like terms,

$$(2x^3 + 2x^2 - 3) + (x^3 - x^2 + x + 2) = 3x^3 + x^2 + x - 1$$

b. Subtracting the coefficients of like terms,

$$(3x^3 - 2x^2 + 2x) - (2x^3 + x^2 - x + 1) = x^3 - 3x^2 + 3x - 1$$

Warning

$$(x + 5) - (x + 2) \neq (x + 5) - x + 2$$

The coefficient -1 must multiply each term in the parentheses. Thus,

$$-(x + 2) = -x - 2$$

Therefore,

$$(x + 5) - (x + 2) = x + 5 - x - 2 = 3$$

while

$$(x + 5) - x + 2 = x + 5 - x + 2 = 7$$

Multiplication of polynomials is based on the rule for exponents developed earlier in this section,

$$a^m a^n = a^{m+n}$$

and on the distributive laws

$$a(b + c) = ab + ac$$
$$(a + b)c = ac + bc$$

Example 8 Multiplication of Polynomials

Multiply $3x^3(2x^3 - 6x^2 + 5)$.

Solution

$3x^3(2x^3 - 6x^2 + 5)$

$\quad = (3x^3)(2x^3) + (3x^3)(-6x^2) + (3x^3)(5)$ Distributive law

$\quad = (3)(2)x^{3+3} + (3)(-6)x^{3+2} + (3)(5)x^3$ $a^m a^n = a^{m+n}$

$\quad = 6x^6 - 18x^5 + 15x^3$

Example 9 Multiplication of Polynomials

Multiply $(x + 2)(3x^2 - x + 5)$.

Solution

$(x + 2)(3x^2 - x + 5)$

$\quad = x(3x^2 - x + 5) + 2(3x^2 - x + 5)$ Distributive law

$\quad = 3x^3 - x^2 + 5x + 6x^2 - 2x + 10$ Distributive law and $a^m a^n = a^{m+n}$

$\quad = 3x^3 + 5x^2 + 3x + 10$ Adding like terms

✔ Progress Check

Multiply.

a. $(x^2 + 2)(x^2 - 3x + 1)$ b. $(x^2 - 2xy + y)(2x + y)$

Answers

a. $x^4 - 3x^3 + 3x^2 - 6x + 2$ b. $2x^3 - 3x^2y + 2xy - 2xy^2 + y^2$

The multiplication in Example 9 can be carried out in "long form" as follows.

$$
\begin{array}{ll}
\begin{array}{r}
3x^2 - x + 5 \\
x + 2 \\
\hline
3x^3 - x^2 + 5x \\
6x^2 - 2x + 10 \\
\hline
3x^3 + 5x^2 + 3x + 10
\end{array}
&
\begin{array}{l}
\\
\\
= x(3x^2 - x + 5) \\
= 2(3x^2 - x + 5) \\
= \text{sum of above lines}
\end{array}
\end{array}
$$

In Example 9, the product of polynomials of degrees 1 and 2 is seen to be a polynomial of degree 3. From the multiplication process, we can derive the following useful rule.

The degree of the product of two nonzero polynomials is the sum of the degrees of the polynomials.

Products of the form $(2x + 3)(5x - 2)$ or $(2x + y)(3x - 2y)$ occur often, and we can handle them by the method sometimes referred to as FOIL: F = first, O = outer, I = inner, L = last.

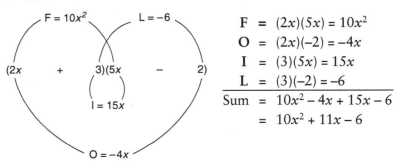

$$
\begin{aligned}
\mathbf{F} &= (2x)(5x) = 10x^2 \\
\mathbf{O} &= (2x)(-2) = -4x \\
\mathbf{I} &= (3)(5x) = 15x \\
\mathbf{L} &= (3)(-2) = -6 \\
\hline
\text{Sum} &= 10x^2 - 4x + 15x - 6 \\
&= 10x^2 + 11x - 6
\end{aligned}
$$

A number of special products occur frequently, and it is worthwhile knowing them.

Special Products

$$(a + b)(a - b) = a^2 - b^2$$

$$(a + b)^2 = (a + b)(a + b) = a^2 + 2ab + b^2$$

$$(a - b)^2 = (a - b)(a - b) = a^2 - 2ab + b^2$$

$$(a + b)^3 = a^3 + 3a^2b + 3ab^2 + b^3$$

$$(a - b)^3 = a^3 - 3a^2b + 3ab^2 - b^3$$

Example 10   Multiplication of Polynomials
Multiply.

a. $(x + 2)^2$ b. $(x - 3)^2$ c. $(x + 4)(x - 4)$

Solution
a. $(x + 2)^2 = (x + 2)(x + 2) = x^2 + 4x + 4$

b. $(x - 3)^2 = (x - 3)(x - 3) = x^2 - 6x + 9$

c. $(x + 4)(x - 4) = x^2 - 16$

✔ Progress Check

a. Multiply $(2x^2 - xy + y^2)(3x + y)$.   b. Multiply $(2x - 3)(3x - 2)$.

Answers

a. $6x^3 - x^2y + 2xy^2 + y^3$ b. $6x^2 - 13x + 6$

Graphing Calculator Power User's Corner

(1) Assigning Values to Variables

Assign values to variables on your graphing calculator using the STORE command. There is usually an arrow key $\boxed{\rightarrow}$ or a key labeled $\boxed{\text{STO}}$. For example, to set $M = 3$, you press

$$\boxed{3} \; \boxed{\rightarrow} \; \boxed{M} \qquad \text{or} \qquad \boxed{3} \; \boxed{\text{STO}} \; \boxed{M}$$

Check your owner's manual for details. The owner's manual may be available online. Look up your calculator by model and number.

(2) Evaluating Algebraic Expressions on a Graphing Calculator

Once specific values have been assigned to variables in your graphing calculator, you can use these variables to evaluate algebraic expressions. For example, evaluate

$$\frac{3m + 4n}{m + n}$$

when $m = 3$ and $n = 2$.

Step 1. Store 3 in memory location M and store 2 in memory location N.

Step 2. Enter and evaluate the expression

$$(3M + 4N) \div (M + N)$$

Note that the numerator expression and the denominator expression must both be enclosed in parentheses. On some calculators, you may need to enter 3 $\times M$ and 4 $\times N$ to multiply.

Step 3. Note that your answer is given in the decimal form 3.4. Use your calculator to verify that $\frac{17}{5} = 3.4$.

Exercise Set 1.3

In Exercises 1–6, evaluate the given expression when $r = 2$, $s = -3$, and $t = 4$.

1. $r + 2s + t$

2. rst

3. $\dfrac{rst}{r + s + t}$

4. $(r + s)t$

5. $\dfrac{r + s}{rt}$

6. $\dfrac{r + s + t}{t}$

7. Evaluate $\frac{2}{3}r + 5$ when $r = 12$.

8. Evaluate $\frac{9}{5}C + 32$ when $C = 37$.

9. If P dollars are invested at a simple interest rate of r percent per year for t years, the amount on hand

at the end of t years is $P + Prt$. Suppose you invest $2000 at 8% per year ($r = 0.08$). Find the amount you will have on hand after

a. 1 year   b. $\frac{1}{2}$ year   c. 8 months.

10. The perimeter of a rectangle is given by the formula $P = 2(L + W)$, where L is the length and W is the width of the rectangle. Find the perimeter if

a. $L = 2$ feet, $W = 3$ feet

b. $L = \frac{1}{2}$ meter, $W = \frac{1}{4}$ meter

 11. Evaluate $0.02r + 0.314st + 2.25t$ when $r = 2.5$, $s = 3.4$, and $t = 2.81$.

 12. Evaluate $10.421x + 0.821y + 2.34xyz$ when $x = 3.21$, $y = 2.42$, and $z = 1.23$.

Evaluate the given expression in Exercises 13–18.

13. $|x| - |x| \cdot |y|$ when $x = -3$, $y = 4$

14. $|x + y| + |x - y|$ when $x = -3$, $y = 2$

15. $\dfrac{|a - 2b|}{2a}$ when $a = 1$, $b = 2$

16. $\dfrac{|x| + |y|}{|x| - |y|}$ when $x = -3$, $y = 4$

17. $\dfrac{-|a - 2b|}{|a + b|}$ when $a = -2$, $b = -1$

18. $\dfrac{|a - b| - 2|c - a|}{|a - b + c|}$ when $a = -2$, $b = 3$, $c = -5$

Carry out the indicated operations in Exercises 19–24.

19. $b^5 \cdot b^2$ 20. $x^3 \cdot x^5$

21. $(4y^3)(-5y^6)$ 22. $(-6x^4)(-4x^7)$

23. $\left(\dfrac{3}{2}x^3\right)(-2x)$ 24. $\left(-\dfrac{5}{3}x^6\right)\left(-\dfrac{3}{10}x^3\right)$

 25. Evaluate the given expressions and verify your answer using your calculator.

a. 1^3 b. 10^8

c. 2^5 d. 7^1

 26. Evaluate the given expressions using your calculator.

a. 9^{10} b. 0.8^6

27. Which of the following expressions are *not* polynomials?

a. $-3x^2 + 2x + 5$ b. $-3x^2y$

c. $-3x^{2/3} + 2xy + 5$ d. $-2x^{-4} + 2xy^3 + 5$

28. Which of the following expressions are *not* polynomials?

a. $4x^5 - x^{1/2} + 6$ b. $\dfrac{2}{5}x^3 + \dfrac{4}{3}x - 2$

c. $4x^5y$ d. $x^{4/3}y + 2x - 3$

In Exercises 29–32, indicate the leading coefficient and the degree of the given polynomial.

29. $2x^3 + 3x^2 - 5$ 30. $-4x^5 - 8x^2 + x + 3$

31. $\dfrac{3}{5}x^4 + 2x^2 - x - 1$ 32. $-1.5 + 7x^3 + 0.75x^7$

In Exercises 33–36, find the degree of the given polynomial.

33. $3x^2y - 4x^2 - 2y + 4$ 34. $4xy^3 + xy^2 - y^2 + y$

35. $2xy^3 - y^3 + 3x^2 - 2$ 36. $\dfrac{1}{2}x^3y^3 - 2$

37. Find the value of the polynomial $3x^2y^2 + 2xy - x + 2y + 7$ when $x = 2$ and $y = -1$.

 38. Find the value of the polynomial $0.02x^2 + 0.3x - 0.5$ when $x = 0.3$.

 39. Find the value of the polynomial $2.1x^3 + 3.3x^2 - 4.1x - 7.2$ when $x = 4.1$.

40. Write a polynomial giving the area of a circle of radius r.

41. Write a polynomial giving the area of a triangle of base b and height h.

42. A field consists of a rectangle and a square arranged as shown in Figure 4. What does each of the following polynomials represent?

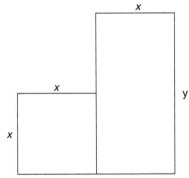

Figure 4   See Exercise 42.

a. $x^2 + xy$ b. $2x + 2y$

c. $4x$ d. $4x + 2y$

43. An investor buys x shares of G.E. stock at $76.50 per share, y shares of Exxon stock at $61 per share, and z shares of AT&T stock at $45 per share. What does the polynomial $76.50x + 61y + 45z$ represent?

Perform the indicated operations in Exercises 44–62.

44. $(4x^2 + 3x + 2) + (3x^2 - 2x - 5)$

45. $(2x^2 + 3x + 8) - (5 - 2x + 2x^2)$

46. $4xy^2 + 2xy + 2x + 3 - (-2xy^2 + xy - y + 2)$

47. $(2s^2t^3 - st^2 + st - s + t) - (3s^2t^2 - 2s^2t - 4st^2 - t + 3)$

48. $3xy^2z - 4x^2yz + xy + 3 - (2xy^2z + x^2yz - yz + x - 2)$

49. $a^2bc + ab^2c + 2ab^3 - 3a^2bc - 4ab^3 + 3$

50. $(x + 1)(x^2 + 2x - 3)$

51. $(2 - x)(2x^3 + x - 2)$

52. $(2s - 3)(s^3 - s + 2)$

53. $(-3s + 2)(-2s^2 - s + 3)$

54. $(x^2 + 3)(2x^2 - x + 2)$

55. $(2y^2 + y)(-2y^3 + y - 3)$

56. $(x^2 + 2x - 1)(2x^2 - 3x + 2)$

57. $(a^2 - 4a + 3)(4a^3 + 2a + 5)$

58. $(2a^2 + ab + b^2)(3a - b^2 + 1)$

59. $(-3a + ab + b^2)(3b^2 + 2b + 2)$

60. $5(2x - 3)^2$

61. $2(3x - 2)(3 - x)$

62. $(x - 1)(x + 2)(x + 3)$

63. An investor buys x shares of IBM stock at \$100 per share at Thursday's opening of the stock market. Later in the day, the investor sells y shares of AT&T stock at \$45 per share and z shares of TRW stock at \$50 per share. Write a polynomial that expresses the amount of money the buyer has invested at the end of the day.

64. An artist takes a rectangular piece of cardboard whose sides are x and y and cuts out a square of side $\frac{x}{2}$ to obtain a mat for a painting, as shown in Figure 5. Write a polynomial giving the area of the mat.

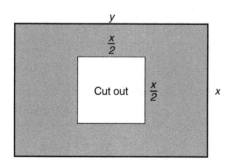

Figure 5   See Exercise 64.

In Exercises 65–78, perform the multiplication mentally.

65. $(x - 1)(x + 3)$

66. $(x + 2)(x + 3)$

67. $(2x + 1)(2x + 3)$

68. $(3x - 1)(x + 5)$

69. $(3x - 2)(x - 1)$

70. $(x + 4)(2x - 1)$

71. $(x + y)^2$

72. $(x - 4)^2$

73. $(3x - 1)^2$

74. $(x + 2)(x - 2)$

75. $(2x + 1)(2x - 1)$

76. $(3a + 2b)^2$

77. $(x^2 + y^2)^2$

78. $(x - y)^2$

79. Simplify the following.

a. $3^{10} + 3^{10} + 3^{10}$ b. $2^n + 2^n + 2^n + 2^n$

80. A student conjectured that the expression $N = m^2 - m + 41$ yields N, a prime number, for integer values of m. Prove or disprove this statement.

81. Perform the indicated operations.

a. $\left(\dfrac{2}{x} - 1\right)\left(\dfrac{2}{x} + 1\right)$ b. $\left(\dfrac{wx}{y} - z\right)^2$

c. $(x + y + z)(x + y - z)$

82. Find the surface area and volume of the open-top box below.

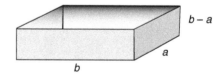

83. Eric can run a mile in 4.23 minutes, and Benjamin can run 4.23 miles in an hour. Who is the faster runner?

84. a. Let $P = \$1000$; that is, store 1000 in memory location P. Evaluate $P + 0.06P$ by entering the expression $P + 0.06P$ into your calculator.

b. Repeat part (a) for $P = \$28,525$.

85. Let $A = 8$ and $B = 32$; that is, store 8 in memory location A and 32 in memory location B. Evaluate the following expressions by entering them into your calculator as they appear below. (Use a multiplication sign if your calculator requires you to do so.)

a. $A(B + 17)$ b. $5B - A^2$

c. A^A d. $16^A - 3AB$

86. Find the value of the polynomial $20t - 0.7t^2$ when t is 28 and when t is 29. Try to find a value for t (other than 0) that gives the expression a value close to zero.

Applications 1.3

1. April 1st, 2011, Tracy bought x shares of WLK (Westlake Chemical Corp) at $54.00 per share, y shares of Ford at $5.12 per share, and z shares of WFMI (Whole Foods Market, Inc.) at $57.23 per share.

   a. What does the polynomial $54x + 5.12y + 57.23z$ represent?

   b. Please find the amount of money Tracy gained/lost if she held these three stocks for four months if she bought 100 shares of WLK, 3000 shares of Ford, and 200 shares of WFMI.

2. A Macy's coupon offered 35% sale on your entire purchase. If x is the price of a product that you would like to buy at Macy's,

   a. What does $x - 0.35x$ represent?

   b. What does $0.35x$ represent?

   c. If you would like to buy a pair of shoes at $130.99, Find $0.35x$ and $x - 0.35x$. What do they represent?

3. A 12-meter long steel beam is to be cut into two pieces so that one piece will be 3 meters longer than the other. How long will each piece be? (Show your work, please.)

4. The length of a rectangular garden is x meters and its width is two meters shorter than the length.

   a. Find the area and the perimeter of the garden.

   b. If the length of your garden is 13 meters, find the area and the perimeter of your garden.

5. The number of enterprise instant message (IM) accounts, in millions, is projected to grow according to the polynomial $3t^2 + 12t + 60$, where $0 \le t \le 5$ and t is measured in years, with $t = 0$ corresponding to 2006.

   a. How many enterprise IM accounts in 2006?

   b. What was the number of enterprise IM accounts expected in 2010?

   c. Can you use the given model to find the number of IM accounts expected in 2014? Explain your answer carefully.

1.4   Factoring

Now that we can find the product of two polynomials, let us consider the reverse problem: given a polynomial, can we find factors whose product yields the given polynomial? This process, known as **factoring**, is one of the basic tools of algebra. In this chapter, a polynomial with *integer* coefficients is to be factored as a product of polynomials of lower degree with *integer* coefficients; a polynomial with *rational* coefficients is to be factored as a product of polynomials of lower degree with *rational* coefficients. We will approach factoring by learning to recognize the situations in which factoring is possible.

Common Factors

Consider the polynomial

$$x^2 + x$$

Since the factor x is common to both terms, we can write

$$x^2 + x = x(x + 1)$$

Example 1   Factoring with Common Factors

Factor.

a. $15x^3 - 10x^2$ b. $4x^2y - 8xy^2 + 6xy$ c. $2x(x + y) - 5y(x + y)$

Solution

a. 5 and x^2 are common to both terms. Therefore,

$$15x^3 - 10x^2 = 5x^2(3x - 2)$$

b. Here we see that 2, x, and y are common to all terms. Therefore,

$$4x^2y - 8xy^2 + 6xy = 2xy(2x - 4y + 3)$$

c. The expression $(x + y)$ is found in both terms. Factoring, we have

$$2x(x + y) - 5y(x + y) = (x + y)(2x - 5y)$$

✔ **Progress Check**

Factor.

a. $4x^2 - x$ b. $3x^4 - 9x^2$ c. $3m(2x - 3y) - n(2x - 3y)$

Answers

a. $x(4x - 1)$ b. $3x^2(x^2 - 3)$ c. $(2x - 3y)(3m - n)$

Factoring by Grouping

It is sometimes possible to discover common factors by first grouping terms. Consider the following examples.

Example 2   Factoring by Grouping

Factor.

a. $2ab + b + 2ac + c$ b. $2x - 4x^2y - 3y + 6xy^2$

Solution

a. Group those terms containing b and those terms containing c.

$$
\begin{aligned}
2ab + b + 2ac + c &= (2ab + b) + (2ac + c) &&\text{Grouping} \\
&= b(2a + 1) + c(2a + 1) &&\text{Common factors } b, c \\
&= (2a + 1)(b + c) &&\text{Common factors } 2a + 1
\end{aligned}
$$

Alternatively, suppose we group terms containing a.

$$
\begin{aligned}
2ab + b + 2ac + c &= (2ab + 2ac) + (b + c) &&\text{Grouping} \\
&= 2a(b + c) + (b + c) &&\text{Common factors } 2, a \\
&= (b + c)(2a + 1) &&\text{Common factor } (b + c)
\end{aligned}
$$

b. $2x - 4x^2y - 3y + 6xy^2$

$$= (2x - 4x^2y) - (3y - 6xy^2) \qquad \text{Grouping with sign change}$$

$$= 2x(1 - 2xy) - 3y(1 - 2xy) \qquad \text{Common factors } 2x, 3y$$

$$= (1 - 2xy)(2x - 3y) \qquad \text{Common factor } 1 - 2xy \quad ■$$

✔ **Progress Check**

Factor.

a. $2m^3n + m^2 + 2mn^2 + n$ b. $2a^2 - 4ab^2 - ab + 2b^3$

Answers

a. $(2mn + 1)(m^2 + n)$ b. $(a - 2b^2)(2a - b)$

Factoring Second-Degree Polynomials

To factor a second-degree polynomial, such as

$$x^2 + 5x + 6$$

we first note that the term x^2 can have come only from $x \cdot x$, so we write two incomplete factors:

$$x^2 + 5x + 6 = (x \quad)(x \quad)$$

The constant term +6 can be the product of either two positive numbers or two negative numbers. Since the middle term +5x is the sum of two other products, both signs must be positive. Thus,

$$x^2 + 5x + 6 = (x + \quad)(x + \quad)$$

Finally, the number 6 can be written as the product of two integers in only two ways: $1 \cdot 6$ and $2 \cdot 3$. The first pair gives a middle term of $7x$. The second pair gives the actual middle term, $5x$. So

$$x^2 + 5x + 6 = (x + 2)(x + 3)$$

Example 3   Factoring Second-Degree Polynomials

Factor.

a. $x^2 - 7x + 10$ b. $x^2 - 3x - 4$

Solution

a. Since the constant term is positive and the middle term is negative, we must have two negative signs. Integer pairs whose product is 10 are 1 and 10, and 2 and 5. We find that

$$x^2 - 7x + 10 = (x - 2)(x - 5)$$

b. Since the constant term is negative, we must have opposite signs. Integer pairs whose product is 4 are 1 and 4, and 2 and 2. Since the coefficient of $-3x$ is negative, we assign the larger integer of a given pair to be negative. We find that

$$x^2 - 3x - 4 = (x + 1)(x - 4)$$

When the leading coefficient of a second-degree polynomial is an integer other than 1, the factoring process becomes more complex, as shown in the following example.

Example 4   Factoring Second-Degree Polynomials

Factor $2x^2 - x - 6$.

Solution

The term $2x^2$ can result only from the factors $2x$ and x, so the factors must be of the form

$$2x^2 - x - 6 = (2x \qquad)(x \qquad)$$

The constant term, -6, must be the product of factors of opposite signs, so we may write

$$2x^2 - x - 6 = \begin{cases} (2x + \quad)(x - \quad) \\ \text{or} \\ (2x - \quad)(x + \quad) \end{cases}$$

The integer factors of 6 are

$$1 \cdot 6 \qquad 6 \cdot 1 \qquad 2 \cdot 3 \qquad 3 \cdot 2$$

By trying these we find that

$$2x^2 - x - 6 = (2x + 3)(x - 2)$$

✔ Progress Check

Factor.

a. $3x^2 - 16x + 21$ b. $2x^2 + 3x - 9$

Answers

a. $(3x - 7)(x - 3)$ b. $(2x - 3)(x + 3)$

Warning

The polynomial $x^2 - 6x$ can be written as

$$x^2 - 6x = x(x - 6)$$

and is then a product of two polynomials of positive degree. Students often fail to consider x to be a "true" factor.

Special Factors

There is a special case of the second-degree polynomial that occurs frequently and factors easily. Given the polynomial $x^2 - 9$, we see that each term is a perfect square, and we can verify that

$$x^2 - 9 = (x + 3)(x - 3)$$

The general rule, which holds whenever we are dealing with a difference of two squares, may be stated as follows.

Difference of Two Squares

$$a^2 - b^2 = (a + b)(a - b)$$

Example 5   Special Factors

Factor.

a. $4x^2 - 25$

b. $9r^2 - 16t^2$

Solution

a. Since

$$4x^2 - 25 = (2x)^2 - (5)^2$$

we may use the formula for the difference of two squares with $a = 2x$ and $b = 5$. Thus,

$$4x^2 - 25 = (2x + 5)(2x - 5)$$

b. Since

$$9r^2 - 16t^2 = (3r)^2 - (4t)^2$$

we have $a = 3r$ and $b = 4t$, resulting in

$$9r^2 - 16t^2 = (3r + 4t)(3r - 4t)$$

✔ **Progress Check**

Factor.

a. $x^2 - 49$

b. $16x^2 - 9$

c. $25x^2 - y^2$

Answers

a. $(x + 7)(x - 7)$

b. $(4x + 3)(4x - 3)$

c. $(5x + y)(5x - y)$

The formulas for a sum of two cubes and a difference of two cubes can be verified by multiplying the factors on the right-hand sides of the following equations.

Sum and Difference of Two Cubes

$$a^3 + b^3 = (a + b)(a^2 - ab + b^2)$$

$$a^3 - b^3 = (a - b)(a^2 + ab + b^2)$$

These formulas provide a direct means of factoring the sum or difference of two cubes and are used in the same way as the formula for a difference of two squares.

Example 6   Special Factors

Factor.

a. $x^3 + 1$ 　　　　　b. $27m^3 - 64n^3$ 　　　　c. $\dfrac{1}{27}u^3 + 8v^3$

Solution

a. With $a = x$ and $b = 1$, the formula for the sum of two cubes yields the following result:

$$x^3 + 1 = (x + 1)(x^2 - x + 1)$$

b. Since

$$27m^3 - 64n^3 = (3m)^3 - (4n)^3$$

we can use the formula for the difference of two cubes with $a = 3m$ and $b = 4n$:

$$27m^3 - 64n^3 = (3m - 4n)(9m^2 + 12mn + 16n^2)$$

c. Note that

$$\frac{1}{27}u^3 + 8v^3 = \left(\frac{1}{3}u\right)^3 + (2v)^3$$

and then use the formula for the sum of two cubes:

$$\frac{1}{27}u^3 + 8v^3 = \left(\frac{u}{3} + 2v\right)\left(\frac{u^2}{9} - \frac{2}{3}uv + 4v^2\right)$$

Combining Methods

We conclude with problems that combine the various methods of factoring that we have studied. As the factoring becomes more complicated, it may be helpful to consider the following strategy:

Remove common factors before attempting any other factoring techniques.

Focus on "MAGICAL" Factoring for Second-Degree Polynomials

Factoring involves a certain amount of trial and error that can become frustrating, especially when the lead coefficient is not 1. You might want to try a scheme that "magically" reduces the number of candidates. We demonstrate the method for the polynomial

$$4x^2 + 11x + 6 \tag{1}$$

Using the lead coefficient of 4, write the pair of incomplete factors

$$(4x \quad)(4x \quad) \tag{2}$$

Next, multiply the coefficient of x^2 and the constant term in Equation (1) to produce $4 \cdot 6 = 24$. Now find two integers whose product is 24 and whose sum is 11, the coefficient of the middle term of (1). Since 8 and 3 work, we write

$$(4x + 8)(4x + 3) \tag{3}$$

Finally, within each parenthesis in Equation (3) discard any common numerical factor. (Discarding a factor may only be performed in this "magical" type of factoring.) Thus $(4x + 8)$ reduces to $(x + 2)$ and we write

$$(x + 2)(4x + 3) \tag{4}$$

which is the factorization of $4x^2 + 11x + 6$.

Will the method always work? Yes—if you first remove all common factors in the original polynomial. That is, you must first write

$$6x^2 + 15x + 6 = 3(2x^2 + 5x + 2)$$

and apply the method to the polynomial $2x^2 + 5x + 2$.

(For a proof that the method works, see M. A. Autrie and J. D. Austin, "A Novel Way to Factor Quadratic Polynomials," *The Mathematics Teacher* 72, no. 2 [1979].)

We use the polynomial $2x^2 - x - 6$ of Example 4 to demonstrate the method when some of the coefficients are negative.

> Try the method on these second-degree polynomials:
>
> $3x^2 + 10x - 8$
>
> $6x^2 - 13x + 6$
>
> $4x^2 - 15x - 4$
>
> $10x^2 + 11x - 6$

Factoring $ax^2 + bx + c$	Example: $2x^2 - x - 6$
Step 1. Use the lead coefficient a to write the incomplete factors $$(ax \quad)(ax \quad)$$	*Step 1.* The lead coefficient is 2, so we write $$(2x \quad)(2x \quad)$$
Step 2. Multiply a and c, the coefficients of x^2, and the constant term.	*Step 2.* $\qquad a \cdot c = (2)(-6) = -12$
Step 3. Find integers whose product is $a \cdot c$ and whose sum equals b. Write these integers in the incomplete factors of *Step 1*.	*Step 3.* Two integers whose product is -12 and whose sum is -1 are 3 and -4. We then write $$(2x + 3)(2x - 4)$$
Step 4. Discard any common factor *within each parenthesis* in *Step 3*. The result is the desired factorization.	*Step 4.* Reducing $(2x - 4)$ to $(x - 2)$ by discarding the common factor 2, we have $$2x^2 - x - 6 = (2x + 3)(x - 2)$$

Example 7   **Common Factors, Grouping, and Special Factors**

Factor.

a. $2x^3 - 8x$
b. $3y(y + 3) + 2(y + 3)(y^2 - 1)$

Solution

a. Observing the common factor $2x$, we find that

$$2x^3 - 8x = 2x(x^2 - 4)$$
$$= 2x(x + 2)(x - 2)$$

b. Observing the common factor $y + 3$, we see that

$$3y(y + 3) + 2(y + 3)(y^2 - 1) = (y + 3)[3y + 2(y^2 - 1)]$$
$$= (y + 3)(3y + 2y^2 - 2)$$
$$= (y + 3)(2y^2 + 3y - 2)$$
$$= (y + 3)(2y - 1)(y + 2)$$

✔ Progress Check

Factor.

a. $x^3 + 5x^2 - 6x$
b. $2x^3 - 2x^2y - 4xy^2$

c. $-3x(x + 1) + (x + 1)(2x^2 + 1)$

Answers

a. $x(x + 6)(x - 1)$
b. $2x(x + y)(x - 2y)$
c. $(x + 1)(2x - 1)(x - 1)$

Irreducible Polynomials

Are there polynomials that cannot be written as a product of polynomials of lower degree with integer coefficients? The answer is yes. Examples are the polynomials $x^2 + 1$ and $x^2 + x + 1$. A polynomial is said to be **prime**, or **irreducible**, if it cannot be written as a product of two polynomials, each of positive degree. Thus, $x^2 + 1$ is irreducible over the integers.

Exercise Set 1.4

Factor completely.

1. $5x - 15$

2. $\dfrac{1}{4}x + \dfrac{3}{4}y$

3. $-2x - 8y$

4. $3x - 6y + 15$

5. $5bc + 25b$

6. $2x^4 + x^2$

7. $-3y^2 - 4y^5$

8. $3abc + 12bc$

9. $3x^2 + 6x^2y - 9x^2z$

10. $9a^3b^3 + 12a^2b - 15ab^2$

11. $x^2 + 4x + 3$

12. $x^2 + 2x - 8$

13. $y^2 - 8y + 15$

14. $y^2 + 7y - 8$

15. $a^2 - 7ab + 12b^2$

16. $x^2 - 49$

17. $y^2 - \dfrac{1}{9}$

18. $a^2 - 7a + 10$

19. $9 - x^2$

20. $4b^2 - a^2$

21. $x^2 - 5x - 14$

22. $x^2y^2 - 9$

23. $\dfrac{1}{16} - y^2$

24. $4a^2 - b^2$

25. $x^2 - 6x + 9$

26. $a^2b^2 - \dfrac{1}{9}$

27. $x^2 - 12x + 20$

28. $x^2 - 8x - 20$

29. $x^2 + 11x + 24$

30. $y^2 - \dfrac{9}{16}$

31. $2x^2 - 3x - 2$

32. $2x^2 + 7x + 6$

33. $3a^2 - 11a + 6$

34. $4x^2 - 9x + 2$

35. $6x^2 + 13x + 6$

36. $4y^2 - 9$

37. $8m^2 - 6m - 9$

38. $9x^2 + 24x + 16$

39. $10x^2 - 13x - 3$

40. $9y^2 - 16x^2$

41. $6a^2 - 5ab - 6b^2$

42. $4x^2 + 20x + 25$

43. $10r^2s^2 + 9rst + 2t^2$

44. $x^{12} - 1$

45. $16 - 9x^2y^2$

46. $6 + 5x - 4x^2$

47. $8n^2 - 18n - 5$

48. $15 + 4x - 4x^2$

49. $2x^2 - 2x - 12$

50. $3y^2 + 6y - 45$

51. $30x^2 - 35x + 10$

52. $x^4y^4 - x^2y^2$

53. $18x^2m + 33xm + 9m$

54. $25m^2n^3 - 5m^2n$

55. $12x^2 - 22x^3 - 20x^4$

56. $10r^2 - 5rs - 15s^2$

57. $x^4 - y^4$

58. $a^4 - 16$

59. $b^4 + 2b^2 - 8$

60. $4b^4 + 20b^2 + 25$

61. $x^3 + 27y^3$

62. $8x^3 + 125y^3$

63. $27x^3 - y^3$

64. $64x^3 - 27y^3$

65. $a^3 + 8$

66. $8r^3 - 27$

67. $\dfrac{1}{8}m^3 - 8n^3$

68. $8a^3 - \dfrac{1}{64}b^3$

69. $(x + y)^3 - 8$

70. $27 + (x + y)^3$

71. $8x^6 - 125y^6$

72. $a^6 + 27b^6$

73. $4(x + 1)(y + 2) - 8(y + 2)$

74. $2(x + 1)(x - 1) + 5(x - 1)$

75. $3(x + 2)^2(x - 1) - 4(x + 2)^2(2x + 7)$

76. $4(2x - 1)^2(x + 2)^3(x + 1) - 3(2x - 1)^5(x + 2)^2(x + 3)$

77. Show that the difference of the squares of two positive, consecutive odd integers must be divisible by 8.

78. A perfect square is a natural number of the form n^2. For example, 9 is a perfect square since $9 = 3^2$. Show that the sum of the squares of two odd numbers cannot be a perfect square.

79. Find a natural number n, if possible, such that $1 + n(n + 1)(n + 2)(n + 3)$ is a perfect square.

80. Prove or disprove that $1 + n(n + 1)(n + 2)(n + 3)$ is a perfect square. (*Hint:* Consider $[1 + n(n + 3)]^2$.)

81. Factor completely.
    a. $(x + h)^3 - x^3$ b. $2^n + 2^{n+1} + 2^{n+2}$
    c. $16 - 81x^{12}$ d. $z^2 - x^2 + 2xy - y^2$

82. Factor completely.
    a. $\left[\dfrac{n(n + 1)}{2}\right]^2 + (n + 1)^3$ b. $\dfrac{n(n + 1)(2n + 1)}{6} + (n + 1)^2$
    c. $\dfrac{1}{b}(a + bx)^2 - \dfrac{a}{b}(a + bx)$

83. Factor the following expressions that arise in different branches of science.
    a. biology (blood flow): $C[(R + 1)^2 - r^2]$
    b. physics (nuclear): $pa^2 + (1 - p)b^2 - [pa + (1 - p)b]^2$
    c. mechanics (bending beams): $X^2 - 3LX + 2L^2$
    d. electricity (resistance): $(R_1 + R_2)^2 - 2r(R_1 + R_2)$
    e. physics (motion): $-16t^2 + 64t + 336$

84. a. Factor this expression, used to find the answers given in the chapter opening.
    $$20t - 0.7t^2$$
    b. Show that the factored form and the original form are identical by using your graphing calculator to compare the GRAPH of each expression. Graphing will be explained in Chapter 3.

85. Factor the general expression $vt - \dfrac{1}{2}at^2$.

86. Suppose we alter the expression from Exercise 85 by adding a constant:
    $$s + vt - \dfrac{1}{2}at^2$$
    Experiment with different values of s, v, and t. Which ones give you an expression that is easy to factor? (Reread Exercise 87 in Section 1.3. The s we have added could represent the original position of the object.)

87. *Mathematics in Writing:* Write a short paragraph explaining the differences in the techniques you used to factor the scientific expressions in Exercise 83 parts a, b and c. Find at least one other problem in this problem set that uses a technique similar to each of the three you have described.

Applications 1.4

1. The revenue of a product is given by a polynomial: $50 + 49x - x^2$, where x is the number of units produced.

   a. Find the value(s) of x for which the revenue is zero.

   b. Explain the meaning of the values you find in part (a).

   c. Find the value(s) of x for which the revenue is less than zero. Explain your answer.

   d. Find the value(s) of x for which the revenue is more than zero. Explain your answer.

2. Your computer store is having an incredible sale. The price on one model is reduced by 40%. Then the sale price is reduced by an additional 60%. If x is the computer's original price,

   a. What does $0.6x$ represent?

   b. What does $0.6x - 0.6(0.6x)$ represent?

   c. Factor out $0.6x$ from each term in part (b). Then simplify the resulting expression.

   d. Use the simplified expression from part (c) to answer these questions: With a 40% reduction followed by a 60% reduction, is the computer selling at 0% of its original price? (For free?) If not, at what percentage of the original price is it selling for?

1.5 Rational Expressions

Much of the terminology and many of the techniques for the arithmetic of fractions carry over to **algebraic fractions**, which are the quotients of algebraic expressions. In particular, we refer to a quotient of two polynomials as a **rational expression**.

Notation

> Any symbol used as a divisor in this text is always assumed to be different from zero.

Therefore, we will not always identify a divisor as being different from zero unless it disappears through some type of mathematical manipulation.

Our objective in this section is to review the procedures for adding, subtracting, multiplying, and dividing rational expressions. We are then able to convert a complicated fraction, such as

$$\frac{1 - \dfrac{1}{x}}{\dfrac{1}{x^2} + \dfrac{1}{x}}$$

into a form that simplifies evaluation of the fraction and facilitates other operations with it.

Multiplication and Division of Rational Expressions

The symbols appearing in rational expressions represent real numbers. We may, therefore, apply the rules of arithmetic to rational expressions. Let a, b, c and d represent any algebraic expressions.

$$\frac{a}{b} \cdot \frac{c}{d} = \frac{ac}{bd}$$ Multiplication of rational expressions

$$\frac{\dfrac{a}{b}}{\dfrac{c}{d}} = \frac{\dfrac{a}{b}}{\dfrac{c}{d}} \cdot \frac{(bd)}{(bd)} = \frac{ad}{cb}$$ Division of rational expressions

Example 1 Multiplication and Division of Rational Expressions

Divide $\dfrac{2x}{y}$ by $\dfrac{3y^3}{x-3}$.

Solution

$$\frac{\dfrac{2x}{y}}{\dfrac{3y^3}{x-3}} = \frac{\dfrac{2x}{y}}{\dfrac{3y^3}{x-3}} \cdot \frac{(y)(x-3)}{(y)(x-3)} = \frac{2x(x-3)}{3y^4}, \quad x \neq 3$$

The basic rule that allows us to simplify rational expressions is the cancellation principle.

Cancellation Principle

$$\frac{ab}{ac} = \frac{b}{c}, \quad a \neq 0$$

This rule results from the fact that $\frac{a}{a} = 1$. Thus,

$$\frac{ab}{ac} = \frac{a}{a} \cdot \frac{b}{c} = 1 \cdot \frac{b}{c} = \frac{b}{c}$$

Once again we find that a rule for the arithmetic of fractions carries over to rational expressions.

Example 2 Factoring and Cancellation

Simplify.

a. $\dfrac{x^2-4}{x^2+5x+6}$ b. $\dfrac{3x^2(y-1)}{y+1} \div \dfrac{6x(y-1)^2}{(y+1)^3}$ c. $\dfrac{x^2-x-6}{3x-x^2}$

Solution

a. $\dfrac{x^2-4}{x^2+5x+6} = \dfrac{(x+2)(x-2)}{(x+3)(x+2)} = \dfrac{x-2}{x+3}, \quad x \neq -2$

b. $\dfrac{\dfrac{3x^2(y-1)}{y+1}}{\dfrac{6x(y-1)^2}{(y+1)^3}} = \dfrac{\dfrac{3x^2(y-1)}{y+1}}{\dfrac{6x(y-1)^2}{(y+1)^3}} \cdot \dfrac{(y+1)^3}{(y+1)^3} = \dfrac{3x^2(y-1)(y+1)^2}{6x(y-1)^2}$

$$= \dfrac{x(y+1)^2}{2(y-1)}, \quad x \neq 0, \quad y \neq -1$$

c. $\dfrac{x^2-x-6}{3x-x^2} = \dfrac{(x-3)(x+2)}{x(3-x)} = \dfrac{(x-3)(x+2)}{-x(x-3)} = \dfrac{x+2}{-x}, \quad x \neq 3$

$$= -\dfrac{x+2}{x}, \quad x \neq 3$$

Note that in Example 2c, we wrote $(3-x)$ as $-(x-3)$. This technique is often used to recognize factors that may be canceled.

✔ **Progress Check**
Simplify.

a. $\dfrac{4-x^2}{x^2-x-6}$ b. $\dfrac{8-2x}{y} \div \dfrac{x^2-16}{y}$

Answers

a. $\dfrac{2-x}{x-3}, \quad x \neq -2$ b. $-\dfrac{2}{x+4}, \quad x \neq 4, \quad y \neq 0$

Warning

a. Only multiplicative factors can be canceled. Thus,

$$\dfrac{2x-4}{x} \neq 2-4$$

Since x is *not a factor* in the numerator, we may *not* perform cancellation.

b. Note that

$$\dfrac{y^2-x^2}{y-x} \neq y-x$$

To simplify correctly, write

$$\dfrac{y^2-x^2}{y-x} = \dfrac{(y+x)(y-x)}{y-x} = y+x, \quad y \neq x$$

Addition and Subtraction of Rational Expressions

Since the variables in rational expressions represent real numbers, the rules of arithmetic for addition and subtraction of fractions apply to rational expressions. When rational expressions have the same denominator, the addition and subtraction rules are as follows.

$$\frac{a}{c} + \frac{b}{c} = \frac{a+b}{c}$$

$$\frac{a}{c} - \frac{b}{c} = \frac{a-b}{c}$$

For example,

$$\frac{2}{x-1} - \frac{4}{x-1} + \frac{5}{x-1} = \frac{2-4+5}{x-1} = \frac{3}{x-1}$$

To add or subtract rational expressions with *different* denominators, we must first rewrite each rational expression as an equivalent one with the same denominator as the others. Although any common denominator will do, we will concentrate on finding the **least common denominator**, or **LCD**, of two or more rational expressions. We now outline the procedure and provide some examples.

Example 3 Least Common Denominator for Rational Numbers

Find the LCD of the following three fractions:

$$\frac{1}{8} \qquad \frac{7}{90} \qquad \frac{3}{25}$$

Solution

Least Common Denominator

Method	Example
Step 1. Factor the denominator of each fraction.	*Step 1.* $\dfrac{1}{2^3}$ $\dfrac{7}{2 \cdot 3^2 \cdot 5}$ $\dfrac{3}{5^2}$
Step 2. Find the different factors in the denominator and the highest power to which each factor occurs.	*Step 2.*

Step 2.

Factor	Highest exponent	Final factors
2	3	8
3	2	9
5	2	25

Step 3. The product of the final factors in *Step 2* is the LCD.	*Step 3.* The LCD is $2^3 \cdot 3^2 \cdot 5^2 = 8 \cdot 9 \cdot 25$.

Example 4   Least Common Denominator for Rational Expressions

Find the LCD of the following three rational expressions:

$$\frac{1}{x^3 - x^2} \qquad \frac{-2}{x^3 - x} \qquad \frac{3x}{x^2 + 2x + 1}$$

Solution

Least Common Denominator

Method	Example
Step 1. Factor the denominator of each fraction.	*Step 1.* $\dfrac{1}{x^2(x-1)} \qquad \dfrac{-2}{x(x-1)(x+1)} \qquad \dfrac{3x}{(x+1)^2}$
Step 2. Find the different factors in the denominator and the highest power to which each factor occurs.	*Step 2.* <table><tr><td>Factor</td><td>Highest exponent</td><td>Final factors</td></tr><tr><td>x</td><td>2</td><td>x^2</td></tr><tr><td>$x-1$</td><td>1</td><td>$x-1$</td></tr><tr><td>$x+1$</td><td>2</td><td>$(x+1)^2$</td></tr></table>
Step 3. The product of the final factors in *Step 2* is the LCD.	*Step 3.* The LCD is $$x^2(x-1)(x+1)^2$$

✔ Progress Check

Find the LCD of the following fractions:

$$\frac{2a}{(3a^2 + 12a + 12)b} \qquad \frac{-7b}{a(4b^2 - 8b + 4)} \qquad \frac{3}{ab^3 + 2b^3}$$

Answer

$12ab^3(a+2)^2(b-1)^2$

Equivalent Fractions

The fractions $\frac{2}{5}$ and $\frac{6}{15}$ are said to be **equivalent**, because we obtain $\frac{6}{15}$ by multiplying $\frac{2}{5}$ by $\frac{3}{3}$, which is the same as multiplying $\frac{2}{5}$ by 1. We also say that algebraic fractions are **equivalent fractions** if we can obtain one from the other by multiplying both the numerator and denominator by the same expression.

To add rational expressions, we must first determine the LCD and then convert each rational expression into an equivalent fraction with the LCD as its denominator. We can accomplish this conversion by multiplying the fraction by the appropriate equivalent of 1. We now outline the procedure and provide an example.

Example 5   Addition and Subtraction of Rational Expressions
Simplify.

$$\frac{x+1}{2x^2} - \frac{2}{3x(x+2)}$$

Solution

Addition of Rational Expressions

Method	Example
Step 1. Find the LCD.	*Step 1.* $\text{LCD} = 6x^2(x+2)$
Step 2. Multiply each rational expression by a fraction whose numerator and denominator are the same, and	*Step 2.* $\dfrac{x+1}{2x^2} \cdot \dfrac{3(x+2)}{3(x+2)} = \dfrac{3x^2+9x+6}{6x^2(x+2)}$
consist of all factors of the LCD that are missing in the denominator of the expression.	$\dfrac{2}{3x(x+2)} \cdot \dfrac{(2x)}{(2x)} = \dfrac{4x}{6x^2(x+2)}$
Step 3. Add the rational expressions. Do not multiply out the denominators since it may be possible to cancel.	*Step 3.* $\dfrac{x+1}{2x^2} - \dfrac{2}{3x(x+2)}$
	$= \dfrac{3x^2+9x+6}{6x^2(x+2)} - \dfrac{4x}{6x^2(x+2)}$
	$= \dfrac{3x^2+5x+6}{6x^2(x+2)}$

✔ Progress Check

Perform the indicated operations.

a. $\dfrac{x-8}{x^2-4} + \dfrac{3}{x^2-2x}$

b. $\dfrac{4r-3}{9r^3} - \dfrac{2r+1}{4r^2} + \dfrac{2}{3r}$

Answers

a. $\dfrac{x-3}{x(x+2)}$, $x \neq 2$

b. $\dfrac{6r^2+7r-12}{36r^3}$

Complex Fractions

At the beginning of this section, we said that we wanted to be able to simplify fractions such as

$$\frac{1-\dfrac{1}{x}}{\dfrac{1}{x^2}+\dfrac{1}{x}}$$

This is an example of a **complex fraction**, which is a fractional form with fractions in the numerator or denominator or both.

Example 6 Division of Rational Expressions

Simplify.

$$\frac{1-\dfrac{1}{x}}{\dfrac{1}{x^2}+\dfrac{1}{x}}$$

Solution

Simplifying Complex Fractions

Method	Example
Step 1. Find the LCD of all fractions in the numerator and denominator.	*Step 1.* The LCD of $\dfrac{1}{x}$ and $\dfrac{1}{x^2}$ is x^2.
Step 2. Multiply the numerator and denominator by the LCD. Since this is multiplication by 1, the result is an equivalent fraction.	*Step 2.* $\dfrac{\left(1-\dfrac{1}{x}\right)}{\left(\dfrac{1}{x^2}+\dfrac{1}{x}\right)}\cdot\dfrac{(x^2)}{(x^2)}=\dfrac{x^2-x}{1+x},\qquad x\neq 0$
	$=\dfrac{x(x-1)}{1+x},\qquad x\neq 0$

✔ Progress Check

Simplify.

a. $\dfrac{2+\dfrac{1}{x}}{1-\dfrac{2}{x}}$

b. $\dfrac{\dfrac{a}{b}+\dfrac{b}{a}}{\dfrac{1}{a}-\dfrac{1}{b}}$

Answers

a. $\dfrac{2x+1}{x-2},\qquad x\neq 0$

b. $-\dfrac{a^2+b^2}{b-a},\qquad a\neq 0,\quad b\neq 0$

Exercise Set 1.5

Perform all possible simplifications in Exercises 1–20.

1. $\dfrac{x+4}{x^2-16}$

2. $\dfrac{y^2-25}{y+5}$

3. $\dfrac{x^2-8x+16}{x-4}$

4. $\dfrac{5x^2-45}{2x-6}$

5. $\dfrac{6x^2-x-1}{2x^2+3x-2}$

6. $\dfrac{2x^3+x^2-3x}{3x^2-5x+2}$

7. $\dfrac{2}{3x-6}\div\dfrac{3}{2x-4}$

8. $\dfrac{5x+15}{8}\div\dfrac{3x+9}{4}$

9. $\dfrac{25-a^2}{b+3}\cdot\dfrac{2b^2+6b}{a-5}$

10. $\dfrac{2xy^2}{x+y}\cdot\dfrac{x+y}{4xy}$

11. $\dfrac{x+2}{3y}\div\dfrac{x^2-2x-8}{15y^2}$

12. $\dfrac{3x}{x+2}\div\dfrac{6x^2}{x^2-x-6}$

13. $\dfrac{6x^2-x-2}{2x^2-5x+3}\cdot\dfrac{2x^2-7x+6}{3x^2+x-2}$

14. $\dfrac{6x^2 + 11x - 2}{4x^2 - 3x - 1} \cdot \dfrac{5x^2 - 3x - 2}{3x^2 + 7x + 2}$

15. $(x^2 - 4) \cdot \dfrac{2x + 3}{x^2 + 2x - 8}$

16. $(a^2 - 2a) \cdot \dfrac{a + 1}{6 - a - a^2}$

17. $(x^2 - 2x - 15) \div \dfrac{x^2 - 7x + 10}{x^2 + 1}$

18. $\dfrac{2y^2 - 5y - 3}{y - 4} \div (y^2 + y - 12)$

19. $\dfrac{x^2 - 4}{x^2 + 2x - 3} \cdot \dfrac{x^2 + 3x - 4}{x^2 - 7x + 10} \cdot \dfrac{x + 3}{x^2 + 3x + 2}$

20. $\dfrac{x^2 - 9}{6x^2 + x - 1} \cdot \dfrac{2x^2 + 5x + 2}{x^2 + 4x + 3} \cdot \dfrac{x^2 - x - 2}{x^2 - 3x}$

In Exercises 21–30, find the LCD.

21. $\dfrac{4}{x}, \dfrac{x - 2}{y}$ 22. $\dfrac{x}{x - 1}, \dfrac{x + 4}{x + 2}$

23. $\dfrac{5 - a}{a}, \dfrac{7}{2a}$ 24. $\dfrac{x + 2}{x}, \dfrac{x - 2}{x^2}$

25. $\dfrac{2b}{b - 1}, \dfrac{3}{(b - 1)^2}$ 26. $\dfrac{2 + x}{x^2 - 4}, \dfrac{3}{x - 2}$

27. $\dfrac{4x}{x - 2}, \dfrac{5}{x^2 + x - 6}$ 28. $\dfrac{3}{y^2 - 3y - 4}, \dfrac{2y}{y + 1}$

29. $\dfrac{3}{x + 1}, \dfrac{2}{x}, \dfrac{x}{x - 1}$ 30. $\dfrac{4}{x}, \dfrac{3}{x - 1}, \dfrac{x}{x^2 - 2x + 1}$

In Exercises 31–50, perform the indicated operations and simplify.

31. $\dfrac{8}{a - 2} + \dfrac{4}{2 - a}$ 32. $\dfrac{x}{x^2 - 4} + \dfrac{2}{4 - x^2}$

33. $\dfrac{x - 1}{3} + 2$ 34. $\dfrac{1}{x - 1} + \dfrac{2}{x - 2}$

35. $\dfrac{1}{a + 2} + \dfrac{3}{a - 2}$ 36. $\dfrac{a}{8b} - \dfrac{b}{12a}$

37. $\dfrac{4}{3x} - \dfrac{5}{xy}$ 38. $\dfrac{4x - 1}{6x^3} + \dfrac{2}{3x^2}$

39. $\dfrac{5}{2x + 6} - \dfrac{x}{x + 3}$ 40. $\dfrac{x}{x - y} - \dfrac{y}{x + y}$

41. $\dfrac{5x}{2x^2 - 18} + \dfrac{4}{3x - 9}$

42. $\dfrac{4}{r} - \dfrac{3}{r + 2}$

43. $\dfrac{1}{x - 1} + \dfrac{2x - 1}{(x - 2)(x + 1)}$

44. $\dfrac{2x}{2x + 1} - \dfrac{x - 1}{(2x + 1)(x - 2)}$

45. $\dfrac{2x}{x^2 + x - 2} + \dfrac{3}{x + 2}$ 46. $\dfrac{2}{x - 2} + \dfrac{x}{x^2 - x - 6}$

47. $\dfrac{2x - 1}{x^2 + 5x + 6} - \dfrac{x - 2}{x^2 + 4x + 3}$

48. $\dfrac{2x - 1}{x^3 - 4x} - \dfrac{x}{x^2 + x - 2}$ 49. $\dfrac{2x}{x^2 - 1} + \dfrac{x + 1}{x^2 + 3x - 4}$

50. $\dfrac{2x}{x + 2} + \dfrac{x}{x - 2} - \dfrac{1}{x^2 - 4}$

In Exercises 51–66, simplify the complex fraction and perform all indicated operations.

51. $\dfrac{1 + \dfrac{2}{x}}{1 - \dfrac{3}{x}}$ 52. $\dfrac{x - \dfrac{1}{x}}{2 + \dfrac{1}{x}}$

53. $\dfrac{x + 1}{1 - \dfrac{1}{x}}$ 54. $\dfrac{1 - \dfrac{r^2}{s^2}}{1 + \dfrac{r}{s}}$

55. $\dfrac{x^2 - 16}{\dfrac{1}{4} - \dfrac{1}{x}}$ 56. $\dfrac{\dfrac{a}{a - b} - \dfrac{b}{a + b}}{a^2 - b^2}$

57. $2 - \dfrac{1}{1 + \dfrac{1}{a}}$ 58. $\dfrac{\dfrac{4}{x^2 - 4} + 1}{\dfrac{x}{x^2 + x - 6}}$

59. $\dfrac{\dfrac{a}{b} - \dfrac{b}{a}}{\dfrac{1}{a} + \dfrac{1}{b}}$ 60. $\dfrac{\dfrac{x}{x - 2} - \dfrac{x}{x + 2}}{\dfrac{2x}{x - 2} + \dfrac{x^2}{x - 2}}$

61. $3 - \dfrac{2}{1 - \dfrac{1}{1 + x}}$ 62. $2 + \dfrac{3}{1 + \dfrac{2}{1 - x}}$

63. $\dfrac{y - \dfrac{1}{1 - \dfrac{1}{y}}}{y + \dfrac{1}{1 + \dfrac{1}{y}}}$ 64. $1 - \dfrac{1 - \dfrac{1}{y}}{y - \dfrac{1}{y}}$

65. $1 - \dfrac{1}{1 + \dfrac{1}{1 - \dfrac{1}{1 + x}}}$ 66. $1 + \dfrac{1}{1 - \dfrac{1}{1 + \dfrac{1}{1 + x}}}$

67. Find the errors in the following and correct the statements.

a. $\dfrac{\dfrac{1}{b}}{\dfrac{1}{a} - \dfrac{1}{b}} = \dfrac{1}{a}$ b. $\dfrac{\dfrac{1}{b}}{\dfrac{1}{a} + \dfrac{1}{b}} = \left(\dfrac{1}{b}\right)\left(\dfrac{a}{1} + \dfrac{b}{1}\right)$

c. $\dfrac{a^2(3b + 4a)}{a^2 + b^2} = \dfrac{3b + 4a}{b^2}$

d. $\dfrac{1 - x}{1 + x} = -1$ e. $(x^2 - y^2)^2 = x^4 - y^4$

f. $\dfrac{a + b}{b} = a$

Applications 1.5

1. The rational expression $\frac{250x}{100 - x}$ describes the cost, in millions of dollars, to inoculate x percent of the population against a particular strain of flu.

   a. Evaluate the expression for $x = 40$, $x = 80$, $x = 95$. Describe the meaning of each inoculated in terms of percentage and cost.

   b. What happens to the cost as x approaches 100%? How can you interpret this observation?

2. Doctors use the rational expression $\frac{DA}{A + 12}$ to determine the dosage of a drug prescribed to children. In the expression, A = child's age, and D = adult dosage.

   a. Find the child's dosage for a 2-year-old child.

   b. What is the difference in the child's dosage for a 2-year-old child and a 7-year-old child?

3. The average speed on a round-trip commute having a one-way distance d is given by the complex rational expression $\dfrac{2d}{\frac{d}{r_1} + \frac{d}{r_2}}$ in which r_1 and r_2 are the speeds on the outgoing and return trips, respectively.

   a. Simplify the expression.

   b. Find the average speed for Tracy who drives from her home to Curry College (12 miles) at 40 miles per hour and returns on the same route average 30 miles per hour. Explain why the answer is not 35 miles per hour.

   c. Find the average speed for Nancy who drives from her home to Curry College (50 miles) at 40 miles per hour and returns on the same route average 30 miles per hour. Explain why the answer is not 35 miles per hour.

   d. Are the answers from part (b) and part (c) the same? Explain your answer.

1.6 Integer Exponents

Positive Integer Exponents

In Section 1.3, we defined a^n for a real number a and a positive integer n as

$$a^n = \underbrace{a \cdot a \cdots \cdot a}_{n \text{ factors}}$$

and we showed that if m and n are positive integers then $a^m a^n = a^{m+n}$. The method we used to establish this rule was to write out the factors of a^m and a^n and count the total

Table 9   Properties of Positive Integer Exponents, $m > 0$ and $n > 0$

Example	Property
$2^2 \cdot 2^3 = 2^5$	$a^m a^n = a^{m+n}$
$4 \cdot 8 = 32$	
$(2^3)^2 = 2^{3 \cdot 2} = 2^6$	$(a^m)^n = a^{mn}$
$8^2 = 64$	
$(2 \cdot 3)^2 = 2^2 \cdot 3^2$	$(ab)^m = a^m b^m$
$6^2 = 4 \cdot 9$	
$\left(\dfrac{6}{2}\right)^2 = \dfrac{6^2}{2^2}$	$\left(\dfrac{a}{b}\right)^m = \dfrac{a^m}{b^m}$
$3^2 = \dfrac{36}{4}$	
$\dfrac{2^5}{2^2} = 2^3$	$\dfrac{a^m}{a^n} = a^{m-n}$ if $m > n$, $a \neq 0$
$\dfrac{32}{4} = 8$	
$\dfrac{2^2}{2^5} = \dfrac{1}{2^3}$	$\dfrac{a^n}{a^m} = \dfrac{1}{a^{m-n}}$ if $m > n$, $a \neq 0$
$\dfrac{4}{32} = \dfrac{1}{8}$	
$\dfrac{5^2}{5^2} = \dfrac{25}{25} = 1$	$\dfrac{a^m}{a^m} = 1$ if $a \neq 0$

number of occurrences of a. The same method can be used to establish the rest of the properties in Table 9 when m and n are positive integers.

Example 1   Multiplication with Positive Integer Exponents
Simplify the following.

a. $(4a^2b^3)(2a^3b)$ b. $(2x^2y)^4$

Solution

a. $(4a^2b^3)(2a^3b) = 4 \cdot 2 \cdot a^2a^3b^3b = 8a^5b^4$ b. $(2x^2y)^4 = 2^4(x^2)^4y^4 = 16x^8y^4$ ■

✔ **Progress Check**

Simplify, using only positive exponents.

a. $(x^3)^4$ b. $x^4(x^2)^3$ c. $\dfrac{a^{14}}{a^8}$ d. $\dfrac{-2(x+1)^n}{(x+1)^{2n}}$

e. $(3ab^2)^3$ f. $\left(\dfrac{-ab^2}{c^3}\right)^3$

Answers

a. x^{12} b. x^{10} c. a^6 d. $-\dfrac{2}{(x+1)^n}$

e. $27a^3b^6$ f. $-\dfrac{a^3b^6}{c^9}$

Zero and Negative Exponents

We next expand our rules to include zero and negative exponents when the base is nonzero. We wish to define a^0 to be consistent with the previous rules for exponents. For example, applying the rule $a^m a^n = a^{m+n}$ yields

$$a^m a^0 = a^{m+0} = a^m$$

Dividing both sides by a^m, we obtain $a^0 = 1$. We therefore *define* a^0 for any nonzero real number by

$$a^0 = 1, \quad a \neq 0$$

The same approach leads us to a definition of negative exponents. For consistency, if $m > 0$, we must have

$$a^m a^{-m} = a^{m-m} = a^0 = 1 \qquad \text{or} \qquad a^m a^{-m} = 1 \tag{1}$$

Division of both sides of Equation (1) by a^m suggests that we define a^{-m} as

$$a^{-m} = \frac{1}{a^m}, \quad a \neq 0$$

Dividing Equation (1) by a^{-m}, we have

$$a^m = \frac{1}{a^{-m}}, \quad a \neq 0$$

Thus, a^m and a^{-m} are reciprocals of one another. The rule for handling negative exponents can be expressed as follows.

A nonzero factor moves from numerator to denominator (or from denominator to numerator) by changing the sign of the exponent.

Warning
It is important to note that

0^0 is not defined. Furthermore, 0^{-m} is also not defined for $m > 0$.

We may also conclude that

$$a^0 \neq 0 \quad \text{and} \quad a^{-m} \neq 0, \quad m > 0$$

We summarize these results in Table 10.

Table 10   Properties of Integer Exponents, $a \neq 0$

Example	Property
$\left(-\dfrac{1}{2}\right)^0 = 1$	$a^0 = 1$
$8 = 2^3 = \dfrac{1}{2^{-3}}$	$a^m = \dfrac{1}{a^{-m}}$
$2^{-3} = \dfrac{1}{2^3} = \dfrac{1}{8}$	$a^{-m} = \dfrac{1}{a^m}$

Example 2   Operations with Integer Exponents
Simplify the following, using only positive exponents.

a. $\dfrac{2}{(x-1)^0}$
b. $(x^2 y^{-3})^{-5}$
c. $\dfrac{y^{3k+1}}{2y^{2k}}, \quad k > 0$

Solution

a. $\dfrac{2}{(x-1)^0} = \dfrac{2}{1} = 2$
b. $(x^2 y^{-3})^{-5} = (x^2)^{-5}(y^{-3})^{-5} = x^{-10}y^{15} = \dfrac{y^{15}}{x^{10}}$

c. $\dfrac{y^{3k+1}}{2y^{2k}} = \dfrac{y^{3k+1}y^{-2k}}{2} = \dfrac{y^{3k+1-2k}}{2} = \dfrac{1}{2}y^{k+1}$

✔ Progress Check
Simplify, using only positive exponents.

a. $x^{-2}y^{-3}$
b. $\dfrac{-3x^4 y^{-2}}{9x^{-8}y^6}$
c. $\left(\dfrac{x^{-3}}{x^{-4}}\right)^{-1}$

Answers

a. $\dfrac{1}{x^2 y^3}$
b. $-\dfrac{x^{12}}{3y^8}$
c. $\dfrac{1}{x}$

Warning

Do not confuse negative numbers and negative exponents.

a. $2^{-4} = \dfrac{1}{2^4}$

   Note that $2^{-4} \neq -2^4$.

b. $(-2)^{-3} = \dfrac{1}{(-2)^3} = \dfrac{1}{-8} = -\dfrac{1}{8}$

   Note that $(-2)^{-3} \neq \dfrac{1}{2^3} = \dfrac{1}{8}$.

Scientific Notation

One of the significant applications of integer exponents is that of scientific notation. This technique enables us to recognize the size of extremely large and extremely small numbers rather quickly and in a more concise form.

Consider the following examples for powers of 10:

$$\text{One thousand} = 1000 = 1 \times 10^3 = 10^3$$

$$\text{One thousandth} = 0.001 = \frac{1}{1000} = \frac{1}{10^3} = 10^{-3}$$

Reversing the procedure we obtain:

1. $10^2 = 1 \times 10^2 = 100.0$, namely, 1 with the decimal point *two* places to the *right* of it.

2. $10^{-2} = 1 \times 10^{-2} = \frac{1}{100} = 0.01$, namely, 1 with the decimal point *two* places to the *left* of it.

> **Scientific Notation**
> A number is written in scientific notation if it is of the form $\pm a \times 10^m$, where $1 \le a < 10$ and m is some integer. If $a = 1$, it is generally omitted.

Example 3   Writing in Scientific Notation
An angstrom (Å) equals 1 ten-billionth of a meter. Write this in scientific notation.

Solution
$1 \text{ Å} = 0.0000000001 \text{ meters} = 10^{-10} \text{ meters}$

Example 4   Writing in Scientific Notation
One light-year is approximately 6 trillion miles. Write this in scientific notation.

Solution

1 light-year ≈ 6,000,000,000,000 miles = 6×10^{12} miles

If $\pm a \times 10^m$ is the result of some calculations or measurements involving scientific notation, then the number of digits present in a are generally taken as the significant digits of the answer. For example, 6×10^{12} has one significant digit.

If we write a number in scientific notation with fewer significant digits than the original number presented, we must round the last significant digit used according to the following rule:

- Add 1 to the last significant digit if the digit following it in the original number is 5, 6, 7, 8, or 9.

- Leave the last significant digit alone if the digit following it in the original number is 0, 1, 2, 3, or 4.

Example 5 Writing in Scientific Notation

The speed of light is approximately 186,282 miles per second. Write it in scientific notation with four significant digits.

Solution

The speed of light ≈ 1.863×10^5 miles per second since 186,282 is rounded to 186,300.

Example 6 Writing in Scientific Notation

There are 31,557,600 seconds in an average year (365.25 days). Write it in scientific notation with four significant digits.

Solution

1 year = 3.156×10^7 seconds.

Example 7 Calculations in Scientific Notation

Find the number of miles in 1 light-year to four significant digits.

Solution

One light-year is the number of miles light travels in 1 year.

$$1 \text{ light-year} = (1.863 \times 10^5 \text{ miles per second})(3.156 \times 10^7 \text{ seconds})$$
$$= 5.880 \times 10^{12} \text{ miles.}$$

Note that this becomes 6×10^{12} miles if we require only one significant digit. The number of significant digits of our answer equals the minimum number of significant digits involved in our calculations.

⌨ **Calculator Alert**

Your calculator has a key that can be used to enter numbers in scientific notation. This key may be labeled $\boxed{\text{EXP}}$, $\boxed{\text{EE}}$, or $\boxed{\text{EEX}}$. Note how numbers entered in this manner appear on the calculator's display window.

Example: 1.863 $\boxed{\text{EXP}}$ 5 × 3.156 $\boxed{\text{EXP}}$ 7 = $\boxed{\text{5.879628 \ 12}}$ or $\boxed{\text{5.879628E \ 12}}$

$$\approx 5.880 \times 10^{12}$$

✔ **Progress Check**

1 ounce = 0.02834952 kilogram

Write this number in scientific notation using:

a. two significant digits

b. three significant digits

c. five significant digits

Answers

a. 2.8×10^{-2} b. 2.83×10^{-2} c. 2.8350×10^{-2}

Exercise Set 1.6

In Exercises 1–6, the right-hand side is incorrect. Find the correct term.

1. $x^2 \cdot x^4 = x^8$

2. $(y^2)^5 = y^7$

3. $\dfrac{b^6}{b^2} = b^3$

4. $\dfrac{x^2}{x^6} = x^4$

5. $(2x)^4 = 2x^4$

6. $\left(\dfrac{4}{3}\right)^4 = \dfrac{4}{3^4}$

In Exercises 7–64, use the rules for exponents to simplify. Write the answers using only positive exponents.

7. $\left(-\dfrac{1}{2}\right)^4\left(-\dfrac{1}{2}\right)^3$

8. $(x^m)^{3m}$

9. $(y^4)^{2n}$

10. $\dfrac{(-4)^6}{(-4)^{10}}$

11. $-\left(\dfrac{x}{y}\right)^3$

12. $-3r^3r^3$

13. $(x^3)^5 \cdot x^4$

14. $\dfrac{x^{12}}{x^8}$

15. $(-2x^2)^5$

16. $-(2x^2)^5$

17. $x^{3n} \cdot x^n$

18. $(-2)^m(-2)^n$

19. $\dfrac{x^n}{x^{n+2}}$

20. $\left(\dfrac{3x^3}{y^2}\right)^5$

21. $(-5x^3)(-6x^5)$

22. $(x^2)^3(y^2)^4(x^3)^7$

23. $\dfrac{(r^2)^4}{(r^4)^2}$

24. $[(3b+1)^5]^5$

25. $\left(\dfrac{3}{2}x^2y^3\right)^n$

26. $\dfrac{(-2a^2b)^4}{(-3ab^2)^3}$

27. $(2x+1)^3(2x+1)^7$

28. $\dfrac{y^3(y^3)^4}{(y^4)^6}$

29. $(-2a^2b^3)^{2n}$

30. $\left(-\dfrac{2}{3}a^2b^3c^2\right)^3$

31. $2^0 + 3^{-1}$

32. $(xy)^0 - 2^{-1}$

33. $\dfrac{3}{(2x^2 + 1)^0}$

34. $(-3)^{-3}$

35. $\dfrac{1}{3^{-4}}$

36. x^{-5}

37. $(-x)^3$

38. $-x^{-5}$

39. $\dfrac{1}{y^{-6}}$

40. $(2a)^{-6}$

41. $5^{-3}5^5$

42. $4y^5y^{-2}$

43. $(3^2)^{-3}$

44. $(x^{-2})^4$

45. $(x^{-3})^{-3}$

46. $[(x + y)^{-2}]^2$

47. $\dfrac{2^2}{2^{-3}}$

48. $\dfrac{x^8}{x^{-10}}$

49. $\dfrac{2x^4y^{-2}}{x^2y^{-3}}$

50. $(x^4y^{-2})^{-1}$

51. $(3a^{-2}b^{-3})^{-2}$

52. $\dfrac{1}{(2xy)^{-2}}$

53. $\left(-\dfrac{1}{2}x^3y^{-4}\right)^{-3}$

54. $\dfrac{(x^{-2})^2}{(3y^{-2})^3}$

55. $\dfrac{3a^5b^{-2}}{9a^{-4}b^2}$

56. $\left(\dfrac{x^3}{x^{-2}}\right)^2$

57. $\left(\dfrac{2a^2b^{-4}}{a^{-3}c^{-3}}\right)^2$

58. $\dfrac{2x^{-3}y^2}{x^{-3}y^{-3}}$

59. $(a - 2b^2)^{-1}$

60. $\left(\dfrac{y^{-2}}{y^{-3}}\right)^{-1}$

61. $\dfrac{(a + b)^{-1}}{(a - b)^{-2}}$

62. $(a^{-1} + b^{-1})^{-1}$

63. $\dfrac{a^{-1} + b^{-1}}{a^{-1} - b^{-1}}$

64. $\left(\dfrac{a}{b}\right)^{-1} + \left(\dfrac{b}{a}\right)^{-1}$

65. Show that $\left(\dfrac{a}{b}\right)^{-n} = \left(\dfrac{b}{a}\right)^{n}$

 Evaluate each expression in Exercises 66–69.

66. $(1.20^2)^{-1}$

67. $[(-3.67)^2]^{-1}$

68. $\left(\dfrac{7.65^{-1}}{7.65^2}\right)^2$

69. $\left(\dfrac{4.46^2}{4.46^{-1}}\right)^{-1}$

In Exercises 70–75, write each number using scientific notation.

70. 7000

71. 0.0091

72. 452,000,000,000

73. 23

74. 0.00000357

75. 0.8×10^{-3}

In Exercises 76–81, write each number without exponents.

76. 4.53×10^5

77. 8.93×10^{-4}

78. 0.0017×10^7

79. 145×10^3

80. 100×10^{-3}

81. 1253×10^{-6}

 82. The dimensions of a rectangular field, measured in meters, are 4.1×10^3 by 3.75×10^5. Find the area of this field expressed in scientific notation.

 83. The volume V of a spherical bubble of radius r is given by the formula

$$V = \dfrac{4}{3}\pi r^3$$

If we take the value of π to be 3.14, find the volume of a bubble, using scientific notation, if its radius is 0.09 inch.

84. Find the distance, expressed in scientific notation, that light travels in 0.000020 seconds if the speed of light is 1.86×10^5 miles per second.

 85. The Republic of Singapore is said to have the highest population density of any country in the world. If its area is 240 square miles and its estimated population is 2,600,000, find the population density, that is, the approximate number of people per square mile, using scientific notation.

 86. Scientists have suggested that the relationship between an animal's weight W and its surface area S is given by the formula
$$S = KW^{\frac{2}{3}}$$

where K is a constant chosen so that W, measured in kilograms, yields a value for S, measured in square meters. If the value of K for a horse is 0.10 and the horse weights 350 kilograms, find the estimated surface area of the horse, using scientific notation.

87. Simplify the following.

a. $\dfrac{2^{n+3} + 2^n + 2^n}{4(2^{n+3} - 2^{n+1})}$

b. $\dfrac{a(1 - r^3)}{1 - r}$

c. $\dfrac{9^{6m}}{3^{2m}}$ d. $\dfrac{8^4 + 8^4 + 8^4 + 8^4}{4^4}$

e. $\dfrac{(6 \times 10^{-2})(2 \times 10^{-3})}{3 \times 10^8}$

 88. Assuming a lifetime is 70 years, how much is that in seconds? Express your answer in scientific notation.

Applications 1.6

1. The exact distance between Earth and the Sun varies with its position in its orbit, which is elliptical. The average distance (the mean distance) between the Earth and the Sun is about 92,955,887.6 miles. Write this number in scientific notation.

2. The 2010 census revealed that the population of Shanghai had reached 23,019,148, including 8,977,000 long-term migrants.

   a. Write the population of long-term migrants using scientific notation.

   b. If the area of Shanghai is 2,401 square miles, find the population density, that is, the approximate number of people per square miles, using scientific notation.

   c. Please find the population density for your home town. Write your answer in scientific notation.

3. The Great Pyramid of Giza in Egypt is the largest of the original Seven Wonders of the World that is basically still intact. This pyramid is an architectural feat that cannot be duplicated with our modern technology and advanced knowledge. The original height of the Great Pyramid was 485 feet, but due to erosion its height declined to 450 feet. Each side of the square base is 755.5 feet in length. Find the base area in square inches in scientific notation.

4. In 1907, the New Year's Eve Ball (Big Apple) first descended from a flagpole at One Times Square, constructed with iron and wood materials with 100 25-watt bulbs weighing 700 pounds and measuring 5 feet in diameter. The volume V of a spherical bubble of radius r is given by the formula $V = \frac{4\pi}{3}r^3$. If we take the value of π as 3.1416, find the volume of the Big Apple, using scientific notation.

5. If the $50 that bought Manhattan Island on May 6, 1626, had been invested at 5% compounded annually, what would it be worth on May 6, 2011? Express the answer in scientific notation, rounded to 2 digits. (Hint: $A = P(1 + r)^t$.)

6. At the present time, the U.S. national debt amounts to 1.4×10^{13}. The population of the United States is approximately 311,277,000. Find the average national debt amount, in scientific notation.

7. Find the average distance (the mean distance) between the Earth and the Moon. Write your answer in scientific notation.

1.7   Rational Exponents and Radicals

nth Roots

Consider a square whose area is 25 cm² (square centimeters), and whose sides are of length a. We can then write

$$a^2 = 25$$

so that a is a number whose square is 25. We say that a is the *square root* of b if $a^2 = b$. Similarly, we say that a is a *cube root* of b if $a^3 = b$, and, in general, if n is a natural number, we say that

a is an **nth root** of b if $a^n = b$

Thus, 5 is a square root of 25 since $5^2 = 25$, and –2 is a cube root of –8 since $(-2)^3 = -8$.

Since $(-5)^2 = 25$, we conclude that –5 is also a square root of 25. More generally, if $b > 0$ and a is a square root of b, then $-a$ is also a square root of b. If $b < 0$, there is no real number a such that $a^2 = b$, since the square of a real number is always nonnegative. (In Section 1.8, we introduce an extended number system in which there is a root when $b < 0$ and n is even.)

We would like to define rational exponents in a manner that is consistent with the rules for integer exponents. If the rule $(a^m)^n = a^{mn}$ is to hold, then we must have

$$(b^{1/n})^n = b^{n/n} = b$$

But a is an nth root of b if $a^n = b$. Then for every natural number n, we say that

$$b^{1/n} \text{ is an } n\text{th root of } b$$

Principal nth Root

If n is even and b is positive, there are two numbers that are nth roots of b. For example,

$$4^2 = 16 \quad \text{and} \quad (-4)^2 = 16$$

There are then two candidates for $16^{1/2}$, namely 4 and –4. To avoid ambiguity we say that $16^{1/2} = 4$ That is, if n is even and b is positive, we always *choose the positive number* a such that $a^n = b$ is the nth root, and call it the *principal nth root* of b. Thus, $b^{1/n}$ denotes the principal nth root of b.

We summarize these results in Table 11.

Example 1　Roots of a Real Number
Evaluate.

a. $144^{1/2}$ 　　 b. $(-8)^{1/3}$ 　　 c. $(-25)^{1/2}$ 　　 d. $-\left(\dfrac{1}{16}\right)^{1/4}$

Solution

a. $144^{1/2} = 12$ 　　　　　　 b. $(-8)^{1/3} = -2$

Table 11　Properties of Powers $a^n = b$ and Roots $a = b^{1/n}$ for Integer $n > 0$

Example		Property
$2^3 = 8$	$(-2)^3 = -8$	Any power of a real number is a real number.
$8^{1/3} = 2$	$(-8)^{1/3} = -2$	The odd root of a real number is a real number.
$0^n = 0$	$0^{1/n} = 0$	A positive power or root of zero is zero.
$4^2 = 16$	$(-4)^2 = 16$	A positive number raised to an even power equals the negative of that number raised to the same even power.
$(16)^{1/2} = 4$		The principal root of a positive number is a positive number.
$(-4)^{1/2}$ is undefined in the real number system		The even root of a negative number is not a real number.

Focus on When Is a Proof Not a Proof?

Books of mathematical puzzles love to include "proofs" that lead to false or contradictory results. Of course, there is always an incorrect step hidden somewhere in the proof. The error may be subtle, but a good grounding in the fundamentals of mathematics will enable you to catch it.

Examine the following "proof."

$$1 = 1^{1/2} \tag{1}$$

$$= [(-1)^2]^{1/2} \tag{2}$$

$$= (-1)^{2/2} \tag{3}$$

$$= (-1)^1 \tag{4}$$

$$= -1 \tag{5}$$

The result is obviously contradictory: we can't have $1 = -1$. Yet each step seems to be legitimate. Did you spot the flaw? The rule

$$(b^m)^{1/n} = b^{m/n}$$

used in going from Equation (2) to (3) does not apply when n is even and b is negative.

---

c. $(-25)^{1/2}$ is not a real number   d. $-\left(\dfrac{1}{16}\right)^{1/4} = -\dfrac{1}{2}$

Rational Exponents

Now we are prepared to define $b^{m/n}$, where m is an integer (positive or negative), n is a positive integer, and $b > 0$ when n is even. We want the rules for exponents to hold for rational exponents as well. That is, we want to have

$$4^{3/2} = 4^{(1/2)(3)} = (4^{1/2})^3 = 2^3 = 8$$

and

$$4^{3/2} = 4^{(3)(1/2)} = (4^3)^{1/2} = (64)^{1/2} = 8$$

To achieve this consistency, we define $b^{m/n}$ for an integer m, a natural number n, and a real number b, by

$$b^{m/n} = (b^{1/n})^m = (b^m)^{1/n}$$

where b must be positive when n is even. With this definition, all the rules of exponents continue to hold when the exponents are rational numbers.

Example 2   Operations with Rational Exponents

Simplify.

a. $(-8)^{4/3}$ b. $x^{1/2} \cdot x^{3/4}$ c. $(x^{3/4})^2$ d. $(3x^{2/3}y^{-5/3})^3$

Solution

a. $(-8)^{4/3} = [(-8)^{1/3}]^4 = (-2)^4 = 16$ b. $x^{1/2} \cdot x^{3/4} = x^{1/2+3/4} = x^{5/4}$

c. $(x^{3/4})^2 = x^{(3/4)(2)} = x^{3/2}$ d. $(3x^{2/3}y^{-5/3})^3 = 3^3 \cdot x^{(2/3)(3)}y^{(-5/3)(3)} = 27x^2y^{-5} = \dfrac{27x^2}{y^5}$ ▪

✔ Progress Check

Simplify. Assume all variables are positive real numbers.

a. $27^{4/3}$ b. $(a^{1/2}b^{-2})^{-2}$ c. $\left(\dfrac{x^{1/3}y^{2/3}}{z^{5/6}}\right)^{12}$

Answers

a. 81 b. $\dfrac{b^4}{a}$ c. $\dfrac{x^4y^8}{z^{10}}$

Radicals

The symbol $\sqrt{b}$ is an alternative way of writing $b^{1/2}$, that is, $\sqrt{b}$ denotes the nonnegative square root of b. The symbol $\sqrt{}$ is called a **radical sign**, and $\sqrt{b}$ is called the **principal square root** of b. Thus,

$$\sqrt{25} = 5 \qquad \sqrt{0} = 0 \qquad \sqrt{-25} \text{ is undefined}$$

In general, the symbol $\sqrt[n]{b}$ is an alternative way of writing $b^{1/n}$, the principal nth root of b. Of course, we must apply the same restrictions to $\sqrt[n]{b}$ that we established for $b^{1/n}$. In summary:

$$\sqrt[n]{b} = b^{1/n} = a \qquad \text{where } a^n = b$$

with these restrictions:

- if n is even and $b < 0$, $\sqrt[n]{b}$ is not a real number;
- if n is even and $b \geq 0$, $\sqrt[n]{b}$ is the *nonnegative* number a satisfying $a^n = b$.

Warning

Many students are accustomed to writing $\sqrt{4} = \pm 2$. This is incorrect, since the symbol $\sqrt{}$ indicates the *principal* square root, which is nonnegative. Get in the habit of writing $\sqrt{4} = 2$. If you want to indicate *all* square roots of 4, write $\pm\sqrt{4} = \pm 2$.

In short, $\sqrt[n]{b}$ is the **radical form** of $b^{1/n}$. We can switch back and forth from one form to the other. For instance,

$$\sqrt[3]{7} = 7^{1/3} \qquad (11)^{1/5} = \sqrt[5]{11}$$

Finally, we treat the radical form of $b^{m/n}$ where m is an integer and n is a positive integer as follows.

and

$$b^{m/n} = (b^m)^{1/n} = \sqrt[n]{b^m}$$

$$b^{m/n} = (b^{1/n})^m = (\sqrt[n]{b})^m$$

Thus

$$8^{2/3} = (8^2)^{1/3} = \sqrt[3]{8^2}$$
$$= (8^{1/3})^2 = (\sqrt[3]{8})^2$$

(Check that the last two expressions have the same value.)

Example 3   Radicals and Rational Exponents

Change from radical form to rational exponent form or vice versa. Assume all variables are nonzero.

a. $(2x)^{-3/2}, \quad x > 0$ b. $\dfrac{1}{\sqrt[7]{y^4}}$ c. $(-3a)^{3/7}$ d. $\sqrt{x^2 + y^2}$

Solution

a. $(2x)^{-3/2} = \dfrac{1}{(2x)^{3/2}} = \dfrac{1}{\sqrt{8x^3}}$ b. $\dfrac{1}{\sqrt[7]{y^4}} = \dfrac{1}{y^{4/7}} = y^{-4/7}$

c. $(-3a)^{3/7} = \sqrt[7]{-27a^3}$ d. $\sqrt{x^2 + y^2} = (x^2 + y^2)^{1/2}$

> ✔ **Progress Check**
> Change from radical form to rational exponent form or vice versa. Assume all variables are positive real numbers.
>
> a. $\sqrt[4]{2rs^3}$ b. $(x + y)^{5/2}$ c. $y^{-5/4}$ d. $\dfrac{1}{\sqrt[4]{m^5}}$
>
> **Answers**
> a. $(2r)^{1/4}s^{3/4}$ b. $\sqrt{(x + y)^5}$ c. $\dfrac{1}{\sqrt[4]{y^5}}$ d. $m^{-5/4}$

Since radicals are just another way of writing exponents, the properties of radicals can be derived from the properties of exponents. In Table 12, n is a positive integer, a and b are real numbers, and all radicals are real numbers.

Table 12   Properties of Radicals

Example	Property
$\sqrt[3]{8^2} = (\sqrt[3]{8})^2 = 4$	$\sqrt[n]{b^m} = (\sqrt[n]{b})^m$
$\sqrt{4}\sqrt{9} = \sqrt{36} = 6$	$\sqrt[n]{a}\sqrt[n]{b} = \sqrt[n]{ab}$
$\dfrac{\sqrt[3]{8}}{\sqrt[3]{27}} = \sqrt[3]{\dfrac{8}{27}} = \dfrac{2}{3}$	$\dfrac{\sqrt[n]{a}}{\sqrt[n]{b}} = \sqrt[n]{\dfrac{a}{b}}$
$\sqrt[3]{(-2)^3} = -2$	$\sqrt[n]{a^n} = a$ if n is odd
$\sqrt{(-2)^2} = \lvert -2 \rvert = 2$	$\sqrt[n]{a^n} = \lvert a \rvert$ if n is even

Here are some examples using these properties.

Example 4   Operations with Radicals

Simplify.

a. $\sqrt{18}$ b. $\sqrt[3]{-54}$ c. $2\sqrt[3]{8x^3y}$ d. $\sqrt{x^6}$

Solution

a. $\sqrt{18} = \sqrt{9 \cdot 2} = \sqrt{9}\sqrt{2} = 3\sqrt{2}$

b. $\sqrt[3]{-54} = \sqrt[3]{(-27)(2)} = \sqrt[3]{-27}\sqrt[3]{2} = -3\sqrt[3]{2}$

c. $2\sqrt[3]{8x^3y} = 2\sqrt[3]{8}\sqrt[3]{x^3}\sqrt[3]{y} = 2(2)(x)\sqrt[3]{y} = 4x\sqrt[3]{y}$

d. $\sqrt{x^6} = \sqrt{x^2} \cdot \sqrt{x^2} \cdot \sqrt{x^2} = \lvert x \rvert \cdot \lvert x \rvert \cdot \lvert x \rvert = \lvert x \rvert^3$

Warning

The properties of radicals state that

$$\sqrt{x^2} = \lvert x \rvert$$

It is a common error to write $\sqrt{x^2} = x$. This can lead to the conclusion that $\sqrt{(-6)^2} = -6$. Since the symbol $\sqrt{}$ represents the principal, or nonnegative, square root of a number, the result cannot be negative. It is therefore essential to write $\sqrt{x^2} = \lvert x \rvert$ (and, in fact, $\sqrt[n]{x^n} = \lvert x \rvert$ whenever n is even) unless we know that $x \geq 0$, in which case we can write $\sqrt{x^2} = x$.

Simplifying Radicals

A radical is said to be in **simplified form** when the following conditions are satisfied:

1. $\sqrt[n]{b^m}$ has $m < n$;

2. $\sqrt[n]{b^m}$ has no common factors between m and n;

3. A denominator is free of radicals.

The first two conditions can always be met by using the properties of radicals and by writing radicals in exponent form. For example,

$$\sqrt[3]{x^4} = \sqrt[3]{x^3 \cdot x} = \sqrt[3]{x^3}\sqrt[3]{x} = x\sqrt[3]{x}$$

and

$$\sqrt[6]{x^4} = x^{4/6} = x^{2/3} = \sqrt[3]{x^2}$$

The third condition can always be satisfied by multiplying the fraction by a properly chosen form of unity, a process called **rationalizing the denominator**. For example, to rationalize $\dfrac{1}{\sqrt{3}}$ we proceed as follows.

$$\frac{1}{\sqrt{3}} = \frac{1}{\sqrt{3}} \cdot \frac{\sqrt{3}}{\sqrt{3}} = \frac{\sqrt{3}}{\sqrt{3^2}} = \frac{\sqrt{3}}{3}$$

In this connection, a useful formula is

$$(\sqrt{m} + \sqrt{n})(\sqrt{m} - \sqrt{n}) = m - n$$

which we will apply in the following examples.

Example 5   Rationalizing Denominators

Rationalize the denominator. Assume all variables denote positive numbers.

a. $\sqrt{\dfrac{x}{y}}$ b. $\dfrac{4}{\sqrt{5} - \sqrt{2}}$ c. $\dfrac{5}{\sqrt{x} + 2}$ d. $\dfrac{5}{\sqrt{x + 2}}$

Solution

a. $\sqrt{\dfrac{x}{y}} = \dfrac{\sqrt{x}}{\sqrt{y}} = \dfrac{\sqrt{x}}{\sqrt{y}} \cdot \dfrac{\sqrt{y}}{\sqrt{y}} = \dfrac{\sqrt{xy}}{\sqrt{y^2}} = \dfrac{\sqrt{xy}}{y}$

b. $\dfrac{4}{\sqrt{5} - \sqrt{2}} = \dfrac{4}{\sqrt{5} - \sqrt{2}} \cdot \dfrac{\sqrt{5} + \sqrt{2}}{\sqrt{5} + \sqrt{2}} = \dfrac{4(\sqrt{5} + \sqrt{2})}{5 - 2} = \dfrac{4}{3}(\sqrt{5} + \sqrt{2})$

c. $\dfrac{5}{\sqrt{x} + 2} = \dfrac{5}{\sqrt{x} + 2} \cdot \dfrac{\sqrt{x} - 2}{\sqrt{x} - 2} = \dfrac{5(\sqrt{x} - 2)}{x - 4}$

d. $\dfrac{5}{\sqrt{x + 2}} = \dfrac{5}{\sqrt{x + 2}} \cdot \dfrac{\sqrt{x + 2}}{\sqrt{x + 2}} = \dfrac{5\sqrt{x + 2}}{x + 2}$

✔ Progress Check

Rationalize the denominator. Assume all variables denote positive numbers.

a. $\dfrac{-9xy^3}{\sqrt{3xy}}$ b. $\dfrac{-6}{\sqrt{2} + \sqrt{6}}$ c. $\dfrac{4}{\sqrt{x} - \sqrt{y}}$

Answers

a. $-3y^2\sqrt{3xy}, \quad x \neq 0, \quad y \neq 0$ b. $\dfrac{3}{2}(\sqrt{2} - \sqrt{6})$ c. $\dfrac{4(\sqrt{x} + \sqrt{y})}{x - y}$

There are times in mathematics when it is necessary to rationalize the numerator instead of the denominator. Although this is in opposition to a simplified form, we illustrate this technique with the following example. Note that if an expression does not display a denominator, we assume a denominator of 1.

Example 6   Rationalizing Numerators

Rationalize the numerator. Assume all variables denote positive numbers.

a. $\dfrac{4}{3}(\sqrt{5} + \sqrt{2})$ b. $\dfrac{x - \sqrt{3}}{x + 4}$

c. $\sqrt{x} + 4$ d. $\dfrac{\sqrt{x} - 2}{x - 4}$

Solution

a. $\dfrac{4}{3}(\sqrt{5} + \sqrt{2}) \cdot \dfrac{\sqrt{5} - \sqrt{2}}{\sqrt{5} - \sqrt{2}} = \dfrac{4}{3} \dfrac{(5 - 2)}{(\sqrt{5} - \sqrt{2})} = \dfrac{4}{\sqrt{5} - \sqrt{2}}$

See Example 5 (b).

b. $\dfrac{x - \sqrt{3}}{x + 4} \cdot \dfrac{x + \sqrt{3}}{x + \sqrt{3}} = \dfrac{x^2 - 3}{(x + 4)(x + \sqrt{3})}$

c. $\dfrac{\sqrt{x} + 4}{1} \cdot \dfrac{\sqrt{x} - 4}{\sqrt{x} - 4} = \dfrac{x - 16}{\sqrt{x} - 4}$

d. $\dfrac{\sqrt{x} - 2}{x - 4} \cdot \dfrac{\sqrt{x} + 2}{\sqrt{x} + 2} = \dfrac{x - 4}{(x - 4)(\sqrt{x} + 2)} = \dfrac{1}{\sqrt{x} + 2}, \quad x \neq 4$

Example 7   Simplified Forms with Radicals

Write in simplified form. Assume all variables denote positive numbers.

a. $\sqrt[4]{y^5}$ b. $\sqrt{\dfrac{8x^3}{y}}$ c. $\sqrt[6]{\dfrac{x^3}{y^2}}$

Solution

a. $\sqrt[4]{y^5} = \sqrt[4]{y^4 \cdot y} = \sqrt[4]{y^4}\sqrt[4]{y} = y\sqrt[4]{y}$

b. $\sqrt{\dfrac{8x^3}{y}} = \dfrac{\sqrt{(4x^2)(2x)}}{\sqrt{y}} = \dfrac{\sqrt{4x^2}\sqrt{2x}}{\sqrt{y}} = \dfrac{2x\sqrt{2x}}{\sqrt{y}} = \dfrac{2x\sqrt{2x}}{\sqrt{y}} \cdot \dfrac{\sqrt{y}}{\sqrt{y}} = \dfrac{2x\sqrt{2xy}}{y}$

c. $\sqrt[6]{\dfrac{x^3}{y^2}} = \dfrac{\sqrt[6]{x^3}}{\sqrt[6]{y^2}} = \dfrac{\sqrt{x}}{\sqrt[3]{y}} = \dfrac{\sqrt{x}}{\sqrt[3]{y}} \cdot \dfrac{\sqrt[3]{y^2}}{\sqrt[3]{y^2}} = \dfrac{\sqrt{x}\sqrt[3]{y^2}}{y}$

✔ Progress Check
Write in simplified form. Assume all variables denote positive numbers.

a. $\sqrt{75}$ b. $\sqrt{\dfrac{18x^6}{y}}$ c. $\sqrt[3]{ab^4c^7}$ d. $\dfrac{-2xy^3}{\sqrt[4]{32x^3y^5}}$

Answers
a. $5\sqrt{3}$ b. $\dfrac{3|x|^3\sqrt{2y}}{y}$ c. $bc^2\sqrt[3]{abc}$ d. $-\dfrac{y}{2}\sqrt[4]{8xy^3}$, $x \neq 0$, $y \neq 0$

Operations with Radicals

We can add or subtract expressions involving exactly the same radical forms. For example,

$$2\sqrt{2} + 3\sqrt{2} = 5\sqrt{2}$$

since

$$2\sqrt{2} + 3\sqrt{2} = (2 + 3)\sqrt{2} = 5\sqrt{2}$$

and

$$3\sqrt[3]{x^2y} - 7\sqrt[3]{x^2y} = 4\sqrt[3]{x^2y}$$

Example 8   Addition and Subtraction of Radicals
Write in simplified form. Assume all variables denote positive numbers.

a. $7\sqrt{5} + 4\sqrt{3} - 9\sqrt{5}$ b. $\sqrt[3]{x^2y} - \dfrac{1}{2}\sqrt{xy} - 3\sqrt[3]{x^2y} + 4\sqrt{xy}$

Solution
a. $7\sqrt{5} + 4\sqrt{3} - 9\sqrt{5} = -2\sqrt{5} + 4\sqrt{3}$

b. $\sqrt[3]{x^2y} - \dfrac{1}{2}\sqrt{xy} - 3\sqrt[3]{x^2y} + 4\sqrt{xy} = -2\sqrt[3]{x^2y} + \dfrac{7}{2}\sqrt{xy}$

Warning
$$\sqrt{9} + \sqrt{16} \neq \sqrt{25}$$

You can perform addition only with identical radical forms. *Adding unlike radicals is one of the most common mistakes made by students in algebra!* You can easily verify that

$$\sqrt{9} + \sqrt{16} = 3 + 4 = 7$$

The product of $\sqrt[n]{a}$ and $\sqrt[m]{b}$ can be readily simplified only when $m = n$. Thus,

$$\sqrt[5]{x^2y} \cdot \sqrt[5]{xy} = \sqrt[5]{x^3y^2}$$

but

$$\sqrt[3]{x^2y} \cdot \sqrt[5]{xy}$$

cannot be readily simplified.

Example 9 Multiplication of Radicals

Multiply and simplify.

a. $2\sqrt[3]{xy^2} \cdot \sqrt[3]{x^2y^2}$ b. $\sqrt[5]{a^2b}\sqrt{ab}\sqrt[5]{ab^2}$

Solution

a. $2\sqrt[3]{xy^2} \cdot \sqrt[3]{x^2y^2} = 2\sqrt[3]{x^3y^4} = 2xy\sqrt[3]{y}$

b. $\sqrt[5]{a^2b}\sqrt{ab}\sqrt[5]{ab^2} = \sqrt[5]{a^3b^3}\sqrt{ab}$

▦ Calculator Alert

Most calculators have a $\boxed{\sqrt{}}$ key. Scientific and graphing calculators sometimes have a special key to evaluate other roots. This key may be $\boxed{\sqrt[x]{y}}$, $\boxed{\sqrt[x]{}}$, or $\boxed{x^{1/y}}$. If your calculator does not have a special root key, you can use the power key to evaluate roots.

Example: Show that $\sqrt[5]{12} = 1.64375183$.

Solution: If your calculator has a root key, evaluate $5\boxed{\sqrt[x]{y}}12$. Otherwise, evaluate $12\boxed{x^y}(1 \div 5)$ or $12\boxed{\wedge}(1 \div 5)$ on your calculator.

Exercise Set 1.7

In Exercises 1–12, simplify, and write the answer using only positive exponents.

1. $16^{3/4}$

2. $(-125)^{-1/3}$

3. $(-64)^{-2/3}$

4. $c^{1/4}c^{-2/3}$

5. $\dfrac{2x^{1/3}}{x^{-3/4}}$

6. $\dfrac{y^{-2/3}}{y^{1/5}}$

7. $\left(\dfrac{x^{3/2}}{x^{2/3}}\right)^{1/6}$

8. $\dfrac{125^{4/3}}{125^{2/3}}$

9. $(x^{1/3}y^2)^6$

10. $(x^6y^4)^{-1/2}$

11. $\left(\dfrac{x^{15}}{y^{10}}\right)^{3/5}$

12. $\left(\dfrac{x^{18}}{y^{-6}}\right)^{2/3}$

In Exercises 13–18, write the expression in radical form.

13. $\left(\dfrac{1}{4}\right)^{2/5}$

14. $x^{2/3}$

15. $a^{3/4}$

16. $(-8x^2)^{2/5}$

17. $(12x^3y^{-2})^{2/3}$

18. $\left(\dfrac{8}{3}x^{-2}y^{-4}\right)^{-3/2}$

In Exercises 19–24, write the expression in exponent form.

19. $\sqrt[4]{8^3}$

20. $\sqrt[5]{3^2}$

21. $\dfrac{1}{\sqrt[5]{(-8)^2}}$

22. $\dfrac{1}{\sqrt[3]{x^7}}$

23. $\dfrac{1}{\sqrt[4]{\dfrac{4}{9}a^3}}$

24. $\sqrt[5]{(2a^2b^3)^4}$

▦ In Exercises 25–33, evaluate the expression. Verify your answer using your calculator.

25. $\sqrt{\dfrac{4}{9}}$

26. $\sqrt{\dfrac{25}{4}}$

27. $\sqrt[4]{-81}$

28. $\sqrt[3]{\dfrac{1}{27}}$

29. $\sqrt{(-5)^2}$

30. $\sqrt{\left(-\dfrac{1}{3}\right)^2}$

31. $\sqrt{\left(\frac{5}{4}\right)^2}$

32. $\sqrt{\left(-\frac{7}{2}\right)^2}$

33. $(14.43)^{3/2}$

In Exercises 34–36, provide a real value for each variable to demonstrate the result.

34. $\sqrt{x^2} \neq x$

35. $\sqrt{x^2 + y^2} \neq x + y$

36. $\sqrt{x}\sqrt{y} \neq xy$

In Exercises 37–56, write the expression in simplified form. Every variable represents a positive number.

37. $\sqrt{48}$

38. $\sqrt{200}$

39. $\sqrt[3]{54}$

40. $\sqrt{x^8}$

41. $\sqrt[3]{y^7}$

42. $\sqrt[4]{b^{14}}$

43. $\sqrt[3]{96x^{10}}$

44. $\sqrt[4]{x^5 y^4}$

45. $\sqrt{x^5 y^3}$

46. $\sqrt[3]{24b^{10}c^{14}}$

47. $\sqrt[4]{16x^8 y^5}$

48. $\sqrt{20x^5 y^7 z^4}$

49. $\sqrt{\dfrac{1}{5}}$

50. $\dfrac{4}{3\sqrt{11}}$

51. $\dfrac{1}{\sqrt{3y}}$

52. $\sqrt{\dfrac{2}{y}}$

53. $\dfrac{4x^2}{\sqrt{2x}}$

54. $\dfrac{8a^2 b^2}{2\sqrt{2b}}$

55. $\sqrt[3]{x^2 y^7}$

56. $\sqrt[4]{48x^8 y^6 z^2}$

In Exercises 57–66, simplify and combine terms.

57. $2\sqrt{3} + 5\sqrt{3}$

58. $4\sqrt[3]{11} - 6\sqrt[3]{11}$

59. $3\sqrt{x} + 4\sqrt{x}$

60. $3\sqrt{2} + 5\sqrt{2} - 2\sqrt{2}$

61. $2\sqrt{27} + \sqrt{12} - \sqrt{48}$

62. $\sqrt{20} - 4\sqrt{45} + \sqrt{80}$

63. $\sqrt[3]{40} + \sqrt{45} - \sqrt[3]{135} + 2\sqrt{80}$

64. $\sqrt{2abc} - 3\sqrt{8abc} + \sqrt{\dfrac{abc}{2}}$

65. $2\sqrt{5} - (3\sqrt{5} + 4\sqrt{5})$

66. $2\sqrt{18} - (3\sqrt{12} - 2\sqrt{75})$

In Exercises 67–74, multiply and simplify.

67. $\sqrt{3}(\sqrt{3} + 4)$

68. $\sqrt{8}(\sqrt{2} - \sqrt{3})$

69. $3\sqrt[3]{x^2 y}\sqrt[3]{xy^2}$

70. $-4\sqrt[5]{x^2 y^3}\sqrt[5]{x^4 y^2}$

71. $(\sqrt{2} - \sqrt{3})^2$

72. $(\sqrt{8} - 2\sqrt{2})(\sqrt{2} + 2\sqrt{8})$

73. $(\sqrt{3x} + \sqrt{2y})(\sqrt{3x} - 2\sqrt{2y})$

74. $(\sqrt[3]{2x} + 3)(\sqrt[3]{2x} - 3)$

In Exercises 75–86, rationalize the denominator.

75. $\dfrac{3}{\sqrt{2} + 3}$

76. $\dfrac{-3}{\sqrt{7} - 9}$

77. $\dfrac{-2}{\sqrt{3} - 4}$

78. $\dfrac{3}{\sqrt{x} - 5}$

79. $\dfrac{-3}{3\sqrt{a} + 1}$

80. $\dfrac{4}{2 - \sqrt{2y}}$

81. $\dfrac{-3}{5 + \sqrt{5y}}$

82. $\dfrac{\sqrt{3}}{\sqrt{3} - 5}$

83. $\dfrac{\sqrt{2} + 1}{\sqrt{2} - 1}$

84. $\dfrac{\sqrt{5} + \sqrt{3}}{\sqrt{5} - \sqrt{3}}$

85. $\dfrac{\sqrt{6} + \sqrt{2}}{\sqrt{3} - \sqrt{2}}$

86. $\dfrac{2\sqrt{a}}{\sqrt{2x} + \sqrt{y}}$

In Exercises 87–90, rationalize the numerator.

87. $\sqrt{12} - \sqrt{10}$

88. $\dfrac{3 - \sqrt{x}}{x - 9}$

89. $\dfrac{\sqrt{x} - 4}{16 - x}$

90. $\dfrac{2 - \sqrt{x + 1}}{3 - x}$

In Exercises 91 and 92, provide real values for x and y and a positive integer value for n to demonstrate the result.

91. $\sqrt{x} + \sqrt{y} \neq \sqrt{x + y}$

92. $\sqrt[n]{x^n + y^n} \neq x + y$

93. Find the step in the following "proof" that is incorrect. Explain.

$$2 = \sqrt{4} = \sqrt{(-2)(-2)} = \sqrt{-2}\sqrt{-2} = -2$$

94. Prove that $|ab| = |a||b|$. (*Hint:* Begin with $|ab| = \sqrt{(ab)^2}$.)

95. Simplify the following.

a. $\sqrt{x\sqrt{x\sqrt{x}}}$

b. $(x^{1/2} - x^{-1/2})^2$

c. $\sqrt{1 + x^2} - \dfrac{\sqrt{1 + x^2}}{2}$

d. $\sqrt[5]{\dfrac{3^4 + 3^4 + 3^4}{5^4 + 5^4 + 5^4 + 5^4 + 5^4}}$

e. $\dfrac{5(1 + x^2)^{1/2} - 5x^2(1 + x^2)^{-1/2}}{1 + x^2}$

96. Write the following in simplest radical form.

 a. $\sqrt{a^{-2} + c^{-2}}$

 b. $\sqrt{1 - \left(\dfrac{a}{c}\right)^2}$

 c. $\sqrt{x + \dfrac{1}{x} + 2}$

97. The frequency of an electrical circuit is given by

$$\frac{1}{2\pi}\sqrt{\frac{Lc_1c_2}{c_1 + c_2}}$$

 Rationalize the denominator.

98. Use your calculator to find $\sqrt{0.4}$, $\sqrt{0.04}$, $\sqrt{0.004}$, $\sqrt{0.0004}$, and so on, until you see a pattern. Can you state a rule about the value of

$$\sqrt{\frac{a}{10^n}}$$

 where a is a perfect square and n is a positive integer? Under what circumstances does this expression have an integer value? Test your rule for large values of n.

Applications 1.7

1. The total surface of the Great Lakes is 80,545 square miles. The amount of evaporation, in inches per day, of a large body of water can be described by the algebraic expression $\frac{w}{20\sqrt{a}}$ where a is the surface area of the water, in square miles, and w is the average wind speed of the air over the water, in miles per hour. Determine the evaporation on the Great Lakes on a day when the wind speed over the water is 8 miles per hour.

2. The algebraic expression $152a^{-1/5}$ describes the percentage of U.S. taxpayers who are a years old who file early. Evaluate the algebraic expression for $a = 40$. Describe what the answer means in practical terms.

3. As broadband Internet grows more popular, video services such as YouTube will continue to expand. The number of online video viewers (in millions) is projected to grow as $56t^{0.521}$, where $0 \leq t \leq 6$ and $t = 0$ corresponds to 2007. How many online video viewers will there be in 2011?

4. The period T, in seconds, of a pendulum of length l, in feet, may be approximated using the formula $T = 2\pi\sqrt{\frac{l}{24}}$. Find the period T of a pendulum whose length is 16 feet.

1.8 Complex Numbers

One of the central problems in algebra is to find solutions to a given polynomial equation. This problem will be discussed in later chapters of this book. For now, observe that there is no real number that satisfies a polynomial equation such as

$$x^2 = -4$$

since the square of a real number is always nonnegative.

To resolve this problem, mathematicians created a new number system built upon an **imaginary unit** i, defined by $i = \sqrt{-1}$. This number i has the property that when we square both sides of the equation we have $i^2 = -1$, a result that cannot be obtained with real numbers. By definition,

$$i = \sqrt{-1}$$
$$i^2 = -1$$

We also assume that i behaves according to all the algebraic laws we have already developed (with the exception of the rules for inequalities for real numbers). This allows us to simplify higher powers of i. Thus,

$$i^3 = i^2 \cdot i = (-1)i = -i$$
$$i^4 = i^2 \cdot i^2 = (-1)(-1) = 1$$

Now we may simplify i^n when n is any natural number. Since $i^4 = 1$, we seek the highest multiple of 4 that is less than or equal to n. For example,

$$i^5 = i^4 \cdot i = (1) \cdot i = i$$
$$i^{27} = i^{24} \cdot i^3 = (i^4)^6 \cdot i^3 = (1)^6 \cdot i^3 = i^3 = -i$$

Example 1   Imaginary Unit i

Simplify.

a. i^{51} b. $-i^{74}$

Solution

a. $i^{51} = i^{48} \cdot i^3 = (i^4)^{12} \cdot i^3 = (1)^{12} \cdot i^3 = i^3 = -i$

b. $-i^{74} = -i^{72} \cdot i^2 = -(i^4)^{18} \cdot i^2 = -(1)^{18} \cdot i^2 = -(1)(-1) = 1$

We may also write square roots of negative numbers in terms of i. For example,

$$\sqrt{-25} = i\sqrt{25} = 5i$$

and, in general, we define

$$\boxed{\sqrt{-a} = i\sqrt{a} \qquad \text{for } a > 0}$$

Any number of the form bi, where b is a real number, is called an **imaginary number**.

- -

Warning

$$\sqrt{-4}\sqrt{-9} \neq \sqrt{36}$$

The rule $\sqrt{a} \cdot \sqrt{b} = \sqrt{ab}$ holds only when $a \geq 0$ and $b \geq 0$. Instead, write

$$\sqrt{-4}\sqrt{-9} = 2i \cdot 3i = 6i^2 = -6$$

- -

Having created imaginary numbers, we next combine real and imaginary numbers. We say that $a + bi$ is a **complex number**, where a and b are real numbers. The number a is called the **real part** of $a + bi$, and b is called the **imaginary part**. The following are examples of complex numbers.

$$3 + 2i \qquad 2 - i \qquad -2i \qquad \frac{4}{5} + \frac{1}{5}i$$

Note that every real number a can be written as a complex number by choosing $b = 0$. Thus,

$$a = a + 0i$$

We see that the real number system is a subset of the complex number system. The desire to find solutions to every quadratic equation has led mathematicians to create a more comprehensive number system, which incorporates all previous number systems. We will show in a later chapter that complex numbers are all that we need to provide solutions to any polynomial equation.

Example 2   Complex Numbers $a + bi$

Write as a complex number.

a. $-\dfrac{1}{2}$ b. $\sqrt{-9}$ c. $-1 - \sqrt{-4}$

Solution

a. $-\dfrac{1}{2} = -\dfrac{1}{2} + 0i$

b. $\sqrt{-9} = i\sqrt{9} = 3i = 0 + 3i$

c. $-1 - \sqrt{-4} = -1 - i\sqrt{4} = -1 - 2i$

Do not be concerned by the word "complex." You already have all the basic tools you need to tackle this number system. We will next define operations with complex numbers in such a way that the rules for the real numbers and the imaginary unit i continue to hold. We begin with equality and say that two complex numbers are **equal** if their real parts are equal and their imaginary parts are equal, that is,

$$a + bi = c + di \qquad \text{if} \qquad a = c \qquad \text{and} \qquad b = d$$

Example 3   Equality of Complex Numbers
Solve the equation $x + 3i = 6 - yi$ for x and y.

Solution
Equating the real parts, we have $x = 6$; equating the imaginary parts, $3 = -y$ or $y = -3$.

Complex numbers are added and subtracted by adding or subtracting the real parts and by adding or subtracting the imaginary parts.

Addition and Subtraction of Complex Numbers

$$(a + bi) + (c + di) = (a + c) + (b + d)i$$

$$(a + bi) - (c + di) = (a - c) + (b - d)i$$

Note that the sum or difference of two complex numbers is again a complex number.

Example 4   Addition and Subtraction of Complex Numbers

Perform the indicated operations.

a. $(7 - 2i) + (4 - 3i)$ b. $14 - (3 - 8i)$

Solution

a. $(7 - 2i) + (4 - 3i) = (7 + 4) + (-2 - 3)i = 11 - 5i$

b. $14 - (3 - 8i) = (14 - 3) + 8i = 11 + 8i$

✔ **Progress Check**

Perform the indicated operations.

a. $(-9 + 3i) + (6 - 2i)$ b. $7i - (3 + 9i)$

Answers

a. $-3 + i$ b. $-3 - 2i$

We now define multiplication of complex numbers in a manner that permits the commutative, associative, and distributive laws to hold, along with the definition $i^2 = -1$. We must have

$$(a + bi)(c + di) = a(c + di) + bi(c + di)$$

$$= ac + adi + bci + bdi^2$$

$$= ac + (ad + bc)i + bd(-1)$$

$$= (ac - bd) + (ad + bc)i$$

The rule for multiplication is

Multiplication of Complex Numbers

$$(a + bi)(c + di) = (ac - bd) + (ad + bc)i$$

This result demonstrates that the product of two complex numbers is a complex number. It need not be memorized. Use the distributive law to form all the products and the substitution $i^2 = -1$ to simplify.

Example 5   Multiplication of Complex Numbers

Find the product of $(2 - 3i)$ and $(7 + 5i)$.

Solution

$$(2 - 3i)(7 + 5i) = 2(7 + 5i) - 3i(7 + 5i)$$
$$= 14 + 10i - 21i - 15i^2$$
$$= 14 - 11i - 15(-1)$$
$$= 29 - 11i$$

✔ Progress Check

Find the product.

a. $(-3 - i)(4 - 2i)$　　　　b. $(-4 - 2i)(2 - 3i)$

Answers

a. $-14 + 2i$　　　　b. $-14 + 8i$

The complex number $a - bi$ is called the **complex conjugate**, or simply the **conjugate**, of the complex number $a + bi$. For example, $3 - 2i$ is the conjugate of $3 + 2i$, $4i$ is the conjugate of $-4i$, and 2 is the conjugate of 2. Forming the product $(a + bi)(a - bi)$, we have

$$(a + bi)(a - bi) = a^2 - abi + abi - b^2i^2$$
$$= a^2 + b^2 \quad \text{Since } i^2 = -1$$

Because a and b are real numbers, $a^2 + b^2$ is also a real number. We can summarize this result as follows.

The Complex Conjugate and Multiplication
The complex conjugate of $a + bi$ is $a - bi$. The product of a complex number and its conjugate is a real number.

$$(a + bi)(a - bi) = a^2 + b^2$$

Before we examine the quotient of two complex numbers, we consider the reciprocal of $a + bi$, namely, $\frac{1}{a + bi}$. This may be simplified by multiplying both numerator and denominator by the conjugate of the denominator.

$$\frac{1}{a + bi} = \left(\frac{1}{a + bi}\right)\left(\frac{a - bi}{a - bi}\right) = \frac{a - bi}{a^2 + b^2} = \frac{a}{a^2 + b^2} - \frac{b}{a^2 + b^2}i$$

In general, the quotient of two complex numbers

$$\frac{a + bi}{c + di}$$

is simplified in a similar manner, that is, by multiplying both numerator and denominator by the conjugate of the denominator.

$$\frac{a + bi}{c + di} = \frac{a + bi}{c + di} \cdot \frac{c - di}{c - di}$$

$$= \frac{(ac + bd) + (bc - ad)i}{c^2 + d^2}$$

$$= \frac{ac + bd}{c^2 + d^2} + \frac{bc - ad}{c^2 + d^2}i$$

Division of Complex Numbers

$$\frac{a + bi}{c + di} = \frac{ac + bd}{c^2 + d^2} + \frac{bc - ad}{c^2 + d^2}i, \qquad c^2 + d^2 \neq 0$$

This result demonstrates that the quotient of two complex numbers is a complex number. Instead of memorizing this formula for division, remember that quotients of complex numbers may be simplified by multiplying the numerator and denominator by the conjugate of the denominator.

Example 6   Division of Complex Numbers

a. Write the quotient $\frac{-2 + 3i}{3 - 2i}$ in the form $a + bi$.

b. Write the reciprocal of $2 - 5i$ in the form $a + bi$.

Solution

a. Multiplying numerator and denominator by the conjugate of the denominator, $3 + 2i$, we have

$$\frac{-2 + 3i}{3 - 2i} = \frac{-2 + 3i}{3 - 2i} \cdot \frac{3 + 2i}{3 + 2i} = \frac{-6 - 4i + 9i + 6i^2}{3^2 + 2^2} = \frac{-6 + 5i + 6(-1)}{9 + 4}$$

$$= \frac{-12 + 5i}{13} = -\frac{12}{13} + \frac{5}{13}i$$

b. The reciprocal is $\frac{1}{2 - 5i}$. Multiplying both numerator and denominator by the conjugate $2 + 5i$, we have

$$\frac{1}{2-5i} \cdot \frac{2+5i}{2+5i} = \frac{2+5i}{2^2+5^2} = \frac{2+5i}{29} = \frac{2}{29} + \frac{5}{29}i$$

Verify that

$$(2-5i)\left(+ i\right) = 1$$

■

Graphing Calculator Alert

Some scientific and graphing calculators have the capability to do computations with complex numbers. Consult your owner's manual for details. The owner's manual may be available online. Look up your calculator by model and number.

Exercise Set 1.8

Simplify in Exercises 1–9.

1. i^{60}
2. i^{27}
3. i^{83}
4. $-i^{54}$
5. $-i^{33}$
6. i^{-15}
7. i^{-84}
8. $-i^{39}$
9. $-i^{-25}$

In Exercises 10–21, write the number in the form $a + bi$.

10. 2
11. $-\frac{3}{4}$
12. -0.3
13. $\sqrt{-25}$
14. $-\sqrt{-5}$
15. $-\sqrt{-36}$
16. $-\sqrt{-18}$
17. $3 - \sqrt{-49}$
18. $-\frac{3}{2} - \sqrt{-72}$
19. $0.3 - \sqrt{-98}$
20. $-0.5 + \sqrt{-32}$
21. $-2 - \sqrt{-16}$

In Exercises 22–26, solve for x and y.

22. $(x + 2) + (2y - 1)i = -1 + 5i$
23. $(3x - 1) + (y + 5)i = 1 - 3i$
24. $\left(\frac{1}{2}x + 2\right) + (3y - 2)i = 4 - 7i$
25. $(2y + 1) - (2x - 1)i = -8 + 3i$
26. $(y - 2) + (5x - 3)i = 5$

In Exercises 27–42, compute the answer and write it in the form $a + bi$.

27. $2i + (3 - i)$
28. $-3i + (2 - 5i)$
29. $2 + 3i + (3 - 2i)$
30. $(3 - 2i) - \left(2 + \frac{1}{2}i\right)$
31. $-3 - 5i - (2 - i)$
32. $\left(\frac{1}{2} - i\right) + \left(1 - \frac{2}{3}i\right)$
33. $-2i(3 + i)$
34. $3i(2 - i)$
35. $i\left(-\frac{1}{2} + i\right)$
36. $\frac{i}{2}\left(\frac{4 - i}{2}\right)$
37. $(2 - i)(2 + i)$
38. $(5 + i)(2 - 3i)$
39. $(-2 - 2i)(-4 - 3i)$
40. $(2 + 5i)(1 - 3i)$
41. $(3 - 2i)(2 - i)$
42. $(4 - 3i)(2 + 3i)$

In Exercises 43–48, multiply by the conjugate and simplify.

43. $2 - i$
44. $3 + i$
45. $3 + 4i$
46. $2 - 3i$
47. $-4 - 2i$
48. $5 + 2i$

In Exercises 49–57, perform the indicated operations and write the answer in the form $a + bi$.

49. $\frac{2 + 5i}{1 - 3i}$
50. $\frac{1 + 3i}{2 - 5i}$
51. $\frac{3 - 4i}{3 + 4i}$
52. $\frac{4 - 3i}{4 + 3i}$

53. $\dfrac{3-2i}{2-i}$ 54. $\dfrac{2-3i}{3-i}$

55. $\dfrac{2+5i}{3i}$ 56. $\dfrac{5-2i}{-3i}$

57. $\dfrac{4i}{2+i}$

In Exercises 58–64, find the reciprocal and write the answer in the form $a + bi$.

58. $3 + 2i$ 59. $4 + 3i$

60. $\dfrac{1}{2} - i$ 61. $1 - \dfrac{1}{3}i$

62. $-7i$ 63. $-5i$

64. $\dfrac{3-i}{3+2i}$

In Exercises 65–68, evaluate the polynomial $x^2 - 2x + 5$ for the given complex value of x.

65. $1 + 2i$ 66. $2 - i$

67. $1 - i$ 68. $1 - 2i$

69. Prove that the commutative law of addition holds for the set of complex numbers.

70. Prove that the commutative law of multiplication holds for the set of complex numbers.

71. Prove that $0 + 0i$ is the additive identity and $1 + 0i$ is the multiplicative identity for the set of complex numbers.

72. Prove that $-a - bi$ is the additive inverse of the complex number $a + bi$.

73. Prove the distributive property for the set of complex numbers.

74. For what values of x is $\sqrt{x-3}$ a real number?

75. For what values of y is $\sqrt{2y-10}$ a real number?

76. Perform the multiplications and simplify.

 a. $(x + yi)(x - yi)$ b. $(1 - i)^5$

 c. $(1 - \sqrt{3})^4$ d. $[x - (2 + 5i)][x - (2 - 5i)]$

In Exercises 77–85, redo Exercises 49–57 using the i key on your graphing calculator. Remember to use parentheses appropriately! (*Note:* The values of a and b in each answer will be in decimal form.)

86. *Mathematics in Writing:* Consider the addition and the multiplication of complex numbers. How does i differ from a variable like x? If you always treat i as though it is a variable, at what step in the procedures of addition or multiplication would you run into trouble?

Terms and Symbols

absolute value, | |	element of a set, ∈	least common denominator (LCD)
algebraic expression	equal	like terms
algebraic fraction	equivalent fractions	member of a set, ∈
algebraic operations	evaluate	monomial
base	exponent	natural numbers
cancellation principle	factor	nonnegative numbers
coefficient	factoring	not a set member, ∉
complex conjugate	imaginary number	nth root
complex fraction	imaginary part	origin
complex number	imaginary unit i	polynomial
constant	inequalities	power
constant term	inequality symbols, $<, >, \leq, \geq$	prime polynomial
degree of a monomial	integers	principal square root
degree of a polynomial	irrational numbers	radical form
distance from point A to point B,	irreducible polynomial	radical sign, $\sqrt{}$
$\overline{AB}$	LCD	rational expression
	leading coefficient	rational numbers

rationalizing the denominator	scientific notation	term
rationalizing the numerator	set	variable
real number line	set notation	zero polynomial
real numbers	simplified form of a radical	
real part	subset	

Key Ideas for Review

Topic	Key Idea
Set	A set is a collection of objects or numbers.
The Set of Real Numbers	The set of real numbers is composed of the rational and irrational numbers. The rational numbers are those that can be written as the ratio of two integers, $\frac{p}{q}$, with $q \neq 0$; the irrational numbers cannot be written as the ratio of two integers.
Properties	The real number system satisfies a number of important properties, including:
	closure commutativity associativity
	identities inverses distributivity
Equality	If two numbers are identical, we say that they are equal.
Properties	Equality satisfies these basic properties:
	reflexive property symmetric property
	transitive property substitution property
Real Number Line	There is a one-to-one correspondence between the set of all real numbers and the set of all points on the real number line. That is, for every point on the line there is a real number, and for every real number there is a point on the line.
Inequalities	Algebraic statements using inequality symbols have geometric interpretations using the real number line. For example, $a < b$ says that a lies to the left of b on the real number line.
Operations	Inequalities can be operated on in the same manner as statements involving an equal sign with one important exception: when an inequality is multiplied or divided by a negative number, the direction of the inequality is reversed.
Absolute Value	Absolute value specifies distance independent of direction. Four important properties of absolute value are: • $\lvert a \rvert \geq 0$ • $\lvert a \rvert = \lvert -a \rvert$ • $\lvert a - b \rvert = \lvert b - a \rvert$ • $\lvert ab \rvert = \lvert a \rvert \lvert b \rvert$
Distance	The distance between points A and B whose coordinates are a and b, respectively, is given by $$\overline{AB} = \lvert b - a \rvert$$
Polynomials	Algebraic expressions of the form $$a_n x^n + a_{n-1} x^{n-1} + \cdots + a_1 x + a_0$$ are called polynomials.

Topic	Key Idea
Operations	To add (subtract) polynomials, just add (subtract) like terms. To multiply polynomials, form all possible products, using the rule for exponents: $$a^m a^n = a^{m+n}$$
Factoring	A polynomial is said to be factored when it is written as a product of polynomials of lower degree.
Rational Expressions	Most of the rules of arithmetic for handling fractions carry over to rational expressions. For example, the LCD has the same meaning except that we deal with polynomials in factored form rather than with integers.
Exponents	The rules for positive integer exponents also apply to zero, negative integer exponents, and, in fact, to all rational exponents.
Scientific Notation	A number in scientific notation is of the form $$\pm\, a \times 10^m$$ where $1 \le a < 10$ and m is some integer.
Radicals	Radical notation is another way of writing a rational exponent. That is, $$\sqrt[n]{b} = b^{1/n}$$
Principal nth Root	If n is even and b is positive, there are two real numbers a such that $b^{1/n} = a$. Under these circumstances, we insist that the nth root be positive. That is, $\sqrt[n]{b}$ is a positive number if n is even and b is positive. Thus $\sqrt{16} = 4$. Similarly, we must write $$\sqrt{x^2} = \lvert x \rvert$$ to ensure that the result is a positive number.
Simplifying	To be in simplified form, a radical must satisfy the following conditions: • $\sqrt[n]{x^m}$ has $m < n$. • $\sqrt[n]{x^m}$ has no common factors between m and n. • The denominator has been rationalized.
Complex Numbers	Complex numbers were created because there were no real numbers that satisfy a polynomial equation such as $$x^2 + 5 = 0$$
Imaginary Unit i	Using the imaginary unit $i = \sqrt{-1}$, a complex number is of the form $a + bi$, where a and b are real numbers; the real part of $a + bi$ is a and the imaginary part of $a + bi$ is b.
Real Number System	The real number system is a subset of the complex number system.

Review Exercises

Solutions to exercises whose numbers are in **bold** are in the Solutions section in the back of the book.

In Exercises 1–3, write each set by listing its elements within braces.

1. The set of natural numbers from -5 to 4, inclusive.

2. The set of integers from -3 to -1, inclusive.

3. The subset of $x \in S$, $S = \{0.5, 1, 1.5, 2\}$ such that x is an even integer.

For Exercises 4–7, determine whether the statement is true (T) or false (F).

4. $\sqrt{7}$ is a real number.

5. -35 is a natural number.

6. -14 is not an integer.

7. 0 is an irrational number.

In Exercises 8–11, identify the property of the real number system that justifies the statement. All variables represent real numbers.

8. $3a + (-3a) = 0$

9. $(3 + 4)x = 3x + 4x$

10. $2x + 2y + z = 2x + z + 2y$

11. $9x \cdot 1 = 9x$

In Exercises 12–14, sketch the given set of numbers on a real number line.

12. The negative real numbers.

13. The real numbers x such that $x > 4$.

14. The real numbers x such that $-1 \le x < 1$.

15. Find the value of $|-3| - |1 - 5|$.

16. Find $\overline{PQ}$ if the coordinates of P and Q are $\frac{9}{2}$ and 6, respectively.

17. A salesperson receives $3.25x + 0.15y$ dollars, where x is the number of hours worked and y is the number of miles driven. Find the amount due the salesperson if $x = 12$ hours and $y = 80$ miles.

18. Which of the following expressions are not polynomials?

   a. $-2xy^2 + x^2y$
   b. $3b^2 + 2b - 6$

   c. $x^{-1/2} + 5x^2 - x$
   d. $7.5x^2 + 3x - \frac{1}{2}x^0$

In Exercises 19 and 20, indicate the leading coefficient and the degree of each polynomial.

19. $-0.5x^7 + 6x^3 - 5$ 20. $2x^2 + 3x^4 - 7x^5$

In Exercises 21–23, perform the indicated operations.

21. $(3a^2b^2 - a^2b + 2b - a) - (2a^2b^2 + 2a^2b - 2b - a)$

22. $x(2x - 1)(x + 2)$

23. $3x(2x + 1)^2$

In Exercises 24–29, factor each expression.

24. $2x^2 - 2$ 25. $x^2 - 25y^2$

26. $2a^2 + 3ab + 6a + 9b$ 27. $4x^2 + 19x - 5$

28. $x^8 - 1$ 29. $27r^6 + 8s^6$

In Exercises 30–33, perform the indicated operations and simplify.

30. $\dfrac{14(y - 1)}{3(x^2 - y^2)} \cdot \dfrac{9(x + y)}{-7xy^2}$

31. $\dfrac{4 - x^2}{2y^2} \div \dfrac{x - 2}{3y}$

32. $\dfrac{x^2 - 2x - 3}{2x^2 - x} \div \dfrac{x^2 - 4x + 3}{3x^3 - 3x^2}$

33. $\dfrac{a + b}{a + 2b} \cdot \dfrac{a^2 - 4b^2}{a^2 - b^2}$

In Exercises 34–37, find the LCD.

34. $\dfrac{-1}{2x^2}$, $\dfrac{2}{x^2 - 4}$, $\dfrac{3}{x - 2}$

35. $\dfrac{4}{x}$, $\dfrac{5}{x^2 - x}$, $\dfrac{-3}{(x - 1)^2}$

36. $\dfrac{2}{(x - 1)y}$, $\dfrac{-4}{y^2}$, $\dfrac{x + 2}{5(x - 1)^2}$

37. $\dfrac{y-1}{x^2(y+1)}$, $\dfrac{x-2}{2xy-2x}$, $\dfrac{3x}{4y^2+8y+4}$

In Exercises 38–41, perform the indicated operations and simplify.

38. $2+\dfrac{4}{a^2-4}$ **39.** $\dfrac{3}{x^2-16}-\dfrac{2}{x-4}$

40. $\dfrac{\dfrac{3}{x+2}-\dfrac{2}{x-1}}{x-1}$ **41.** $x^2+\dfrac{\dfrac{1}{x}+1}{x-\dfrac{1}{x}}$

In Exercises 42–50, simplify and express the answers using only positive exponents. All variables are positive numbers.

42. $(2a^2b^{-3})^{-3}$ **43.** $2(a^2-1)^0$

44. $\left(\dfrac{x^3}{y^{-6}}\right)^{-4/3}$ **45.** $\dfrac{x^{3+n}}{x^n}$

46. $\sqrt{80}$ **47.** $\dfrac{2}{\sqrt{12}}$

48. $\sqrt{x^7y^5}$ **49.** $\sqrt[4]{32x^8y^6}$

50. $\dfrac{\sqrt{x}}{\sqrt{x}+\sqrt{y}}$

 51. Compute
$$\dfrac{(5.10\times10^7)(3.45\times10^{-2})}{7.10\times10^4}$$

to two decimal places and express the answer in scientific notation.

52. Rationalize the numerator for
$$\dfrac{\sqrt{x}-\sqrt{y}}{x-y}$$

In Exercises 53 and 54, perform the indicated operations. Simplify the answer.

53. $\sqrt[4]{x^2y^2}+2\sqrt[4]{x^2y^2}$ **54.** $(\sqrt{3}+\sqrt{5})^2$

55. Evaluate the given expressions using your calculator.

a. $\dfrac{12}{5}-\dfrac{3}{7}$ b. $\left|(-4)^3-5^6\right|$

c. $\sqrt{8}$ d. π^8

e. $\sqrt[5]{-27}$ f. $\dfrac{|2+\sqrt{3}|}{-6}$

g. $\sqrt[3]{4}+\sqrt{\dfrac{1}{8}}$ h. $\sqrt[10]{0.5}$

i. $\left(\dfrac{2}{3}\right)^4$ j. $9^{5/8}$

56. Solve for x and y:
$$(x-2)+(2y-1)i=-4+7i$$

57. Simplify i^{47}.

In Exercises 58–61, perform the indicated operations and write all answers in the form $a+bi$.

58. $2+(6-i)$ **59.** $(2+i)^2$

60. $(4-3i)(2+3i)$ **61.** $\dfrac{4-3i}{2+3i}$

62. Perform the indicated operations.

a. Combine into one term with a common denominator
$$\dfrac{1}{a}+\dfrac{1}{b}+\dfrac{1}{c}$$

b. Simplify the quotient
$$\dfrac{\dfrac{1}{a}+\dfrac{1}{b}}{\dfrac{1}{c}+\dfrac{1}{d}}$$

63. Dan, at 200 pounds, wishes to reduce his weight to 180 pounds in time to attend his college reunion in 8 weeks. He learns that it takes 2400 calories per day to maintain his weight. A reduction of his caloric intake to 1900 calories per day will result in his losing weight at the rate of 1 pound per week. What should his daily caloric intake be to achieve this goal?

64. The executive committee of the student government association consists of a president, vice-president, secretary, and treasurer.

a. In how many ways can a committee of three persons be formed from among the executive committee members?

b. According to the by-laws, there must be at least three affirmative votes to carry a motion. If the president automatically has two votes, list all the minimal winning coalitions.

65. If 6 children can devour 6 hot dogs in $\frac{1}{10}$ of an hour, how many would it take to devour 100 hot dogs in 6000 seconds?

66. A tape recorder costs a dealer $80. If he wishes to make a profit of at least 25% of his cost, what must be the lowest selling price for the recorder?

67. Find the area of the shaded rectangle.

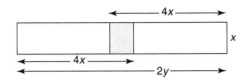

68. An open box is to be made from a 4 feet × 5 feet piece of tin by cutting out squares of equal size from the four corners and bending up the flaps to form sides. Find a formula for the volume in terms of s, the side of the square. Write the inequality that describes the restriction on s.

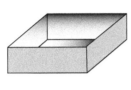

69. Compute the following products.

   a. $(x - y)(x^2 + xy + y^2)$

   b. $(x - y)(x^3 + x^2y + xy^2 + y^3)$

   c. $(x - y)(x^4 + x^3y + x^2y^2 + xy^3 + y^4)$

70. Using Exercise 69, find a general formula that allows you to factor $x^n - y^n$, where n is a positive integer.

71. In ancient Alexandria, numbers were multiplied by using an abacus as follows:

$$19 \times 28 = (20 - 1)(30 - 2)$$
$$= (20)(30) - (20)(2) - 30 + 2$$
$$= 600 - 40 - 30 + 2$$
$$= 532$$

   Set up a comparable sequence of steps for 13×17.

72. Find two ways of grouping and then factoring $ac + ad - bc - bd$.

73. The following calculation represents a sum. If each letter represents a different digit, find the appropriate correspondence between letters and digits so that the sum is correct.

$$\begin{array}{r} FORTY \\ TEN \\ TEN \\ \hline SIXTY \end{array}$$

74. A natural number is said to be perfect if it is the sum of its divisors other than itself. For example, 6 is the first perfect number since $6 = 1 + 2 + 3$. Show that 28 is the second perfect number.

   Every number of the form $2^{p-1}(2^p - 1)$, where $2^p - 1$ is prime, is an even perfect number. (Check your answer when $p = 2$.) Find the third and fourth even perfect numbers. The ancient Greeks could not find the fifth even perfect number. See if you can.

75. The speed of light is 3×10^8 meters per second. Write all answers using scientific notation.

   a. How many seconds does it take an object traveling at the speed of light to go 1×10^{26} meters?

   b. How many seconds are there in 1 year of 365 days?

   c. Write the answer to part (a) in years. (This answer is the approximate age of the universe.)

76. Write $\sqrt{x + \sqrt{x + \sqrt{x}}}$ using exponents.

77. Determine if $(\sqrt{5} - \sqrt{24})^2$ and $(\sqrt{2} - \sqrt{3})^2$ have the same value.

78. The irrational number called the golden ratio

$$T = \frac{\sqrt{5} + 1}{2}$$

   has properties that have intrigued artists, philosophers, and mathematicians through the ages. Show that T satisfies the identity

$$T = 1 + \frac{1}{T}$$

79. Rationalize the numerator in the following.

   a. $\dfrac{\sqrt{x + h + 1} - \sqrt{x - 1}}{h}$

   b. $\dfrac{\sqrt{3 + x} - \sqrt{3}}{x}$

80. In alternating-current theory, the current I (amps), voltage V (volts), and impedance Z (ohms) are treated as complex numbers. The formula relating these quantities is $V = IZ$. If $I = 2 - 3i$ amps and $Z = 6 + 2i$ ohms, find the voltage across this part of the circuit.

Review Test

In Problems 1 and 2, write each set by listing its elements within braces.

1. The set of positive, even integers less than 13.

2. The subset of $x \in S$, $S = \{-1, 2, 3, 5, 7\}$, such that x is a multiple of 3.

In Problems 3 and 4, determine whether the statement is true (T) or false (F).

3. -1.36 is an irrational number.

4. π is equal to $\frac{22}{7}$.

In Problems 5 and 6, identify the property of the real number system that justifies the statement. All variables represent real numbers.

5. $xy(z + 1) = (z + 1)xy$

6. $(-6)\left(-\frac{1}{6}\right) = 1$

In Problems 7 and 8, sketch the given set of numbers on a real number line.

7. The integers that are greater than -3 and less than or equal to 3.

8. The real numbers x such that $-2 \le x < \frac{1}{2}$.

9. Find the value of $|2 - 3| - |4 - 2|$.

10. Find $\overline{AB}$ if the coordinates of A and B are -6 and -4, respectively.

11. The area of a region is given by the expression $3x^2 - xy$. Find the area if $x = 5$ meters and $y = 10$ meters.

12. Evaluate the expression
$$\frac{-|y - 2x|}{|xy|}$$
if $x = 3$ and $y = -1$.

13. Which of the following expressions are not polynomials?

    a. x^5

    b. $5x^{-4}y + 3x^2 - y$

    c. $4x^3 + x$

    d. $2x^2 + 3x^0$

In Problems 14 and 15, indicate the leading coefficient and the degree of each polynomial.

14. $-2.2x^5 + 3x^3 - 2x$ 15. $14x^6 - 2x + 1$

In Problems 16 and 17, perform the indicated operations.

16. $3xy + 2x + 3y + 2 - (1 - y - x + xy)$

17. $(a + 2)(3a^2 - a + 5)$

In Problems 18 and 19, factor each expression.

18. $8a^3b^5 - 12a^5b^2 + 16a^2b$ 19. $4 - 9x^2$

In Problems 20 and 21, perform the indicated operations and simplify.

20. $\dfrac{m^4}{3n^2} \div \left(\dfrac{m^2}{9n} \cdot \dfrac{n}{2m^3}\right)$ 21. $\dfrac{16 - x^2}{x^2 - 3x - 4} \cdot \dfrac{x - 1}{x + 4}$

22. Find the LCD of
$$\frac{-1}{2x^2} \qquad \frac{2}{4x^2 - 4} \qquad \frac{3}{x - 2}$$

In Problems 23 and 24, perform the indicated operations and simplify.

23. $\dfrac{2x}{x^2 - 9} + \dfrac{5}{3x + 9}$ 24. $\dfrac{2 - \dfrac{4}{x + 1}}{x - 1}$

In Problems 25–28, simplify and express the answers using only positive exponents.

25. $\left(\dfrac{x^{7/2}}{x^{2/3}}\right)^{-6}$ 26. $\dfrac{y^{2n}}{y^{n-1}}$

27. $\dfrac{-1}{(x - 1)^0}$ 28. $(2a^2b^{-1})^2$

In Problems 29–31, perform the indicated operations.

29. $3\sqrt[3]{24} - 2\sqrt[3]{81}$ 30. $(\sqrt{7} - 5)^2$

31. $\dfrac{1}{2}\sqrt{\dfrac{xy}{4}} - \sqrt{9xy}$

32. For what values of x is $\sqrt{2 - x}$ a real number?

In Problems 33–35, perform the indicated operations and write all answers in the form $a + bi$.

33. $(2 - i) + (-3 + i)$ 34. $(5 + 2i)(2 - 3i)$

35. $\dfrac{5 + 2i}{2 - i}$

Writing Exercises

1. Evaluate $(8)(1.4142)$ and $(8)(\sqrt{2})$. Are these results close to one another? Why?

2. Discuss the need for the complex number system.

3. Compare and contrast the properties of the complex numbers with those of the real numbers.

4. Discuss why division by zero is not permitted.

Chapter 1 Project

Polynomial expressions are used by physicists to study the motion of objects in free fall. Free fall means that the attraction of gravity is the only force operating on the object. In reality, other forces like air resistance play a role.

Take a look at Exercises 86 and 87 in Section 1.3 and Exercises 84–86 in Section 1.4. Set up a table for various planets or moons in our solar system, and use the Internet or other resources to find the data you need to write free-fall equations for objects on those worlds. (*Hint:* The value of a is all you need.) Here are some values to start you off:

Mars: $a = 3.72$

Earth: $a = 4.9$

The Moon: $a = 1.6$

All these values are in SI units, so the accelerations given above are in meters per second squared.

Try to redo the Exercises listed above for various planets. Write a paragraph explaining the problem described in the chapter opener.

CHAPTER 2

Equations and Inequalities

The Internet is a short form of the word "internetworking." The Internet is a vast data network, with humble origins in the 1960s. A network, whether it connects computers or people, is just a way of facilitating communication. In a **full-mesh network**, elements are linked pairwise—that is, any two elements in the system are linked directly, without intermediary.

How many elements (users) could be linked in a full-mesh network with 190 two-way links? The answer to this problem is found by solving a quadratic equation (see the Chapter Project). This chapter will show you how.

http://www.math-atlas
.org

Explore the Internet for its many mathematical offerings! Check out a site which is organized according to the Mathematics Subject Classification created by the American Mathematical Society. Look up graph theory to learn more about networking.

A major concern of algebra is the solution of equations. Does a given equation have a solution? Is it possible for an equation to have more than one solution? Is there a procedure for solving an equation? In this chapter we will explore the answers to these questions for polynomial equations of the first and second degree. We will also see that the ability to solve equations enables us to tackle a wide variety of applications and word problems.

Linear inequalities also play an important role in solving word problems. For example, if we are required to combine food products in such a way that a specified minimum daily requirement for various nutrients is provided, we need to use inequalities. Many important industries, including steel and petroleum, use computers daily to solve problems that involve thousands of inequalities. The solutions to such problems enable a company to optimize its "product mix" and its profitability.

2.1   Linear Equations in One Unknown

Solving Equations

Expressions of the form

$$x - 2 = 0 \qquad x^2 - 9 = 0 \qquad 3(2x - 5) = 3$$

$$2x + 5 = \sqrt{x - 7} \qquad \frac{1}{2x + 3} = 5 \qquad x^3 - 3x^2 = 32$$

are examples of equations in the unknown x. An **equation** states that two algebraic expressions are equal. We refer to these expressions as the **left-hand side** and the **right-hand side** of the equation.

Our task is to find values of the unknown for which the equation is satisfied. These values are called **solutions** or **roots** of the equation, and the set of all solutions is called the **solution set**. For example, 2 is a solution of the equation $3x - 1 = 5$ since $3(2) - 1 = 5$. However, -2 is *not* a solution since $3(-2) - 1 \neq 5$.

Equations that do not have solutions in one number system may have solutions in a larger number system. For example, the equation $2x - 5$ has no integer solutions but does have a solution among the rational numbers, namely $\frac{5}{2}$. Similarly, the equation $x^2 = -4$ has no solutions among the real numbers but does have solutions if we consider complex numbers, namely $2i$ and $-2i$. The solution sets of these two equations are $\{\frac{5}{2}\}$ and $\{2i, -2i\}$, respectively.

Identities and Conditional Equations
We say that an equation is an **identity** if it is true for every real number for which both sides of the equation are defined. For example, the equation

$$x^2 - 1 = (x + 1)(x - 1)$$

is an identity because it is true for all real numbers. (Try any number and check that this equation holds.) The equation

$$x - 5 = 3$$

is only true when $x = 8$. (Try any number not equal to 8 and check that this equation does not hold.) An equation such as $x - 5 = 3$, which is not true for all values of x, is called a **conditional equation**.

When we say that we want to "solve an equation," we mean that we want to find *all* solutions or roots. If we can replace an equation with another, simpler equation that has the same solutions, we will have an approach to solving equations. Equations having the same solutions are called **equivalent equations**. For example, $3x - 1 = 5$ and $3x = 6$ are equivalent equations because it can be shown that $\{2\}$ is the solution set of both equations.

There are two important rules that allow us to replace an equation with an equivalent equation.

Equivalent Equations

The solutions of a given equation are not affected by the following operations:

1. addition (or subtraction) of the same number or expression on both sides of the equation,

2. multiplication (or division) by the same number, different from 0, on both sides of the equation.

Example 1   Solving Equations

Solve $3x + 4 = 13$.

Solution

We apply the preceding rules to this equation. The strategy is to isolate x, so we *subtract 4 from both sides of the equation.*

$$3x + 4 - 4 = 13 - 4$$
$$3x = 9$$

Dividing both sides by 3, we obtain the solution

$$x = 3$$

We check by substitution to make sure that 3 does, indeed, satisfy the original equation.

$$\text{left-hand side} = 3x + 4 \qquad \text{right-hand side} = 13$$
$$= 3(3) + 4$$
$$= 13$$

Although $x = 3$ is an equation that is *equivalent* to the original equation, in common usage we say that $3x + 4 = 13$ "has the solution $x = 3$."

When the given equation contains rational expressions, we eliminate fractions by first multiplying by the least common denominator of all fractions present. This technique is illustrated in Examples 2, 3, and 4.

Example 2   Solving Equations

Solve the equation.

$$\frac{5}{6}x - \frac{4}{3} = \frac{3}{5}x + 1$$

Solution

We first eliminate fractions by multiplying both sides of the equation by the LCD of all fractions, which is 30.

$$\left(\frac{5}{6}x - \frac{4}{3}\right)(30) = \left(\frac{3}{5}x + 1\right)(30)$$

$$25x - 40 = 18x + 30$$

$$7x = 70$$

$$x = 10$$

Verify that $x = 10$ is a solution of the original equation.

✔ Progress Check

Solve and check.

a. $-\frac{2}{3}(x - 5) = \frac{3}{2}(x + 1)$ b. $\frac{1}{3}x + 2 - 3\left(\frac{x}{2} + 4\right) = 2\left(\frac{x}{4} - 1\right)$

Answers

a. $\frac{11}{13}$ b. $-\frac{24}{5}$

Solving Linear Equations

The equations we have solved are all of the first degree and involve only one un-known. Such equations are called **first-degree equations in one unknown,** or more simply, **linear equations.** The general form of such equations is

$$ax + b = 0$$

where a and b are any real numbers and $a \neq 0$. Let us see how to solve this equation.

$$ax + b = 0$$

$$ax + b - b = 0 - b \qquad \text{Subtract } b \text{ from both sides.}$$

$$ax = -b$$

$$\frac{ax}{a} = \frac{-b}{a} \qquad \text{Divide both sides by } a \neq 0.$$

$$x = -\frac{b}{a}$$

We verify that this is a solution.

$$a\left(-\frac{b}{a}\right) + b = 0$$

Furthermore, it can be shown that this is the only solution. We have thus obtained the following result.

Roots of a Linear Equation
The linear equation $ax + b = 0$, $a \neq 0$, has exactly one solution:

$$x = -\frac{b}{a}$$

Sometimes we are led to linear equations in the course of solving other equations. The following example illustrates this situation.

Example 3   Solving Equations
Solve.

$$\frac{5x}{x + 3} - 3 = \frac{1}{x + 3}$$

Solution
The LCD of all fractions is $x + 3$. Multiplying both sides of the equation by $x + 3$ to eliminate fractions, we obtain

$$5x - 3(x + 3) = 1$$
$$5x - 3x - 9 = 1$$
$$2x = 10$$
$$x = 5$$

Checking the solution, we have

$$\text{left-hand side} = \frac{5x}{x + 3} - 3 \qquad\qquad \text{right-hand side} = \frac{1}{x + 3}$$

$$= \frac{5(5)}{5 + 3} - 3 \qquad\qquad\qquad\qquad = \frac{1}{5 + 3}$$

$$= \frac{25}{8} - 3 \qquad\qquad\qquad\qquad\qquad = \frac{1}{8}$$

$$= \frac{25}{8} - \frac{24}{8}$$

$$= \frac{1}{8}$$

We said earlier that multiplication (or division) of both sides of an equation by any nonzero number results in an equivalent equation. What happens if we multiply or divide an equation by an expression that contains an unknown? In Example 3, this procedure worked and gave us a solution. However, this may not always be so, since the answer we obtain may produce a zero denominator when substituted back into the original equation. Therefore, the following rule must be carefully observed.

Multiplying by an Unknown

Multiplication (or division) by the same expression on both sides of an equation may result in an equation that is *not* equivalent to the original equation. Always verify that the answer obtained to the subsequent equation is, indeed, a solution to the original equation.

Example 4   Equations with No Solution

Solve and check.

$$\frac{8x + 1}{x - 2} + 4 = \frac{7x + 3}{x - 2}$$

Solution

The LCD of all fractions is $x - 2$. Multiplying both sides of the equation by $x - 2$, we eliminate fractions and obtain

$$8x + 1 + 4(x - 2) = 7x + 3$$
$$8x + 1 + 4x - 8 = 7x + 3$$
$$5x = 10$$
$$x = 2$$

Checking our answer, we find that $x = 2$ is not a solution, since substituting $x = 2$ in the original equation yields a denominator of zero. We conclude that the given equation has no solution.   ■

✔ Progress Check

Solve and check.

a. $\dfrac{3}{x} - 1 = \dfrac{1}{2} - \dfrac{6}{x}$ b. $-\dfrac{2x}{x + 1} = 1 + \dfrac{2}{x + 1}$

Answers

a. $x = 6$ b. no solution

Example 5   Equations with No Solution

Solve the equation $2x + 1 = 2x - 3$.

Solution

Subtracting $2x$ from both sides, we have

$$2x + 1 - 2x = 2x - 3 - 2x$$
$$1 = -3$$

This equivalent equation is a contradiction, so we conclude that the given equation has no solution.   ■

Exercise Set 2.1

In Exercises 1–4, determine whether the given statement is true (T) or false (F).

1. $x = -5$ is a solution of $2x + 3 = -7$.

2. $x = \frac{5}{2}$ is a solution of $3x - 4 = \frac{5}{2}$.

3. $x = \dfrac{6}{4 - k}, \quad k \ne 4$
   is a solution of $kx + 6 = 4x$.

4. $x = \dfrac{7}{3k}, \quad k \ne 0$
   is a solution of $2kx + 7 = 5x$.

In Exercises 5–24, solve the given linear equation and check your answer.

5. $3x + 5 = -1$

6. $5r + 10 = 0$

7. $2 = 3x + 4$

8. $\frac{1}{2}s + 2 = 4$

9. $\frac{3}{2}t - 2 = 7$

10. $-1 = -\frac{2}{3}x + 1$

11. $0 = \frac{1}{2}a - \frac{2}{3}$

12. $4r + 4 = 3r - 2$

13. $-5x + 8 = 3x - 4$

14. $2x - 1 = 3x + 2$

15. $-2x + 6 = -5x - 4$

16. $6x + 4 = -3x - 5$

17. $2(3b + 1) = 3b - 4$

18. $-3(2x + 1) = -8x + 1$

19. $4(x - 1) = 2(x + 3)$

20. $-3(x - 2) = 2(x + 4)$

21. $2(x + 4) - 1 = 0$

22. $3a + 2 - 2(a - 1) = 3(2a + 3)$

23. $-4(2x + 1) - (x - 2) = -11$

24. $3(a + 2) - 2(a - 3) = 0$

Solve for x in Exercises 25–28.

25. $kx + 8 = 5x$

26. $8 - 2kx = -3x$

27. $2 - k + 5(x - 1) = 3$

28. $3(2 + 3k) + 4(x - 2) = 5$

Solve and check in Exercises 29–44.

29. $\frac{x}{2} = \frac{5}{3}$

30. $\frac{3x}{4} - 5 = \frac{1}{4}$

31. $\frac{}{x} + 1 = \frac{}{x}$

32. $\frac{}{a} - \frac{}{2} = \frac{}{4}$

33. $\frac{2y - 3}{y + 3} = \frac{5}{7}$

34. $\frac{1 - 4x}{1 - 2x} = \frac{9}{8}$

35. $\frac{1}{x - 2} + \frac{1}{2} = \frac{2}{x - 2}$

36. $\frac{4}{x - 4} - 2 = \frac{1}{x - 4}$

37. $\frac{2}{x - 2} + \frac{2}{x^2 - 4} = \frac{3}{x + 2}$

38. $\frac{3}{x - 1} + \frac{2}{x + 1} = \frac{5}{x^2 - 1}$

39. $\frac{x}{x - 1} - 1 = \frac{3}{x + 1}$

40. $\frac{2}{x - 2} + 1 = \frac{x + 2}{x - 2}$

41. $\frac{4}{b} - \frac{1}{b + 3} = \frac{3b + 2}{b^2 + 2b - 3}$

42. $\frac{3}{x^2 - 2x} + \frac{2x - 1}{x^2 + 2x - 8} = \frac{2}{x + 4}$

43. $\frac{3r + 1}{r + 3} + 2 = \frac{5r - 2}{r + 3}$

44. $\frac{2x - 1}{x - 5} + 3 = \frac{3x - 2}{5 - x}$

In Exercises 45–48, indicate whether the equation is an identity (I) or a conditional equation (C).

45. $x^2 + x - 2 = (x + 2)(x - 1)$

46. $(x - 2)^2 = x^2 - 4x + 4$

47. $2x + 1 = 3x - 1$

48. $3x - 5 = 4x - x - 2 - 3$

In Exercises 49–54, write (T) if the equations within each exercise are all equivalent equations and (F) if they are not equivalent.

49. $2x - 3 = 5$ $\qquad$ $2x = 8$ $\qquad$ $x = 4$

50. $5(x - 1) = 10$ $\qquad$ $x - 1 = 2$ $\qquad$ $x = 3$

51. $x(x - 1) = 5x$ $\qquad$ $x - 1 = 5$ $\qquad$ $x = 6$

52. $x = 5$ $\quad$ $x^2 = 25$

53. $3(x^2 + 2x + 1) = -6$ $\quad$ $x^2 + 2x + 1 = -2$
    $(x + 1)^2 = -2$

54. $(x + 3)(x - 1) = x^2 - 2x + 1$
    $(x + 3)(x - 1) = (x - 1)^2$ $\quad$ $x + 3 = x - 1$

55. Write repeating decimal fractions as rational equivalents.

    Example:
    $$N = 0.1515\ldots = 0.\overline{15}$$
    $$100N = 15.\overline{15}$$
    $$-N = -0.\overline{15}$$
    $$\overline{99\,N = 15}$$
    $$N = \frac{15}{99} = \frac{5}{33}$$

    a. $0.\overline{2}$ b. $0.\overline{123}$

    c. $1.\overline{35}$ d. $0.\overline{9}$

56. Find the error in the following argument. Assume that $a = b \neq 0$.

    $$a^2 = ab$$
    $$a^2 - b^2 = ab - b^2$$
    $$(a + b)(a - b) = b(a - b)$$
    $$a + b = b$$
    $$b + b = b \text{ (since } a = b)$$
    $$2b = b$$
    $$2 = 1 \text{ (since } b \neq 0)$$

57. Solve

    a. $\dfrac{w - c}{w - d} = \dfrac{c^2}{d^2}$ for w

    b. $a^2 = \dfrac{a + c}{x} + c^2$ for x

    c. $(a - y)(y + b) - c(y + c)$
    $= (c - y)(y + c) + ab$ for y

58. Solve for y.

    a. $y + \dfrac{c}{y - 3} = 3 + \dfrac{c}{y - 3}$

    b. $y + \dfrac{c}{y - 3} = -3 + \dfrac{c}{y - 3}$

59. The golden ratio is given by
    $$T = \frac{1 + \sqrt{5}}{2}$$

    (See Chapter 1, Review Exercise 78.) Show that
    $$T = 1 + \cfrac{1}{1 + \cfrac{1}{1 + \cfrac{1}{T}}}$$

 60. Determine if the equation is an identity experimentally by setting up a TABLE in your graphing calculator, and entering a variety of values for x.
    $$(x^2 + 5x + 6)(x - 3) = (x^2 - x - 6)(x + 3)$$

Example for Exercise 60.

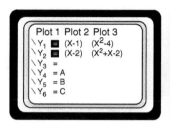 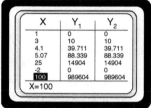

61. *Mathematics in Writing:* Set up a table like the one in Exercise 60, but pick a Y1 and Y2 so that Y1 = Y2 is a conditional equation. Explain in a brief paragraph how the tables differ, and what the difference tells you about the equations.

Applications 2.1

1. A rule of thumb for estimating the maximum affordable monthly mortgage note M for prospective homeowners is $M = \frac{m - b}{4}$, where m is the gross monthly income and b is the total of the monthly bills. What must the gross monthly income be to justify a monthly note of $900 if monthly bills are $500?

2. If P dollars are invested at a simple interest rate r (in decimals), the amount A that will be available after t years is $A = P(1 + rt)$.

   a. If $2000 is invested at a rate of 4.5%, how long will it be before the amount of money available is $3000?

   b. How long will it take to double your investment if the interest rate is 4.5%?

   c. If $2000 is invested at a rate of 10%, how long will it be before the amount of money available is $3000?

   d. How long will it take to double your investment if the interest rate is 10%?

3. The price P (in dollars) for which a manufacturer will sell a computer is related to the number q of computers ordered by the formula: $P = 600 - 0.03q$ where $200 \leq q \leq 4000$. How many computers must be ordered for a customer to pay $500 for a computer?

4. There is a relationship between the vocabulary of a child and the child's age. The equation $60A - V = 900$ describes the relationship, where A is the age of the child, in months, and V is the number of words that

the child uses. Suppose that a child uses 1200 words, find the age of the child, in months.

5. The Curry College book store marks up the price that it pays the publisher for a book by 30%. If the selling price of a math book is $125.99, how much did the book store pay for this book?

6. You made two investments in 2010 at $2000 each. On one investment, you gained 15%, and on the other investment, you lost 15%. What is your percentage gain or loss?

7. One of your stocks went up 20% and then down 20%. What is your percentage gain or loss?

8. Jing Yang, who is a well-known artist in Cape Cod, can produce and sell x craft items per month. The total cost C (in dollars) for producing x craft items is $C = 600 + 20x$ and the total revenue R (in dollars) is $R = 50x$.

   a. Find the break-even point. Please explain your answer so Jing could understand your mathematical result.

   b. Find the profit P obtained by selling 10 craft items per month. Please explain your answer.

   c. Find the profit P obtained by selling 30 craft items per month. Please explain your answer.

2.2 Applications: From Words to Algebra

Many applied problems lead to linear equations. The challenge of applied problems is translating words into appropriate algebraic forms.

The steps listed here can guide you in solving word problems.

Step 1. Read the problem through the first time to get a general idea of what is being asked.

Step 2. Read the problem a second time to recognize what may be important in determining that which is to be found.

Step 3. If possible, estimate the solution to this problem, and then compare this estimate with your final answer.

Step 4. Let some algebraic symbol denote the quantity to be found.

Step 5. If possible, represent other quantities in the problem in terms of the algebraic symbol designated in *Step 4*.

Step 6. Find various relationships (equations or inequalities) in the problem.

Step 7. Use relationships established in *Step 6* to find the solution to the problem.

Step 8. Verify that your answer is, indeed, the solution to the problem.

The words and phrases in Table 1 may prove helpful in translating a word problem into an algebraic expression that can be solved.

Example 1   Prices and Discounts
If you pay $66 for a car radio after receiving a 25% discount, what was the price of the radio before the discount?

Table 1 Translation of Words into Algebraic Expressions

Word or Phrase	Algebraic Symbol	Example	Algebraic Expression
Sum	+	Sum of two numbers	$a + b$
Difference	−	Difference of two numbers	$a - b$
		Difference of a number and 3	$x - 3$
Product	× or ·	Product of two numbers	$a \cdot b$, $(a)(b)$, or ab
Quotient	÷ or /	Quotient of two numbers	$\frac{a}{b}$, a/b, or $a \div b$
Exceeds		a exceeds b by 3	$a = b + 3$
More than		a is 3 more than b	or
More of		There are 3 more of a than of b	$a - 3 = b$
Twice		Twice a number	$2x$
		Twice the difference of x and 3	$2(x - 3)$
		3 more than twice a number	$2x + 3$
		3 less than twice a number	$2x - 3$
Is or equals	=	The sum of a number and 3 is 15.	$x + 3 = 15$

Solution

Let p = the price of the radio (in dollars) before the discount. Then

$$0.25p = \text{the amount discounted}$$

and the price of the radio after the discount is given by

$$p - 0.25p$$

Hence

$$p - 0.25p = 66$$
$$0.75p = 66$$
$$p = \frac{66}{0.75} = 88$$

The price of the radio was $88 before the discount.

Coin Problems

When interpreting coin problems, always distinguish between the *number* of coins and the *value* of the coins. You may also find it helpful to use a chart, as in the following example.

Example 2   Coins

A purse contains $3.20 in quarters and dimes. If there are 3 more quarters than dimes, how many coins of each type are there?

Solution

In this problem, we may let the unknown represent either the number of quarters or the number of dimes. Let

$$q = \text{the number of quarters}$$

Then

$$q - 3 = \text{the number of dimes}$$

since there are 3 more quarters than dimes.

Note that the number of coins times the value of each coin in cents is equal to the total value in cents using that particular coin.

	Number of coins $\times$ Value of each coin in cents = Total value in cents using that coin		
Quarters	q	25	$25q$
Dimes	$q - 3$	10	$10(q - 3)$

We know that

$$\text{total value} = (\text{value of quarters}) + (\text{value of dimes})$$
$$320 = 25q + 10(q - 3)$$
$$320 = 25q + 10q - 30$$
$$350 = 35q$$
$$10 = q$$

Then

$$q = \text{number of quarters} = 10$$
$$q - 3 = \text{number of dimes} = 7$$

Now verify that the total value of all the coins is \$3.20.

Simple Interest

Interest is the fee charged for borrowing money. In this section we will deal only with simple interest, which assumes the fee to be a fixed percentage r of the amount borrowed. We call the amount borrowed the **principal** and denote it by P.

If the principal P is borrowed at a simple annual interest rate r, then the interest due at the end of each year is Pr, and the total interest I due at the end of t years is

$$I = Prt$$

Consequently, if S is the total amount owed at the end of t years, then

$$S = P + I = P + Prt$$

since both the principal and interest are to be repaid. Thus, the basic formulas for simple interest calculations are

$$I = Prt$$
$$S = P + Prt$$

Example 3   Simple Interest

A part of $7000 was borrowed at 6% simple annual interest and the remainder at 8%. If the total amount of interest due after 3 years is $1380, how much was borrowed at each rate?

Solution

Let

$$s = \text{the amount borrowed at 6\%}$$

Then

$$7000 - s = \text{the amount borrowed at 8\%}$$

since the total amount is $7000. We can display the information in table form using the equation $I = Prt$.

	P	$\times$	r	$\times$	t	$=$	Interest
6% Portion	s		0.06		3		$0.18s$
8% Portion	$7000 - s$		0.08		3		$0.24(7000 - s)$

Note that we write the rate r in its decimal form, so that 6% = 0.06 and 8% = 0.08.

Since the total interest of $1380 is the sum of the interest from the two portions, we have

$$1380 = 0.18s + 0.24(7000 - s)$$
$$1380 = 0.18s + 1680 - 0.24s$$
$$0.06s = 300$$
$$s = 5000$$

We conclude that $5000 was borrowed at 6% and $2000 was borrowed at 8%.   ■

Distance Problems (Uniform Motion)

Here is the key to the solution of distance problems.

Distance = (Rate)(Time)

or

$$d = r \cdot t$$

The relationships that permit you to write an equation are sometimes obscured by the words. Here are some questions to ask as you set up a distance problem.

1. Are there two distances that are equal? (Will two objects have traveled the same distance? Is the distance on a return trip the same as the distance going?)

2. Is the sum (or difference) of two distances equal to a constant? (When two objects are traveling toward each other, they meet when the sum of the distances traveled by them equals the original distance between them.)

Example 4 Travel

Two trains leave New York for Chicago. The first train travels at an average speed of 60 mph. The second train, which departs an hour later, travels at an average speed of 80 mph. How long will it take the second train to overtake the first train?

Solution

Since we are interested in the time the second train travels, we let

$$t = \text{the number of hours the second train travels}$$

Then

$$t + 1 = \text{the number of hours the first train travels}$$

since the first train departs 1 hour earlier. We display the information in table form using the equation $d = rt$.

	Rate	×	Time	=	Distance
First train	60		$t + 1$		$60(t + 1)$
Second train	80		t		$80t$

At the moment the second train overtakes the first, they must both have traveled the *same* distance. Thus,

$$60(t + 1) = 80t$$
$$60t + 60 = 80t$$
$$60 = 20t$$
$$3 = t$$

It takes the second train 3 hours to catch up with the first train.

Mixture Problems

One type of mixture problem involves mixing varieties of a commodity, say two or more types of coffee, to obtain a mixture with a desired value. If the commodity is measured in pounds, the relationships we need are

> (Number of pounds)(Price per pound) = Value of commodity
>
> Sum of weights of all varieties = Weight of mixture
>
> Sum of values of all varieties = Value of mixture

Example 5　Mixtures

How many pounds of Brazilian coffee worth $5 per pound must be mixed with 20 pounds of Colombian coffee worth $4 per pound to produce a mixture worth $4.20 per pound?

Solution

Let B = number of pounds of Brazilian coffee. We display all the information, using cents in place of dollars.

Type of coffee	Number of pounds	× Price per pound	= Value (in cents)
Brazilian	B	500	$500B$
Colombian	20	400	8000
Mixture	$B + 20$	420	$420(B + 20)$

Note that the weight of the mixture equals the sum of the weights of the Brazilian and Colombian coffees that make up the mixture. Since the value of the mixture is the sum of the values of the two types of coffee,

$$\text{value of mixture} = (\text{value of Brazilian}) + (\text{value of Colombian})$$
$$420(B + 20) = 500B + 8000$$
$$420B + 8400 = 500B + 8000$$
$$400 = 80B$$
$$5 = B$$

We must add 5 pounds of Brazilian coffee to make the required mixture.

Work Problems

Work problems typically involve two or more people or machines working on the same task. The key to these problems is to express the *rate of work per unit of time,* whether an hour, a day, a week, or some other unit. For example, if a machine can do a job in 5 days, then

$$\text{rate of machine} = \frac{1}{5} \text{ job per day}$$

If this machine is used for 2 days, it performs $2(\frac{1}{5}) = \frac{2}{5}$ of the job. In summary:

> If a machine (or person) can complete a job in n days, then
> $$\text{Rate of machine (or person)} = \frac{1}{n} \text{ Job per day}$$
> $$\text{Work done} = (\text{Rate})(\text{Time})$$

Example 6   Work

Using a small mower, at 12 noon a student begins to mow a lawn, a job that would take 9 hours working alone. At 1 P.M. another student, using a tractor, joins the first student, and they complete the job together at 3 P.M. How many hours would it take to do the job using only the tractor?

Solution

Let t = number of hours to do the job by tractor alone. The small mower works from 12 noon to 3 P.M., or 3 hours. The tractor is used from 1 P.M. to 3 P.M., or 2 hours.

All the information can be displayed in table form.

	Rate	$\times$ Time	$=$ Work done
Small mower	$\dfrac{1}{9}$	3	$\dfrac{3}{9} = \dfrac{1}{3}$
Tractor	$\dfrac{1}{t}$	2	$\dfrac{2}{t}$

Since

$$\text{Work done by small mower} + \text{Work done by tractor} = 1 \text{ Whole job}$$
$$\frac{1}{3} + \frac{2}{t} = 1$$

To solve, multiply both sides by the LCD, which is $3t$.

$$\left(\frac{1}{3} + \frac{2}{t}\right)(3t) = 1(3t)$$
$$t + 6 = 3t$$
$$t = 3$$

Thus, by tractor alone, the job can be done in 3 hours.

Formulas

The circumference C of a circle is given by the formula

$$C = 2\pi r$$

where r is the radius of the circle. For every value of r, the formula gives us a value of C. If $r = 20$, we have

$$C = 2\pi(20) = 40\pi$$

It is sometimes convenient to be able to turn a formula around, that is, to be able to solve for a different variable. For example, if we want to express the radius of a circle in terms of the circumference, we have

$$C = 2\pi r$$
$$\frac{C}{2\pi} = \frac{2\pi r}{2\pi} \qquad \text{Dividing by } 2\pi$$
$$\frac{C}{2\pi} = r$$

Now, given a value of C, we can determine a value of r.

Example 7 Manipulation of Formulas

If an amount P is borrowed at the simple annual interest rate r, then the amount S due at the end of t years is

$$S = P + Prt$$

Solve for P.

Solution

$$P + Prt = S$$
$$P(1 + rt) = S \qquad \text{Common factor } P$$
$$P = \frac{S}{1 + rt} \qquad \text{Dividing both sides by } (1 + rt)$$

Calculator Alert

A formula may be stored as a PROGRAM in your graphing calculator. The program may be written merely to display the formula, or to ask the user for the input values and then evaluate the formula for those particular values. Many formulas are available online, or you could learn to write your own. Consult your owner's manual for details. The owner's manual may be available online.

Exercise Set 2.2

In Exercises 1–3, let n represent the unknown. Translate from words to an algebraic expression or equation.

1. The number of blue chips is 3 more than twice the number of red chips.

2. The number of station wagons on a parking lot is 20 fewer than 3 times the number of sedans.

3. Five less than 6 times a number is 26.

In Exercises 4–41, translate from words to an algebraic problem and solve.

4. Janis is 3 years older than her sister. Thirty years from now the sum of their ages will be 111. Find the current ages of the sisters.

5. John is presently 12 years older than Fred. Four years ago John was twice as old as Fred. How old is each now?

6. The larger of two numbers is 3 more than twice the smaller. If their sum is 18, find the numbers.

7. Find three consecutive integers whose sum is 21.

8. A certain number is 5 less than another number. If their sum is 11, find the two numbers.

9. A resort guarantees that the average temperature over the period Friday, Saturday, and Sunday will be exactly 80°F, or else each guest pays only half price for the facilities. If the temperatures on Friday and Saturday were 90°F and 82°F, respectively, what must the temperature be on Sunday so that the resort does not lose half of its revenue?

10. A patient's temperature was taken at 6 A.M., 12 noon, 3 P.M., and 8 P.M. The first, third, and fourth readings were 102.5°, 101.5°, and 102°F, respectively. The nurse forgot to write down the second reading, but recorded that the average of the four readings was 101.5°F. What was the second temperature reading?

11. A 12-meter long steel beam is to be cut into two pieces so that one piece will be 4 meters longer than the other. How long will each piece be?

12. A rectangular field whose length is 10 meters longer than its width is to be enclosed with exactly 100 meters of fencing material. What are the dimensions of the field?

13. A vending machine contains $3.00 in nickels and dimes. If the number of dimes is 5 more than twice the number of nickels, how many coins of each type are there?

14. A wallet contains $460 in $5, $10, and $20 bills. The number of $5 bills exceeds twice the number of $10 bills by 4, and the number of $20 bills is 6 fewer than the number of $10 bills. How many bills of each type are there?

15. A movie theater charges $3 admission for an adult and $1.50 for a child. If 700 tickets are sold on a particular day and the total revenue received is $1650, how many tickets of each type are sold?

16. A student bought 5-cent, 10-cent, and 15-cent stamps with a total value of $6.70. If the number of 5-cent stamps is 2 more than the number of 10-cent stamps, and the number of 15-cent stamps is 5 more than one-half the number of 10-cent stamps, how many stamps of each denomination did the student obtain?

17. An amateur theater group is converting a classroom to an auditorium for a forthcoming play. The group sells $3, $5, and $6 tickets, and receives exactly $503 from the sale of tickets. If the number of $5 tickets is twice the number of $6 tickets, and the number of $3 tickets is 1 more than 3 times the number of $6 tickets, how many tickets of each type are there?

18. To pay for their child's college education, the parents invested $10,000, part in a certificate of deposit paying 8.5% annual interest, the rest in a mutual fund paying 7% annual interest. The annual income from the certificate of deposit is $200 more than the annual income from the mutual fund. How much money was put into each type of investment?

19. A bicycle store is closing out its entire stock of a certain brand of three-speed and ten-speed models. The profit on a three-speed bicycle is 11% of the sale price, and the profit on a ten-speed model is 22% of the sale price. If the entire stock is sold for $16,000 and the profit on the entire stock is 19%, how much is obtained from the sale of each type of bicycle?

20. A film shop carrying black-and-white film and color film has $4000 in inventory. The profit on black-and-white film is 12%, and the profit on color film is 21%. If all the film is sold, and if the profit on color film is $150 less than the profit on black-and-white film, how much was invested in each type of film?

21. A firm borrowed $12,000 at a simple annual interest rate of 8% for a period of 3 years. At the end of the first year, the firm found that its needs were reduced. The firm returned a portion of the original loan and retained the remainder until the end of the 3-year period. If the total interest paid was $1760, how much was returned at the end of the first year?

22. A finance company lent a certain amount of money to Firm A at 7% annual interest. An amount $100 less than that lent to Firm A was lent to Firm B at 8%, and an amount $200 more than that lent to Firm A was lent to Firm C at 8.5%. All loans were for one year. If the total annual income is $126.50, how much was lent to each firm?

23. Two trucks leave Philadelphia for Miami. The first truck to leave travels at an average speed of 50 kilometers per hour. The second truck, which leaves 2 hours later, travels at an average speed of 55 kilometers per hour. How long does it take the second truck to overtake the first truck?

24. Jackie either drives or bicycles from home to school. Her average speed when driving is 36 mph, and her average speed when bicycling is 12 mph. If it takes her $\frac{1}{2}$ hour less to drive to school than to bicycle, how long does it take her to go to school, and how far is the school from her home?

25. Professors Roberts and Jones, who live 676 miles apart, are exchanging houses and jobs for the summer. They start out for their new locations at exactly the same time, and they meet after 6.5 hours of driving. If their average speeds differ by 4 mph, what are their average speeds?

26. Steve leaves school by moped for spring vacation. Forty minutes later his roommate, Frank, notices that Steve forgot to take his camera. So, Frank decides to try to catch up with Steve by car. If Steve's average speed is 25 mph and Frank averages 45 mph, how long does it take Frank to overtake Steve?

27. An express train and a local train start out from the same point at the same time and travel in opposite directions. The express train travels twice as fast as the local train. If after 4 hours they are 480 kilometers apart, what is the average speed of each train?

28. How many pounds of raisins worth $1.50 per pound must be mixed with 10 pounds of peanuts worth $1.20 per pound to produce a mixture worth $1.40 per pound?

29. How many ounces of Ceylon tea worth $1.50 per ounce and how many ounces of Formosa tea worth $2.00 per ounce must be mixed to obtain a mixture of 8 ounces that is worth $1.85 per ounce?

30. A copper alloy that is 40% copper is to be combined with a copper alloy that is 80% copper to produce 120 kilograms of an alloy that is 70% copper. How many kilograms of each alloy must be used?

31. A vat contains 27 gallons of water and 9 gallons of acetic acid. How many gallons of water must be evaporated if the resulting solution is to be 40% acetic acid?

32. A producer of packaged frozen vegetables wants to market mixed vegetables at $1.20 per kilogram. How many kilograms of green beans worth $1.00 per kilogram must be mixed with 100 kilograms of corn worth $1.30 per kilogram and 90 kilograms of peas worth $1.40 per kilogram to produce a satisfactory mixture?

33. A certain number is 3 times another. If the difference of their reciprocals is 8, find both numbers.

34. If $\frac{1}{3}$ is subtracted from 3 times the reciprocal of a certain number, the result is $\frac{25}{6}$. Find the number.

35. Computer A can carry out an engineering analysis in 6 hours, but computer B can do the same job in 4 hours. How long does it take to complete the job if both computers work together?

36. Jackie can paint a certain room in 3 hours, Lisa in 4 hours, and Susan in 2 hours. How long does it take to paint the room if they all work together?

37. A senior copy editor together with a junior copy editor can edit a book in 3 days. The junior editor, working alone, would take twice as long to complete the job as the senior editor would require if working alone. How long would it take each editor to complete the job by herself?

38. Hose A can fill a certain vat in 3 hours. After 2 hours of pumping, hose A is turned off. Hose B is then turned on and completes filling the vat in 3 more hours. How long would it take hose B to fill the vat alone?

39. A printing shop starts a job at 10 A.M. on press A. Using this press alone, it would take 8 hours to complete the job. At 2 P.M. press B is also turned on, and both presses together finish the job at 4 P.M. How long would it take press B to do the job alone?

40. A boat travels 20 kilometers upstream in the same time that it would take the same boat to travel 30 kilometers downstream. If the rate of the stream is 5 kilometers per hour, find the speed of the boat in still water.

41. An airplane flying against the wind travels 300 miles in the same time that it would take the same plane, flying the same speed, to travel 400 miles with the wind. If the wind speed is 20 mph, find the speed of the airplane in still air.

In Exercises 42–51 solve for the indicated variable in terms of the remaining variables.

42. $A = Pr$ for r

43. $C = 2\pi r$ for r

44. $V = \frac{1}{3}\pi r^2 h$ for h

45. $F = \dfrac{9}{5}C + 32$ for C

46. $S = \dfrac{1}{2}gt^2 + vt$ for v

47. $A = \dfrac{1}{2}h(b + b')$ for b

48. $A = P(1 + rt)$ for r

49. $\dfrac{1}{f} = \dfrac{1}{f_1} + \dfrac{1}{f_2}$ for f_2

50. $a = \dfrac{v_1 - v_0}{t}$ for v_0

51. $S = \dfrac{a - rL}{L - r}$ for L

52. Translate the following from words to an algebraic expression or equation, denoting the unknown by n.

   a. The express train travels 5 mph faster than the local train.

   b. The length of a rectangle is 7 inches more than its width.

   c. the area of a triangle, if the altitude is twice the base

   d. the sum of 3 consecutive even numbers

   e. 15% of the amount by which a number exceeds 10,000

53. If r and s represent two numbers, write

   a. twice the sum of the two numbers

   b. 5% of the difference between the two numbers

   c. 5 less than twice the second number

   d. the ratio of the first to the second number

   e. the sum of the squares of the two numbers

   f. the average of the two numbers

   g. 6 times the first number less 4 times the second number

54. Write formulas for each of the following:

   a. the charge in cents for a telephone call between two cities lasting n minutes, n greater than 3, if the charge for the first 3 minutes is $1.20 and each additional minute costs 33 cents

   b. the taxi fare for m miles, if the initial charge is $2.50 and the driver charges 70 cents for every $\frac{1}{5}$ mile traveled

   c. the amount in an account at the end of a year, if simple interest is paid at the rate of 16%, and the account contains d dollars at the beginning of the year

   d. the fine a company paid for dumping acid into the Mississippi River for d days, if the U.S. Environmental Protection Agency fined the company $150,000 plus $1000 per day until the company complied with the federal water pollution regulations.

55. Find three consecutive even numbers such that twice the first plus 3 times the second is 4 times the third.

56. When exercising, Mary walks a distance to warm up, jogs $3\frac{1}{2}$ times as far as she walks, and sprints $3\frac{1}{3}$ times as far as she jogs. If she covers 4171 meters, find the distances that she walked, jogged, and sprinted.

57. A 10-quart radiator has 30% antifreeze. How much of the fluid should be drained and replaced with pure antifreeze to double the strength of the mixture?

58. There are two identical beakers in a chemistry laboratory, both filled to the same level. One contains sulfuric acid and the other contains water. First, one spoon of acid is put into the beaker with the water and mixed thoroughly. Then one spoon of this mixture is put back into the beaker with the acid. Is there more water in the acid or more acid in the water?

59. Two bicyclists leave cities A and B at the same time, heading toward each other. Their speeds are 20 mph and 30 mph, respectively. The distance between these cities is 100 miles. Simultaneously, a bird leaves city A, heading toward B, traveling at 40 mph. When it meets the bicyclist who left from B, it turns around and heads back toward A. When it subsequently meets the bicyclist who came from A, it turns around and heads back toward B, and so on. Find the total distance the bird will have flown by the time the two bicyclists meet.

60. To determine the number of deer in a forest, a conservationist catches 225 deer, tags them and then releases them. A week later, 102 deer are caught and, of those, 15 are found to be tagged. Assuming that the proportion of tagged deer in the second sample was the same as the proportion of all tagged deer in the total population, estimate the number of deer in the forest.

61. In a Tour de France bicycle race, Stefan averaged 20 mph for the first third of the race and 35 mph for the remainder. Enrique maintained a constant speed of 30 mph throughout the race. Of these two, who finished first?

Applications 2.2

1. Curry College pays time-and-a-half for all hours worked in excess of 40 hours. Sharon made $551 last week by working 52 hours at the Curry College Admission Office. With this information, can you determine Sharon's regular hourly wage? Please show your work step by step.

2. We measure temperature in both degrees Fahrenheit (°F) and degrees Celsius (°C), which are related by the formula $5F - 9C = 160$.

   a. Write the degrees Celsius (°C) as an expression of degrees Fahrenheit (°F)

   b. If the Fahrenheit (°F) is 32 degrees, find the degrees Celsius.

3. A total of $50,000 is invested, some in stocks and the rest in bonds. If the amount invested in bonds is half that invested in stocks, how much is invested in each category?

4. Kim invests $5000, some in stocks and the rest in bonds. Let x = amount invested in stocks. Write an algebraic expression in x for "the amount invested in bonds."

5. You own a small farm. Dried pears sell for $6.00 per pound, and dried apricots sell for $8.00 per pound. Let x = number of pounds of dried pears in a 15-pound mixture of dried pears and dried apricots. Write an algebraic expression in x for

   a. The number of pounds of dried apricots in the 15-pound mixture.

   b. The value of the dried apricots in the 15-pound mixture.

   c. The number of pounds of dried pears in the 15-pound mixture.

   d. The value of the dried pears in the 15-pound mixture.

   e. If one 15-pound mixture sells for $108, find the numbers of pounds of dried pears and dried apricots in the 15-pound mixture.

6. An air conditioning repair bill for $329.96 showed a charge of $80 for parts, with the remainder of the charge for labor. Let x = number of hours of labor it took to repair the air conditioner.

   a. Write an algebraic expression in x for the labor charge per hour.

   b. It took Joe 2 hours to repair the air conditioner, find the labor charge per hour.

7. Stacey bought a math book for $165.99, including sales tax of 6.75%. Let x = the price of the math book before tax.

   a. Write an algebraic expression in x for "the tax paid on the math book."

   b. Find the tax paid on the math book.

2.3   The Quadratic Equation

We now turn our attention to equations involving second-degree polynomials. A **quadratic equation** is an equation of the form

$$ax^2 + bx + c = 0, \qquad a \neq 0$$

where a, b and c are real numbers. In this section we will explore techniques for solving this important class of equations. We will also show that there are several kinds of equations that can be transformed into quadratic equations and then solved.

Solving by Factoring

If we can factor the left-hand side of the quadratic equation

$$ax^2 + bx + c = 0, \qquad a \neq 0$$

into two linear factors, then we can solve the equation. For example, the quadratic equation

$$x^2 - 5x + 6 = 0$$

can be written as

$$(x - 2)(x - 3) = 0$$

since 0 is the only number with the following property:

If $ab = 0$, then $a = 0$ or $b = 0$.

We can set each factor of the above quadratic equation equal to 0.

$$x - 2 = 0 \qquad \text{or} \qquad x - 3 = 0$$
$$x = 2 \qquad \text{or} \qquad x = 3$$

The solutions of the given quadratic equation are 2 and 3.

Example 1   Solving by Factoring

Solve the equation $2x^2 - 3x - 2 = 0$ by factoring.

Solution

Factoring, we have

$$2x^2 - 3x - 2 = 0$$
$$(2x + 1)(x - 2) = 0$$

Since the product of the factors is 0, at least one factor must be 0. Setting each factor equal to 0, we have

$$2x + 1 = 0 \qquad \text{or} \qquad x - 2 = 0$$
$$x = -\frac{1}{2} \qquad \text{or} \qquad x = 2$$

Example 2   Solving by Factoring

Solve the equation $3x^2 + 5x - 2 = 0$ by factoring.

Solution

Factoring, we have

$$(3x - 1)(x + 2) = 0$$

$$3x - 1 = 0 \quad \text{or} \quad x + 2 = 0$$
$$x = \frac{1}{3} \quad \text{or} \quad x = -2$$

Example 3   Solving by Factoring

Solve the equation $3x^2 - 4x = 0$ by factoring.

Solution

Factoring, we have

$$3x^2 - 4x = 0$$
$$x(3x - 4) = 0$$

Setting each factor equal to zero,

$$x = 0 \quad \text{or} \quad x = \frac{4}{3}$$

Warning

When considering an equation with a common factor, such as

$$3x^2 - 4x = 0$$
$$x(3x - 4) = 0$$

always set each factor equal to zero. A common error of students is to divide both sides of the above equation by x.

$$\frac{x(3x - 4)}{x} = \frac{0}{x}$$

concluding that

$$3x - 4 = 0$$
$$x = \frac{4}{3}$$

The only time this operation is permitted is if $x \neq 0$. If $x = 0$ were possible, then you would have "lost" this root of the original equation.

✔ Progress Check

Solve each of the given equations by factoring.

a. $4x^2 - x = 0$ b. $3x^2 - 11x - 4 = 0$

Answers

a. $0, \dfrac{1}{4}$ b. $-\dfrac{1}{3}, 4$

One cannot always find "simple" factors to solve quadratic equations. For the most part, we will only attempt to use the factoring method for general quadratic equations with rational roots. In those cases, the factors only have integer coefficients.

Furthermore, there are some quadratic equations that cannot even be factored over the real numbers. Consider using the factoring method to solve

$$x^2 + x + 1 = 0$$

There do not exist any real numbers r and s such that

$$x^2 + x + 1 = (x + r)(x + s)$$

However, it can be written in this form if we permit r and s to be complex numbers. For this reason, it is necessary to develop solution techniques that are more powerful than factoring.

Special Cases: $x^2 - p = 0$, $x^2 + p = 0$, $a(x+h)^2 + c = 0$

There are certain quadratic equations that do not necessarily require the use of factoring when finding solutions. Because of their special form, we may use the method of taking roots.

Example 4 Special Cases
Solve the equation $x^2 - 3 = 0$.

Solution
We may write the original equation as

$$x^2 = 3$$

Taking the square root of both sides, we obtain

$$x = \sqrt{3} \qquad \text{or} \qquad x = -\sqrt{3}$$

Sometimes these solutions are written in the abbreviated form $x = \pm\sqrt{3}$.

Alternatively, if we recognize that the original equation can be factored as

$$x^2 - 3 = (x - \sqrt{3})(x + \sqrt{3}) = 0$$

we obtain the same results by setting each factor equal to 0. ■

For a positive number p, consider $x^2 - p = 0$ or, equivalently, $x^2 = p$. Taking the square root of both sides of this equation, we obtain $x = \pm\sqrt{p}$. Alternatively, we may factor

$$x^2 - p = (x - \sqrt{p})(x + \sqrt{p})$$

(Check this by multiplying the factors of the right-hand side of the equation.) This leads to the following result.

If $p > 0$ and $x^2 = p$, then $x = \pm\sqrt{p}$. Furthermore, the equation can be written in factored form as

$$x^2 - p = (x - \sqrt{p})(x + \sqrt{p}) = 0$$

Example 5   Special Cases

Solve the equation $x^2 + 4 = 0$.

Solution

We may write the original equation as

$$x^2 = -4$$

Taking the square root of both sides, we obtain

$$x = \pm 2i$$

Alternatively, if we recognize that the original equation can be factored as

$$x^2 + 4 = (x - 2i)(x + 2i) = 0$$

we obtain the same results by setting each factor equal to 0.

For a positive number p, consider $x^2 + p = 0$ or, equivalently, $x^2 = -p$. Taking the square root of both sides of this equation we obtain $x = \pm\sqrt{p}\,i$. Alternatively, we may factor

$$x^2 + p = (x - \sqrt{p}\,i)(x + \sqrt{p}\,i)$$

(Check by multiplying the factors of the right-hand side.)

This leads to the following result.

If $p > 0$ and $x^2 = -p$, then $x = \pm\sqrt{p}\,i$. Furthermore, the equation can be written in factored form as

$$x^2 + p = (x - \sqrt{p}\,i)(x + \sqrt{p}\,i) = 0$$

Example 6   Special Cases

Solve the equation $2x^2 - 6 = 0$.

Solution

$$2x^2 - 6 = 0$$
$$2x^2 = 6$$
$$x^2 = 3$$
$$x = \pm\sqrt{3}$$

Example 7 Special Cases

Solve the equation $2(x - 1)^2 - 6 = 0$.

Solution

$$2(x - 1)^2 - 6 = 0$$
$$2(x - 1)^2 = 6$$
$$(x - 1)^2 = 3$$
$$x - 1 = \pm\sqrt{3}$$
$$x = 1 \pm \sqrt{3}$$

Example 8 Special Cases

Solve the equation $4(x + 3)^2 + 20 = 0$.

Solution

$$4(x + 3)^2 + 20 = 0$$
$$4(x + 3)^2 = -20$$
$$(x + 3)^2 = -5$$
$$x + 3 = \pm\sqrt{5}i$$
$$x = -3 \pm \sqrt{5}i$$

Equations of the form $a(x + h)^2 + c = 0$ may be solved using the techniques of Examples 7 and 8 as follows.

$$a(x + h)^2 + c = 0$$
$$a(x + h)^2 = -c$$
$$(x + h)^2 = -\frac{c}{a}$$
$$x + h = \pm\sqrt{-\frac{c}{a}}$$
$$x = -h \pm \sqrt{-\frac{c}{a}}$$

✔ **Progress Check**

Solve the given equation.

a. $5x^2 + 13 = 0$ b. $(2x - 7)^2 - 5 = 0$

Answers

a. $\pm\frac{\sqrt{65}}{5}i$ b. $\frac{7 \pm \sqrt{5}}{2}$

We have seen that the solutions of a quadratic equation may be complex numbers, whereas the solution of a linear equation is a real number. In addition, quadratic equations appear to have two solutions. We will have more to say about these observations when we study the roots of polynomial equations in a later chapter.

We have shown that we can always find a solution to a quadratic equation of the form

$$a(x + h)^2 + c = 0 \tag{1}$$

A technique known as **completing the square** permits us to rewrite *any* quadratic equation in the form of Equation (1). Beginning with the expression $x^2 + dx$, we seek a constant h^2 to complete the square so that

$$x^2 + dx + h^2 = (x + h)^2$$

Expanding and solving, we have

$$x^2 + dx + h^2 = x^2 + 2hx + h^2$$
$$dx = 2hx$$
$$h = \frac{d}{2}$$
$$h^2 = \left(\frac{d}{2}\right)^2$$

so $h^2 = (\frac{d}{2})^2$ is the amount to be added to $x^2 + dx$ to form a perfect square.

Example 9   Completing the Square
Complete the square for each of the following.

a. $x^2 - 6x$ 　　　　　　b. $x^2 + 3x$

Solution

a. The coefficient of x is -6, so $h = -\frac{6}{2} = -3$ and $h^2 = 9$. Then
$$x^2 - 6x + 9 = (x - 3)^2$$

b. The coefficient of x is 3, and $h^2 = (\frac{3}{2})^2 = \frac{9}{4}$. Then
$$x^2 + 3x + \frac{9}{4} = \left(x + \frac{3}{2}\right)^2.$$

We are now in a position to use this method to solve a quadratic equation.

Example 10   Completing the Square
Solve the quadratic equation $2x^2 - 10x + 1 = 0$ by completing the square.

Solution
We outline and explain each step of the process in Table 2 (next page).

Table 2 Completing the Square

Method	Example
Step 1. Rewrite the equation with the constant term on the right-hand side.	*Step 1.* $2x^2 - 10x = -1$
Step 2. Factor out a, the coefficient of x^2.	*Step 2.* $2(x^2 - 5x) = -1$
Step 3. Divide both sides of the equation by a.	*Step 3.* $x^2 - 5x = -\dfrac{1}{2}$
Step 4. Find $h = \frac{d}{2}$ and $h^2 = (\frac{d}{2})^2$, where d is the coefficient of x in *Step 3*.	*Step 4.* $h = \dfrac{-5}{2}, \quad h^2 = \dfrac{25}{4}$
Step 5. Add h^2 to both sides of the equation.	*Step 5.* $x^2 - 5x + \dfrac{25}{4} = -\dfrac{1}{2} + \dfrac{25}{4}$
Step 6. Simplify.	*Step 6.* $\left(x - \dfrac{5}{2}\right)^2 = \dfrac{23}{4}$
Step 7. Solve for x.	*Step 7.* $x - \dfrac{5}{2} = \pm \sqrt{\dfrac{23}{4}}$ $x = \dfrac{5}{2} \pm \dfrac{\sqrt{23}}{2}$ $x = \dfrac{5 \pm \sqrt{23}}{2}$

✔ **Progress Check**

Solve by completing the square.

a. $x^2 - 3x + 2 = 0$
b. $3x^2 - 4x + 2 = 0$

Answers

a. $1, 2$
b. $\dfrac{2 \pm \sqrt{2}\,i}{3}$

The Quadratic Formula

We can apply the method of completing the square to the general quadratic equation

$$ax^2 + bx + c = 0, \qquad a \neq 0$$

Following the steps of the method as shown in Table 2, we proceed as follows:

1. Move the constant term to the right-hand side.

$$ax^2 + bx = -c$$

2. Factor out a, the coefficient of x^2.

$$a\left(x^2 + \frac{b}{a}x\right) = -c$$

3. Divide both sides of the equation by a.

$$x^2 + \frac{b}{a}x = -\frac{c}{a}$$

4. Find $h = \frac{d}{2}$ and $h^2 = (\frac{d}{2})^2$, where d is the coefficient of x.

$$h = \frac{b}{2a}, \quad h^2 = \frac{b^2}{4a^2}$$

5. Add h^2 to both sides of the equation.

$$x^2 + \frac{b}{a}x + \frac{b^2}{4a^2} = -\frac{c}{a} + \frac{b^2}{4a^2}$$

6. Simplify.

$$\left(x + \frac{b}{2a}\right)^2 = \frac{b^2}{4a^2} - \frac{c(4a)}{a(4a)}$$

$$\left(x + \frac{b}{2a}\right)^2 = \frac{b^2 - 4ac}{4a^2}$$

7. Solve for x.

$$x + \frac{b}{2a} = \pm\sqrt{\frac{b^2 - 4ac}{4a^2}}$$

$$x = \frac{-b}{2a} \pm \frac{\sqrt{b^2 - 4ac}}{2a}$$

$$x = \frac{-b \pm \sqrt{b^2 - 4ac}}{2a}$$

The quadratic equation

$$ax^2 + bx + c = 0, \qquad a \neq 0$$

has *two* roots often written in the compact form

$$x = \frac{-b \pm \sqrt{b^2 - 4ac}}{2a}, \qquad a \neq 0$$

Example 11   The Quadratic Formula

Solve $2x^2 - 3x - 3 = 0$ by the quadratic formula.

Solution

Since $a = 2$, $b = -3$ and $c = -3$, we have

$$x = \frac{-b \pm \sqrt{b^2 - 4ac}}{2a}$$

$$x = \frac{-(-3) \pm \sqrt{(-3)^2 - 4(2)(-3)}}{2(2)}$$

$$x = \frac{3 \pm \sqrt{33}}{4}$$

Example 12   The Quadratic Formula

Solve $-5x^2 + 3x = 2$ by the quadratic formula.

Solution

We first rewrite the given equation as $-5x^2 + 3x - 2 = 0$. Then $a = -5$, $b = 3$ and $c = -2$. Substituting into the quadratic formula, we have

$$x = \frac{-b \pm \sqrt{b^2 - 4ac}}{2a}$$

$$x = \frac{-3 \pm \sqrt{3^2 - 4(-5)(-2)}}{2(-5)}$$

$$x = \frac{-3 \pm \sqrt{-31}}{-10}$$

$$x = \frac{-3 \pm \sqrt{31}\,i}{-10}$$

(Show that this is equivalent to $x = \frac{3 \pm \sqrt{31}\,i}{10}$.)

✔ Progress Check

Solve by the quadratic formula.

a. $x^2 - 8x = -10$ b. $4x^2 - 2x + 1 = 0$

Answers

a. $4 \pm \sqrt{6}$ b. $\dfrac{1 \pm \sqrt{3}\,i}{4}$

Warning

There are a number of errors that students make in using the quadratic formula.

a. To solve $x^2 - 3x = -4$, you must write the equation in the form

$$x^2 - 3x + 4 = 0$$

to properly identify a, b and c. Note that $b = -3$, *not* 3.

b. The quadratic formula is

$$x = \frac{-b \pm \sqrt{b^2 - 4ac}}{2a}$$

Note that

$$x \neq -b \pm \frac{\sqrt{b^2 - 4ac}}{2a}$$

since the term $-b$ must also be divided by $2a$.

- -

Now that there is a formula that works for any quadratic equation, it may be tempting to use it all the time. However, if you see an equation such as

$$x^2 = 15$$

it may be easier to obtain the answer: $x = \pm\sqrt{15}$. Similarly, when faced with

$$x^2 + 3x + 2 = 0$$

it may be faster to solve it if you see that

$$x^2 + 3x + 2 = (x + 1)(x + 2)$$

The method of completing the square is generally not used for solving quadratic equations once the quadratic formula is learned. The *technique* of completing the square is helpful in a variety of applications, and we will use it in a later chapter when we graph second-degree equations.

The Discriminant

By analyzing the quadratic formula

$$x = \frac{-b \pm \sqrt{b^2 - 4ac}}{2a}$$

we can learn a great deal about the roots of the quadratic equation

$$ax^2 + bx + c = 0, \qquad a \neq 0$$

The key to the analysis is the **discriminant** $b^2 - 4ac$ found under the radical.

- If $b^2 - 4ac$ is negative, we have the square root of a negative number, and the roots of the quadratic equation are complex numbers as conjugate pairs.

- If $b^2 - 4ac$ is positive, we have the square root of a positive number, and the roots of the quadratic equation are two different real numbers.

- If $b^2 - 4ac = 0$, then $x = -\frac{b}{2a}$, which we call a **double root** or **repeated root** of the quadratic equation. For example, if $x^2 - 10x + 25 = 0$, then the discriminant is 0 and $x = 5$. But

$$x^2 - 10x + 25 = (x - 5)(x - 5) = 0$$

We call $x = 5$ a double root because the factor $x - 5$ is a double factor of $x^2 - 10x + 25 = 0$. This hints at the importance of the relationship between roots and factors, a relationship that we will explore later in Chapter 4. We summarize as follows in Table 3.

Table 3   Discriminant-Root Analysis

The quadratic equation $ax^2 + bx + c = 0$, $a \neq 0$, has exactly two roots, the nature of which are determined by the discriminant $b^2 - 4ac$.

Discriminant	Roots
Negative	Two complex roots as conjugate pairs
0	One real double root
Positive	Two different real roots

If the roots of the quadratic equation are real, and a, b and c are rational numbers, the discriminant enables us to determine whether the roots are rational or irrational. Since $\sqrt{k}$ is a rational number only if k is a perfect square, we see that the quadratic formula produces a rational result only if $b^2 - 4ac$ is a perfect square.

Example 13   Discriminant-Root Analysis

Without solving, determine the nature of the roots of the quadratic equation $3x^2 - 4x + 6 = 0$.

Solution

We evaluate $b^2 - 4ac$ using $a = 3$, $b = -4$ and $c = 6$:

$$b^2 - 4ac = (-4)^2 - 4(3)(6) = 16 - 72 = -56$$

The discriminant is negative, so the equation has two complex roots.

Example 14   Discriminant-Root Analysis

Without solving, determine the nature of the roots of the equation $2x^2 - 7x = -1$.

Solution

We rewrite the equation in the standard form

$$2x^2 - 7x + 1 = 0$$

and then substitute $a = 2$, $b = -7$ and $c = 1$ in the discriminant. Therefore,

$$b^2 - 4ac = (-7)^2 - 4(2)(1) = 49 - 8 = 41$$

The discriminant is positive and is not a perfect square. Thus, the roots are real, unequal, and irrational.

✔ **Progress Check**

Without solving, determine the nature of the roots of the quadratic equation by using the discriminant.

a. $4x^2 - 20x + 25 = 0$ b. $5x^2 - 6x = -2$

c. $10x^2 = x + 2$ d. $x^2 + x - 1 = 0$

Answers

a. a real, double root   b. two complex roots

c. two real, rational roots   d. two real, irrational roots

Forms Leading to Quadratics

Certain types of equations can be transformed into quadratic equations that can be solved by the methods discussed in this section. One form that leads to a quadratic equation is the **radical equation**, such as

$$x - \sqrt{x - 2} = 4$$

which is solved in Example 15. To solve the equation, we isolate the radical and raise both sides to a suitable power. The following is the key to the solution of such equations.

Solving Radical Equations

Step 1. If possible, isolate the radical on one side of the equation.	*Step 1.* $\qquad x - 4 = \sqrt{x - 2}$
Step 2. Raise both sides of the equation to a suitable power to eliminate the radical. If necessary, go back to *Step 1.*	*Step 2.* Squaring both sides, we have $$x^2 - 8x + 16 = x - 2$$
Step 3. Solve for the unknown.	*Step 3.* $\qquad x^2 - 9x + 18 = 0$ $(x - 3)(x - 6) = 0$ $x = 3 \qquad x = 6$
Step 4. Check each solution by substituting in the *original* equation.	*Step 4.* LHS $= x - \sqrt{x - 2} \qquad$ RHS $= 4$ Check $x = 3$ LHS $= 3 - \sqrt{3 - 2} = 2 \neq 4 =$ RHS Check $x = 6$ LHS $= 6 - \sqrt{6 - 2} = 6 - 2 = 4 =$ RHS

> If P and Q are algebraic expressions, then the solution set of the equation
>
> $$P = Q$$
>
> is a subset of the solution set of the equation
>
> $$P^n = Q^n$$
>
> where n is a natural number.

This suggests that we can solve radical equations if we observe a precaution.

> If both sides of an equation are raised to the same power, the solutions of the resulting equation must be checked to see that they satisfy the original equation.

Example 15   Radical Equations
Solve $x - \sqrt{x - 2} = 4$.

Solution
We will use the abbreviation LHS for left-hand side and RHS for right-hand side.
We conclude that 6 is a solution of the original equation, and 3 is not a solution of the original equation. We say that 3 is an **extraneous solution** that was introduced when we raised both sides of the original equation to the second power.   ■

> ✔ **Progress Check**
> Solve $x - \sqrt{1 - x} = -5$.
>
> **Answer**
> -3

The equation in the next example contains more than one radical. Solving this equation requires that we square both sides *twice*.

Example 16   Radical Equations
Solve $\sqrt{2x - 4} - \sqrt{3x + 4} = -2$.

Solution
Before squaring, rewrite the equation so that we isolate one of the radicals on one side of the equation.

$$\sqrt{2x - 4} = \sqrt{3x + 4} - 2$$

$$2x - 4 = (3x + 4) - 4\sqrt{3x + 4} + 4 \qquad \text{Square both sides.}$$

$$-x - 12 = 4\sqrt{3x + 4} \qquad \text{Isolate the radical.}$$

$$x^2 + 24x + 144 = 16(3x + 4) \qquad \text{Square both sides.}$$

$$x^2 - 24x + 80 = 0$$

$$(x - 20)(x - 4) = 0$$

$$x = 20 \qquad x = 4$$

Verify that both 20 and 4 are solutions of the original equation.

✔ Progress Check

Solve $\sqrt{5x - 1} - \sqrt{x + 2} = 1$.

Answer

2

Although the equation

$$x^4 - x^2 - 2 = 0$$

is not a quadratic in the unknown x, it is a quadratic in the unknown x^2:

$$(x^2)^2 - (x^2) - 2 = 0$$

This may be seen more clearly by replacing x^2 with a new unknown u such that $u = x^2$. Substituting, we have

$$u^2 - u - 2 = 0$$

which is a quadratic equation in the unknown u. Solving, we find

$$(u + 1)(u - 2) = 0$$

$$u = -1 \quad \text{or} \quad u = 2$$

Since $x^2 = u$, we must next solve the equations

$$x^2 = -1 \quad \text{and} \quad x^2 = 2$$

$$x = \pm i \qquad \qquad x = \pm\sqrt{2}$$

The original equation has four solutions: i, $-i$, $\sqrt{2}$, and $-\sqrt{2}$.

The technique we have used is called a **substitution of variable**. This is a powerful method that is commonly used in calculus.

✔ Progress Check

Indicate an appropriate substitution of variable and solve each of the following equations.

a. $3x^4 - 10x^2 - 8 = 0$

b. $4x^{2/3} + 7x^{1/3} - 2 = 0$

c. $\dfrac{2}{x^2} + \dfrac{1}{x} - 10 = 0$

d. $\left(1 + \dfrac{2}{x}\right)^2 - 8\left(1 + \dfrac{2}{x}\right) + 15 = 0$

Answers

a. $u = x^2$; ± 2, $\pm\dfrac{\sqrt{6}i}{3}$

b. $u = x^{1/3}$; $\dfrac{1}{64}$, -8

c. $u = \dfrac{1}{x}$; $-\dfrac{2}{5}$, $\dfrac{1}{2}$

d. $u = 1 + \dfrac{2}{x}$; 1, $\dfrac{1}{2}$

Calculator Alert

There are programs available for most graphing calculators which allow the user to input the values of a, b, and c, and then display the solutions. Look online for a program you could download. You may find a site which gives you the lines of code needed; you would then write the program line-by-line using the "edit" option in your graphing calculator's program menu.

Exercise Set 2.3

In Exercises 1–14, solve by factoring.

1. $x^2 - 3x + 2 = 0$
2. $x^2 - 6x + 8 = 0$
3. $x^2 + x - 2 = 0$
4. $3r^2 - 4r + 1 = 0$
5. $x^2 + 6x = -8$
6. $x^2 + 6x + 5 = 0$
7. $y^2 - 4y = 0$
8. $2x^2 - x = 0$
9. $2x^2 - 5x = -2$
10. $2s^2 - 5s - 3 = 0$
11. $t^2 - 4 = 0$
12. $4x^2 - 9 = 0$
13. $6x^2 - 5x + 1 = 0$
14. $6x^2 - x = 2$

In Exercises 15–24, solve the given equation.

15. $3x^2 - 27 = 0$
16. $4x^2 - 64 = 0$
17. $5y^2 - 25 = 0$
18. $6x^2 - 12 = 0$
19. $(2r + 5)^2 = 8$
20. $(3x - 4)^2 = -6$
21. $(3x - 5)^2 - 8 = 0$
22. $(4t + 1)^2 - 3 = 0$
23. $9x^2 + 64 = 0$
24. $81x^2 + 25 = 0$

In Exercises 25–36, solve by completing the square.

25. $x^2 - 2x = 8$
26. $t^2 - 2t = 15$
27. $2r^2 - 7r = 4$
28. $9x^2 + 3x = 2$
29. $3x^2 + 8x = 3$
30. $2y^2 + 4y = 5$
31. $2y^2 + 2y = -1$
32. $3x^2 - 4x = -3$
33. $4x^2 - x = 3$
34. $2x^2 + x = 2$
35. $3x^2 + 2x = -1$
36. $3u^2 - 3u = -1$

In Exercises 37–48, solve by the quadratic formula.

37. $2x^2 + 3x = 0$
38. $2x^2 + 3x + 3 = 0$
39. $5x^2 - 4x + 3 = 0$
40. $2x^2 - 3x - 2 = 0$
41. $5y^2 - 4y + 5 = 0$
42. $x^2 - 5x = 0$
43. $3x^2 + x - 2 = 0$
44. $2x^2 + 4x - 3 = 0$

45. $3y^2 - 4 = 0$

46. $2x^2 + 2x + 5 = 0$

47. $4u^2 + 3u = 0$

48. $4x^2 - 1 = 0$

In Exercises 49–58, solve by any method.

49. $2x^2 + 2x - 5 = 0$

50. $2t^2 + 2t + 3 = 0$

51. $3x^2 + 4x - 4 = 0$

52. $x^2 + 2x = 0$

53. $2x^2 + 5x + 4 = 0$

54. $2r^2 - 3r + 2 = 0$

55. $4u^2 - 1 = 0$

56. $x^2 + 2 = 0$

57. $4x^3 + 2x^2 + 3x = 0$

58. $4s^3 + 4s^2 - 15s = 0$

In Exercises 59–64, solve for the indicated variable in terms of the remaining variables.

59. $a^2 + b^2 = c^2$, for b

60. $s = \frac{1}{2}gt^2$, for t

61. $V = \frac{1}{3}\pi r^2 h$, for r

62. $A = \pi r^2$, for r

63. $s = \frac{1}{2}gt^2 + vt$, for t

64. $F = g\frac{m_1 m_2}{d^2}$, for d

Without solving, determine the nature of the roots of each quadratic equation in Exercises 65–80.

65. $x^2 - 2x + 3 = 0$

66. $3x^2 + 2x - 5 = 0$

67. $4x^2 - 12x + 9 = 0$

68. $2x^2 + x + 5 = 0$

69. $-3x^2 + 2x + 5 = 0$

70. $-3y^2 + 2y - 5 = 0$

71. $3x^2 + 2x = 0$

72. $4x^2 + 20x + 25 = 0$

73. $2r^2 = r - 4$

74. $3x^2 = 5 - x$

75. $3x^2 + 6 = 0$

76. $4x^2 - 25 = 0$

77. $6r = 3r^2 + 1$

78. $4x = 2x^2 + 3$

79. $12x = 9x^2 + 4$

80. $4s^2 = -4s - 1$

In Exercises 81–84, find a value or values of k for which the quadratic has a double root.

81. $kx^2 - 4x + 1 = 0$

82. $2x^2 + 3x + k = 0$

83. $x^2 - kx - 2k = 0$

84. $kx^2 - 4x + k = 0$

In Exercises 85–92, find the solution set.

85. $x + \sqrt{x + 5} = 7$

86. $x - \sqrt{13 - x} = 1$

87. $2x + \sqrt{x + 1} = 8$

88. $3x - \sqrt{1 + 3x} = 1$

89. $\sqrt{3x + 4} - \sqrt{2x + 1} = 1$

90. $\sqrt{4 - 4x} - \sqrt{x + 4} = 3$

Applications 2.3

1. A manufacturer of a certain commodity has estimated that her profit in thousands of dollars is given by the expression $-6x^2 + 30x - 10$ where x (in thousands) is the number of units produced.

   a. Find the break-even point and explain your answer(s).

   b. How many units must be sold to reach a profit of $2400?

2. Suppose you throw a ball straight up from the ground with a velocity of 120 feet per second. As the ball moves up, gravity slows it. Eventually, the ball begins to fall back to the ground. The height h of his ball after t seconds in the air is given by the equation $-16t^2 + 112t$.

   a. Find the height of the ball after 1 second.

   b. When will the ball reach its peak height?

   c. How long will it take the ball to reach a height of 96 feet?

   d. How long after you throw the ball will it return to the ground?

3. Sky drivers are in free fall from the time they jump out of a plane until they open their parachutes. A sky diver jumps from 6000 feet. The diver's height h above the ground t seconds after the jump is described by the algebraic expression $-16t^2 + 6000$. Find the time during which the diver is in free fall assuming that the parachute opens at 1000 feet.

4. In a 50-inch television set, the length of the screen's diagonal is 50 inches. If the screen's height is 37 inches, what is its width? (Hint: Use Pythagorean Theorem.)

5. The rectangular shaped Curry College Faculty Parking Lot has a length that is 68-yards greater than the width. The area of the lot is 7888 square yards. Find the length and the width.

2.4 Applications of Quadratic Equations

As your knowledge of mathematical techniques and ideas grows, you will become capable of solving an ever wider variety of applied problems. In Section 2.2 we explored many types of word problems that lead to linear equations. We can now tackle a group of applied problems that lead to quadratic equations.

One word of caution: It is possible to arrive at a solution that makes no sense. For example, a negative solution that represents hours worked or the age of an individual is meaningless and must be rejected.

Example 1 Quadratic Equations and Word Problems

The larger of two positive numbers exceeds the smaller by 2. If the sum of the squares of the two numbers is 74, find the two numbers.

Solution
If we let

$$x = \text{the larger number}$$

then

$$x - 2 = \text{the smaller number}$$

The sum of the squares of the numbers is 74.

$$(\text{larger number})^2 + (\text{smaller number})^2 = 74$$
$$x^2 + (x - 2)^2 = 74$$
$$x^2 + x^2 - 4x + 4 = 74$$
$$2x^2 - 4x - 70 = 0$$
$$x^2 - 2x - 35 = 0$$
$$(x + 5)(x - 7) = 0$$
$$x = 7 \qquad \text{Reject } x = -5.$$

The numbers are then 7 and $(7 - 2) = 5$. Verify that the sum of the squares is indeed 74. ■

Example 2 Quadratic Equations and Word Problems

The length of a pool is 3 times its width, and the pool is surrounded by a grass walk 4 feet wide. If the total area covered and enclosed by the walk is 684 square feet, find the dimensions of the pool.

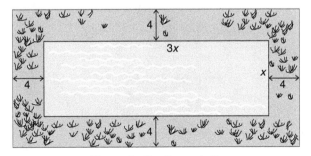

Figure 1 See Example 2.

Solution

Drawing diagrams is useful in solving geometric problems. For example, as shown in Figure 1, if we let x = width of the pool, then $3x$ = length of the pool, and the region enclosed by the walk has length $3x + 8$ and width $x + 8$. The total area is the product of the length and width, so

$$\text{length} \times \text{width} = 684$$
$$(3x + 8)(x + 8) = 684$$
$$3x^2 + 32x + 64 = 684$$
$$3x^2 + 32x - 620 = 0$$
$$(3x + 62)(x - 10) = 0$$
$$x = 10 \qquad \text{Reject } x = -\frac{62}{3}.$$

The dimensions of the pool are 10 feet by 30 feet.

Example 3   Quadratic Equations and Word Problems

Working together, two cranes can unload a ship in 4 hours. The slower crane, working alone, requires 6 hours more than the faster crane to do the job. How long does it take each crane to do the job by itself?

Solution

Let x = number of hours for the faster crane to do the job. Then $x + 6$ = number of hours for the slower crane to do the job. The rate of the faster crane is $\frac{1}{x}$, the portion of the whole job that it completes in 1 hour. Similarly, the rate of the slower crane is $\frac{1}{x + 6}$. We display this information in a table.

	Rate	×	Time	=	Work done
Faster crane	$\dfrac{1}{x}$		4		$\dfrac{4}{x}$
Slower crane	$\dfrac{1}{x + 6}$		4		$\dfrac{4}{x + 6}$

When the two cranes work together, we must have

$$\begin{pmatrix} \text{work done by} \\ \text{fast crane} \end{pmatrix} + \begin{pmatrix} \text{work done by} \\ \text{slow crane} \end{pmatrix} = 1 \text{ whole job}$$

or

$$\frac{4}{x} + \frac{4}{x + 6} = 1$$

To solve, we multiply by the LCD, $x(x + 6)$, obtaining

$$4(x + 6) + 4x = x^2 + 6x$$
$$0 = x^2 - 2x - 24$$
$$0 = (x + 4)(x - 6)$$
$$x = -4 \qquad \text{or} \qquad x = 6$$

The solution $x = -4$ is rejected, because it makes no sense to speak of negative hours of work. Then

$x = 6$ is the number of hours in which the fast crane can do the job alone.

$x + 6 = 12$ is the number of hours in which the slow crane can do the job alone.

Exercise Set 2.4

1. Working together, computers A and B can complete a data-processing job in 2 hours. Computer A working alone can do the job in 3 hours less than computer B working alone. How long does it take each computer to do the job by itself?

2. A graphic designer and her assistant working together can complete an advertising layout in 6 days. The assistant working alone could complete the job in 16 more days than the designer working alone. How long would it take each person to do the job alone?

3. A roofer and his assistant working together can finish a roofing job in 4 hours. The roofer working alone could finish the job in 6 hours less than the assistant working alone. How long would it take each person to do the job alone?

4. A 16- by 20-inch mounting board is used to mount a photograph. How wide a uniform border is needed if the photograph occupies $\frac{3}{5}$ of the area of the mounting board?

5. The length of a rectangle exceeds twice its width by 4 feet. If the area of the rectangle is 48 square feet, find the dimensions.

6. The length of a rectangle is 4 centimeters less than twice its width. Find the dimensions if the area of the rectangle is 96 square centimeters.

7. The area of a rectangle is 48 square centimeters. If the length and width are each increased by 4 centimeters, the area of the newly formed rectangle is 120 square centimeters. Find the dimensions of the original rectangle.

8. The base of a triangle is 2 feet more than twice its altitude. If the area is 12 square feet, find the dimensions.

9. Find the width of a strip that has been mowed around a rectangular field 60 feet by 80 feet if $\frac{1}{2}$ the lawn has not yet been mowed.

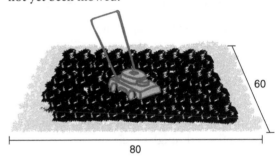

10. The sum of the reciprocals of two consecutive numbers is $\frac{7}{12}$. Find the numbers.

11. The sum of a number and its reciprocal is $\frac{26}{5}$. Find the number.

12. The difference of a number and its reciprocal is $\frac{35}{6}$. Find the number.

13. The smaller of two numbers is 4 less than the larger. If the sum of their squares is 58, find the numbers.

14. The sum of the reciprocals of two consecutive odd numbers is $\frac{8}{15}$. Find the numbers.

15. The sum of the reciprocals of two consecutive even numbers is $\frac{7}{24}$. Find the numbers.

16. A number of students rented a car for $160 for a one-week camping trip. If another student had joined the original group, each person's share of expenses would have been reduced by $8. How many students were in the original group?

17. An investor placed an order totaling $1200 for a certain number of shares of a stock. If the price of each share of stock were $2 more, the investor would get

30 fewer shares for the same amount of money. How many shares did the investor buy?

18. A fraternity charters a bus for a ski trip at a cost of $360. When 6 more students join the trip, each person's cost decreases by $2. How many students were in the original group of travelers?

19. A salesman worked a certain number of days to earn $192. If he had been paid $8 more per day, he would have earned the same amount of money in 2 fewer days. How many days did he work?

20. A freelance photographer worked a certain number of days for a newspaper to earn $480. If she had been paid $8 less per day, she would have earned the same amount in 2 more days. What was her daily rate of pay?

21. A wire 48 centimeters long is cut into two pieces. Each piece is bent to form a square. Where should the wire be cut so that the sum of the areas of the squares is equal to 1280 square centimeters?

22. A circuit has a resistance of 25 ohms and a voltage of 110 volts. The power P in watts when a current I in amperes flows through the circuit is

$$P = 110I - I^2$$

If the power is 121 watts, find the current I.

The following are needed for Exercises 23 and 24: If an object is thrown with an initial speed of v_0, then the distance d the object travels in t seconds is

$$d = 16t^2 + v_0t$$

if the distance is measured in feet and

$$d = 4.9t^2 + v_0t$$

if the distance is measured in meters.

23. An object is thrown off the Gateway Arch in St. Louis with an initial velocity of 68 feet per second. The Gateway Arch is 630 feet tall. How long will it take for the object to reach the ground?

24. A warhead fired from an enemy ship in the Persian Gulf is a dud and travels only 100 meters before it hits the water. If it had an initial velocity of 489 meters per second, find the time from the initial launch of the warhead to impact.

25. A principal amount P is invested at a rate of $r \times 100\%$ per year. After 2 years the amount of the investment

becomes $S = P(1 + r)^2$. Rachel invests $7000 at the start of her junior year in high school. What interest rate does her investment require so that she will have $9100 for her freshman tuition in college 2 years later?

26. The spread of a certain variety of ivy follows the investment model given in Exercise 25, $S = P(1 + r)^2$. Thirty square feet of ivy are planted. Two years later there are 75 square feet of ground cover. At what rate is the plant spreading?

27. According to Einstein's theory, relative to earth time, space travelers will not age as fast as those who remain on earth. In fact, if a space traveler could travel at the speed of light, relative to those on earth, the traveler would not age at all. The relationship between time on earth t_e, and time in space t_s is given by

$$t_s = t_e \sqrt{1 - \frac{v^2}{c^2}}$$

where v is the velocity of the space traveler and c is the speed of light. One of two brothers makes a round trip to Arcturus. The elapsed time of the trip for the brother on earth is 80.8 years, whereas the elapsed time for the traveling brother is 11.4 years. If the traveling brother maintained a constant speed for the entire trip, find this speed in terms of c.

28. There exists a gravitational force of attraction between all particles. Newton's law of gravitation defines the relationship between the force F exerted by a particle of mass m_1 on another particle of mass m_2 when the distance between the two particles is r.

$$F = \frac{Gm_1m_2}{r^2}$$

where $G = 6.67 \times 10^{-11}$ Nm²/kg² is the universal gravitational constant. (N is the abbreviation for Newtons, a measure of force.) The gravitational force that attracts a 65-kilogram boy to a 50-kilogram girl is 8.67×10^{-7} N. How many meters apart are the boy and the girl?

29. Angular displacement θ is defined by:

$$\theta = \theta_0 + \omega_0 t + \frac{1}{2}\alpha_0 t^2$$

where θ_0, ω_0 and α_0 are the angular displacement, angular velocity, and angular acceleration, respectively, all at time $t = 0$.

a. Let $\theta = 11$ radians, $\theta_0 = 1$ radian, $\omega_0 = 3$ radians per second and $\alpha_0 = 2$ radians per second squared. Solve for t.

b. Find a general formula for t by using the quadratic formula.

30. The equilibrium point in economic theory is that price where demand equals supply. For the following supply and demand equations, find the equilibrium point.

a. $d = \dfrac{1500}{p}, \quad s = 500p - 250$

b. $d = \dfrac{1400}{p}, \quad s = 1200p - 3800$

31. In probability theory, a binomial random variable x can be approximated by a normal random variable z by the equation

$$z = \frac{x - np}{\sqrt{np(1 - p)}}$$

where n is the number of trials in a binomial experiment and p is the probability of success in one trial of the experiment. If the number of trials is 16, $x = 1$ and $z = -2.48$, what is p?

32. An oil company has decided to replace two old cylindrical storage tanks with one new cylindrical storage tank constructed from a material guaranteed to keep the oil at a constant temperature. The old tanks were both 25 feet high, however, one tank had a radius of 12 feet whereas the other had a radius of 16 feet. The new tank will also be 25 feet high. Find the radius of the new tank if it is to hold the same amount of oil as both of the old tanks. (*Hint:* The volume of a cylinder is $V = \pi r^2 h$, where r is the radius and h is the height.)

33. The area of a circle is 10π. What is the radius?

34. The surface area of a cube is 294 square inches. What is the length of each edge of the cube?

35. It is believed that the most visually pleasing rectangle with length L and width W satisfies the following equation

$$\frac{L + W}{L} = \frac{L}{W}$$

a. What is L if $W = 5$?

b. Solve this equation for W in terms of L.

Applications 2.4

1. A manufacturer of a certain commodity has estimated that her profit in thousands of dollars is given by the expression $-6x^2 + 30x - 10$ where x (in thousands) is the number of units produced. What production range will enable the manufacturer to have a profit of $15,000 on the commodity? What is the break-even point? Explain your answer.

2. The Curry College book store purchased some shirts for $540. Then the book store sold all but eight of them. On each shirt sold, a profit of $6 was made. The shirts sold brought in revenue of $750.

a. How many shirts were bought initially?

b. What was the purchase price?

c. What was the selling price of each shirt?

3. After a U.S. president makes a politically unpopular decision, his approval rating usually drops. After some time, the approval rating rises again. We will model this drop in approval by a quadratic equation. Assume that before the president signs an unpopular tax bill, the approval rating is at 59 percent. One week after the president signs the bill, the rating is at 50 percent, at two weeks it is at 42 percent, and at three weeks it is at 53 percent. Using quadratic regression we can show that $A = 5x^2 - 17.6x + 59.9$ is the best quadratic equation that fits the data. How many weeks after the signing of the tax bill will the approval rating be back to what it was before the signing of the tax bill?

4. After a U.S. president makes a politically unpopular decision, his approval rating usually drops. After some time, the approval rating rises again. We will model this drop in approval by a quadratic equation. Assume that before the president signs an unpopular tax bill, the approval rating is at 42 percent. One week after the president signs the bill, the rating is at 38 percent, at two weeks it is at 32 percent, and at three weeks it is at 39 percent. Using quadratic regression we can show that $A = 4.5x^2 - 13x + 42$ is the best quadratic equation that fits the data. How many weeks after the signing of the tax bill will the approval rating be back to what it was before the signing of the tax bill? Explain your answer.

2.5   Linear and Quadratic Inequalities

Much of the terminology of equations carries over to inequalities. A **solution of an inequality** is a value of the unknown that satisfies the inequality, and the solution set is composed of all solutions. The properties of inequalities listed in Section 1.2 enable us to use the same procedures in solving inequalities as in solving equations *with one exception.*

> Multiplication or division of an inequality by a negative number reverses the direction of the inequality.

We will concentrate for now on solving a **linear inequality**, that is, an inequality in which the unknown appears only in the first degree.

Example 1   Linear Inequalities
Solve the inequality $2x + 11 \geq 5x - 1$.

Solution
We perform addition and subtraction for inequalities to collect terms in x just as we did for equations.

$$2x + 11 \geq 5x - 1$$
$$2x \geq 5x - 12$$
$$-3x \geq -12$$

We now divide both sides of the inequality by -3, a negative number, and therefore reverse the sense of the inequality.

$$\frac{-3x}{-3} \leq \frac{-12}{-3}$$
$$x \leq 4$$

✔ Progress Check
Solve the inequality $3x - 2 \geq 5x + 4$.

Answer
$x \leq -3$

Warning
Given the inequality

$$-2x \geq -6$$

it is a common error to conclude that dividing by -2 gives $x \leq -3$. Multiplication or division by a negative number changes the sense of the inequality, but the *signs* obey the usual rules of algebra. Thus,

$$-2x \geq -6$$

$$\frac{-2x}{-2} \leq \frac{-6}{-2} \qquad \text{Reverse sense of the inequality.}$$

$$x \leq 3$$

There are three methods commonly used to describe subsets of the real numbers: graphs on a real number line, interval notation, and set notation. Since there will be occasions when we want to use each of these schemes, this is a convenient time to introduce them and to apply them to inequalities.

The **graph of an inequality** is the set of all points satisfying the inequality. The graph of the inequality $a \leq x < b$ is shown in Figure 2. The portion of the real number line that is in bold is the solution set of the inequality. The circle at point a is filled in to indicate that a is also a solution of the inequality; the circle at point b is left open to indicate that b is not a member of the solution set.

Figure 2   Graph of $a \leq x < b$

An **interval** is a set of numbers on the real number line that forms a line segment, a half line, or the entire real number line. The subset shown in Figure 2 is written in **interval notation** as $[a, b)$, where a and b are the **endpoints** of the interval. A bracket, [or], indicates that the endpoint is included, and a parenthesis, (or), indicates that the endpoint is not included. The interval $[a, b]$ is called a **closed interval** because both endpoints are included. The interval (a, b) is called an **open interval** because neither endpoint is included. Finally, the intervals $[a, b)$ and $(a, b]$ are called **half-open intervals.**

The set of all real numbers satisfying a given property P is written as

$$\{x \mid x \text{ satisfies property } P\}$$

which is read as "the set of all x such that x satisfies property P." This form, called **set notation,** provides a third means of designating subsets of the real number line. Thus, the interval $[a, b)$ shown in Figure 1 is written as

$$\{x \mid a \leq x < b\}$$

which indicates the x must satisfy the inequalities $x \geq a$ and $x < b$.

Example 2   Graphs of Finite Intervals

Graph each of the given intervals on a real number line and indicate the same subset of the real number line in set notation.

a. $(-3, 2]$ b. $(1, 4)$ c. $[-4, -1]$

Solution

a.

$\{x \mid -3 < x \le 2\}$

b.

$\{x \mid 1 < x < 4\}$

c.

$\{x \mid -4 \le x \le -1\}$

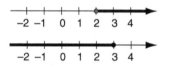

Figure 3   Graphs of Infinite Intervals

To describe the inequality $x > 2$ or the inequality $x \le 3$ in interval notation, we need to introduce the symbols ∞ and $-\infty$, read "**infinity**" and "minus infinity," respectively. The inequality $x > 2$ is then written as $(2, \infty)$, and the inequality $x \le 3$ is written as $(-\infty, 3]$. They are graphed on a real number line as shown in Figure 3. Note that ∞ and $-\infty$ are symbols, not numbers, indicating that the intervals extend indefinitely. An interval using one of these symbols is called an **infinite interval**. The interval $(-\infty, \infty)$ designates the entire real number line. Square brackets must never be used around ∞ and $-\infty$ since they are not real numbers.

If the endpoint of the graph of an inequality is *not* specifically identified by an *open circle* or by a *filled-in circle*, then we assume that the graph continues forever in the direction where the endpoint is "missing." (See Figure 3.) (There are some texts that indicate that a graph continues forever in a particular direction by placing an arrow on the graph pointing in that direction. We shall *not* use this "arrow" notation in this text.)

Example 3   Graphing and Solving Linear Inequalities
Graph each inequality and write the solution set in interval notation.

a. $x \le -2$ b. $x \ge -1$ c. $x < 3$

Solution

a.

$(-\infty, -2]$

b.

$[-1, \infty)$

c.

$(-\infty, 3)$

Example 4   Graphing and Solving Linear Inequalities
Solve the inequality.

$$\frac{x}{2} - 9 < \frac{1 - 2x}{3}$$

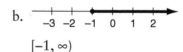

Graph the solution set, and write the solution set in both interval notation and set notation.

Solution

To clear the inequality of fractions, we multiply both sides by the LCD of all fractions, which is 6.

$$3x - 54 < 2(1 - 2x)$$
$$3x - 54 < 2 - 4x$$
$$7x < 56$$
$$x < 8$$

We may write the solution set as $\{x \mid x < 8\}$ or as the infinite interval $(-\infty, 8)$. The graph of the solution set is shown in Figure 4. ▪

−1 0 1 2 3 4 5 6 7 8

Figure 4 Graph of the Solution Set of Example 4

Example 5   Linear Inequalities

Solve the inequalities.

a. $\dfrac{2(x + 1)}{3} < \dfrac{2x}{3} - \dfrac{1}{5}$ b. $2(x - 1) < 2x + 5$

Solution

a. The LCD of all fractions is 15. Multiplying both sides of the inequality by 15, we obtain

$$10(x + 1) < 10x - 3$$
$$10x + 10 < 10x - 3$$
$$10 < -3$$

Our procedure has led to a contradiction, indicating that there is no solution to the inequality.

b. Expanding and simplifying leads to the inequality

$$-2 < 5$$

Since this inequality is true for all real values of x, we conclude that the solution set is the set of all real numbers. ▪

✔ Progress Check

Solve, and write the answers in interval notation.

a. $\dfrac{3x - 1}{4} + 1 > 2 + \dfrac{x}{3}$ b. $\dfrac{2x - 3}{2} \geq x + \dfrac{2}{5}$

Answers

a. $(3, \infty)$ b. no solution

Example 6 Inequalities and Word Problems

A taxpayer may choose to pay a 20% tax on the gross income or a 25% tax on the gross income less $4000. Above what income level should the taxpayer elect to pay at the 20% rate?

Solution

If we let x = gross income, then the choice available to the taxpayer is

a. pay at the 20% rate on the gross income, that is, pay $0.20x$, or

b. pay at the 25% rate on the gross income less $4000, that is, pay

$$0.25(x - 4000)$$

To determine when (a) produces a lower tax than (b), we must solve

$$0.20x < 0.25(x - 4000)$$
$$0.20x < 0.25x - 1000$$
$$-0.05x < -1000$$
$$x > \frac{-1000}{-0.05} = 20,000$$

The taxpayer should choose to pay at the 20% rate if the gross income is more than $20,000.

✔ Progress Check

A customer is offered the following choice of telephone services: unlimited local calls at a fixed $20 monthly charge, or a base rate of $8 per month plus $0.06 per message unit. At what level of use does it cost less to choose the unlimited service?

Answer

Unlimited service costs less when the anticipated use exceeds 200 message units.

Compound Inequalities

We can solve compound inequalities such as

$$1 < 3x - 2 \le 7$$

by operating on both inequalities at the same time.

$3 < 3x \le 9$ Add +2 to each member.

$1 < x \le 3$ Divide each member by 3.

The solution set is the half-open interval (1, 3].

Note that the statement of the compound inequality

$$1 < 3x - 2 \leq 7$$

actually represents three inequalities:

$$1 < 3x - 2$$
$$3x - 2 \leq 7$$
$$1 \leq 7$$

Example 7   Compound Inequalities

Solve the inequality $-3 \leq 1 - 2x < 6$, and write the answer in interval notation.

Solution

Operating on this inequality, we have

$$-4 \leq -2x < 5 \qquad \text{Add } -1 \text{ to each member.}$$

$$2 \geq x > -\frac{5}{2} \qquad \text{Divide each member by } -2.$$

The solution set is the half-open interval $(-\frac{5}{2}, 2]$.

 Calculator Alert

With many graphing calculators, you can use the GRAPH option to visualize the number-line solution to a linear inequality. The x-axis on the graph display represents the number line, and a horizontal line just above it represents the solution. Try by letting $Y1 = (x \leq 6)(x \geq 2)$.

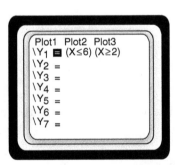 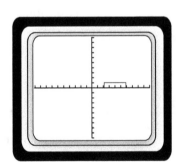

✔ Progress Check

Solve the inequality $-5 < 2 - 3x < -1$, and write the answer in interval notation.

Answer

$$\left(1, \frac{7}{3}\right)$$

Critical Value Method

The **Critical Value Method** is an alternative approach to solving inequalities. In fact, we shall be relying upon this method throughout the remainder of the text.

> The **critical values** of an inequality are
>
> 1. those values for which either side of the inequality is not defined (such as a denominator equal to 0),
>
> 2. those values that are solutions to the equation obtained by replacing the inequality sign with an equal sign.

The critical values determine endpoints of intervals on the real number line. The inequality in question either satisfies all points in a given interval, or no points in a given interval. In order to find out in which intervals the inequality holds, we may test *any* point from each interval. We call such points **test points**. We follow this technique using Example 1 in Table 4.

Example 8   Rational Expression Inequalities

Solve the inequality.

$$\frac{x + 1}{x - 1} \geq 2$$

Solution

The inequality is not defined where $x - 1 = 0$, that is, where $x = 1$. Solving the equation

$$\frac{x + 1}{x - 1} = 2$$
$$x + 1 = 2x - 2$$
$$x = 3$$

Therefore, the critical values are 1 and 3 as shown in Figure 5.

Figure 5 Critical Values for Example 8

Solution by the Critical Value Method

Interval, Critical Value	Test Point	Substitution	Verification
$x < 1$	$x = 0$	$\frac{0 + 1}{0 - 1} \geq 2$	False
$x = 1$	$x = 1$	$\frac{1 + 1}{1 - 1} \geq 2$	False
$1 < x < 3$	$x = 2$	$\frac{2 + 1}{2 - 1} \geq 2$	True
$x = 3$	$x = 3$	$\frac{3 + 1}{3 - 1} \geq 2$	True
$x > 3$	$x = 4$	$\frac{4 + 1}{4 - 1} \geq 2$	False

Table 4 Solving Inequalities by the Critical Value Method

Method	Example: $2x + 11 \geq 5x - 1$

Step 1. Find the critical values of the inequality.
 	
    a. values where the inequality is not defined
 	
    b. replace the inequality sign by an equal sign and solve.
	Step 1. a. Both sides of the inequality are defined everywhere.
	
	    b. $2x + 11 = 5x - 1$
	        $12 = 3x$
	         $x = 4$

Step 2. Plot the critical values on the real line.	*Step 2.* ⟶ (number line with point at 4)

Step 3. Try a test point in each interval, and try each critical value.	*Step 3.* Interval: $x < 4$ Test point: $x = 0$
	       $2(0) + 11 \geq 5(0) - 1$ True
	
	Critical Value: $x = 4$ Test point: $x = 4$
	       $2(4) + 11 \geq 5(4) - 1$ True
	
	Interval: $x > 4$ Test point: $x = 5$
	       $2(5) + 11 \geq 5(5) - 1$ False

Step 4. Find the solution.	*Step 4.* $x \leq 4$

Figure 6 Summary of Critical Value Analysis

These results are summarized in Figure 6. Therefore, the solution set consists of all real numbers

$$\{x \mid 1 < x \leq 3\}$$

Second-Degree Inequalities

The Critical Value Method can also be applied to **second-degree inequalities.** This requires the solution of a quadratic equation rather than a linear equation.

Example 9 Quadratic Inequalities

Solve the inequality $x^2 - 2x > 15$ and graph the solution.

Solution

The inequality is defined everywhere. Solving the equation

$$x^2 - 2x = 15$$
$$x^2 - 2x - 15 = 0$$
$$(x + 3)(x - 5) = 0$$
$$x = -3, 5$$

Therefore, the critical values are -3 and 5 as shown in Figure 7.

Figure 7 Critical Values for Example 9

Solution by the Critical Value Method

Interval, Critical Value	Test Point	Substitution	Verification
$x < -3$	$x = -5$	$(-5)^2 - 2(-5) > 15$	True
$x = -3$	$x = -3$	$(-3)^2 - 2(-3) > 15$	False
$-3 < x < 5$	$x = 0$	$0^2 - 2(0) > 15$	False
$x = 5$	$x = 5$	$(5)^2 - 2(5) > 15$	False
$x > 5$	$x = 6$	$(6)^2 - 2(6) > 15$	True

These results are summarized in Figure 8.

Figure 8 Summary of Critical Value Analysis

Therefore, the solution set is

$$\{x \mid x < -3 \quad \text{or} \quad x > 5\}$$

which consists of the real numbers in the open intervals $(-\infty, -3)$ and $(5, \infty)$. The solution set is shown in Figure 9.

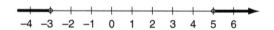

Figure 9 Graph of Solution Set for Example 9

✔ Progress Check

Solve the inequalities:

a. $2x^2 \geq 5x + 3$

b. $\dfrac{2x - 3}{1 - 2x} \geq 0$

Answers

a. $\left\{x \mid x \leq -\dfrac{1}{2} \quad \text{or} \quad x \geq 3\right\}$

b. $\left\{x \mid \dfrac{1}{2} < x \leq \dfrac{3}{2}\right\}$

Example 10   Polynomial Inequalities

Solve the inequality $(x - 2)(2x + 5)(3 - x) < 0$.

Solution

The inequality is defined everywhere. Solving the equation

$$(x - 2)(2x + 5)(3 - x) = 0$$

$$x = 2, -\frac{5}{2}, 3$$

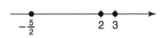

Figure 10   Critical Values for Example 10

Therefore the critical values are $-\frac{5}{2}$, 2 and 3 as shown in Figure 10.

Solution by the Critical Value Method

Interval, Critical Value	Test Point	Substitution	Verification
$x < -\frac{5}{2}$	$x = -3$	$(-3 - 2)(2(-3) + 5)(3 - (-3)) < 0$	False
$x = -\frac{5}{2}$	$x = -\frac{5}{2}$	$\left(-\frac{5}{2} - 2\right)\left(2\left(-\frac{5}{2}\right) + 5\right)\left(3 - \left(-\frac{5}{2}\right)\right) < 0$	False
$-\frac{5}{2} < x < 2$	$x = 0$	$(0 - 2)(2(0) + 5)(3 - 0) < 0$	True
$x = 2$	$x = 2$	$(2 - 2)(2(2) + 5)(3 - 2) < 0$	False
$2 < x < 3$	$x = \frac{5}{2}$	$\left(\frac{5}{2} - 2\right)\left(2\left(\frac{5}{2}\right) + 5\right)\left(3 - \frac{5}{2}\right) < 0$	False
$x = 3$	$x = 3$	$(3 - 2)(2(3) + 5)(3 - 3) < 0$	False
$x > 3$	$x = 4$	$(4 - 2)(2(4) + 5)(3 - 4) < 0$	True

These results are summarized in Figure 11.

Figure 11   Summary of Critical Value Analysis

Therefore, the solution set consists of all real numbers

$$\{x \mid -\frac{5}{2} < x < 2 \quad \text{or} \quad x > 3\}$$

which consists of the real numbers in the open intervals $(-\frac{5}{2}, 2)$, $(3, \infty)$.

✔ **Progress Check**
Solve the inequality $(2y - 9)(6 - y)(y + 5) \geq 0$.

Answer
$$\left\{y \mid y \leq -5 \quad \text{or} \quad \frac{9}{2} \leq y \leq 6\right\} \quad \text{or} \quad (-\infty, -5], \left[\frac{9}{2}, 6\right]$$

Example 11   Quadratic Inequalities
Solve the inequality $x^2 + 1 > 0$.

Solution
The inequality is defined everywhere. The equation $x^2 = -1$ has no real roots. Thus, we have no critical values, and there is only one interval, namely, the entire real number line. If we choose our test point to be 0, we have

$$0^2 > -1$$

which is true. Therefore, the solution set consists of all real numbers.

Exercise Set 2.5

In Exercises 1–9, express the given inequality in interval notation.

1. $-5 \leq x < 1$

2. $-4 < x \leq 1$

3. $x > 9$

4. $x \leq -2$

5. $-12 \leq x \leq -3$

6. $x \geq -5$

7. $3 < x < 7$

8. $x < 17$

9. $-6 < x \leq -4$

In Exercises 10–18, express the given interval as an inequality.

10. $(-4, 3]$

11. $[5, 8]$

12. $(-\infty, -2]$

13. $(3, \infty)$

14. $[-3, 10)$

15. $(-\infty, 5]$

16. $(-2, -1)$

17. $[0, \infty)$

18. $(-5, 7)$

In Exercises 19–36, solve the inequality and graph the result.

19. $x + 4 < 8$

20. $x + 5 < 4$

21. $x + 3 < -3$

22. $x - 2 \leq 5$

23. $x - 3 \geq 2$

24. $x + 5 \geq -1$

25. $2 < a + 3$

26. $-5 > b - 3$

27. $2y < -1$

28. $3x < 6$

29. $2x \geq 0$

30. $-\dfrac{1}{2}y \geq 4$

31. $2r + 5 < 9$

32. $3x - 2 > 4$

33. $3x - 1 \geq 2$

34. $\dfrac{-1}{2x + 3} > 0$

35. $\dfrac{4}{5 - 3x} < 0$

36. $\dfrac{3}{3x - 1} > 0$

Solve the given inequality in Exercises 37–60, and write the solution set in interval notation.

37. $4x + 3 \leq 11$

38. $\dfrac{1}{2}y - 2 \leq 2$

39. $\frac{3}{2}x + 1 \geq 4$

40. $-5x + 2 > -8$

41. $4(2x + 1) < 16$

42. $3(3r - 4) \geq 15$

43. $2(x - 3) < 3(x + 2)$

44. $4(x - 3) \geq 3(x - 2)$

45. $3(2a - 1) > 4(2a - 3)$

46. $2(3x - 1) + 4 < 3(x + 2) - 8$

47. $\frac{2}{3}(x + 1) + \frac{5}{6} \geq \frac{1}{2}(2x - 1) + 4$

48. $\frac{1}{4}(3x + 2) - 1 \leq -\frac{1}{2}(x - 3) + \frac{3}{4}$

49. $\frac{x - 1}{3} + \frac{1}{5} < \frac{x + 2}{5} - \frac{1}{3}$

50. $\frac{x}{5} - \frac{1 - x}{2} > \frac{x}{2} - 3$

51. $3(x + 1) + 6 \geq 2(2x - 1) + 4$

52. $4(3x + 2) - 1 \leq -2(x - 3) + 15$

53. $-2 < 4x \leq 5$

54. $3 \leq 6x < 12$

55. $-4 \leq 2x + 2 \leq -2$

56. $5 \leq 3x - 1 \leq 11$

57. $3 \leq 1 - 2x < 7$

58. $5 < 2 - 3x \leq 11$

59. $-8 < 2 - 5x \leq 7$

60. $-10 < 5 - 2x < -5$

In Exercises 61–67, translate from words to an algebraic problem and solve.

61. A student has grades of 42 and 70 on the first two tests of the semester. If an average of 70 is required to obtain a C grade, what is the minimum score the student must achieve on the third exam to obtain a C?

62. A compact car can be rented from firm A for $160 per week with no charge for mileage or from firm B for $100 per week plus 20 cents for each mile driven. If the car is driven m miles, for what values of m does it cost less to rent from firm A?

63. An appliance salesperson is paid $30 per day plus $25 for each appliance sold. How many appliances must be sold for the salesperson's income to exceed $130 per day?

64. A pension trust invests $6000 in a bond that pays 5% simple interest per year. Additional funds are to be invested in a more speculative bond paying 9% simple interest per year, so that the return on the total investment will be at least 6%. What is the minimum amount that must be invested in the more speculative bond?

65. A book publisher spends $38,000 on editorial expenses and $12 per book for manufacturing and sales expenses in the course of publishing a psychology textbook. If the book sells for $25, how many copies must be sold to show a profit?

66. If the area of a right triangle is not to exceed 80 square inches and the base is 10 inches, what values may be assigned to the altitude h?

67. A total of 70 meters of fencing material is available with which to enclose a rectangular area. If the width of the rectangle is 15 meters, what values can be assigned to the length L?

In Exercises 68–95, indicate the solution set of each inequality on a real number line.

68. $x^2 + 5x + 6 > 0$

69. $x^2 + 3x - 4 \leq 0$

70. $2x^2 - x - 1 < 0$

71. $3x^2 - 4x - 4 \geq 0$

72. $4x - 2x^2 < 0$

73. $r^2 + 4r \geq 0$

74. $\frac{x + 5}{x + 3} \leq 0$

75. $\frac{x - 6}{x + 4} \geq 0$

76. $\frac{2r + 1}{r - 3} \leq 0$

77. $\frac{x - 1}{2x - 3} \geq 0$

78. $\frac{3s + 2}{2s - 1} \geq 0$

79. $\frac{4x + 5}{x^2} \leq 0$

80. $(x + 2)(3x - 2)(x - 1) > 0$

81. $(x - 4)(2x + 5)(2 - x) \leq 0$

82. $x^2 + x - 6 > 0$

83. $x^2 - 3x - 10 \geq 0$

84. $2x^2 - 3x - 5 < 0$

85. $3x^2 - 4x - 4 \leq 0$

86. $\frac{2r + 3}{2r - 1} < 0$

87. $\frac{3x + 2}{2x - 3} \geq 0$

88. $\frac{x - 1}{x + 1} \geq 0$

89. $\frac{2x - 1}{x + 2} \leq 0$

90. $6x^2 + 8x + 2 \geq 0$

91. $2x^2 + 5x + 2 \leq 0$

92. $(y - 3)(2 - y)(2y + 4) \geq 0$

93. $(2x + 5)(3x - 2)(x + 1) < 0$

94. $(x - 3)(1 + 2x)(3x + 5) > 0$

95. $(1 - 2x)(2x + 1)(x - 3) \leq 0$

In Exercises 96–99, find the values of x for which the given expression has real values.

96. $\sqrt{(x - 2)(x + 1)}$

97. $\sqrt{(2x + 1)(x - 3)}$

98. $\sqrt{2x^2 + 7x + 6}$

99. $\sqrt{2x^2 + 3x + 1}$

100. A manufacturer of solar heaters finds that when x units are made and sold, the profit (in thousands of dollars) is given by $x^2 - 50x - 5000$. For what values of x will the firm show a loss?

101. A ball thrown directly upward from ground level at an initial velocity of 40 feet per second attains a height d given by $d = 40t - 16t^2$ after t seconds. During what time interval is the ball at a height of at least 16 feet?

102. A rectangle has length x and width $x - 4$.

    a. Find the inequality that states that the perimeter of the rectangle must be at least 24 units, and solve for x.

    b. Find the inequality that states that the area of the rectangle must be less than 12 square units, and solve for x.

103. Each of the two congruent sides of an isosceles triangle are 10 centimeters more than $\frac{1}{2}$ the length of the base. If the perimeter of the triangle is to be at most 100 centimeters, what is the maximum length of the base?

104. Morry's best time in the 70-meter track event is 9.5 seconds. Rob wants to beat Morry's best time. He runs the first half of the event at a speed of 7 meters per second. What is the maximum time Rob has left to run the second half of the event?

105. A carpet factory manufactures bolts of carpet 10 feet wide. A large bolt of carpet covers 8 linear feet more than a small bolt of carpet. If the large bolt of carpet covers at most 200 square feet of floor, what is the largest length of a small bolt?

106. Charles and Morry face each other at opposite ends of an 880-meter track. Charles runs this distance at 420 meters per minute, and Morry runs the same distance at 300 meters per minute. At the sound of the gun, the boys start running toward each other. Charles always arrives at a point P on the track before Morry. What is the farthest distance P could be from Charles's end of the track?

107. The power P in watts, total resistance R in ohms, and current I in amperes of a circuit are related by the equation

$$P = I^2R$$

The power output can be at most 1200 watts. What is the maximum current in the circuit if the total resistance is 48 ohms?

108. Michael earned 310 points before the final exam in his college algebra and trigonometry course. He must have at least 80% of a total of 600 points to get a B in this class. The final is worth 200 points. What is the lowest possible score Michael can get on his final exam and still get a B?

109. An economist hired by the Hiccup Seed Company has found that the company's profit, in hundred thousands of dollars, is

$$P = 6x^2 - 70x + 50$$

where x is the amount, in thousands, of seed packets sold. For what values of x does the Hiccup Seed Company make a profit?

110. The relationship between degrees Celsius and degrees Fahrenheit is given by

$$F = \frac{9}{5}C + 32$$

What temperature range in °F corresponds to –10°C to 20°C?

111. Graph the left side of the inequality below as Y1, and the right side as Y2. Your graphing calculator may be able to locate the points of intersection. Find the solution interval, rounding if necessary.

$$\frac{x - 1}{3x + 2} \le 1$$

112. *Mathematics in Writing:* Write a three-paragraph essay. In the first paragraph, describe in your own words how to solve a quadratic inequality algebraically. In the second paragraph, describe how to solve it graphically. In the final paragraph, compare the two methods and state which one you prefer.

Applications 2.5

1. The percentage method of withholding for federal income tax (2010) states that a single person whose annual wages, after subtracting withholding allowances, are over $34,000 but not over $82,400, shall have $4681.25 plus 25 percent of the excess over $34,000 withheld. Over what range does the

amount withheld vary if the annual wages vary from $50,000 to $80,000?

2. A used car salesperson is paid a commission of $100 plus 35 percent of the selling price in excess of the owner's cost. The owner claims that used cars typically sell for at least the owner's cost plus $120 and at most the owner's cost plus $420. For each sale made, over what range can the salesperson expect the commission to vary?

3. The markup over the dealer's cost of a new car ranges from 10 percent to 20 percent. If the sticker price is $26,000, over what range will the dealer's cost vary?

4. The town of Sharon charges homeowners $21.99 per quarter-year plus $4.50 per 1000 gallons for water usage in excess of 10,000 gallons. In 2010 one homeowner's quarterly bill ranged from a high of $150.00 to a low of $25.00. Over what range did water usage vary?

5. In your Math 1190 class, you have scores of 78, 85, and 92 on the first three of four tests. To get a grade of B, the average of the first four test scores must be greater than or equal to 80 and less than 90.

   a. Write an inequality which represents the range of the score that you need on the last test to get a B.

   b. Solve the inequality in part (a).

   c. What score do you need if the fourth test counts double?

   d. Solve an inequality to find the range of the score that you need on the last test to get a letter grade A, the average of the first four test scores must be greater than or equal to 90.

6. Tracy wants to lose weight. For healthy weight loss, the American College of Sports Medicine (ACSM) recommends 200 to 300 minutes of exercise per week. For the first six days of the week, Tracy exercised 45, 50, 30, 0, 60 and 20 minutes. How long should Tracy exercise on the seventh day in order to stay within the ACSM guidelines?

7. For food products to be labeled "light," the U.S. Food and Drug Administration requires that the altered product must either contain one-third or fewer calories than the regular product or it must contain one-half or less fat than the regular product. If a serving of Miracle Whip Light contains 20 calories and 1.5 grams of fat, then what must be true about either the number of calories or the grams of fat in a serving of regular Miracle Whip?

2.6   Absolute Value in Equations and Inequalities

In Section 1.2, we discussed the use of absolute value notation to indicate distance, and we provided this formal definition.

$$|x| = \begin{cases} x & \text{when } x \geq 0 \\ -x & \text{when } x < 0 \end{cases}$$

The following example illustrates the application of this definition to the solution of equations involving absolute value.

Example 1   Absolute Value in Equations
Solve the equation $|2x - 7| = 11$.

Solution
We apply the definition of absolute value and consider two cases.

Case 1. $2x - 7 \geq 0$

With the first part of the definition,

$$|2x - 7| = 2x - 7 = 11$$
$$2x = 18$$
$$x = 9$$

Case 2. $2x - 7 < 0$

With the second part of the definition,

$$|2x - 7| = -(2x - 7) = 11$$
$$-2x + 7 = 11$$
$$x = -2$$

Alternatively, we can solve $2x - 7 = 11$ to obtain $x = 9$ and $2x - 7 = -11$ to obtain $x = -2$.

✔ Progress Check
Solve each equation and check the solution(s).

a. $|x + 8| = 9$

b. $|3x - 4| = 7$

Answers

a. $1, -17$

b. $\dfrac{11}{3}, -1$

When used in inequalities, absolute value notation plays an important and frequently used role in higher mathematics. To solve inequalities involving absolute value, we recall that $|x|$ is the distance between the origin and the point on the real number line corresponding to x. For $a > 0$, the solution set of the inequality $|x| < a$ is then seen to consist of all real numbers whose distance from the origin is less than a, that is, all real numbers in the open interval $(-a, a)$, shown in Figure 12. Similarly, if $|x| > a > 0$, the solution set consists of all real numbers whose distance from the origin is greater than a, that is, all points in the two infinite intervals $(-\infty, -a)$ and (a, ∞), shown in Figure 13. Of course, $|x| \leq a$ and $|x| \geq a$ include the endpoints a and $-a$, and the circles are filled in. An alternative statement of the solution set is

$$\{x \mid x < -a \quad \text{or} \quad x > a\}$$

We will use the Critical Value Method for solving inequalities involving the absolute value in a manner similar to that found in Section 2.5.

Figure 12 Graph of Solution Set for $|x| < a$

Figure 13 Graph of Solution Set for $|x| > a$

Example 2   Absolute Value in Inequalities
Solve the inequality $2|2x - 5| \leq 14$, write the solution set in interval notation and graph the solution.

Solution
The inequality is defined everywhere. Solving the equation

$$2|2x - 5| = 14 \qquad \text{or} \qquad |2x - 5| = 7$$
$$2x - 5 = 7 \qquad \text{or} \qquad 2x - 5 = -7$$
$$x = 6 \qquad \text{or} \qquad x = -1$$

Therefore, the critical values are -1 and 6 as shown in Figure 14.

Figure 14   Critical Values for Example 2

Solution by the Critical Value Method

Interval, Critical Value	Test Point	Substitution	Verification
$x < -1$	$x = -2$	$2\left\|2(-2) - 5\right\| \leq 14$	False
$x = -1$	$x = -1$	$2\left\|2(-1) - 5\right\| \leq 14$	True
$-1 < x < 6$	$x = 0$	$2\left\|2(0) - 5\right\| \leq 14$	True
$x = 6$	$x = 6$	$2\left\|2(6) - 5\right\| \leq 14$	True
$x > 6$	$x = 7$	$2\left\|2(7) - 5\right\| \leq 14$	False

These results are summarized in Figure 15.

Figure 15   Summary of Critical Value Analysis

Therefore, the solution set consists of all real numbers in the closed interval $[-1, 6]$ and the graph of the solution set is shown in Figure 16.

Figure 16   Graph of Solution Set for Example 2

✔ Progress Check

Solve each inequality, graph the solution set, and write the solution set in interval notation.

a. $|x| < 3$ b. $|3x - 1| \leq 8$ c. $|x| < -2$

Answers

a. $(-3, 3)$ b. $\left[-\dfrac{7}{3}, 3\right]$

c. No solution since $|x|$ is always nonnegative and thus cannot be less than -2.

Example 3   Absolute Value in Inequalities

Solve the inequality $|2x - 6| > 4$, write the solution set in interval notation, and graph the solution.

Solution

The inequality is defined everywhere. Solving the equation

$$|2x - 6| = 4$$

$$2x - 6 = 4 \qquad \text{or} \qquad 2x - 6 = -4$$
$$x = 5 \qquad \text{or} \qquad x = 1$$

Figure 17 Critical Values for Example 3

Therefore, the critical values are 1 and 5 as shown in Figure 17.

Solution by the Critical Value Method

Interval, Critical Value	Test Point	Substitution	Verification
$x < 1$	$x = 0$	$\lvert 2(0) - 6 \rvert > 4$	True
$x = 1$	$x = 1$	$\lvert 2(1) - 6 \rvert > 4$	False
$1 < x < 5$	$x = 2$	$\lvert 2(2) - 6 \rvert > 4$	False
$x = 5$	$x = 5$	$\lvert 2(5) - 6 \rvert > 4$	False
$x > 5$	$x = 6$	$\lvert 2(6) - 6 \rvert > 4$	True

Figure 18 Summary of Critical Value Analysis

These results are summarized in Figure 18. Therefore, the solution set consists of all real numbers in the infinite intervals $(-\infty, 1)$ and $(5, \infty)$. The graph of the solution set is shown in Figure 19.

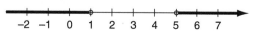

Figure 19 Graph of Solution Set for Example 3

- -

Warning

Students sometimes write

$$1 > x > 5$$

This is a misuse of the inequality notation since it states that x is simultaneously less than 1 *and* greater than 5, which is impossible. What is usually intended is the pair of infinite intervals $(-\infty, 1)$ and $(5, \infty)$, and the inequalities must be written

$$x < 1 \qquad \text{or} \qquad x > 5$$

Two additional misuses of the inequality notation are

$$1 < x > 5 \qquad \text{and} \qquad 1 > x < 5$$

- -

We summarize some facts concerning absolute values in equations and inequalities.

If $a > 0$, then

- $\lvert x \rvert = a$ is equivalent to $x = \pm a$.

- $\lvert x \rvert < a$ is equivalent to $-a < x < a$.

- $\lvert x \rvert > a$ is equivalent to $x < -a$ or $x > a$.

Verify these results using the Critical Value Method.

✔ Progress Check

Solve each inequality, write the solution set in interval notation, and graph the solution.

a. $|5x - 6| > 9$ b. $|2x - 2| \geq 8$

Answers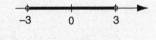

a. $\left(-\infty, -\dfrac{3}{5}\right), (3, \infty)$

b. $(-\infty, -3], [5, \infty)$

Example 4   Graphing the Solution to an Absolute Value Inequality

You can use your graphing calculator to visualize the solution set of an absolute value inequality. Enter the inequality as seen below. Ignore the y-axis, and think of the x-axis as a number line. Note that the graph will not tell you whether the endpoints are included in the solution set.

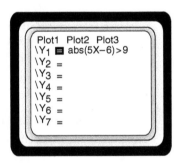
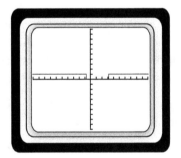

Exercise Set 2.6

In Exercises 1–9, solve and check.

1. $|x + 2| = 3$
2. $|r - 5| = \dfrac{1}{2}$
3. $|2x - 4| = 2$
4. $|5y + 1| = 11$
5. $|-3x + 1| = 5$
6. $|2t + 2| = 0$
7. $3|-4x - 3| = 27$
8. $\dfrac{1}{|x|} = 5$
9. $\dfrac{1}{|s - 1|} = \dfrac{1}{3}$

In Exercises 10–15, solve the inequality and graph the solution set.

10. $|x + 3| < 5$
11. $|x + 1| > 3$
12. $|3x + 6| \leq 12$
13. $|4x - 1| > 3$
14. $|3x + 2| \geq -1$
15. $\left|\dfrac{1}{3} - x\right| < \dfrac{2}{3}$

In Exercises 16–24, solve the inequality, and write the solution set using interval notation.

16. $|x - 2| \leq 4$
17. $|x - 3| \geq 4$

18. $|2x + 1| < 5$

19. $\dfrac{|2x - 1|}{4} < 2$

20. $\dfrac{|3x + 2|}{2} \leq 4$

21. $\dfrac{|2x + 1|}{3} < 0$

22. $\left|\dfrac{4}{3x - 2}\right| < 1$

23. $\left|\dfrac{5 - x}{3}\right| > 4$

24. $\left|\dfrac{2x + 1}{3}\right| \leq 5$

In Exercises 25–28, solve for x.

25. $|2x + 1| - 3 = -2$

26. $3 - |2x + 4| = 1$

27. $2|3 - x| + 3 = 5$

28. $4 - 3|2x + 7| = -5$

In Exercises 29 and 30, x and y are real numbers.

29. Prove that $\left|\dfrac{x}{y}\right| = \dfrac{|x|}{|y|}$. (*Hint:* Consider four cases.)

30. Prove that $|x|^2 = x^2$.

31. A machine that packages 100 vitamin pills per bottle can make an error of 2 pills per bottle. If x is the number of pills in a bottle, write an inequality, using absolute value, that indicates a maximum error of 2 pills per bottle. Solve the inequality.

32. The weekly income of a worker in a manufacturing plant differs from $300 by no more than $50. If x is the weekly income, write an inequality, using absolute value, that expresses this relationship. Solve the inequality.

33. Express the statement $x > 6$ or $x < -6$ as a single inequality using absolute value.

34. Express the statement $-10 < x < 10$ as an inequality using absolute value.

35. Express the statement $x \geq 5$ or $x \leq 1$ as a single inequality using absolute value.

36. Express the statement $2d - 5 \leq x \leq 2d + 5$ as an inequality using absolute value.

37. Write an equation that states that x is 10 units from 4 on the real number line. Solve this equation.

38. Find all points x on the real number line such that x is 5 times as far from the origin as from 20.

39. Find all points x on the real number line such that x is 3 times as far from 4 as $2x$ is from 6.

Applications 2.6

1. In the U.S., normal household voltage is 110 volts. However, it is not uncommon for actual voltage to differ from normal voltage by at most 4 volts. Express this situation as an inequality involving an absolute value. Use x as the actual voltage and solve for x.

2. "Normal" human body temperature is 98.6 F. If a temperature x that differs from normal by at least 1.5 is considered unhealthy

   a. write the condition for an unhealthy temperature x as an inequality involving an absolute value, and solve for x.

   b. write the condition for a healthy temperature x as an inequality involving an absolute value, and solve for x.

   c. sketch your solutions for parts (a) and (b) on a number line.

3. The Department of Sciences and Mathematics at Curry College budgeted $30,000 for office supplies in 2009. The actual expense for budget supplies must be within ±80.00 of this figure. Let x = actual expense for the office supplies. Write an absolute value inequality in x whose solution is the range of possible amounts for expense of the office supplies.

4. A car has approximately 5 gallons of gas, with an error margin of $\pm\frac{2}{7}$ per gallon. If the car gets 29 miles per gallon of gas, how many miles can the car travel?

5. Suppose 75% of the scores on a national achievement exam will be within ±85 points of a score of 490. Let x = a score among the 75% just described. Write an absolute value inequality in x whose solution is the range of possible scores within ±85 points of 490.

6. Marie expects about 45 students at the 2011 Science Senior Club party. She knows that this estimation could be off by 7 people (more or less). Food for the event costs $16 per person. How much might Marie's food expense be?

7. Bonuses at Curry College are usually given to about 15 people each year. The bonuses are $20,000 each, and the estimation of 15 recipients may be off by 4 people (more or less). How much might the Curry College spend on bonuses this year?

8. A weight scale is accurate to within ±0.07 pound. Marie weighs 126 pounds on this scale. Let x = the actual weight of Marie. Write an absolute value inequality in x whose solution is the range of possible values for the actual weight of Marie.

Terms and Symbols

closed interval	half-open interval	radical equation
completing the square	identity	repeated root
conditional equation	infinite interval	right-hand side (RHS)
critical value	infinity, ∞	root
Critical Value Method	interval	second-degree inequality
discriminant	interval notation	set notation
double root	left-hand side (LHS)	solution
endpoints	linear equation	solution of an inequality
equation	linear inequality	solution set
equivalent equations	open interval	substitution of variable
extraneous solution	principal	test points
first-degree equation in one unknown	quadratic equation	
graph of an inequality	quadratic formula	

Key Ideas for Review

Topic	Key Idea
Solutions of an Equation	A solution of an equation is a value that satisfies the equation.
Solution Process	To solve an equation, we generally form a succession of simpler, equivalent equations. We may add to or subtract from both sides of the equation any number or expression. We may also multiply both sides by any nonzero number. If we multiply the equation by an expression containing a variable, the answers must be substituted into the original equation to verify that they are solutions.
Linear Equations	The linear equation $$ax + b = 0, \quad a \neq 0$$ has precisely one solution $$x = -\frac{b}{a}$$
Completing the Square	$$x^2 + dx + \frac{d^2}{4} = \left(x + \frac{d}{2}\right)^2$$ Therefore, add $\frac{d^2}{4}$ to $x^2 + dx$ to "complete the square."

Topic	Key Idea
Quadratic Equations	The quadratic equation $$ax^2 + bx + c = 0, \quad a \neq 0$$ always has two solutions that are given by the quadratic formula $$x = \frac{-b \pm \sqrt{b^2 - 4ac}}{2a}, \quad a \neq 0$$ If $b = 0$ or if the quadratic equation can be factored, then faster solution methods are available.
Discriminant	The solutions or roots of a quadratic equation may be complex numbers. The expression $$b^2 - 4ac$$ under the radical of the quadratic formula is called the discriminant. Its value determines the nature of the roots of the quadratic equation.
Radical Equations	Radical equations often can be transformed into quadratic equations. Since the process involves raising both sides of an equation to a power, the answers must be checked to see that they satisfy the original equation.
Substitution of Variable	The method called *substitution of variable* can be used to transform certain equations into quadratic equations. This is a valuable technique that will be used in other chapters of this book.
Solutions of an Inequality	A solution of an inequality is a value that satisfies the inequality.
Solution Process	The permissible operations in solving an inequality are the same as those for solving equations with this proviso: multiplication or division by a negative number reverses the direction of the inequality.
Solution Set Representation	The solution set of an inequality can be represented by using set notation, interval notation, or a graph on the real number line.
Critical Value Method	The critical values of an inequality are 1. those values for which either side of the inequality is not defined (such as a denominator equal to 0), 2. those values that are solutions to the equation obtained by replacing the inequality sign with an equal sign. An inequality can be solved by finding the critical values and checking a test point in each interval determined by those critical values.

Review Exercises

Solutions to exercises whose numbers are in **bold** are in the Solutions section in the back of the book.

In Exercises 1–4, solve for x.

1. $3x - 5 = 3$

2. $2(2x - 3) - 3(x + 1) = -9$

3. $\dfrac{2 - x}{3 - x} = 4$

4. $k - 2x = 4kx$

5. The width of a rectangle is 4 centimeters less than twice its length. If the perimeter is 12 centimeters, find the measurement of each side.

6. A donation box contains coins consisting of dimes and quarters. The number of dimes is 4 more than twice the number of quarters. If the total value of the coins is $2.65, how many coins of each type are there?

7. It takes 4 hours for a bush pilot in Australia to pick up mail at a remote village and return to home base. If the average speed going is 150 mph and the average speed returning is 100 mph, how far from the home base is the village?

8. Copying machines A and B, working together, can prepare enough copies of the annual report for the board of directors in 2 hours. Machine A, working alone, would require 3 hours to do the job. How long would it take machine B to do the job by itself?

In Exercises 9 and 10 indicate whether the statement is true (T) or false (F).

9. The equation $3x^2 = 9$ is an identity.

10. $x = 3$ is a solution of the equation $3x - 1 = 10$.

11. Solve $x^2 - x - 20 = 0$ by factoring.

12. Solve $6x^2 - 11x + 4 = 0$ by factoring.

13. Solve $x^2 - 2x + 6 = 0$ by completing the square.

14. Solve $2x^2 - 4x + 3 = 0$ by the quadratic formula.

15. Solve $3x^2 + 2x - 1 = 0$ by the quadratic formula.

In Exercises 16–18, solve for x.

16. $49x^2 - 9 = 0$

17. $kx^2 - 3\pi = 0$

18. $x^2 + x = 12$

In Exercises 19–21, determine the nature of the roots of the quadratic equation without solving.

19. $3r^2 = 2r + 5$

20. $4x^2 + 20x + 25 = 0$

21. $6y^2 - 2y = -7$

In Exercises 22–25, solve the given equation.

22. $\sqrt{x} + 2 = x$

23. $\sqrt{x + 3} + \sqrt{2x - 3} = 6$

24. $x^4 - 4x^2 + 3 = 0$

25. $\left(1 - \dfrac{2}{x}\right)^2 - 8\left(1 - \dfrac{2}{x}\right) + 15 = 0$

26. A charitable organization rented an auditorium for a meeting at a cost of $420 and split the cost among the attendees. If 10 additional persons had attended the meeting, the cost per person would have decreased by $1. How many persons actually attended?

27. Solve and graph $3 \le 2x + 1$.

28. Solve and graph $-4 < -2x + 1 \le 10$.

In Exercises 29–31, solve the inequality and express the solution set in interval notation.

29. $2(a + 5) > 3a + 2$

30. $\dfrac{-1}{2x - 5} \le 0$

31. $\dfrac{2x}{3} + \dfrac{1}{2} \ge \dfrac{x}{2} - 1$

32. Solve $|3x + 2| = 7$ for x.

33. Solve and graph $|4x - 1| = 5$.

34. Solve and graph $|2x + 1| > 7$.

35. Solve $|2 - 5x| < 1$ and write the solution in interval notation.

36. Solve $|3x - 2| \ge 6$ and write the solution in interval notation.

37. Find the values of x for which $\sqrt{2x^2 - x - 6}$ has real values.

38. Using interval notation, write the solution set of the inequality $x^2 + 4x - 5 \le 0$.

39. Write the solution set for $\dfrac{2x + 1}{x + 5} \geq 0$ in interval notation.

40. Write the solution set for

$$(3 - x)(2x + 3)(x + 2) < 0$$

in interval notation.

41. A local school board is debating the question of whether or not to close an elementary school in its district. The board expects a larger than average number of local residents at this meeting. The typical meeting seats the residents in a rectangular formation of 10 rows, 15 seats to a row. In order to double the seating capacity with a new rectangular formation, the board decides to add an equal number of seats to each existing row and to add that same number of additional rows to the original formation. Find the number of chairs needed to add to each row.

Review Test

In Problems 1 and 2, solve for y.

1. $5 - 4y = 2$

2. $\dfrac{2 + 5y}{3y - 1} = 6$

3. One side of a triangle is 2 meters shorter than the base, and the other side is 3 meters longer than half the base. If the perimeter is 15 meters, find the length of each side.

4. A trust fund invested a certain amount of money at 6.5% simple annual interest, a second amount $200 more than the first amount at 7.5%, and a third amount $300 more than twice the first amount at 9%. If the total annual income from these investments is $1962, how much was invested at each rate?

5. Indicate whether the statement is true (T) or false (F): The equation $(2x - 1)^2 = 4x^2 - 4x + 1$ is an identity.

6. Solve $x^2 - 5x = 14$ by factoring.

7. Solve $5x^2 - x + 4 = 0$ by completing the square.

8. Solve $12x^2 + 5x - 3 = 0$ by the quadratic formula.

In Problems 9 and 10, solve for x.

9. $(2x - 5)^2 + 9 = 0$

10. $2 + \dfrac{1}{x} - \dfrac{3}{x^2} = 0$

In Problems 11 and 12, determine the nature of the roots of the quadratic equation without solving.

11. $6x^2 + x - 2 = 0$

12. $3x^2 - 2x = -6$

In Problems 13 and 14, solve the given equation.

13. $x - \sqrt{4 - 3x} = -8$

14. $3x^4 + 5x^2 - 2 = 0$

15. The area of a rectangle is 96 square meters. If the length and the width are each increased by 2 meters, the area of the newly formed rectangle is 140 square meters. Find the dimensions of the original rectangle.

16. Solve $-1 \leq 2x + 3 < 5$ and graph the solution set.

In Problems 17 and 18, solve the inequality and express the solution set in interval notation.

17. $3(2a - 1) - 4(a + 2) \leq 4$

18. $-2 \leq 2 - x \leq 6$

19. Solve $|4x - 1| = 9$.

20. Solve $|2x - 1| \leq 5$ and graph the solution set.

21. Solve $|1 - 3x| > 5$ and write the solution in interval notation.

22. Find the values of x for which $\sqrt{3x^2 - 4x + 1}$ has real values.

In Problems 23–25, write the solution set in interval notation.

23. $-2x^2 + 3x - 1 \leq 0$

24. $(x - 1)(2 - 3x)(x + 2) \leq 0$

25. $\dfrac{2x - 5}{x + 1} > -\dfrac{1}{3}$

Writing Exercises

In Exercises 1–3, write in complete sentences the procedure that you follow in solving the following problems.

1. An automatic teller machine gives you $150 in five and ten dollar bills. There are 2 more than twice as many five dollar bills as there are ten dollar bills. How many of each denomination are there?

2. A pound of raisins costs $2.50 whereas a pound of chocolate bits costs $4.00. If we want to make a one-pound mixture of these items to sell for $3.25, how much of each item must be used?

3. Two students work in a library shelving books. Eric can shelve 50 books per hour and Steve can shelve 40 books per hour. If Steve starts work in the morning and then is relieved by Eric later in the day, how long did each student work if 355 books were shelved in an 8-hour day?

4. Why is it a good practice to check your answers? Give an example to show how not following this practice can lead to a wrong conclusion.

Chapter 2 Project

Have you ever considered the challenges involved in linking computers and databases across the world into a user-friendly network? The mathematics involved in any such project are very sophisticated. The type of network we discussed in this chapter is far simpler!

In Section 2.3, do Exercise 119, and in Section 2.5, do Exercise 116.

In a **central relay network**, all users are connected to one central point. Therefore, the number of users is exactly equal to the number of links necessary. For how many users would a central relay network actually require fewer links than a full-mesh network? The same number? Sketch a diagram to illustrate.

Functions

http://scienceworld
.wolfram.com
/biography/

Try this experiment. Listen to a cricket chirping, and count the number of times it chirps in one minute. Divide that number by 4, then add 40. Now compare that result to the temperature in degrees Fahrenheit. Is your result close? It probably is.

This is one example of a *function*. For this experiment, the outside temperature in degrees Fahrenheit is treated as a function of the number of times a cricket chirps in fifteen seconds. This rule of thumb has actually been shown to have validity. Find out how by looking up Svante Arrhenius at http://scienceworld.wolfram.com/biography/.

We will look at this function more closely in several sections of this chapter. By looking at its graph, determining the slope, finding its inverse, etc., you will see how functions help us to predict events in the world around us. (See the Chapter Project.)

What is the result of increased fertilization on the growth of an azalea? If the minimum wage is increased, what will be the effect on the number of unemployed workers? When a submarine dives, can we calculate the water pressure against the hull at a given depth?

Each of the questions posed above seeks a relationship between phenomena. The search for relationships, or correspondence, is a central activity in our attempts to understand the universe; it is used in mathematics, engineering, the physical and biological sciences, the social sciences, business and economics.

The concept of a function has been developed as a means of organizing and assisting the study of relationships. Since graphs are powerful means of exhibiting relationships, we begin with a study of the Cartesian, or rectangular, coordinate system. We then formally define a function and offer a number of ways of viewing the concept of a function. Function notation will be introduced to provide a convenient means of writing functions.

We will also explore some special types of functional relationships (increasing and decreasing functions), the effect of combining functions in various ways and how functions can be used to describe certain processes.

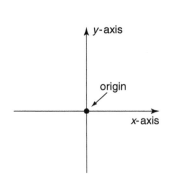

Figure 1   The Rectangular Coordinate System

3.1   The Rectangular Coordinate System

In Chapter 1 we associated the system of real numbers with points on the real number line. That is, we saw that there is a one-to-one correspondence between the system of real numbers and points on the real number line.

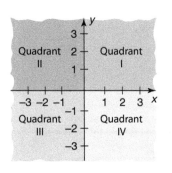

Figure 2   The Rectangular Coordinate System

We will now develop an analogous way to handle points in a plane. We begin by drawing a pair of perpendicular lines intersecting at a point called the **origin**. As shown in Figure 1, one of the lines, called the **x-axis,** is usually horizontal, and the other line, called the **y-axis,** is usually vertical.

If we think of the x-axis as a real number line, we may mark off some convenient unit of length, with positive numbers to the right of the origin and negative numbers to the left of the origin. Similarly, we may think of the y-axis as a real number line. Again, we may mark off a convenient unit of length (usually the same as the unit of length on the x-axis) with the upward direction representing positive numbers and the downward direction negative numbers. The x and y axes are called **coordinate axes,** and together they constitute a **rectangular,** or **Cartesian, coordinate system.** The coordinate axes divide the plane into four **quadrants,** which we label I, II, III and IV as in Figure 2.

By using the coordinate axes, we can outline a procedure for labeling any point in the plane. Consider the point P that is 2 units to the right of the y-axis and 3 units above the x-axis as shown in Figure 3. This means that the line from P, perpendicular to the x-axis, meets the x-axis 2 units to the right of the origin. Furthermore, the line from P, perpendicular to the y-axis, meets the y-axis 3 units above the origin. We now give the point P the label (2, 3).

More generally, consider the point P in Figure 4. Starting from P, draw a line perpendicular to the x-axis, and let it meet the x-axis where x has the value a. Also starting from P, draw a line perpendicular to the y-axis, and let it meet the y-axis where y has the value b. Note the rectangle drawn in Figure 4, hence the name: *rectangular*

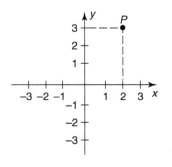

Figure 3 P with Coordinates (2, 3)

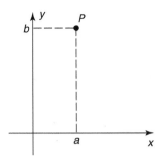

Figure 4 *P* with
Coordinates (*a*, *b*)

coordinates. (The alternative name, "Cartesian," was given to honor the French mathematician and philosopher, René Descartes (1596–1650).) We say that the **coordinates** of *P* are given by the **ordered pair** (*a*, *b*). The term, "ordered pair," means that the order is significant; the ordered pair (*a*, *b*) is different from the ordered pair (*b*, *a*) when $a \neq b$.

The first number of the ordered pair (*a*, *b*) is called the **abscissa**, or ***x*-coordinate**, of *P*. The second number is called the **ordinate**, or ***y*-coordinate**, of *P*.

We have now developed a procedure for associating with each point *P* in plane a unique ordered pair of real numbers (*a*, *b*) that we write as *P*(*a*, *b*). Conversely, every ordered pair of real numbers (*a*, *b*) determines a unique point *P* in the plane. The point *P* is located at the intersection of two lines: one perpendicular to the *x*-axis at $x = a$ and one perpendicular to the *y*-axis at $y = b$. This establishes a one-to-one correspondence between the set of all points in the plane and the set of all ordered pairs of real numbers.

We have indicated a number of points in Figure 5. Note that all points on the *x*-axis have a *y*-coordinate of 0 and all points on the *y*-axis have an *x*-coordinate of 0.

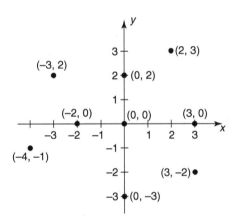

Figure 5 Points with Coordinates

📟 Graphing Calculator Alert

(1) Viewing Rectangle

Graphing calculators display a portion of the Cartesian coordinate plane in a "viewing rectangle." The boundary of the portion of the plane that is displayed is controlled by numbers called "range values," or "plot parameters." We will use the term WINDOW to refer to these values. Consult your owner's manual for details on changing the WINDOW values on your calculator. The owner's manual may be available online.

We now define two special viewing rectangles for your graphing calculator:

• DEFAULT: The WINDOW values for this viewing rectangle are $-10 \leq X \leq 10$ and $-10 \leq Y \leq 10$. (The minimum and maximum values of the X and Y coordinates are called XMIN, XMAX, YMIN and YMAX, respectively. The scale for values corresponding to the tick marks on the graph for X and Y are called XSCL and YSCL, respectively. For the DEFAULT viewing rectangle, XMIN = −10, XMAX = 10, XSCL = 1, YMIN = −10, YMAX = 10, YSCL = 1.)

• EQUAL: The WINDOW values for this viewing rectangle depend on your calculator model. "EQUAL" stands for _EQ_ual _U_nit _AL_ignment. It is chosen so that the origin is at the center of the screen and each pixel of your viewing rectangle represents 0.1 unit.

We will be using these special viewing rectangles throughout this book.

(2)   Plotting Points

The PLOT or PT-ON command allows you to plot points on your graphing calculator. Set the EQUAL viewing rectangle and use this command to plot the points in Figure 5.

It is important to note that the absolute value of the x-coordinate of point P is the distance from P to the y-axis. Analogously, the absolute value of the y-coordinate of point P is the distance from P to the x-axis. For example, the origin (0, 0) is simultaneously 0 units from both the x-axis and y-axis. Also the point (−3, 2) is 3 units from the y-axis and 2 units from the x-axis. (Recall that the negative sign, as part of the x-coordinate −3, indicates that this point is to the *left* of the y-axis, and that the positive sign, as part of the y-coordinate 2, indicates that this point is *above* the x-axis.)

The Distance Formula

Consider the problem of finding the distance between two points that are horizontal relative to each other, say (−3, −1) and (1, −1), as shown in Figure 6. We see that (−3, −1) is 3 units from the y-axis and (1, −1) is 1 unit from the other side of the y-axis. Therefore, since $1 > −3$, the distance between these points is given by $d_1 = 1 − (−3) = 4$.

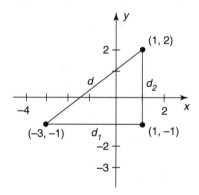

Figure 6   Finding the Distance between (−3, −1) and (1, 2)

If we consider finding the distance between two points that are vertical relative to each other, say $(1, -1)$ and $(1, 2)$, as shown in Figure 6, we see that the first point is 1 unit from the x-axis, and the second point is 2 units from the other side of the x-axis. Therefore, since $2 > -1$, the distance between these points is given by $d_2 = 2 - (-1) = 3$.

A more complicated problem is to find the distance between $(-3, -1)$ and $(1, 2)$. (See Figure 6.) Since the triangle with vertices $(-3, -1)$, $(1, -1)$ and $(1, 2)$ is a right triangle, we may use the Pythagorean Theorem. Thus

$$d^2 = d_1^2 + d_2^2 = 4^2 + 3^2 = 25$$

Therefore, $d = 5$, since distance is always nonnegative.

We can generalize this approach to derive a formula that gives the distance between any two points $P(x_1, y_1)$ and $Q(x_2, y_2)$, denoted $\overline{PQ}$. Choose R so that it has the same y-coordinate as $P(x_1, y_1)$ and the same x-coordinate as $Q(x_2, y_2)$, as shown in Figure 7. This makes PRQ a right triangle. Therefore, since $x_2 > x_1$ and $y_2 > y_1$,

$$d_1 = x_2 - x_1 \qquad \text{and} \qquad d_2 = y_2 - y_1$$

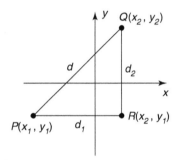

Figure 7   Deriving the Distance Formula

Hence, we can apply the Pythagorean Theorem.

$$d^2 = d_1^2 + d_2^2$$
$$d^2 = (x_2 - x_1)^2 + (y_2 - y_1)^2$$
$$d = \sqrt{(x_2 - x_1)^2 + (y_2 - y_1)^2}$$

because distance is always nonnegative.

Although points P and Q in Figure 7 are in quadrants III and I, respectively, the same result is true for any two points in the plane. Hence, we have

The Distance Formula
The distance $\overline{PQ}$ between the points $P(x_1, y_1)$ and $Q(x_2, y_2)$ in the plane is

$$\overline{PQ} = \sqrt{(x_2 - x_1)^2 + (y_2 - y_1)^2}$$

Use the distance formula to verify that $\overline{PQ} = \overline{QP}$.

Example 1 The Distance Formula
Find the distance between the points $P(-2, -3)$ and $Q(1, 2)$.

Solution
Using the distance formula, we have

$$\overline{PQ} = \sqrt{[1 - (-2)]^2 + [2 - (-3)]^2} = \sqrt{3^2 + 5^2} = \sqrt{34}$$

> ✔ **Progress Check**
> Find the distance between the points $P(-3, 2)$ and $Q(4, -2)$.
>
> **Answer**
> $\sqrt{65}$

Example 2 Applications of the Distance Formula
Show that the triangle with vertices $A(-2, 3)$, $B(3, -2)$ and $C(6, 1)$ is a right triangle.

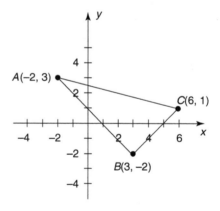

Figure 8 See Example 2.

Solution
We draw a diagram as shown in Figure 8 and compute the lengths of the three sides.

$$\overline{AB} = \sqrt{(3 + 2)^2 + (-2 - 3)^2} = \sqrt{50}$$
$$\overline{BC} = \sqrt{(6 - 3)^2 + (1 + 2)^2} = \sqrt{18}$$
$$\overline{AC} = \sqrt{(6 + 2)^2 + (1 - 3)^2} = \sqrt{68}$$

If the Pythagorean Theorem holds, then triangle ABC is a right triangle. We see that

$$(\overline{AC})^2 = (\overline{AB})^2 + (\overline{BC})^2 \qquad \text{since} \qquad 68 = 50 + 18$$

and we conclude that triangle ABC is a right triangle whose hypotenuse is AC.

The Midpoint Formula

Consider the line segment with endpoints $P(x_1, y_1)$ and $Q(x_2, y_2)$, as shown in Figure 9. Let $M(x_m, y_m)$ denote the midpoint of this segment. Since M is the midpoint of PQ, then $c_1 = c_2$. From plane geometry, if $c_1 = c_2$, then $a_1 = a_2$ and $b_1 = b_2$. Since $x_2 > x_m > x_1$ and $y_2 > y_m > y_1$, $a_1 = x_m - x_1$, $a_2 = x_2 - x_m$, $b_1 = y_m - y_1$ and $b_2 = y_2 - y_m$. We may substitute into the equations as follows:

$$a_1 = a_2 \qquad\qquad\qquad b_1 = b_2$$
$$x_m - x_1 = x_2 - x_m \qquad\qquad y_m - y_1 = y_2 - y_m$$
$$2x_m = x_1 + x_2 \qquad\qquad 2y_m = y_1 + y_2$$
$$x_m = \frac{x_1 + x_2}{2} \qquad\qquad y_m = \frac{y_1 + y_2}{2}$$

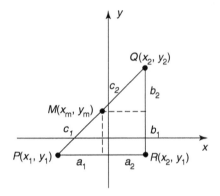

Figure 9   Deriving the Midpoint Formula

Although points P and Q in Figure 9 are in quadrants III and I, respectively, the same result is true for any two points in the plane. Hence, we have

---

The Midpoint Formula

The coordinates (x_m, y_m) of the midpoint M of the line segment with endpoints $P(x_1, y_1)$ and $Q(x_2, y_2)$ are given by

$$x_m = \frac{x_1 + x_2}{2} \qquad\qquad y_m = \frac{y_1 + y_2}{2}$$

Equivalently, we may say that the midpoint of a line segment is the average of the corresponding coordinates of its endpoints.

Example 3   The Midpoint Formula

Find the coordinates (x_m, y_m) of the midpoint of the line segment with endpoints $P(2, 1)$ and $Q(6, 4)$.

Solution

$P(x_1, y_1) = P(2, 1)$ and $Q(x_2, y_2) = Q(6, 4)$.

$$x_m = \frac{2 + 6}{2} = \frac{8}{2} = 4 \qquad y_m = \frac{1 + 4}{2} = \frac{5}{2}$$

The midpoint of PQ is $(4, \frac{5}{2})$.

✔ Progress Check

Find the coordinates of the midpoint of the line segment with endpoints $P(-2, -3)$ and $Q(1, 2)$.

Answer

$(-\frac{1}{2}, -\frac{1}{2})$

Example 4   Applications of the Midpoint Formula

Find the coordinates of the midpoint between $P(-4, 2)$ and the midpoint of the line segment with endpoints $P(-4, 2)$ and $Q(6, -2)$.

Solution

The midpoint of PQ is

$$\left(\frac{-4 + 6}{2}, \frac{2 - 2}{2}\right) = (1, 0)$$

The midpoint of $(-4, 2)$ and $(1, 0)$ is

$$\left(\frac{-4 + 1}{2}, \frac{2 + 0}{2}\right) = \left(-\frac{3}{2}, 1\right)$$

(Check that $(-\frac{3}{2}, 1)$ divides the line segment PQ into two line segments whose lengths are in the ratio $1:3$.)

✔ Progress Check

If $(1, 2)$ is the midpoint of PQ, where the coordinates of P are $(0, 1)$, find the coordinates of Q.

Answer

$(2, 3)$

Graphs of Equations

The **graph of an equation in two variables** x and y is the set of all points $P(x, y)$ whose coordinates satisfy the equation. We say that the ordered pair (a, b) is a **solution** of the equation if substituting a for x and b for y yields a true statement.

To graph $y = x^2 - 4$, an equation in the variables x and y, we proceed as follows: assign arbitrary values for x and compute the corresponding values of y. Thus, if $x = 3$, then $y = 3^2 - 4 = 5$, and the ordered pair $(3, 5)$ is a solution of the equation. Table 1 shows a number of solutions. Next, we plot the points corresponding to these ordered pairs. Since the equation has an infinite number of solutions, the plotted points represent only a portion of the graph. We must plot enough points to feel reasonably certain of the curve, as shown in Figure 10(a). (Check intermediate values with a calculator.)

(Some texts indicate that a graph continues forever in a particular direction by placing an arrow on the graph pointing in that direction. We shall *not* use this "arrow" notation in this text.)

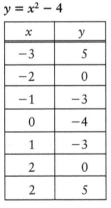

Graphing Calculator Alert

Set the WINDOW values for your viewing rectangle to $-5 \le X \le 5$ and $-5 \le Y \le 6$. GRAPH $y = x^2 - 4$. (See Figure 10(b).) Note the difference between the actual graph of the function and the calculator display. With practice you will learn to interpret the calculator display correctly and to sketch an accurate graph. Use the TRACE command to observe the points that have been plotted on your calculator. Note that the points in Table 1 do not appear on your screen. Why? Repeat this activity using the EQUAL viewing rectangle. Do you see why these WINDOW values were selected for the EQUAL viewing rectangle?

Table 1
$y = x^2 - 4$

x	y
-3	5
-2	0
-1	-3
0	-4
1	-3
2	0
2	5

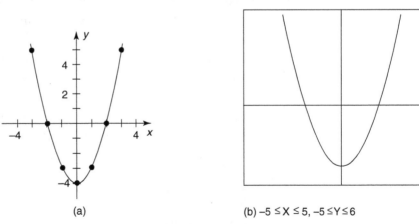

(a)   (b) $-5 \le X \le 5$, $-5 \le Y \le 6$

Figure 10   Graph of $y = x^2 - 4$, XSCL = 1, YSCL = 1

The abscissa of a point at which a graph meets the x-axis is called an **x-intercept**. Since the graph in Figure 10 meets the x-axis at points $(2, 0)$ and $(-2, 0)$, we see that 2 and -2 are the x-intercepts. Similarly, we define the **y-intercept** as the ordinate of a point at which the graph meets the y-axis. In Figure 10, the y-intercept is -4. Therefore, to find the x-intercept, set $y = 0$ and solve the resulting equation for x. Similarly, to find the y-intercept, set $x = 0$ and solve for y. Intercepts may be useful in sketching a graph.

Example 5   Graphs and Intercepts
Sketch the graph of the equation $y = 2x + 1$. Determine the x- and y-intercepts, if any.

Solution
We form a short table of values and sketch the graph in Figure 11. The graph appears to be a line that intersects the x-axis at $(-\frac{1}{2}, 0)$ and the y-axis at $(0, 1)$, implying that the x-intercept is $-\frac{1}{2}$ and the y-intercept is 1.

Alternatively, we can find the y-intercept algebraically by letting $x = 0$ so that

$$y = 2x + 1 = 2(0) + 1 = 1$$

and the x-intercept by letting $y = 0$ so that

$$y = 2x + 1$$
$$0 = 2x + 1$$
$$x = -\frac{1}{2}$$

x	y
-2	-3
-1	-1
0	1
1	3
2	5

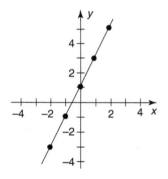

Figure 11   Graph of $y = 2x + 1$

Symmetry

If we folded the graph of Figure 12(a) along the x-axis, the top and bottom portions would match exactly. This is what we mean when we speak of symmetry about the x-axis. We would like to develop a way of testing for symmetry that does not require examining the graph. We can then use this information to improve our sketching ability.

Returning to Figure 12(a), we see that every point typically labeled (x_1, y_1) on the portion of the curve above the x-axis is reflected in a point $(x_1, -y_1)$ that lies on the portion of the curve below the x-axis. Similarly, using the graph of Figure 12(b), we observe symmetry about the y-axis if every point (x_1, y_1) on the curve implies that $(-x_1, y_1)$ also lies on the curve. Finally, using the graph sketched in Figure 12(c), we see that symmetry occurs about the origin if every point (x_1, y_1) on the curve implies that $(-x_1, -y_1)$ also lies on the curve. We now summarize these results.

Tests for Symmetry
The graph of an equation is **symmetric with respect to the**

  i. **x-axis** if replacing y with $-y$ results in an equivalent equation

  ii. **y-axis** if replacing x with $-x$ results in an equivalent equation

  iii. **origin** if replacing x with $-x$ and y with $-y$ results in an equivalent equation

---

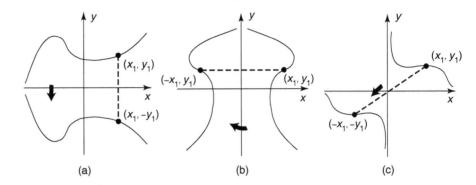

Figure 12   Symmetry with Respect to: (a) x-axis, (b) y-axis, (c) origin

Example 6   Applications of Intercepts and Symmetry
Use intercepts and symmetry to assist in graphing the equations.

a. $y = 1 - x^2$ b. $x = y^2 + 1$ c. $x^2 + y^2 = 25$

Solution

a. To determine the intercepts, set $x = 0$ to yield $y = 1$ as the y-intercept. Setting $y = 0$, we have $x^2 = 1$ or $x = \pm 1$ as the x-intercepts.

To test for symmetry, replace x with $-x$ in the equation $y = 1 - x^2$ to obtain

$$y = 1 - (-x)^2 = 1 - x^2$$

Since the equation is unaltered, the curve is symmetric with respect to the y-axis. Now, replacing y with $-y$, we have

$$-y = 1 - x^2$$

which is *not* equivalent to the original equation. The curve is therefore not symmetric with respect to the x-axis. Finally, replacing x with $-x$ and y with $-y$ repeats the last result and shows that the curve is not symmetric with respect to the origin.

We can now form a table of values for $x \geq 0$ and use symmetry with respect to the y-axis to help sketch the graph of the equation, as shown in Figure 13.

b. The y-intercepts occur where $x = 0$. Since this leads to the equation $y^2 = -1$, which has no real roots, there are no y-intercepts. Setting $y = 0$, we have $x = 1$ as the x-intercept.

Replacing x with $-x$ in the equation $x = y^2 + 1$ gives us

$$-x = y^2 + 1$$

which is *not* an equivalent equation. The curve is therefore not symmetric with respect to the y-axis. Replacing y with $-y$, we find that

$$x = (-y)^2 + 1 = y^2 + 1$$

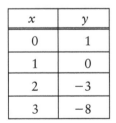

x	y
0	1
1	0
2	−3
3	−8

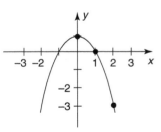

Figure 13   Graph of $y = 1 - x^2$

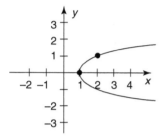

y	x
0	1
1	2
2	5
3	10

Figure 14   Graph of $x = y^2 + 1$

which is the same as the original equation. Thus, the curve is symmetric with respect to the x-axis. Replacing x with $-x$ and y with $-y$ also results in the equation

$$-x = y^2 + 1$$

and demonstrates that the curve is not symmetric with respect to the origin. We next form the table of values shown in Figure 14 by assigning nonnegative values to y and calculating the corresponding values of x from the equation. (Note that we have reversed the order of the table, putting y first and x second.) Symmetry enables us to sketch the lower half of the graph without plotting points.

Solving the given equation for y yields $y = \pm\sqrt{x - 1}$, which confirms the symmetry about the x-axis. The upper half of the curve in Figure 14 is the graph of the equation $y = \sqrt{x - 1}$ and the lower half is the graph of the equation $y = -\sqrt{x - 1}$.

c. We find the y-intercepts when $x = 0$, that is, $y^2 = 25$ so $y = \pm 5$. The x-intercepts occur when $y = 0$, that is, $x^2 = 25$, hence $x = \pm 5$. Since x and y are raised to an even power, replacing x with $-x$, replacing y with $-y$ or replacing both x and y with $-x$ and $-y$, respectively, leaves the equation unchanged. Therefore, this curve is symmetric with respect to the x-axis, the y-axis and the origin. If we only plot points in the first quadrant, the three symmetries will give us the complete graph. If $x^2 + y^2 = 25$, then $y = \pm\sqrt{25 - x^2}$. Then, for x and y in the first quadrant, we form the table of values shown in Figure 15. (Approximate $\sqrt{24}$ and $\sqrt{21}$ with a calculator.) Symmetry enables us to sketch the remainder of the graph without plotting points.

The upper half of the curve in Figure 15 is the graph of $y = \sqrt{25 - x^2}$ and the lower half is the graph of $y = -\sqrt{25 - x^2}$.

x	y
0	5
1	$\sqrt{24}$
2	$\sqrt{21}$
3	4
4	3
5	0

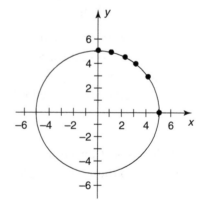

Figure 15   Graph of $x^2 + y^2 = 25$

Graphing Calculator Alert

Set the WINDOW values on your graphing calculator to $-6 \leq X \leq 6$ and $-6 \leq Y \leq 6$. GRAPH $y = \sqrt{25 - x^2}$ and $y = -\sqrt{25 - x^2}$ in the same viewing rectangle. Does the graph look like a circle? Why? If your calculator has a SQUARE command, use it to make the circle in your viewing rectangle have a better "shape." (In some viewing rectangles, the ends of the semicircles do not touch the x-axis.)

Example 7   Determining Symmetry

Without sketching the graph, determine symmetry with respect to the x-axis, the y-axis and the origin.

a. $x^2 + 4y^2 - y = 1$ b. $xy = 5$ c. $y^2 = \dfrac{x^2 + 1}{x^2 - 1}$

Solution

a. Replacing x with $-x$ in the equation, we have

$$(-x^2) + 4y^2 - y = 1$$
$$x^2 + 4y^2 - y = 1$$

Since the equation is unaltered, the curve is symmetric with respect to the y-axis. Next, replacing y with $-y$, we have

$$x^2 + 4(-y)^2 - (-y) = 1$$
$$x^2 + 4y^2 + y = 1$$

which is *not* an equivalent equation. Replacing x with $-x$ and y with $-y$ repeats the last result. The curve is therefore not symmetric with respect to either the x-axis or the origin.

b. Replacing x with $-x$, we have $-xy = 5$, which is *not* an equivalent equation. Replacing y with $-y$, we again have $-xy = 5$. Thus, the curve is not symmetric with respect to either axis. However, replacing x with $-x$ and y with $-y$ gives us

$$(-x)(-y) = 5$$

which is equivalent to $xy = 5$. We conclude that the curve is symmetric with respect to the origin.

c. Since x and y both appear to the second power only, all tests lead to an equivalent equation. The curve is therefore symmetric with respect to both axes and the origin.

✔ Progress Check

Without graphing, determine symmetry with respect to the coordinate axes and the origin.

a. $x^2 - y^2 = 1$ b. $x + y = 10$ c. $y = x + \dfrac{1}{x}$

Answers

a. Symmetric with respect to the x-axis, the y-axis and the origin.

b. Not symmetric with respect to either axis or the origin.

c. Symmetric with respect to the origin only.

Note that in Example 7(c) and in Progress Check (a) above, the curves are symmetric with respect to both the x-axis and y-axis, as well as the origin. In fact, we have the following rule.

> A curve that is symmetric with respect to both coordinate axes is also symmetric with respect to the origin. However, a curve that is symmetric with respect to the origin need not be symmetric with respect to the coordinate axes.

The curve in Figure 12(c) illustrates this last point, namely, that it is symmetric with respect to the origin but not with respect to the coordinate axes.

Exercise Set 3.1

In each of Exercises 1 and 2, plot the given points on the same coordinate axes.

1. $(2, 3), (-3, -2), \left(-\dfrac{1}{2}, \dfrac{1}{2}\right), \left(0, \dfrac{1}{4}\right), \left(-\dfrac{1}{2}, 0\right), (3, -2)$

2. $(-3, 4), (5, -2), (-1, -3), \left(-1, \dfrac{3}{2}\right), (0, 1.5)$

In Exercises 3–8, find the distance between each pair of points and find the midpoint.

3. $(5, 4), (2, 1)$ 4. $(-4, 5), (-2, 3)$

5. $(-1, -5), (-5, -1)$ 6. $(-3, 0), (2, -4)$

7. $\left(\dfrac{2}{3}, \dfrac{3}{2}\right), (-2, -4)$ 8. $\left(-\dfrac{1}{2}, 3\right), \left(-1, -\dfrac{3}{4}\right)$

In Exercises 9–12, find the length of the shortest side of the triangle determined by the three given points.

9. $A(6, 2), B(-1, 4), C(0, -2)$

10. $P(2, -3), Q(4, 4), R(-1, -1)$

11. $R\left(-1, \dfrac{1}{2}\right), S\left(-\dfrac{3}{2}, 1\right), T(2, -1)$

12. $F(-5, -1), G(0, 2), H(1, -2)$

In Exercises 13–16, determine if the given points form a right triangle. (*Hint:* A triangle is a right triangle if and only if the lengths of the sides satisfy the Pythagorean Theorem.)

13. $(1, -2), (5, 2), (2, 1)$

14. $(2, -3), (-1, -1), (3, 4)$

15. $(-4, 1), (1, 4), (4, -1)$

16. $(1, -1), (-6, 1), (1, 2)$

In Exercises 17–20, show that the points lie on the same line. (*Hint:* Three points are collinear if and only if the sum of the lengths of two sides equals the length of the third side.)

17. $(-1, 2), (1, 1), (5, -1)$

18. $(-1, -4), (1, 10), (0, 3)$

19. $(-1, 2), (1, 5), \left(-2, \dfrac{1}{2}\right)$

20. $(-1, -5), (1, 1), (-2, -8)$

21. Find the perimeter of the quadrilateral whose vertices are $(-2, -1), (-4, 5), (3, 5), (4, -2)$.

22. Show that the points $(-2, -1), (2, 2)$ and $(5, -2)$ are the vertices of an isosceles triangle.

23. Show that the points $(9, 2), (11, 6), (3, 5)$ and $(1, 1)$ are the vertices of a parallelogram.

24. Show that the point $(-1, 1)$ is the midpoint of the line segment whose endpoints are $(-5, -1)$ and $(3, 3)$.

25. The points $A(1, 7), B(4, 3)$ and $C(x, 5)$ determine a right triangle whose hypotenuse is AB. Find x. (*Hint:* There is more than one answer.)

26. The points $A(2, 6), B(4, 6), C(4, 8)$ and $D(x, y)$ form a rectangle. Find x and y.

In Exercises 27–32, determine the intercepts and sketch the graph of the given equation.

27. $y = 2x + 4$

28. $y = -2x + 5$

29. $y = \sqrt{x}$

30. $y = \sqrt{x - 1}$

31. $y = |x + 3|$

32. $y = 2 - |x|$

In Exercises 33–38, determine the intercepts and use symmetry to assist in sketching the graph of the given equation.

33. $y = 3 - x^2$

34. $y = 3x - x^2$

35. $y = x^3 + 1$

36. $x = y^3 - 1$

37. $x = y^2 - 1$

38. $y = 3x$

In Exercises 39–44, use your graphing calculator to GRAPH the given equations in the indicated viewing rectangle. Set the XSCL and YSCL values appropriately. Use the TRACE command to estimate the intercepts of each graph.

39. $y = 7 - x$ $-5 \le X \le 15$ $-5 \le Y \le 15$

40. $y = 2x + 1$ $-5 \le X \le 5$ $-3 \le Y \le 3$

41. $y = |x| - x^2$ $-5 \le X \le 5$ $-3 \le Y \le 1$

42. $y = \sqrt{4 - x}$ $-3 \le X \le 5$ $-1 \le Y \le 3$

43. $y = x^3 - x^2 - x$ $-5 \le X \le 5$ $-3 \le Y \le 3$

44. $y = 3x^2 + 4x$ $-5 \le X \le 5$ $-3 \le Y \le 3$

Without graphing, determine whether each curve in Exercises 45–59 is symmetric with respect to the x-axis, the y-axis and the origin.

45. $3x + 2y = 5$

46. $y = 4x^2$

47. $y^2 = x - 4$

48. $x^2 - y = 2$

49. $y^2 = 1 + x^3$

50. $y = (x - 2)^2$

51. $y^2 = (x - 2)^2$

52. $y^2x + 2x = 4$

53. $y^2x + 2x^2 = 4x^2y$

54. $y^3 = x^2 - 9$

55. $y = \dfrac{x^2 + 4}{x^2 - 4}$

56. $y = \dfrac{1}{x^2 + 1}$

57. $y^2 = \dfrac{x^2 + 1}{x^2 - 1}$

58. $4x^2 + 9y^2 = 36$

59. $xy = 4$

60. A ladder leans against a wall. The foot of the ladder is 8 feet from the wall, and the top of the ladder is 6 feet from the floor. The foot of the ladder is pulled 1 foot away from the wall. How far will the top of the ladder slide down the wall? (*Hint:* Draw the coordinate axes and place the ladder up against the y-axis.)

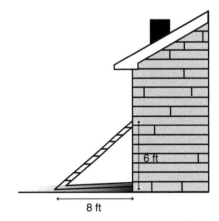

6 ft

8 ft

61. Show that the points $(0, 0), (4, 3)$ and $(3, 4)$ form an isosceles triangle.

62. Graph the points $(0, 0)$, $(-3, 3)$, $(2, 8)$ and $(5, 5)$.

    a. Show that these points form a rectangle.

    b. Find the area of the rectangle.

63. Find the midpoint of the line segment whose endpoints are $(-3, 6)$ and $(5, -2)$.

64. A line segment has midpoint $(-3, -2)$. One endpoint of the line segment is $(1, -5)$. Find the other endpoint.

65. A line segment has midpoint $(2, 7)$. One endpoint has coordinates $(x, 10)$ and the other endpoint has coordinates $(6, y)$. Find the values of x and y.

66. The points $(0, 0)$, $(x, 5)$ and $(4, 4)$ form a triangle.

    a. Find x so that these three points form an isosceles triangle.

    b. Find the midpoint of the line segment whose endpoints are $(0, 0)$ and $(4, 4)$.

    c. The line segment from $(x, 5)$ to the midpoint from part (b) is the height of the triangle. Find the area of this triangle.

67. Prove that the midpoint of the hypotenuse of a right triangle is equidistant from the three vertices. Locate the right triangle as in the figure below.

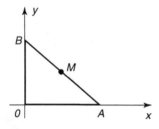

For Exercises 68–71, recall the definition of a median of a triangle: a line joining a vertex to the midpoint of the opposite side.

68. Prove that the medians from the equal angles of an isosceles triangle are of equal length. (*Hint*: Place the triangle so that its vertices are at the points $A(-a, 0)$, $B(a, 0)$ and $C(0, b)$.)

69. Show that the sum of the squares of the lengths of the medians of a triangle equals $\frac{3}{4}$ the sum of the squares of the lengths of the sides. (*Hint*: Place the triangle so that its vertices are at the points $(-a, 0)$, $(b, 0)$ and $(0, c)$.)

70. Prove that a triangle with two equal medians is isosceles.

71. Show that the midpoints of the sides of a rectangle are the vertices of a rhombus (a quadrilateral with four equal sides). (*Hint*: Place the rectangle so that its vertices are at the points $(0, 0)$, $(a, 0)$, $(0, b)$ and (a, b).)

72. Prove that the lengths of the diagonals of a rectangle are equal. (*Hint*: Place the rectangle so that its vertices are at the points $(0, 0)$, $(a, 0)$, $(0, b)$ and (a, b).)

Applications 3.1

1. The following table gives the time x in hours invested in concentrated study for five different algebra exams and the resulting score y. Plot the points whose coordinates are given in the table. Please label your axes.

Study Time (in hours)	3	2.5	5	4.3	2
Test Scores	78	72	95	92	68

2. The tuition at Curry College from 2007 to 2011 is given in the following table. Plot the points whose coordinates are given in the table. Please label your axes.

Year	2007	2008	2009	2010	2011
Tuition	24,500	25,600	27,000	29,000	30,700

3. The enrollment at Curry College from 2007 to 2011 is given in the following table. Plot the points whose coordinates are given in the table. Please label your axes. Explain the trend of enrollment at Curry College.

Year	2007	2008	2009	2010	2011
Enrollment	1329	1396	1412	1430	1459

4. Has the tsunami in Japan affected the U.S. economy? On March 15, 2011, Tracy recorded the Dow Jones Industrial Average into the following table. Plot the points whose coordinates are given in the table. Please label your axes and explain the trend of the market.

Time	9 AM	10 AM	11 AM	12 PM	1 PM
Dow Average	11,992	11,723	11,768	11,800	11,849

5. Has the tsunami in Japan affected the world economy? To answer this question, Tracy recorded the world market data on March 15, 2011 into the following table.. Plot the points whose coordinates are given in the table.

Location	DOW	Brazil	Mexico	Canada	Chile
Market	−1.15%	−0.68%	−1.02%	−0.94%	+0.25%

6. Curry College's baseball "diamond" is in fact a square with a distance of 90 feet between each of the consecutive bases. Use an appropriate coordinate system to calculate the distance the ball travels when the third baseman throws it from the third base to the first base. (Hint: Your home is at (0, 0) and your first base is located at (90, 0).)

3.2   Functions and Function Notation

The equation

$$y = 2x + 3$$

assigns a value to y for every value of x. If we let X denote the set of values that we can assign to x, and let Y denote the set of values that the equation assigns to y, we can show the correspondence schematically as in Figure 16. The equation can be thought of as a rule defining the correspondence from the set X to the set Y.

Figure 16   Correspondence Defined by $y = 2x + 3$

We are particularly interested in the situation where, for each element x in X, there corresponds one and only one element y in Y, that is, the rule assigns exactly one y for a given x. This type of correspondence plays a fundamental role in mathematics and is called a function.

Function, Domain, Image and Range
A **function** is a rule that, for each x in a set X, assigns exactly one y in a set Y. The element y is called the **image** of x. The set X is called the **domain** of the function and the set of all images is called the **range** of the function.

We can think of the rule defined by the equation $y = 2x + 3$ as a function machine as shown in Figure 17. Each time we drop a value of x from the domain into the input hopper, exactly one value of y falls out of the output chute. If we drop in $x = 5$, the function machine follows the rule and produces $y = 13$. Since we are free to choose the values of x that we drop into the machine, we call x the **independent variable**; the value of y that drops out depends upon the choice of x, so y is called the **dependent variable**. We say that the dependent variable is a function of the independent variable, that is, *the output is a function of the input.*

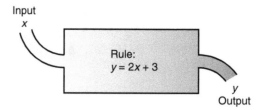

Figure 17   A Function Machine

Let us look at a few schematic presentations. The correspondence in Figure 18(a) is a function: for each x in X there is exactly one corresponding value of y in Y. The fact that y_1 is the image of both x_1 and x_2 does not violate the definition of a function. However, the correspondence in Figure 18(b) is not a function. Here x_1 has two images assigned to it, namely, y_1 and y_2, thus violating the definition of a function.

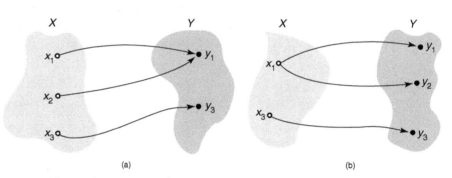

Figure 18   Correspondence: (a) is a Function, (b) is not a Function

Vertical Line Test

The **graph of the function** f is defined as the graph of the equation $y = f(x)$. Therefore, it is possible to use the *graph of an equation* to test whether it determines a function. If we consider all vertical lines on the graph of Figure 19(a), we see that no vertical line intersects the graph at more than one point. This means that the correspondence used in sketching the graph assigns exactly one y-value for each x-value and therefore determines y as a function of x. If we consider all vertical lines on the graph of Figure 19(b), however, some vertical lines intersect the graph at two points. Since the correspondence graphed in Figure 19(b) assigns the values y_1 and y_2 to x_1, it does not determine y as a function of x. Thus, *not every equation or correspondence* in the variables x and y determines y as a function of x.

Figure 19   Vertical Line Test: (a) is a Function, (b) is not a Function.

Vertical Line Test

A graph represents y as a function of x if and only if no vertical line meets the graph at more than one point.

Example 1 Determining Functions with the Vertical Line Test

Which of the following graphs determine y as a function of x?

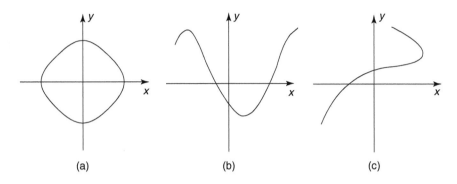

(a)   (b)   (c)

Solution

a. Not a function. Some vertical line meets the graph in more than one point.

b. A function. Passes the vertical line test.

c. Not a function. Fails the vertical line test.

Domain and Range

We have defined the domain of a function as the set of values assumed by the independent variable. In more advanced courses in mathematics, the domain may include complex numbers. In this book, we will restrict the domain of a function to those real numbers for which the image is also a real number, and we say that the function is *defined at* such values. When a function is defined by an equation, we must always be alert to two potential problems.

1. *Division by zero.* For example, the domain of the function

$$y = \frac{2}{x - 1}$$

   is the set of all real numbers other than $x = 1$. When $x = 1$, the denominator is 0, and division by 0 is not defined.

2. *Even roots of negative numbers.* For example, the function

$$y = \sqrt{x - 1}$$

   is defined only in the real number system for $x \geq 1$, since we exclude the square root of negative numbers. Hence the domain of the function consists of all real numbers $x \geq 1$.

In general, the range of a function is not as easily determined as its domain. The range is the set of all y-values that occur in the correspondence, that is, it is the set of

x	y
0	0
1	1
4	2
9	3

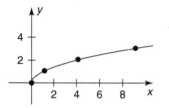

Figure 20   Graph of $y = \sqrt{x}$

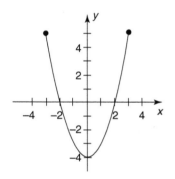

Figure 21   Graph of $y = x^2 - 4$

all outputs of the function. For our purposes, it will suffice to determine the range by examining the graph of the function.

Example 2   Graphing and the Vertical Line Test
Graph the equation $y = \sqrt{x}$. If the correspondence determines a function, find the domain and range.

Solution
We obtain the graph of the equation by plotting points and connecting them to form a smooth curve. Applying the vertical line test to the graph as shown in Figure 20, we see that the equation determines a function. The domain of the function is the set $\{x \mid x \geq 0\}$ and the range is the set $\{y \mid y \geq 0\}$.   ■

✔ **Progress Check**
Graph the equation $y = x^2 - 4$, $-3 \leq x \leq 3$. If the correspondence determines a function, find the domain and range.

Answer
The graph is shown in Figure 21. The domain is $\{x \mid -3 \leq x \leq 3\}$; the range is $\{y \mid -4 \leq y \leq 5\}$.

Function Notation

If we use the letter f to designate a function, then we denote the output corresponding to x by $f(x)$, which is read "f of x." Frequently, we use the letter y to denote the output corresponding to the input x. For example,

$$f(x) = 2x + 3$$

specifies a rule f for determining an output $f(x)$ for a given value of x. In other words, the symbol x can be thought of as holding a place. Equivalently, we might write

$$f(\ ) = 2(\ ) + 3$$

To find y, that is, $y = f(x)$ when $x = 5$, we substitute 5 for x and obtain

$$y = f(5) = 2(5) + 3 = 13$$

The notation $f(5)$ is a convenient way of specifying "the value of the function f that corresponds to $x = 5$." The symbol f represents the function or rule; the notation $f(x)$ or y represents the output produced by the rule. However, in common usage, the symbols f, $f(x)$ and y are often used interchangeably.

Example 3 Evaluating Functions

a. If $f(x) = 2x^2 - 2x + 1$, find $f(-1)$.

b. If $f(t) = 3t^2 - 1$, find $f(2a)$.

Solution

a. We substitute -1 for x.

$$f(-1) = 2(-1)^2 - 2(-1) + 1 = 5$$

b. We substitute $2a$ for t.

$$f(2a) = 3(2a)^2 - 1 = 3(4a^2) - 1 = 12a^2 - 1$$

✔ **Progress Check**
a. If $f(u) = u^3 + 3u - 4$, find $f(-2)$.   b. If $f(t) = t^2 + 1$, find $f(t - 1)$.

Answers
a. -18 b. $t^2 - 2t + 2$

Example 4 Evaluating Functions

Consider the function $f(x) = x^2 + 3$. Find the number (or numbers) whose image is

a. 3   b. 7   c. 2

Solution

a. We seek values of x such that

$$f(x) = x^2 + 3 = 3$$

Solving for x, we obtain

$$x = 0$$

b. If $f(x) = x^2 + 3 = 7$, then

$$x^2 = 4$$
$$x = \pm 2$$

Note that $f(2) = 7$ and $f(-2) = 7$.

c. If $f(x) = x^2 + 3 = 2$, then

$$x^2 = 1$$

This has no solution for real values of x. Therefore, 2 is not the image of any element in the domain.

Example 5   Evaluating Functions

Let the function f be defined by $f(x) = x^2 - 1$. Find

a. $f(-2)$ b. $f(a)$ c. $f(a + h)$ d. $f(a + h) - f(a)$ e. $\dfrac{f(a + h) - f(a)}{h}$

Solution

a. $f(-2) = (-2)^2 - 1 = 4 - 1 = 3$

b. $f(a) = a^2 - 1$

c. $f(a + h) = (a + h)^2 - 1 = a^2 + 2ah + h^2 - 1$

d. $f(a + h) - f(a) = (a + h)^2 - 1 - (a^2 - 1)$
$$= a^2 + 2ah + h^2 - 1 - a^2 + 1$$
$$= 2ah + h^2$$

e. $\dfrac{f(a + h) - f(a)}{h} = \dfrac{2ah + h^2}{h} = \dfrac{h(2a + h)}{h} = 2a + h, \quad h \neq 0$

Warning

a. Note that $f(a + 3) \neq f(a) + f(3)$. Function notation is not to be confused with the distributive law.

b. Note that $f(x^2) \neq f \cdot x^2$. The use of parentheses in function notation does *not* imply multiplication.

We may use letters other than f to designate a function as we see in the next example.

Example 6   Functions and Word Problems

A newspaper makes this offer to its advertisers: The first column inch will cost $40, and each subsequent column inch will cost $30. If T is the total cost of running an ad whose length is n column inches, and the minimum space is 1 column inch,

a. express T as a function of n;   b. find T when $n = 4$.

Solution

a. After paying $40 for the first inch, we must pay $30 for each of the remaining $n - 1$ inches. Therefore, the equation

$$T = 40 + 30(n - 1)$$
$$= 10 + 30n$$

gives the correspondence between n and T. In function notation,

$$T(n) = 10 + 30n \quad n \geq 1$$

b. When $n = 4$,

$$T(4) = 10 + 30(4) = 130$$

Exercise Set 3.2

In Exercises 1–6, graph the equation. If the graph determines y as a function of x, find the domain and use the graph to determine the range of the function.

1. $y = 2x - 3$

2. $y = x^2 + x, \quad -2 \le x \le 1$

3. $x = y + 1$

4. $x = y^2 - 1$

5. $y = \sqrt{x - 1}$

6. $y = |x|$

In Exercises 7–12, determine the domain of the function defined by the given rule. Then, determine the appropriate WINDOW values and GRAPH the function on your graphing calculator.

7. $f(x) = \sqrt{2x - 3}$

8. $f(x) = \sqrt{5 - x}$

9. $f(x) = \dfrac{1}{\sqrt{x - 2}}$

10. $f(x) = \dfrac{-2}{x^2 + 2x - 3}$

11. $f(x) = \dfrac{\sqrt{x - 1}}{x - 2}$

12. $f(x) = \dfrac{x}{x^2 - 4}$

In Exercises 13–16, find the number (or numbers) whose image is 2.

13. $f(x) = 2x - 5$

14. $f(x) = x^2$

15. $f(x) = \dfrac{1}{x - 1}$

16. $f(x) = \sqrt{x - 1}$

In Exercises 17–23, determine the following if f is defined by $f(x) = 2x^2 + 5$.

17. $f(0)$

18. $f(-2)$

19. $f(a)$

20. $f(3x)$

21. $3f(x)$

22. $-f(x)$

23. $\dfrac{f(a + h) - f(a)}{h}$

In Exercises 24–29, determine the following if g is defined by $g(x) = x^2 + 2x$.

24. $g(-3)$

25. $g\left(\dfrac{1}{x}\right)$

26. $\dfrac{1}{g(x)}$

27. $g(-x)$

28. $g(a + h)$

29. $\dfrac{g(a + h) - g(a)}{h}$

In Exercises 30–34, determine the following if F is defined by
$$F(x) = \frac{x^2 + 1}{3x - 1}$$

30. $F(-2.73)$ to two decimal places

31. $\dfrac{1}{F(x)}$

32. $F(-x)$

33. $2F(2x)$

34. $F(x^2)$

In Exercises 35–40, determine the following if r is defined by
$$r(t) = \frac{t - 2}{t^2 + 2t - 3}$$

35. $r(-8.27)$

36. $r(2.04)$

37. $r(2a)$

38. $2r(a)$

39. $r(a + 1)$

40. $\dfrac{r(a + h) - r(a)}{h}$

41. If x dollars are borrowed at 7% simple annual interest, express the interest I at the end of 4 years as a function of x.

42. Express the area A of an equilateral triangle as a function of the length s of its side.

43. Express the diameter d of a circle as a function of its circumference C.

44. Express the perimeter P of a square as a function of its area A.

45. Container Corporation of America wants to manufacture a box with no top from a 10 inch by 12 inch piece of metal by cutting equal-sized squares from each corner and bending up the sides. Express the volume of the container as a function of its height.

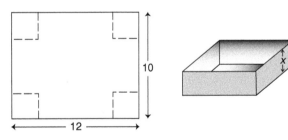

46. A rectangular box with a depth of 10 inches and a square base is to be manufactured by the Bold Box Company. The top of the box costs $1.20 per square inch, the bottom costs $.95 per square inch and the sides cost $.75 per square inch. Express the cost of manufacturing this box as a function of length.

47. The owners of an audio-video store have found that they can sell 400 compact disc players per month at $300 per player. For each $5.00 drop in price, they can sell 10 more compact disc players.

a. Express the gross sales as a function of each $5.00 decrease in price.

b. What would the gross sales of compact disc players be for ten $5.00 decreases?

48. A power line runs due north. Westown is 5 miles due west from a point *A* on the power line. Another town, Westwood, is 12 miles west from a point *B* on the power line. Points *A* and *B* are 8 miles apart. A power company wants to locate a transformer between *A* and *B*. Express the sum of the distances from each town to the transformer as a function of the distance *d* from point *A* to the transformer.

49. *Mathematics in Writing:*

a. Explain in your own words the phrase *domain of a function.*

b. Give an example of a function whose domain excludes the number 2. Explain in a complete sentence.

c. Give an example of a function whose domain excludes all real numbers less than 5. Explain in a complete sentence.

d. How can your graphing calculator help you to determine the range of a function? Give an example.

Applications 3.2

1. The Curry College Book Store has found that they can sell 350 Curry College notebooks per month at $6.00 each. For each 50 cents drop in price, they can sell 80 more notebooks.

a. Express the gross sales as a function of each 50 cents decrease in price. Identify your independent variable and dependent variable in terms of the content.

b. Sketch the graph of the function.

c. What would the gross sales be for six 50 cents decreases?

2. You would like to hang a wallpaper border on the walls close to the ceiling in your dorm room. You know the cost of the wallpaper border is $2.99 per foot.

a. Measure your room first and then calculate the perimeter of your room.

b. Find the cost of the wallpaper to cover your walls close to the ceiling.

c. Write the cost of wallpaper for any room if the perimeter of the room is measured as *x*.

d. Sketch the graph of the function you wrote in part (b).

3. Assume that postage rates are $0.60 for the first ounce, plus $0.21 for each additional ounce, and that each letter carries one $0.30 stamp and as many $0.21 stamps as necessary.

a. Find the number of $0.30 stamps and $0.21 stamps are needed if you would like to send a package which weighs 7 ounces?

b. Write a function that models the number of stamps on a letter weighing *x* ounces over the interval (0, 8].

c. Sketch the graph of the function that you wrote in part (b).

4. The cost of parking a car at the Logan Airport hourly parking lot is $3 for the first half-hour and $3 each additional half-hour or fraction of a half hour.

a. Find the cost if you have to park your car for 40 minutes.

b. Write a function that models the cost of parking a car for *x* hours over the interval (0, 2].

c. Sketch the graph of the function you wrote in part (b).

5. A book author invests her royalties in a savings account for three years. The account pays 5% simple interest.

a. Find the amount of interest she will earn if she invests $3,000.

b. If she invests *x* dollars in this account, write an expression for y_1 in terms of *x*, where y_1 represents the amount of interest earned.

c. Sketch the graph of the function you wrote in part (b).

3.3 Graphs of Functions

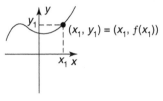

Figure 22 Points on Graphs of Functions

We have used the graph of an equation to help us find out when the equation determines a function. For example, the graph of the function f defined by the rule $f(x) = \sqrt{x}$ is the graph of the equation $y = \sqrt{x}$, which was sketched in Figure 20.

There are times when different notation is used to identify points on the graph of the equation $y = f(x)$. One method is to identify specific points with numbered coordinates. For example, if $f(1) = 3$, then we would identify the point associated with this equation as $(1, 3)$. More generally, if $f(x_1) = y_1$, then we may either identify this equation with the point (x_1, y_1) or with the point $(x_1, f(x_1))$ as shown in Figure 22.

"Special" Functions and Their Graphs

There are a number of "special" functions that can be very useful in understanding many of the concepts presented here. Furthermore, these functions tend to arise quite frequently in many practical situations. Therefore, we will present a brief list of these functions, along with their graphs and information about symmetry, intercepts, domain and range.

As you look at the graph of each function, see if you can anticipate the answers concerning the various characteristics mentioned above.

$f(x) = x$ Identity Function

The domain of f is the set of all real numbers. We form a table of values and use it to sketch the graph of $y = x$ in Figure 23. The graph is symmetric with respect to the origin. (Note that $-y = -x$ is equivalent to $y = x$.) The range of f is the set of all real numbers. The x-intercept and the y-intercept are both 0.

x	y
-2	-2
-1	-1
0	0
1	1
2	2

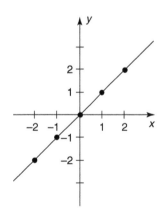

Figure 23   Graph of $y = x$

$f(x) = -x$ **Negation Function**

The domain of f is the set of all real numbers. A table of values is used to sketch the graph of $y = -x$ in Figure 24. The graph is symmetric with respect to the origin. (Note that $-y = x$ is equivalent to $y = -x$.) The range of f is the set of all real numbers. The x-intercept and the y-intercept are both 0.

x	y
-2	2
-1	1
0	0
1	-1
2	-2

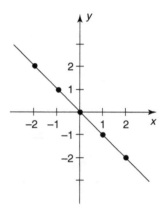

Figure 24   Graph of $y = -x$

$f(x) = |x|$ **Absolute Value Function**

The domain of f is the set of all real numbers. A table of values allows us to sketch the graph in Figure 25. The graph is symmetric with respect to the y-axis. (Note that $y = |-x| = |x|$.) Since the graph lies on or above the x-axis, the range of f is the set of all nonnegative real numbers, that is, $\{y \mid y \geq 0\}$. The x-intercept and y-intercept are both 0. Note that we may also write

$$y = f(x) = |x| = \begin{cases} x & \text{if } x \geq 0 \\ -x & \text{if } x < 0 \end{cases}$$

Thus, $y = x$ if $x \geq 0$ whereas $y = -x$ if $x < 0$.

x	y
-2	2
-1	1
0	0
1	1
2	2

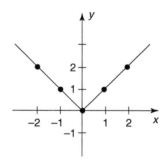

Figure 25   Graph of $y = |x|$

$f(x) = c$ **Constant Function**

The domain of f is the set of all real numbers. In fact, the value of f is the same for all values of x, as shown in Figure 26. The range of f is the set $\{c\}$. The graph is symmetric with respect to the y-axis. (Note that $y = c$ is unaltered when x is replaced by $-x$.) The y-intercept is c; there is no x-intercept.

x	y
-2	c
-1	c
0	c
1	c
2	c

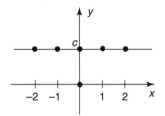

Figure 26 Graph of $y = c$, $c > 0$

$f(x) = x^2$ **Squaring Function**

The domain of f is the set of all real numbers. The graph in Figure 27 is called a **parabola** and illustrates the general shape of all second-degree polynomials. The graph of f is symmetric with respect to the y-axis. (Note that $y = (-x)^2 = x^2$.) Since the graph lies on or above the x-axis, the range of f is $\{y \mid y \geq 0\}$. Both the x-intercept and y-intercept are 0.

x	y
-2	4
-1	1
0	0
1	1
2	4

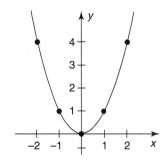

Figure 27 Graph of $y = x^2$

$f(x) = \sqrt{x}$ **Square Root Function**

Since $\sqrt{x}$ is not defined for $x < 0$, the domain is the set of nonnegative real numbers, that is, $\{x \mid x \geq 0\}$. The graph in Figure 28 always lies on or above the x-axis, so the range of f is $\{y \mid y \geq 0\}$. The graph is not symmetric with respect to either axis or the origin. Both the x-intercept and y-intercept are 0.

x	y
0	0
1	1
4	2
9	3

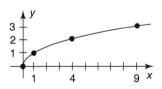

Figure 28 Graph of $y = \sqrt{x}$

$f(x) = x^3$ Cubic or Cubing Function

The domain is the set of all real numbers. From the graph in Figure 29, we see that the range is also the set of all real numbers. The graph is symmetric with respect to the origin. (Note that $-y = (-x)^3 = -x^3$ is equivalent to $y = x^3$.) Both the x-intercept and y-intercept are 0.

x	y
-2	-8
-1	-1
0	0
1	1
2	8

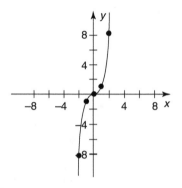

Figure 29   Graph of $y = x^3$

Additional Graphing Techniques

Although it is always possible to sketch a graph by finding many points, there are other methods that can make graph sketching a bit easier. We shall focus on specific transformations that create families of graphs. We will see how these transformations change graphs in predictable ways.

Consider the graphs of $y = x^2$, $y = x^2 + 1$, $y = x^2 + 2$, $y = x^2 - 1$ and $y = x^2 - 2$, as shown in Figure 30.

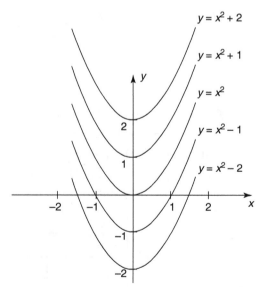

Figure 30   Vertical Shift of a Graph

We have a family of parabolas that are related as follows: each graph is an exact copy of the graph $y = x^2$, shifted up or down an appropriate number of units. For example, the graph of $y = x^2 + 2$ is the graph of $y = x^2$ shifted up 2 units; the graph of $y = x^2 - 1$ is the graph of $y = x^2$ shifted down 1 unit. This example illustrates the concept of vertical shifts.

Vertical Shift

If $p > 0$, the graph of $y = f(x) + p$ is the graph of $y = f(x)$ shifted up p units. Similarly, the graph of $y = f(x) - p$ is the graph of $y = f(x)$ shifted down p units.

Next, consider the graphs $y = x^3$, $y = (x - 1)^3$, $y = (x - 2)^3$, $y = (x + 1)^3$, and $y = (x + 2)^3$, as shown in Figure 31. We have a family of cubic functions that are related as follows: each graph is an exact copy of the graph of $y = x^3$, shifted to the right or left an appropriate number of units. For example, the graph of $y = (x - 2)^3$ is the graph of $y = x^3$ shifted 2 units to the right; the graph of $y = (x + 1)^3$ is the graph of $y = x^3$ shifted 1 unit to the left. This example illustrates the concept of horizontal shifts.

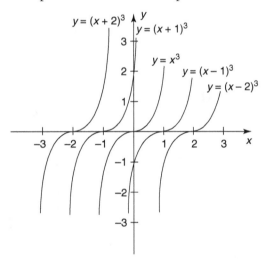

Figure 31   Horizontal Shift of a Graph

Horizontal Shift

If $p > 0$, the graph of $y = f(x - p)$ is the graph of $y = f(x)$ shifted p units to the right. Similarly, the graph of $y = f(x + p)$ is the graph of $y = f(x)$ shifted p units to the left.

Now, consider the graphs of $y = x^2$ and $y = -x^2$ as shown in Figure 32(a), or the graphs of $y = x^3$ and $y = -x^3$ as shown in Figure 32(b). We have two families of curves, parabolic and cubic. One member of a given family is the reflection about the x-axis of the other member of that family. This leads to the concept of reflection.

Note that $f(-x) = -x^3$ as well. This is equivalent to reflection about the y-axis of the graph of $y = x^3$. (In Figure 32(b), observe that the reflection of $y = x^3$ about either the x- or y-axis yields the same graph.)

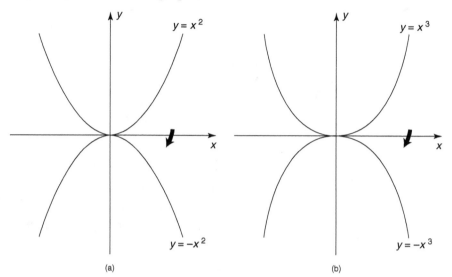

(a)   (b)

Figure 32   Reflection of a Graph about the x-axis

Reflection
The graph of $y = -f(x)$ is the reflection about the x-axis of the graph $y = f(x)$. The graph of $y = f(-x)$ is the reflection about the y-axis of the graph $y = f(x)$.

We summarize these results in Table 2.

Table 2   Graphing Techniques

Form	Relationship to the Graph of $y = f(x)$, $p > 0$
$y = f(x) + p$	Shift $f(x)$ p units up.
$y = f(x) - p$	Shift $f(x)$ p units down.
$y = f(x - p)$	Shift $f(x)$ p units to the right.
$y = f(x + p)$	Shift $f(x)$ p units to the left.
$y = -f(x)$	Reflect $f(x)$ about the x-axis.
$y = f(-x)$	Reflect $f(x)$ about the y-axis.

Example 1   Applications of Graphing Techniques
Sketch the graph of $y = \sqrt{x + 2} + 1$.

Solution

Take the graph of $y = \sqrt{x}$ and shift it 2 units to the left. Now take this graph and shift it up 1 unit. We show this process in Figure 33.

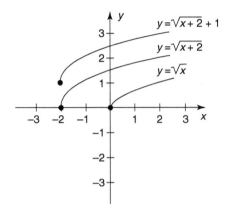

Figure 33   Graphs Associated with Example 1

Consider the graphs of $y = x^2$, $y = 2x^2$ and $y = \frac{1}{2}x^2$ as shown in Figure 34. This is another family of parabolas. If we use the graph of $y = x^2$ as our reference point once again, we see that this graph will expand or contract depending upon whether the multiplying coefficient of x^2 is greater than 1 or less than 1.

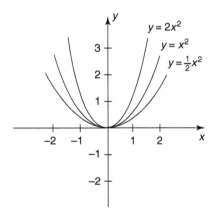

Figure 34   Stretching and Shrinking Graphs

✔ **Progress Check**

Determine what must be done to the graph of $y = |x|$ in order to sketch the graph $y = -|x - 1| + 3$.

Answer

Take the graph of $y = |x|$ and shift it 1 unit to the right. Now, reflect this graph about the x-axis. Finally, shift this reflected graph up 3 units. (As a check, try sketching this graph by plotting points.)

x	y
-2	4
-1	1
0	0
1	1
2	4
3	7
4	9
5	11

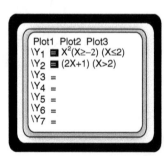

Figure 35 Graph for Example 2

Piecewise-Defined Functions

Thus far we have defined each function by means of an equation. A function can also be defined by a table, by a graph or by several equations. When a function is defined in different ways over different parts of its domain, it is said to be a **piecewise-defined function**. We illustrate this idea by several examples.

Example 2   Graphing Piecewise-Defined Functions

Sketch the graph of the function f defined by

$$f(x) = \begin{cases} x^2 & \text{if} & -2 \leq x \leq 2 \\ 2x + 1 & \text{if} & x > 2 \end{cases}$$

Solution

We form a table of points to be plotted as shown in Figure 35, being careful to use the first equation when $-2 \leq x \leq 2$ and the second equation when $x > 2$. Note that the graph in Figure 35 has a gap. Also note that the point $(2, 5)$ has been marked with an *open circle* to indicate that it is *not included* on the graph of the function, whereas the points $(-2, 4)$ and $(2, 4)$ have been marked with *filled-in circles* to indicate that these points *are included* on the graph.

Graphing Calculator Alert

Some graphing calculators have the capability to graph piecewise-defined functions. Consult your owner's manual for details. Note that the graphing calculator does not provide information about the function at the endpoints of the "pieces."

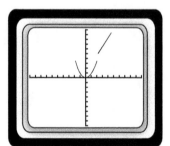

Example 3   Graphing with Absolute Value

Sketch the graph of the function $f(x) = |x + 1|$.

Solution

We apply the definition of absolute value to obtain

$$y = |x + 1| = \begin{cases} x + 1 & \text{if} & x + 1 \geq 0 \\ -(x + 1) & \text{if} & x + 1 < 0 \end{cases}$$

or

$$y = \begin{cases} x + 1 & \text{if} \quad x \ge -1 \\ -x - 1 & \text{if} \quad x < -1 \end{cases}$$

From this example, we see that a function involving absolute value is usually a piecewise-defined function. As usual, we form a table of values, being careful to use $y = x + 1$ when $x \ge -1$ and $y = -x - 1$ when $x < -1$. It is a good idea to include the value of x in the table where the change occurs. The change in this example is at $x = -1$.

The graph consists of two rays or half-lines intersecting at $(-1, 0)$, as shown in Figure 36.

x	y
-3	2
-2	1
-1	0
0	1
1	2
2	3
3	4

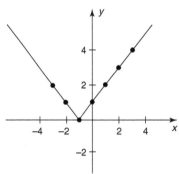

Figure 36   Graph of $y = |x + 1|$

Alternatively, we may obtain the same result by shifting the graph of $y = |x|$ one unit to the left. See Table 2.   ■

Example 4   Piecewise-Defined Functions and Word Problems

The commission earned by a door-to-door cosmetics salesperson is determined as shown in the accompanying table.

a. Express the commission C as a function of sales s.

b. Find the commission if the weekly sales are \$425.

c. Sketch the graph of the function.

Weekly Sales	Commission
less than \$300	20% of sales
\$300 or more but less than \$400	\$60 + 40% of sales over \$300
\$400 or more	\$100 + 60% of sales over \$400

Solution
a. The function C can be described by three equations.

$$C(s) = \begin{cases} 0.20s & \text{if} \quad 0 \le s < 300 \\ 60 + 0.40(s - 300) & \text{if} \quad 300 \le s < 400 \\ 100 + 0.60(s - 400) & \text{if} \quad s \ge 400 \end{cases}$$

b. When $s = 425$, we must use the third equation and substitute to determine $C(425)$.

$$C(425) = 100 + 0.60(425 - 400)$$
$$= 100 + 0.60(25)$$
$$= 115$$

The commission on sales of $425 is $115.

c. The graph of the function C consists of three line segments as shown in Figure 37.

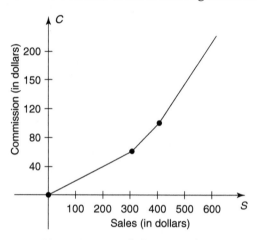

Figure 37   Graph for Example 4,
Commission as a Function of Sales

✔ **Progress Check**

Let N denote the number of 50-cent stamps one can purchase with x dollars, assuming $0 \leq x \leq 1$. Express N as a function of x and sketch the graph.

Answer

$$N(x) = \begin{cases} 0 & \text{if} & 0 \leq x < \frac{1}{2} \\ 1 & \text{if} & \frac{1}{2} \leq x < 1 \\ 2 & \text{if} & x = 1 \end{cases}$$

The graph consists of two line segments and an isolated point as shown in Figure 38.

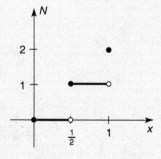

Figure 38   Number of 50¢ Stamps Purchased
as a Function of Money

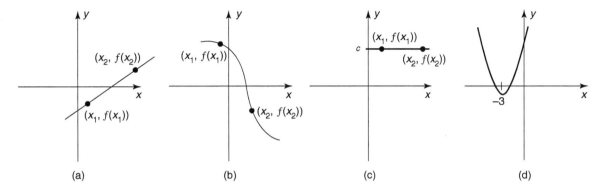

Figure 39   Functions: (a) Increasing, (b) Decreasing, (c) Constant, (d) Decreasing then Increasing

Increasing and Decreasing Functions

When we apply the terms **increasing** and **decreasing** to the graph of a function, we assume that we are viewing the graph from left to right. The line of Figure 39(a) is increasing, since the values of y increase as we move from left to right. Similarly, the graph in Figure 39(b) is decreasing, since the values of y decrease as we move from left to right. The graph in Figure 39(c) is a **constant**, hence it is neither increasing nor decreasing. One portion of the graph in Figure 39(d) is decreasing and another is increasing. Observe that in Figure 39, the notation $f(x_1)$ and $f(x_2)$ represents the y-coordinates at $x = x_1$ and $x = x_2$, respectively. (See Figure 22.)

In general, a function may increase over some intervals, decrease over others and remain constant in still other intervals. Recall that there are four types of intervals to consider, namely, $[a, b]$, $(a, b]$, $[a, b)$ or (a, b). We define increasing, decreasing and constant on an interval I.

Let x_1 and x_2 be any numbers in interval I in the domain of a function f. Then,

- f is increasing on I if $f(x_1) < f(x_2)$ whenever $x_1 < x_2$
- f is decreasing on I if $f(x_1) > f(x_2)$ whenever $x_1 < x_2$
- f is constant on I if $f(x_1) = f(x_2)$ for all x_1, x_2

Returning to Figure 39(d), note that the function is decreasing when $x \leq -3$ and increasing when $x \geq -3$. In other words, the function is decreasing on the interval $(-\infty, -3]$ and increasing on the interval $[-3, \infty)$. Observe that the point whose x-coordinate is -3 actually plays a dual role. The graph shows that the function has a minimum value at this point. It can be very useful, when sketching a graph, to find **turning points**, namely, those points where the graph changes from increasing to decreasing or from decreasing to increasing.

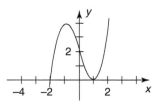

Figure 40 Graph of
$y = x^3 - 3x + 2$

Example 5 Increasing and Decreasing Functions

Use the graph of the function $f(x) = x^3 - 3x + 2$, shown in Figure 40, to determine where the function is increasing and where it is decreasing.

Solution

From the graph, we see that there are turning points at $(-1, 4)$ and at $(1, 0)$. We conclude that

- f is increasing on the intervals $(-\infty, -1]$ and $[1, \infty)$

- f is decreasing on the interval $[-1, 1]$

Graphing Calculator Alert

If you use the TRACE feature of your graphing calculator to locate the "turning points" of a graph, keep in mind that the actual maximum and minimum values may not have been plotted on your calculator. For example, GRAPH $y = x^3 - 3x + 2$ in the viewing rectangle $-2 \leq X \leq 2$ and $-1 \leq Y \leq 5$. When you TRACE on your graphing calculator, you skip over the points $(-1, 4)$ and $(1, 0)$, but you can reasonably estimate these values with practice. On some models with the TRACE feature, you can ENTER a value. Try entering -1 and see what the result is.

Example 6 Increasing and Decreasing Functions

The function f is defined by

$$f(x) = \begin{cases} |x| & \text{if} \quad x \leq 2 \\ -3 & \text{if} \quad x > 2 \end{cases}$$

Use the graph to find the values of x for which the function is increasing, decreasing and constant.

Solution

Note that the piecewise-defined function f is composed of the absolute value function when $x \leq 2$ and a constant function when $x > 2$. Therefore, we sketch the graph of f as shown in Figure 41. From this graph, we determine that

- f is decreasing on the interval $(-\infty, 0]$

- f is increasing on the interval $[0, 2]$

- f is constant and has value -3 on the interval $(2, \infty)$

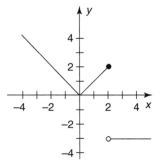

Figure 41 Graph for
Example 6

✔ **Progress Check**

The function f is defined by

$$f(x) = \begin{cases} 2x + 1 & \text{if} & x < -1 \\ 0 & \text{if} & -1 \leq x \leq 3 \\ -2x + 1 & \text{if} & x > 3 \end{cases}$$

Use the graph to find the values of x for which the function is increasing, decreasing and constant.

Answer

Increasing on the interval $(-\infty, -1)$, decreasing on $(3, \infty)$ and constant on $[-1, 3]$.

Polynomial Functions

The polynomial function of first degree

$$f(x) = ax + b$$

is called a **linear function**. We have already graphed a number of such functions in this chapter: $f(x) = 2x + 1$ (Figure 11), $f(x) = x$ (Figure 23) and $f(x) = -x$ (Figure 24). In each case, the graph appeared to be a line. We will prove in the next section that the graph of every linear function is indeed a line.

The polynomial function of second degree

$$f(x) = ax^2 + bx + c, \quad a \neq 0$$

is called a **quadratic function**. We have graphed a few quadratic functions: $f(x) = x^2 - 4$ (Figure 10), $f(x) = 1 - x^2$ (Figure 13) and $f(x) = x^2$ (Figure 27). The graph of the quadratic function is called a **parabola** and will be studied in detail in Chapter 5. For now, we offer an example for which a, b and c are all nonzero.

Example 7   Graphs of Polynomials

Sketch the graph of $f(x) = 2x^2 - 4x + 3$.

Solution

We need to graph $y = 2x^2 - 4x + 3$. We form a table of values, plot the corresponding points and connect them by a smooth curve, as shown in Figure 42.   ▪

An investigation of polynomials of any degree reveals that they are all functions. The graphs of polynomials are always smooth curves. However, their shapes are not easily determined for degree greater than 2. We will take another look at this topic in the next chapter after learning more about the roots of polynomial equations. Note, however, that it may be difficult to graph polynomial functions accurately without results obtained by methods taught in calculus courses.

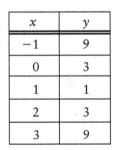

x	y
-1	9
0	3
1	1
2	3
3	9

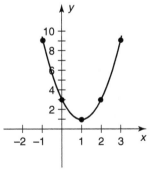

Figure 42   Graph of $y = 2x^2 - 4x + 3$

Exercise Set 3.3

 In Exercises 1–16, sketch the graph of the function and state where it is increasing, decreasing and constant. In Exercises 1–12, determine appropriate WINDOW values, and check your answer using your graphing calculator. Exercises 9–12 require piecewise graphing capability.

1. $f(x) = 3x + 1$

2. $f(x) = 3 - 2x$

3. $f(x) = x^2 + 1$

4. $f(x) = x^2 - 4$

5. $f(x) = 9 - x^2$

6. $f(x) = 4x - x^2$

7. $f(x) = |2x + 1|$

8. $f(x) = |1 - x|$

9. $f(x) = \begin{cases} 2x & \text{if } x > -1 \\ -x - 1 & \text{if } x \le -1 \end{cases}$

10. $f(x) = \begin{cases} x + 1 & \text{if } x > 2 \\ 1 & \text{if } -1 \le x \le 2 \\ -x + 1 & \text{if } x < -1 \end{cases}$

11. $f(x) = \begin{cases} x & \text{if } x < 2 \\ 2 & \text{if } x \ge 2 \end{cases}$

12. $f(x) = \begin{cases} -x & \text{if } x \le -2 \\ x^2 & \text{if } -2 < x \le 2 \\ -x & \text{if } 3 \le x \le 4 \end{cases}$

13. $f(x) = \begin{cases} -x^2 & \text{if } -3 < x < 1 \\ 0 & \text{if } 1 \le x \le 2 \\ -3x & \text{if } x > 2 \end{cases}$

14. $f(x) = \begin{cases} 2 & \text{if } x \text{ is an integer} \\ -1 & \text{if } x \text{ is not an integer} \end{cases}$

15. $f(x) = \begin{cases} -2 & \text{if } x < -2 \\ -1 & \text{if } -2 \le x \le -1 \\ 1 & \text{if } x > -1 \end{cases}$

16. $f(x) = \begin{cases} \dfrac{x^2 - 1}{x - 1} & \text{if } x \ne 1 \\ 3 & \text{if } x = 1 \end{cases}$

 In Exercises 17–24, sketch the graphs of the given functions on the same coordinate axes. Then, determine appropriate WINDOW values, and check your answers using your graphing calculator.

17. $f(x) = x^2, \quad g(x) = 2x^2, \quad h(x) = \frac{1}{2}x^2$

18. $f(x) = \frac{1}{2}x^2, \quad g(x) = \frac{1}{3}x^2, \quad h(x) = \frac{1}{4}x^2$

19. $f(x) = 2x^2, \quad g(x) = -2x^2$

20. $f(x) = x^2 - 2, \quad g(x) = 2 - x^2$

21. $f(x) = x^3, \quad g(x) = 2x^3$

22. $f(x) = \frac{1}{2}x^3, \quad g(x) = \frac{1}{4}x^3$

23. $f(x) = x^3, \quad g(x) = -x^3$

24. $f(x) = -2x^3, \quad g(x) = -4x^3$

25. The telephone company charges a fee of $6.50 per month for the first 100 message units and an additional fee of $0.06 for each of the next 100 message units. A reduced rate of $0.05 is charged for each message unit after the first 200 units. Express the monthly charge C as a function of the number of message units u.

26. The annual dues of a union are as shown in the table.

Employee's Annual Salary	Annual Dues
less than $8000	$60
$8000 or more but less than $15,000	$60 + 1% of the salary in excess of $8000
$15,000 or more	$130 + 2% of the salary in excess of $15,000

Express the annual dues d as a function of the salary S.

27. A tour operator who runs charter flights to Rome has established the following pricing schedule. For a group of no more than 100 people, the round trip fare per person is $300, with a minimum rental of $30,000 for the plane. For a group of more than 100, the fare per person for all passengers is reduced by $1 for each passenger in excess of 100. Write the tour operator's total revenue R as a function of the number of people x in the group.

28. A firm packages and ships 1-pound jars of instant coffee. The cost C of shipping is 40 cents for the first pound and 25 cents for each additional pound.

    a. Write C as a function of the weight w in pounds for $0 < w \le 30$.

    b. What is the cost of shipping a package containing 24 jars of instant coffee?

29. The daily rates of a car rental firm are $14 plus $0.08 per mile.

    a. Express the cost C of renting a car as a function of m, the number of miles traveled.

    b. What is the domain of the function?

c. How much would it cost to rent a car for a 100-mile trip?

30. In a wildlife preserve, the population P of eagles depends on the population x of its basic food supply, rodents. Suppose that P is given by

$$P(x) = 0.002x + 0.004x^2$$

Find the eagle population when the rodent population is

    a. 500   b. 2000

31. A parking lot in center city Philadelphia charges \$2.00 for any part of the first half-hour of parking. After the first half-hour, the rate is \$1.20 for any part of each additional half hour to a maximum rate of \$8.00 for the entire day.

    a. Express the parking fee F as a function of time t in hours.

    b. What does it cost to park if you enter the lot at 11:20 A.M. and leave at 1:05 P.M.?

    c. Sketch the graph of the function.

Graph functions (a) through (h) and then answer Exercises 32–36. Then, for each function, determine appropriate WINDOW values and GRAPH the function on your graphing calculator.

    a. $f(x) = x^2 + 1$ b. $f(x) = 3x - \dfrac{1}{4}$

    c. $f(x) = -2x - 1$ d. $f(x) = -3x^2$

    e. $f(x) = \begin{cases} -x & \text{if } x \le 0 \\ x & \text{if } 0 < x \le 3 \\ 3 & \text{if } x > 3 \end{cases}$

    f. $f(x) = |x| - 2$ g. $f(x) = |x^2 - 9|$

    h. $f(x) = \sqrt{1 - x}$

32. For each function, find the domain.

33. For each function, find the range.

34. For each function, find the intervals on which $f(x)$ is increasing.

35. For each function, find the intervals on which $f(x)$ is decreasing.

36. For each function, find the intervals on which $f(x)$ is neither increasing nor decreasing.

37. Graph the function in which the second coordinate is always -3 and in which the first coordinate may be any real number.

38. Graph the function in which the second coordinate is always 5 less than the first coordinate and in which the first coordinate may be any real number.

39. Graph the function whose second coordinate is always one more than the square of the first coordinate and whose first coordinate may be any real number.

40. Graph the function whose second coordinate is always the square root of the first coordinate and whose first coordinate may be any nonnegative real number.

The following is the graph of $y = f(x)$, associated with Exercises 41–44.

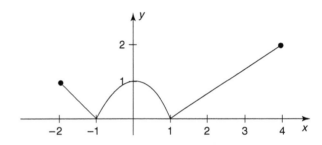

41. Sketch the graph of $y = 2 + f(x)$.

42. Sketch the graph of $y = f(x - 1)$.

43. Sketch the graph of $y = -f(x)$.

44. Sketch the graph of $y = f(-x)$.

The following is the graph of $y = f(x)$, associated with Exercises 45–49.

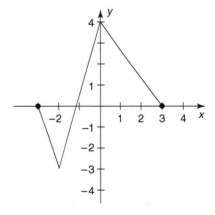

45. Sketch the graph of $y = f(x) - 3$.

46. Sketch the graph of $y = f(x + 2)$.

47. Sketch the graph of $y = -f(x)$.

48. Sketch the graph of $y = |f(x)|$.

49. Sketch the graph of $y = f(-x)$.

The following is the graph of $y = f(x)$, associated with Exercises 50–55.

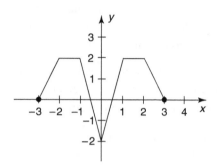

50. Sketch the graph of $y = f(x) + 5$.

51. Sketch the graph of $y = f(x + 1)$.

52. Sketch the graph of $y = -f(x)$.

53. Sketch the graph of $y = 5 - f(x)$.

54. Sketch the graph of $y = |f(x)|$.

55. Sketch the graph of $y = f(-x)$.

 56. The following graphs are variations of the function $y = \sqrt{x}$. Determine each function and verify your answer by graphing the function on your graphing calculator. (All graphs are drawn in the EQUAL viewing rectangle with XSCL = YSCL = 1.)

a.

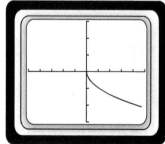

b.

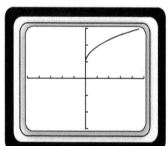

c.

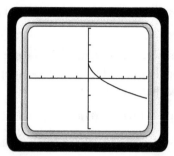

d.

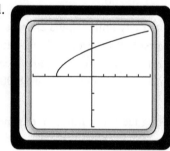

e.

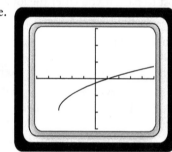

f.

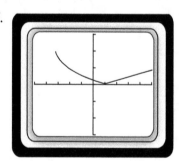

57. If your graphing calculator can graph piecewise-defined functions, use it to confirm graphically that

$$|x + 1| = \begin{cases} x + 1 & \text{if } x \geq -1 \\ -x - 1 & \text{if } x < -1 \end{cases}$$

by completing the following steps.

a. Set the EQUAL viewing rectangle on your graphing calculator.

b. GRAPH $y = |x + 1|$.

c. Clear the viewing rectangle.

d. GRAPH $y = \begin{cases} x + 1 & \text{if} \quad x \geq -1 \\ -x - 1 & \text{if} \quad x < -1 \end{cases}$

e. Compare your graphs from parts (b) and (d). (See Example 2 in this Section.)

58. A ball is thrown upward from a bridge 96 feet over a river with an initial velocity of 80 feet per second. Its height after t seconds is: $s = -16t^2 + 80t + 96$.

   a. Graph this function.

   b. From the graph, find the maximum height of the ball.

   c. At what time t after the ball is released does it reach its maximum height?

   d. Find the time when the ball reaches the water.

59. Johnny Appleseed currently has 20 winesap apple trees on one acre of ground. Each tree has an average yield of 40 bushels of apples. For every tree the farm adds, the yield per tree is one less bushel of apples due to overcrowding.

   a. Express the total number of bushels of apples as a function of the number of trees.

   b. Graph this function.

   c. From the graph, determine the number of trees that should be planted so that the yield of apples is a maximum.

   d. Find the maximum yield of apples, giving your answer in bushels.

60. *Mathematics in Writing:* Store the LIST {3, 4, 5, 6} at L_1, then graph

$$y = 3x + L_1$$

Write a brief paragraph explaining your results.

Applications 3.3

1. You bought an auto insurance policy with a $500 deductible. Let x be the amount of a claim that you filed and y be the amount of money that your insurance company will pay for the incident.

   a. Write a piecewise function which reflects the relationship between x and y.

   b. Sketch the graph of the function that you found in part (a).

2. The following table gives the tax bracket in year 2010.

Tax Bracket	Married Filing Jointly	Single
10%	$0–$17,000	$0–$8,500
15%	$17,001–$69,000	$8,501–$34,500
25%	$69,001–$139,350	$34,501–$83,600
28%	$139,351–$212,300	$83,601–$174,400
33%	$212,301–$379,150	$174,401–$379,150
35%	Over $379,150	Over $379,150

   a. Mike made $10,000 in 2010. How much tax does he need to pay?

   b. Write a piecewise function which reflects the amount of tax you need to pay as a single.

   c. Sketch the graph of the function that you found in part (a).

   d. Mike made one million dollars in 2010. How much tax does he need to pay?

   e. Can you claim that the richer pays more tax? Explain your answer.

3. Curry College Admissions Office packages and ships New Student Welcome Kit to all freshmen. The cost of shipping is 20 cents for the first pound and 15 cents for each additional pound.

   a. Write the shipping amount as a function of weight in pounds.

   b. Sketch the graph of the function that you found in part (b).

   c. Find the shipping amount if the package weights 0.7 pounds.

   d. Find the shipping amount if the package weights 1.7 pounds.

4. A ball is thrown upward from the top of Prudential Center in Boston, which is 749 feet from the ground, with an initial velocity of 80 feet per second. Its height after t seconds is given as $h = -16t^2 + 80t + 749$.

   a. Graph the function and find the maximum height of the ball.

   b. At what time after the ball is released does it reach its maximum height?

   c. Find the time when the ball reaches the ground.

3.4   Linear Functions

In the previous section, we said that the polynomial function of first degree

$$f(x) = ax + b$$

is called a linear function, and we observed that the graph of such a function *appears* to be a line. In this section, we will look at the property of a line that distinguishes it from all other curves. We will then develop equations for the line, and we will show that the graph of a linear function is indeed a line.

Slope of a Line

In Figure 43, we have drawn a line L that is not vertical. We have indicated the distinct points $P_1(x_1, y_1)$ and $P_2(x_2, y_2)$ on L. When moving from P_1 to P_2, the increment or change in the x-coordinate is $x_2 - x_1$ and in the y-coordinate, $y_2 - y_1$. Note that the increment $x_2 - x_1$ cannot be zero since L is not vertical.

If $P_3(x_3, y_3)$ and $P_4(x_4, y_4)$ are another pair of points on L, the increments $x_4 - x_3$ and $y_4 - y_3$ will, in general, be different from the increments obtained by using P_1 and P_2. However, since triangles P_1AP_2 and P_3BP_4 are similar, the corresponding sides are proportional to one another, that is,

$$\frac{y_2 - y_1}{x_2 - x_1} = \frac{y_4 - y_3}{x_4 - x_3}$$

This ratio is called the **slope of the line** L and is denoted by m.

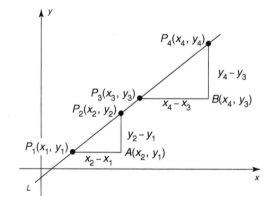

Figure 43   All Points on a Line
Produce the Same Slope

Slope of a Line

The slope m of a line that is not vertical is given by

$$m = \frac{y_2 - y_1}{x_2 - x_1}$$

where $P_1(x_1, y_1)$ and $P_2(x_2, y_2)$ are any two points on the line.

For a vertical line, $x_1 = x_2$, so $x_2 - x_1 = 0$. Since division by 0 is not defined, we say that a vertical line has no slope, or the slope of a vertical line does not exist.

The property of constant slope characterizes the line, that is, no other curve has this property.

Example 1   Finding the Slope of a Line

Find the slope of the line that passes through the points $(5, 6)$ and $(1, -2)$.

Solution

$$(x_1, y_1) = (5, 6) \quad \text{and} \quad (x_2, y_2) = (1, -2)$$

$$m = \frac{y_2 - y_1}{x_2 - x_1} = \frac{-2 - 6}{1 - 5} = \frac{-8}{-4} = 2$$

Verify that reversing the choice of P_1 and P_2 produces the same result for the slope m. Although we may choose either point as P_1 and the other as P_2, we must use this choice consistently once it has been made.

Slope is a means of measuring the steepness of a line. That is, slope specifies the number of units we must move up or down to reach the line after moving 1 unit to the left or right of the line. Specifically in Example 1 above, if we move 1 unit to the right of the line, we must move up 2 units to reach the line. Alternatively, if we move 1 unit to the left of the line, we must move down 2 units to reach the line. (See Figure 44.)

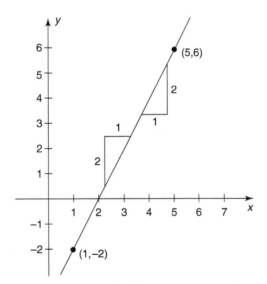

Figure 44   Graph of the Line for Example 1

In Figure 45, we have displayed several lines with positive and negative slopes. We can summarize as follows.

Let *m* be the slope of a line.

1. When $m > 0$, the line is the graph of an increasing function.

2. When $m < 0$, the line is the graph of a decreasing function.

3. When $m = 0$, the line is the graph of a constant function.

4. Slope does not exist for a vertical line, and a vertical line is not the graph of a function.

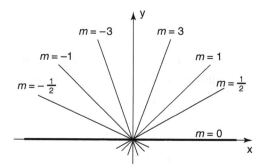

Figure 45 Lines with Different Slopes

🖩 Graphing Calculator Alert

The function $y = x$ is graphed below in four different viewing rectangles as shown in Figure 46. The slope *appears* to be different in each viewing rectangle. TRACE to locate two points on each line and *compute* the slope to verify that each line has slope $m = 1$. *You cannot estimate the slope of a line on a graphing calculator "by eye."*

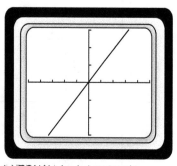

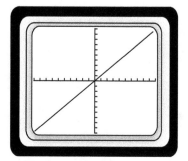

(a) EQUAL viewing rectangle
XSCL = 1, YSCL = 1

(b) Default viewing rectangle
XSCL = 1, YSCL = 1

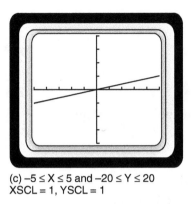 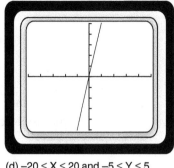

(c) $-5 \leq X \leq 5$ and $-20 \leq Y \leq 20$
XSCL = 1, YSCL = 1

(d) $-20 \leq X \leq 20$ and $-5 \leq Y \leq 5$
XSCL = 5, YSCL = 1

Figure 46   Graph of $y = x$

Equations of a Line

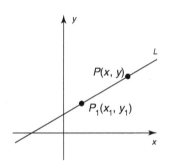

Figure 47   Graph of Line Using Point–Slope Form

We can apply the concept of slope to develop two important forms of the equation of a line. In Figure 47, the point $P_1(x_1, y_1)$ lies on a line L whose slope is assumed to be m. If $P(x, y)$ is any other point on L, then we may use P and P_1 to compute m. Therefore,

$$m = \frac{y - y_1}{x - x_1}$$

which can be written in the form

$$y - y_1 = m(x - x_1)$$

Since (x_1, y_1) satisfies this equation, every point on L satisfies this equation. Conversely, any point satisfying this equation must lie on the line L, since there is only one line through $P_1(x_1, y_1)$ with slope m. This equation is called the **point–slope form** of a line.

Point–Slope Form

The equation

$$y - y_1 = m(x - x_1)$$

is that of the line with slope m that passes through the point (x_1, y_1).

Example 2   Application of Point–Slope Form

Find an equation of the line that passes through the points $(6, -2)$ and $(-4, 3)$.

Solution

First we find the slope. Let $(x_1, y_1) = (6, -2)$ and $(x_2, y_2) = (-4, 3)$. Then

$$m = \frac{y_2 - y_1}{x_2 - x_1} = \frac{3 - (-2)}{-4 - 6} = \frac{5}{-10} = -\frac{1}{2}$$

Next, the point–slope form is used with $m = -\frac{1}{2}$ and $(x_1, y_1) = (6, -2)$.

$$y - y_1 = m(x - x_1)$$

$$y - (-2) = -\frac{1}{2}(x - 6)$$

$$y = -\frac{1}{2}x + 1$$

Verify that using the point $(-4, 3)$ and $m = -\frac{1}{2}$ in the point–slope form will also yield the same equation.

✔ Progress Check

Find an equation of the line that passes through the points $(-5, 0)$ and $(2, -5)$.

Answer

$$y = -\frac{5}{7}x - \frac{25}{7}$$

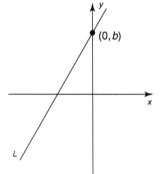

Figure 48   Graph of Line Using Slope–Intercept Form

There is another form of the equation of the line that is very useful. In Figure 48, the line L meets the y-axis at the point $(0, b)$ and is assumed to have slope m. Then, we can let $(x_1, y_1) = (0, b)$ and use the point–slope form:

$$y - y_1 = m(x - x_1)$$

$$y - b = m(x - 0)$$

$$y = mx + b$$

Recalling that b is the y-intercept, we call this equation the **slope–intercept form** of the line.

Slope–Intercept Form

The equation

$$y = mx + b$$

is that of the line with slope m and y-intercept b.

The last result leads to the important conclusion mentioned in the introduction to this section. Since the graph of $y = mx + b$ is the graph of the function $f(x) = mx + b$, we have indeed shown that the *graph of a linear function is a line.*

Example 3   Application of Slope–Intercept Form
Find the slope and y-intercept of the line $y - 3x + 1 = 0$.

Solution
The equation must be placed in the form $y = mx + b$. Solving for y gives

$$y = 3x - 1$$

and we find that $m = 3$ is the slope and $b = -1$ is the y-intercept.

✔ Progress Check
Find the slope and y-intercept of the line $2y + x - 3 = 0$.

Answer
slope $= m = -\dfrac{1}{2}$; y-intercept $= b = \dfrac{3}{2}$

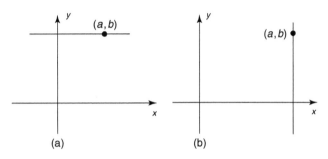

Figure 49   Horizontal and Vertical Lines

Horizontal and Vertical Lines

In Figure 49(a), we have drawn a horizontal line through the point (a, b). Every point on this line has the form (x, b), since the y-coordinate remains constant. If $P_1(x_1, b)$ and $P_2(x_2, b)$ are any two distinct points on the line, then the slope is

$$m = \frac{b - b}{x_2 - x_1} = 0$$

We have established the following.

Horizontal Lines
The equation

$$y = b$$

is that of the horizontal line through the point (a, b). The slope of a horizontal line is 0.

In Figure 49(b), every point on the vertical line through the point (a, b) has the form (a, y), since the x-coordinate remains constant. Calculating the slope using any two points $P_1(a, y_1)$ and $P_2(a, y_2)$ on the line produces

$$m = \frac{y_2 - y_1}{a - a} = \frac{y_2 - y_1}{0}$$

Since we cannot divide by 0, slope is not defined for a vertical line.

> **Vertical Lines**
> The equation
>
> $$x = a$$
>
> is that of the vertical line through the point (a, b). A vertical line has no slope.

Note that a vertical line is the only line that is *not* the graph of a function.

Example 4 Application of Horizontal and Vertical Line Forms
Find the equations of the horizontal and vertical lines through $(-4, 7)$.

Solution
The horizontal line has the equation $y = 7$. The vertical line has the equation $x = -4$. ■

Warning
Do not confuse "no slope" with "zero slope." A horizontal line has zero slope. A vertical line has no slope, in other words, its slope is undefined.

Graphing Calculator Alert
Function graphers can only graph expressions of the form $y = f(x)$. To display a vertical line on your graphing calculator, you can use the LINE command or you can "trick" the calculator by choosing a "large" slope. For example, to display the line $x = 2$ in the default viewing rectangle, GRAPH $y = 100(x - 2)$. To display the line $x = 2$ in the viewing rectangle $-10 \leq X \leq 10$ and $-100 \leq Y \leq 100$, GRAPH $y = 1000(x - 2)$.

General First-Degree Equation

The general first-degree equation in x and y can always be written in the form

$$Ax + By + C = 0$$

where A, B and C are constants, and A and B are *not both* zero. We can rewrite this equation as

$$By = -Ax - C$$

If $B \neq 0$, the equation becomes

$$y = -\frac{A}{B}x - \frac{C}{B}$$

which we recognize as the equation of a line with slope $-\frac{A}{B}$ and y-intercept $-\frac{C}{B}$. If $B = 0$, the original equation becomes $Ax + C = 0$, whose graph is the vertical line

$x = -\frac{C}{A}$. If $A = 0$, the original equation becomes $By + C = 0$, whose graph is the horizontal line $y = -\frac{C}{B}$.

The General First-Degree Equation
- The graph of the general first-degree equation

$$Ax + By + C = 0, \qquad A \text{ and } B \text{ not both zero}$$

  is a line.

- If $A = 0$, the graph is a horizontal line.

- If $B = 0$, the graph is a vertical line.

Parallel and Perpendicular Lines

The concept of slope of a line can be used to determine when two lines are parallel or perpendicular. Since parallel lines have the same "steepness," we recognize that they must have the same slope.

Two lines with slopes m_1 and m_2 are parallel if and only if

$$m_1 = m_2$$

The criterion for perpendicular lines can be stated in this way.

Two lines with slopes m_1 and m_2 are perpendicular if and only if

$$m_1 m_2 = -1 \quad \text{or equivalently,} \quad m_2 = -\frac{1}{m_1}, \quad m_1 \neq 0$$

These two theorems do not apply to vertical lines, since the slope of a vertical line is undefined. The proofs of these theorems are geometric in nature and are outlined in Exercises 56 and 57.

Example 5 Application of Parallel and Perpendicular Lines
Given the line $y = 3x - 2$, find an equation of the line passing through the point $(-5, 4)$ that is (a) parallel to the given line; (b) perpendicular to the given line.

Solution

We first note that the line $y = 3x - 2$ has slope $m_1 = 3$.

a. Every line parallel to the line $y = 3x - 2$ must have slope $m_2 = m_1 = 3$. Therefore, we seek a line with slope 3 that passes through the point $(-5, 4)$. Using the point–slope formula, we have

$$y - y_1 = m(x - x_1)$$
$$y - 4 = 3(x + 5)$$
$$y = 3x + 19$$

b. Since the line $y = 3x - 2$ has slope $m_1 = 3$, every line perpendicular to this line must have slope

$$m_2 = -\frac{1}{m_1} = -\frac{1}{3}$$

Then, the line we seek has slope $-\frac{1}{3}$ and passes through the point $(-5, 4)$. We can apply the point–slope formula once again to obtain

$$y - y_1 = m(x - x_1)$$
$$y - 4 = -\frac{1}{3}(x + 5)$$
$$y = -\frac{1}{3}x + \frac{7}{3}$$

The three lines are shown in Figure 50.

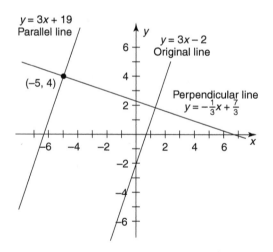

Figure 50   Graphs of Parallel and Perpendicular Lines

Summary

The slope m of a line can tell us a great deal about its graph. The slopes m_1 and m_2 of a pair of lines can be useful in determining some special relationship between their graphs. Various facts about the slope of a line are presented in Table 3.

Table 3 Slope of a Line

Slope(s)	Graph(s)	Example
$m > 0$	rising	
$m < 0$	falling	
$m = 0$	horizontal	
m undefined	vertical	
$m_1 = m_2$	parallel	
$m_1 m_2 = -1$	perpendicular	

Exercise Set 3.4

In Exercises 1–6, determine the slope of the line through the given points. State whether the line is the graph of an increasing function, a decreasing function, a constant function or not a function.

1. $(2, 3), (-1, -3)$
2. $(1, 2), (-2, 5)$
3. $(-2, 3), (0, 0)$
4. $(2, 4), (-3, 4)$
5. $\left(\frac{1}{2}, 2\right), \left(\frac{3}{2}, 1\right)$
6. $(-4, 1), (-1, -2)$

7. Use slopes to show that the points $A(-1, -5)$, $B(1, -1)$ and $C(3, 3)$ are collinear, that is, they lie on the same line.

8. Use slopes to show that the points $A(-3, 2)$, $B(3, 4)$, $C(5, -2)$ and $D(-1, -4)$ are the vertices of a parallelogram.

In Exercises 9–12, determine an equation of the line with the given slope m that passes through the given point.

9. $m = 2, (-1, 3)$
10. $m = -\frac{1}{2}, (1, -2)$
11. $m = 3, (0, 0)$
12. $m = 0, (-1, 3)$

In Exercises 13–18, determine an equation of the line through the given points.

13. $(2, 4), (-3, -6)$
14. $(-3, 5), (1, 7)$
15. $(0, 0), (3, 2)$
16. $(-2, 4), (3, 4)$
17. $\left(-\frac{1}{2}, -1\right), \left(\frac{1}{2}, 1\right)$
18. $(-8, -4), (3, -1)$

In Exercises 19–24, determine an equation of the line with the given slope m and the given y-intercept b.

19. $m = 3, b = 2$
20. $m = -3, b = -3$
21. $m = 0, b = 2$
22. $m = -\frac{1}{2}, b = \frac{1}{2}$
23. $m = \frac{1}{3}, b = -5$
24. $m = -2, b = -\frac{1}{2}$

In Exercises 25–30, determine the slope m and y-intercept b of the given line.

25. $3x + 4y = 5$
26. $2x - 5y + 3 = 0$
27. $y - 4 = 0$
28. $x = -5$
29. $3x + 4y + 2 = 0$
30. $x = -\frac{1}{2}y + 3$

In Exercises 31–36, write an equation of (a) the horizontal line passing through the given point and (b) the vertical line passing through the given point.

31. $(-6, 3)$
32. $(-5, -2)$
33. $(-7, 0)$
34. $(0, 5)$
35. $(9, -9)$
36. $\left(-\frac{3}{2}, 1\right)$

In Exercises 37–40, determine the slope of (a) every line that is parallel to the given line and (b) every line that is perpendicular to the given line.

37. $y = -3x + 2$
38. $2y - 5x + 4 = 0$
39. $3y = 4x - 1$
40. $5y + 4x = -1$

In Exercises 41–44, determine an equation of the line through the given point that (a) is parallel to the given line; (b) is perpendicular to the given line.

41. $(1, 3); \quad y = -3x + 2$
42. $(-1, 2); \quad 3y + 2x = 6$
43. $(-3, 2); \quad 3x + 5y = 2$
44. $(-1, -3); \quad 3y + 4x - 5 = 0$

45. The Celsius (C) and Fahrenheit (F) temperature scales are related by a linear equation. Water boils at 212°F or 100°C, and freezes at 32°F or 0°C.

   a. Write a linear equation expressing F in terms of C.

   b. What is the Fahrenheit temperature when the Celsius temperature is 20°?

46. The college bookstore sells a textbook that costs $40 for $43.50, and a textbook that costs $42 for $45.90. If the markup policy of the bookstore is linear, write a linear function that relates sales price S and cost C. What is the cost of a book that sells for $52?

47. An appliance manufacturer finds that it had sales of $200,000 five years ago and sales of $600,000 this year. If the growth in sales is assumed to be linear, what will the sales amount be 5 years from now?

48. A product that cost $2.50 three years ago sells for $3 this year. If price increases are assumed to be linear, how much will the product cost 6 years from now?

49. Find a real number c such that $P(-2, 2)$ is on the line $3x + cy = 4$.

50. Find a real number c such that the line $cx - 5y + 8 = 0$ has x-intercept 4.

51. If the points $(-2, -3)$ and $(-1, 5)$ are on the graph of a linear function f, find $f(x)$.

52. If $f(1) = 4$ and $f(-1) = 3$ and the function f is linear, find $f(x)$.

53. Prove that the linear function $f(x) = ax + b$ is an increasing function if $a > 0$, a decreasing function if $a < 0$ and a constant function if $a = 0$.

54. Find a viewing rectangle on your graphing calculator so that line $y = \frac{1}{3}x$ *appears* to have slope $m = 5$. (*Note:* GRAPH $y = \frac{x}{3}$.)

55. Prove that if two lines have the same slope, they are parallel.

56. In the accompanying figure, lines L_1 and L_2 are parallel. Points A and D are selected on lines L_1 and L_2, respectively. Lines parallel to the x-axis are constructed through A and D that intersect the y-axis at points B and E. Supply a reason for each of the steps in the following proof.

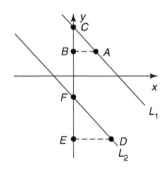

a. Angles ABC and DEF are equal.

b. Angles ACB and DFE are equal.

c. Triangles ABC and DEF are similar.

d. $\dfrac{\overline{CB}}{\overline{BA}} = \dfrac{\overline{FE}}{\overline{ED}}$

e. $m_1 = \dfrac{\overline{CB}}{\overline{BA}}, \quad m_2 = \dfrac{\overline{FE}}{\overline{ED}}$

f. $m_1 = m_2$

g. Parallel lines have the same slope.

57. In the accompanying figure, lines perpendicular to each other, with slopes m_1 and m_2, intersect at a point Q. A perpendicular from Q to the x-axis intersects the x-axis at the point C. Supply a reason for each of the steps in the following proof.

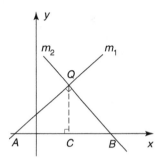

a. Angles CAQ and BQC are equal.

b. Triangles ACQ and BCQ are similar.

c. $\dfrac{\overline{CQ}}{\overline{AC}} = \dfrac{\overline{CB}}{\overline{CQ}}$

d. $m_1 = \dfrac{\overline{CQ}}{\overline{AC}}, \quad m_2 = -\dfrac{\overline{CQ}}{\overline{CB}}$

e. $m_2 = -\dfrac{1}{m_1}$

58. Prove that if two lines have slopes m_1 and m_2 such that $m_2 = -1/m_1$, the lines are perpendicular.

59. If x_1 and x_2 are the abscissas of two points on the graph of the function $y = f(x)$, show that the slope m of the line connecting the two points can be written as

$$m = \frac{f(x_2) - f(x_1)}{x_2 - x_1}$$

 In Exercises 60–63,

   a. Plot the data in the tables that follow.

   b. If the graph is a line, find the linear relationship.

   c. On your graphing calculator, GRAPH the line in an appropriate viewing rectangle for the problem and TRACE (approximately) to the points given in the table.

60. The table below shows the surface tension T in dynes per centimeter for pure water in contact with air at various temperatures C in °C

C	10	20	50
T	74	72	66

61. The table below gives the volume V of 1 gram of water at various temperatures T in °C.

T	0	50	75	100
V	1.00	1.01	1.02	1.04

62. The next table shows the number N of earthquakes per year of different magnitudes M as measured on the Richter Scale.

M	7	5	4	2
N	14	1000	1493	2479

63. The profit P in dollars for selling G gallons of gasoline at a service station is shown in the following table.

G	2	10	50	85
P	−4	20	140	245

Exercises 64–70 require the following information.

   The distance traveled by a moving object is a function of time. The average speed is defined as the ratio of the total distance traveled between two points to the elapsed time of travel, that is, *Average Speed* $= \frac{Distance\ Traveled}{Elapsed\ Time}$. It is also the slope of the straight line connecting the two points on the graph of the function.

64. What is the distance a car will travel in 12 minutes if it is going 50 mph?

65. An American Airlines jet leaves Raleigh-Durham at 10:05 A.M. nonstop to Fort Lauderdale. The jet arrives in Fort Lauderdale at 12:00 noon. If the distance between Raleigh-Durham and Fort Lauderdale is 683 air miles, find the average speed of the plane.

66. A particle is at $x = 2$ meters at $t = 0$ seconds, $x = -3$ meters at $t = 5$ seconds and $x = 5$ meters at $t = 7$ seconds. Find the average speed during the intervals:

   a. $t = 0$ seconds to $t = 5$ seconds

   b. $t = 5$ seconds to $t = 7$ seconds

   c. $t = 0$ seconds to $t = 7$ seconds

67. An out-of-shape junior high school student is asked to run 0.25 miles during the last 5 minutes of a 50-minute gym class. The student starts running, but eventually ends up walking around the track. If the student's average speed is 2.5 miles per hour, will the

student complete the full distance before the gym class ends?

The following two graphs show the position of a particle versus time. In Exercises 68 and 69, find the average speed during the given time intervals.

68. a. from $t = 0$ to $t = 2$

   b. from $t = 2$ to $t = 5$

   c. from $t = 5$ to $t = 7$

   d. from $t = 0$ to $t = 5$

   e. from $t = 0$ to $t = 7$

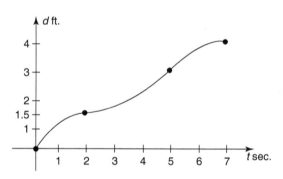

69. a. from $t = 0$ to $t = 4$

   b. from $t = 4$ to $t = 7$

   c. from $t = 7$ to $t = 10$

   d. from $t = 0$ to $t = 7$

   e. from $t = 4$ to $t = 10$

   f. from $t = 0$ to $t = 10$

   g. What conclusion can you draw about the particle between 4 and 7 seconds?

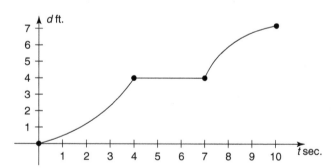

70. The speed of sound is 1100 feet per second. A clap of thunder occurs 5 miles from a school. How long will it take before the school children hear the thunder?

71. Assume that the pressure one experiences descending the depths of the ocean is linear.

a. If the pressure is 15 pounds per square inch on the surface of the water and the pressure is 35 pounds per square inch 45 feet below the surface, find the equation giving the relationship between pressure p and depth d.

b. What is the pressure 10,800 feet below the surface of the water?

c. How far below the surface of the water would you be to experience a pressure of 99 pounds per square inch?

d. Graph this function.

72. Katy buys a car for $20,500. In 3 years the value of the car is $14,500.

a. If the value of the car depreciates linearly, find the equation relating time and the value of the car.

b. In how many years would the car be worthless?

73. Refer to Katy's car purchase in Exercise 72. Suppose that 6 years after Katy purchased her car, the manufacturer stops producing the model that she purchased. This manufacturing decision causes the value of the car to begin to appreciate. After 8 years of ownership, Katy's car is now worth $900 more than it was worth after 6 years.

a. If the appreciation of the car is again taken to be linear, express the relationship between the value of the car and time.

b. Graph the relationship.

c. What is the value of Katy's car after 10 years?

Applications 3.4

1. Zeep Car Rental charges $45.00 for a weekend, plus 20 cents per mile driven. Let C be the rental cost, in dollars, and let d be the distance driven, in miles.

a. Express C symbolically as a function of d.

b. Graph C as a function of d. Please label your axes.

c. Zeep Car Rental also offers free drop off and pick up service. How much do you need to pay to drive from Curry College to your home? (Answer might vary.)

2. In a study conducted in early 2006, experts projected a rise in the market for cholesterol-reducing drugs. A mathematical model giving the approximate U.S.

market over the period from 2006 to 2010 in question is given by $M(t) = 1.875t + 13.2$, where M is measured in billions of dollars and t is measured in years, with $t = 0$ corresponding to 2006.

a. Sketch the graph of $M(t)$.

b. Assuming that the projection held and the trend continued, what was the market for cholesterol-reducing drugs in 2010?

c. What is the rate of increase of the market for cholesterol-reducing drugs over the period in question? Explain your answer.

3. The tuition at Curry College from 2007 to 2011 is given in the following table.

Year	2007	2008	2009	2010	2011
Tuition($)	24,500	25,600	27,000	29,000	30,700

A linear mathematical model giving the approximate tuition over the period in the question is given by $T(t) = 1580t + 24,200$ where t is measured in years, with $t = 0$ corresponding to 2007.

a. Sketch the graph of the function and the given data on the same set of axes.

b. Assuming that the projection held and the trend continued, what will be Curry College tuition in 2012?

c. Can you use this model to predict Curry College tuition in 2025? Explain your answer.

4. Curry College enrolled of 928 students in 2001. During the next nine years, the enrollment increased by approximately 75 students per year.

a. Write an equation of the line giving the enrollment N in terms of the year t. (Let $t = 0$ correspond to the year 2001.)

b. Find and interpret the slope of the line.

c. Sketch the graph of the line which you found in part (a). Label your axes.

d. Find and interpret the y-intercept.

e. Assuming the trend of enrollment will be held, estimate the enrollment at Curry College in 2011.

3.5   The Algebra of Functions; Inverse Functions

Functions such as

$$f(x) = x^2 \quad \text{and} \quad g(x) = x - 1$$

can be combined by the usual operations of addition, subtraction, multiplication and division. Using these functions f and g, we can form

$$(f + g)(x) = f(x) + g(x) = x^2 + x - 1$$

$$(f - g)(x) = f(x) - g(x) = x^2 - (x - 1) = x^2 - x + 1$$

$$(f \cdot g)(x) = f(x) \cdot g(x) = x^2(x - 1) = x^3 - x^2$$

$$\frac{f}{g}(x) = \frac{f(x)}{g(x)} = \frac{x^2}{x - 1}$$

In each case, we have combined two functions f and g to form a new function. Note, however, that the domain of the new function need not be the same as the domain of either of the original functions. The function formed by division in the above example has as its domain the set of all real numbers x except $x = 1$, since we cannot divide by 0. On the other hand, the original functions $f(x) = x^2$ and $g(x) = x - 1$ are both defined at $x = 1$.

Example 1   Algebra of Functions

Given $f(x) = x - 4$ and $g(x) = x^2 - 4$, find the following.

a. $(f + g)(x)$ b. $(f - g)(x)$

c. $(f \cdot g)(x)$ d. $\left(\dfrac{f}{g}\right)(x)$

e. the domain of $\left(\dfrac{f}{g}\right)(x)$

Solution

a. $(f + g)(x) = f(x) + g(x) = x - 4 + x^2 - 4 = x^2 + x - 8$

b. $(f - g)(x) = f(x) - g(x) = x - 4 - (x^2 - 4) = -x^2 + x$

c. $(f \cdot g)(x) = f(x) \cdot g(x) = (x - 4)(x^2 - 4) = x^3 - 4x^2 - 4x + 16$

d. $\left(\dfrac{f}{g}\right)(x) = \dfrac{f(x)}{g(x)} = \dfrac{x - 4}{x^2 - 4}$

e. The domain of $(\frac{f}{g})(x)$ must exclude values of x for which $x^2 - 4 = 0$. Thus, the domain consists of the set of all real numbers except 2 and -2.

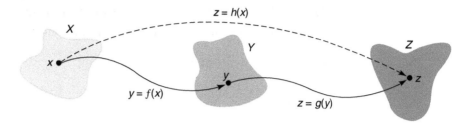

Figure 51   Correspondence for the Composition of Two Functions

✔ **Progress Check**

Given $f(x) = 2x^2$ and $g(x) = x^2 - 5x + 6$, find the following.

a. $(f + g)(x)$ b. $(f - g)(x)$

c. $(f \cdot g)(x)$ d. $\left(\dfrac{f}{g}\right)(x)$

e. the domain of $\left(\dfrac{f}{g}\right)(x)$

Answers

a. $3x^2 - 5x + 6$ b. $x^2 + 5x - 6$

c. $2x^4 - 10x^3 + 12x^2$ d. $\dfrac{2x^2}{x^2 - 5x + 6}$

e. The set of all real numbers except 2 and 3.

Composite Functions

There is another important way in which two functions f and g can be combined to form a new function. In Figure 51, the function f takes the point x in set X and assigns it the value y in set Y. Then, the function g takes the point y in set Y and assigns it the value z in set Z. The net effect of this combination of f and g is a new function h, called the **composite function of g and f**, denoted $g \circ f$. This function takes the point x in set X and assigns it the value z in set Z directly. We write the new function as

$$h(x) = (g \circ f)(x) = g[f(x)]$$

which is read "g of f of x." (The square bracket "[ ]" has been introduced in the notation regarding composite functions to form a more pronounced separation between g and f. We return to the use of parentheses "( )" when a "single substitution" is to take place.) Furthermore, if the notation $g[f(x)]$ is to make sense, then the domain of $g[f(x)]$ must consist only of those x in X for which $y = f(x)$ and $g(y) = g[f(x)]$ are both defined.

Example 2 Evaluation of Composite Functions

Given $f(x) = x^2$ and $g(x) = x - 1$, find the following.

a. $f[g(3)]$ b. $g[f(3)]$ c. $f[g(x)]$ d. $g[f(x)]$

Solution

a. We begin by evaluating $g(3)$:

$$g(x) = x - 1$$
$$g(3) = 3 - 1 = 2$$

Therefore,

$$f[g(3)] = f(2)$$

Since

$$f(x) = x^2$$

then

$$f(2) = 2^2 = 4$$

Thus,

$$f[g(3)] = 4$$

b. Beginning with $f(3)$, we have

$$f(3) = 3^2 = 9$$

Then we find by substituting $f(3) = 9$ that

$$g[f(3)] = g(9) = 9 - 1 = 8$$

c. Since $g(x) = x - 1$, we make the substitution

$$f[g(x)] = f(x - 1) = (x - 1)^2 = x^2 - 2x + 1$$

d. Since $f(x) = x^2$, we make the substitution

$$g[f(x)] = g(x^2) = x^2 - 1$$

Note that in general, $f[g(x)] \neq g[f(x)]$, or equivalently $(f \circ g)(x) \neq (g \circ f)(x)$.

Example 3 Composition of Two Functions

Given $f(x) = \sqrt{x} + 1$ and $g(x) = x - 1$, find the following.

a. $(f \circ g)(x)$ b. $(g \circ f)(x)$

c. the domain of $f(x)$ d. the domain of $g(x)$

e. the domain of $(f \circ g)(x)$ f. the domain of $(g \circ f)(x)$

Solution

a. $(f \circ g)(x) = f[g(x)] = f(x - 1) = \sqrt{x - 1} + 1$

b. $(g \circ f)(x) = g[f(x)] = g(\sqrt{x} + 1) = (\sqrt{x} + 1) - 1 = \sqrt{x}$

c. If $f(x) = \sqrt{x} + 1$ is to be a real number, the domain is $\{x \mid x \geq 0\}$.

d. The domain of $g(x) = x - 1$ is the set of all real numbers.

e. If $(f \circ g)(x) = \sqrt{x - 1} + 1$ is to be a real number, then we must have $x - 1 \geq 0$, so its domain is $\{x \mid x \geq 1\}$.

f. If $(g \circ f)(x) = \sqrt{x}$ is to be a real number, then its domain is $\{x \mid x \geq 0\}$.

(Verify that the only value for which $(f \circ g)(x) = (g \circ f)(x)$ in this example is $x = 1$.) ■

✔ Progress Check
Given $f(x) = x^2 - 2x$ and $g(x) = 3x$, find the following.

a. $f[g(-1)]$ b. $g[f(-1)]$ c. $f[g(x)]$

d. $g[f(x)]$ e. $(f \circ g)(2)$ f. $(g \circ f)(2)$

Answers

a. 15   b. 9   c. $9x^2 - 6x$

d. $3x^2 - 6x$ e. 24   f. 0

Example 4   Composition of Two Functions
Find two functions $f(x)$ and $g(x)$, such that $h(x) = (f \circ g)(x)$ where $h(x) = (5x - 2)^8$.

Solution
One way to examine $h(x) = (5x - 2)^8$ is to focus on what happens inside the parentheses, namely, $5x - 2$. After we find the value of $5x - 2$, we raise that value to the eighth power. Thus, if we let $g(x) = 5x - 2$ and $f(x) = x^8$, we obtain

$$(f \circ g)(x) = f[g(x)] = f[5x - 2] = (5x - 2)^8 = h(x)$$

✔ Progress Check
Find two functions $f(x)$ and $g(x)$, such that $h(x) = (f \circ g)(x)$ where

$$h(x) = \frac{2}{7 - x}$$

Answer

$f(x) = \dfrac{2}{x}, g(x) = 7 - x$

One-to-One Functions

An element in the range of a function may correspond to more than one element in the domain of the function. In Figure 52, we see that y in Y corresponds to both x_1 and x_2 in X. If we demand that every element in the domain be assigned to a *different* element of the range, then the function is called **one-to-one**. More formally:

A function f is one to one if $f(a) = f(b)$ only when $a = b$.

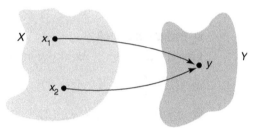

Figure 52   Correspondence of a Function that is not One-to-One

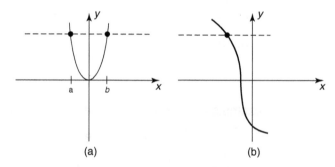

(a)   (b)

Figure 53   Horizontal Line Test: (a) is Not One-to-One, (b) is One-to-One

There is a simple means of determining if a function f is one-to-one by examining the graph of the function. In Figure 53(a), we see that a horizontal line meets the graph in more than one point. Thus, $f(a) = f(b)$ although $a \neq b$; hence the function is not one-to-one. On the other hand, no horizontal line meets the graph in Figure 53(b) in more than one point; the graph thus determines a one-to-one function. In summary, we have the following test.

Horizontal Line Test
If no horizontal line meets the graph of a function in more than one point, then the function is one-to-one.

Example 5   Determining One-to-One Functions
Which of the graphs in Figure 54 are graphs of one-to-one functions?

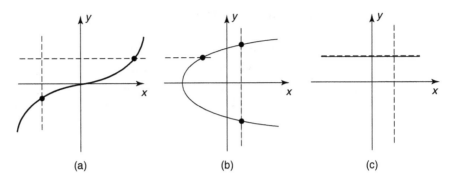

Figure 54   Determining One-to-One Functions with the Horizontal Line Test

Solution

a. No *vertical* line meets the graph in more than one point, hence, it is the graph of a function. No *horizontal* line meets the graph in more than one point, hence, it is the graph of a one-to-one function.

b. Although no *horizontal* line meets the graph in more than one point, at least one *vertical* line does meet the graph in more than one point. It is therefore not the graph of a function and consequently not the graph of a one-to-one function.

c. No *vertical* line meets the graph in more than one point, hence, it is the graph of a function. However, at least one *horizontal* line does meet the graph in more than one point. This is the graph of a function but not of a one-to-one function. ■

✔ Progress Check

Which of the graphs in Figure 55 are graphs of one-to-one functions?

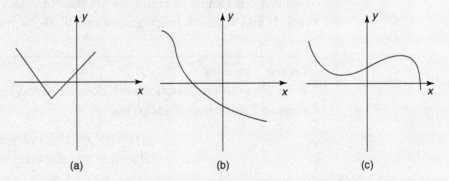

Figure 55   Determining One-to-One Functions with the Horizontal Line Test

Answer

(b)

Inverse Functions

Suppose the function *f* in Figure 56(a) is a one-to-one function and that $y = f(x)$. Since *f* is one-to-one, we know that the correspondence is unique, that is, *x* in *X* is the *only* element of the domain for which $y = f(x)$. It is then possible to define a function *g* as shown in Figure 56(b) with domain *Y* and range *X* that reverses the correspondence, that is,

$$g(y) = x \quad \text{for every } x \text{ in } X$$

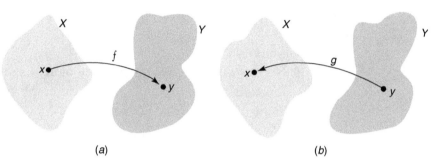

(a)   (b)

Figure 56   Correspondence of Inverse Functions

If we substitute $y = f(x)$, we have

$$g[f(x)] = x \quad \text{for every } x \text{ in } X \tag{1}$$

Substituting $g(y) = x$ in the equation $f(x) = y$ yields

$$f[g(y)] = y \quad \text{for every } y \text{ in } Y \tag{2}$$

The functions *f* and *g* of Figure 56 are therefore seen to satisfy the properties of Equations (1) and (2). Such functions are called inverse functions.

Inverse Functions

If *f* is a one-to-one function with domain *X* and range *Y*, then the function *g* with domain *Y* and range *X* satisfying

$$g[f(x)] = x \quad \text{for every } x \text{ in } X$$
$$f[g(y)] = y \quad \text{for every } y \text{ in } Y$$

is called an **inverse function** of *f*.

It can be proven that the inverse of a one-to-one function is unique. (See Exercise 63.)

Since the multiplicative inverse of a real number $x \neq 0$ can be written as x^{-1}, it seems reasonable to write the inverse of a function *f* as f^{-1}. Thus, we have

$$f^{-1}[f(x)] = x \quad \text{for every } x \text{ in } X$$
$$f[f^{-1}(y)] = y \quad \text{for every } y \text{ in } Y$$

Equivalently,

$$y = f(x) \text{ and } x = f^{-1}(y) \quad \text{for every } x \text{ in } X, \text{ every } y \text{ in } Y$$

Figure 57 is a graphical representation.

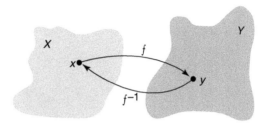

Figure 57   Correspondence for Inverse Functions
and One-to-One Functions

We can define the inverse function of f only if f is one-to-one.

Example 6   *Composition of Two Functions*
Given $f(x) = x + 5$ and $g(x) = x - 5$, find $(f \circ g)(x)$ and $(g \circ f)(x)$.

Solution

$$(f \circ g)(x) = f[g(x)] = f[x - 5] = (x - 5) + 5 = x$$
$$(g \circ f)(x) = g[f(x)] = g[x + 5] = (x + 5) - 5 = x$$

In Example 6, we have shown that $f[g(x)] = x$ and $g[f(x)] = x$. Therefore, we may conclude that $f^{-1}(x) = x - 5$ and $g^{-1}(x) = x + 5$.

✔ **Progress Check**
Given $f(x) = 5x$ and $g(x) = \frac{x}{5}$, find

a. $(f \circ g)(x)$ b. $(g \circ f)(x)$

c. Does $f^{-1}(x)$ exist?   d. Does $g^{-1}(x)$ exist?

Answers
a. x b. x c. Yes   d. Yes

Example 7   Verification of Inverse Functions

Let f be the function defined by

$$f(x) = x^2 - 4, \quad x \geq 0$$

Verify that the inverse of f is given by

$$f^{-1}(x) = \sqrt{x + 4}$$

Solution
We must verify that $f[f^{-1}(x)] = x$ and $f^{-1}[f(x)] = x$. Thus,

$$f[f^{-1}(x)] = f(\sqrt{x + 4})$$
$$= (\sqrt{x + 4})^2 - 4$$
$$= x + 4 - 4 = x$$

and

$$f^{-1}[f(x)] = f^{-1}(x^2 - 4)$$
$$= \sqrt{(x^2 - 4) + 4}$$
$$= \sqrt{x^2} = |x|$$

Since $x \geq 0$,

$$f^{-1}[f(x)] = |x| = x$$

We have verified that the equations defining inverse functions hold, and we conclude that the inverse of f is as given. Verify that: (a) the domain of f is the set of all real numbers in the interval $[0, \infty)$, and the range of f is the set of all real numbers in the interval $[-4, \infty)$; (b) the domain of f^{-1} is the range of f, and the range of f^{-1} is the domain of f. ■

It is sometimes possible to find an inverse by algebraic methods, as shown in the following example.

Example 8   Finding Inverse Functions

Find the inverse function of $f(x) = 2x - 3$.

Solution
If $f^{-1}(x)$ exists, then $y = f(x)$ implies that $x = f^{-1}(y)$. Thus,

$$y = f(x) = 2x - 3$$

and solving for x

$$2x - 3 = y$$
$$2x = y + 3$$
$$x = \frac{y + 3}{2}$$

But if $x = f^{-1}(y)$ and

$$x = \frac{y + 3}{2}$$

then

$$f^{-1}(y) = \frac{y + 3}{2}$$

We verify that

$$f^{-1}[f(x)] = f^{-1}(2x - 3) = \frac{(2x - 3) + 3}{2} = \frac{2x}{2} = x$$

and

$$f[f^{-1}(x)] = f\left[\frac{x + 3}{2}\right] = 2\left(\frac{x + 3}{2}\right) - 3 = x + 3 - 3 = x$$

In Table 4, we summarize a method for finding the inverse of a function when that inverse exists. We illustrate this method using an example to find the inverse of $f(x) = x^5 + 4$.

Table 4   To Find the Inverse of a Function

Method	Example
Step 1. Given the function $f(x)$, set $y = f(x)$.	*Step 1.* $y = f(x) = x^5 + 4$
Step 2. If possible, solve for x in terms of y, that is, $x = g(y)$.	*Step 2.* $x = \sqrt[5]{y - 4} = g(y)$
Step 3. The function g is the inverse of f. Using the same variable we write $g(x) = f^{-1}(x)$.	*Step 3.* $g(y) = f^{-1}(y) = \sqrt[5]{y - 4}$ Therefore, $$f^{-1}(x) = \sqrt[5]{y - 4}$$

There are some inverses that cannot be found using the method from Table 4. Sometimes, the inverse must be "created." (See Section 6.3.)

The inverse of a function that is not one-to-one does not exist. However, by restricting the domain of that function to where it is one-to-one, we are able to find the inverse of the restricted function

Consider the function $f(x)$ defined in the table below.

x	$f(x)$
1	4
2	5
3	4

Since $f(1) = 4$ and $f(3) = 4$ this function is not one-to-one. Let $g(x)$ denote the restriction of $f(x)$ to the domain $\{1, 2\}$.

x	$g(x)$
1	4
2	5

The function $g(x)$ is one-to-one, hence its inverse $g^{-1}(x)$ exists.

x	$g^{-1}(x)$
4	1
5	2

Consider $h(x) = x^2 - 4$. This function is not one-to-one since $h(2) = 0$ and $h(-2) = 0$. However, let us call $f(x)$ the restriction of $h(x)$ to $x \geq 0$, that is,

$$f(x) = x^2 - 4, \qquad x \geq 0$$

In Example 7, we verified that $f^{-1}(x) = \sqrt{x + 4}$. Similarly, let us call $g(x)$ the restriction of $h(x)$ to $x \leq 0$, that is,

$$g(x) = x^2 - 4, \qquad x \leq 0$$

Verify that $g^{-1}(x) = -\sqrt{x + 4}$. We show the graphs of $f(x)$, $g(x)$ and $h(x)$ in Figure 58.

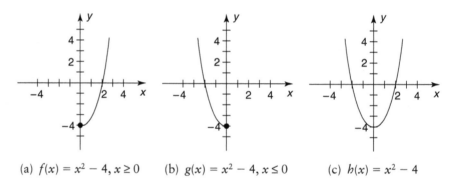

(a) $f(x) = x^2 - 4, x \geq 0$ (b) $g(x) = x^2 - 4, x \leq 0$ (c) $h(x) = x^2 - 4$

Figure 58   Graphs of $f(x)$, $g(x)$ and $h(x)$

✔ Progress Check

Given $f(x) = 3x + 5$, find f^{-1}.

Answer

$$f^{-1}(x) = \frac{x - 5}{3}$$

We may also think of the function f defined by $y = f(x)$ as the set of all ordered pairs $(x, f(x))$, where x assumes all values in the *domain* of f. Since the inverse function reverses the correspondence, the function f^{-1} is the set of all ordered pairs $(f(x), x)$, where $f(x)$ assumes all values in the *range* of f. With this approach, we see that the graphs of inverse functions are related in a specific manner. First, note that the points (a, b) and (b, a) in Figure 59(a) are located symmetrically with respect to the graph of the line $y = x$. That is, if we fold the paper along the line $y = x$, the two points will coincide. Furthermore, if (a, b) lies on the graph of the function f, then (b, a) must lie on the graph f^{-1}. Therefore,

> The graphs of a function and its inverse are **reflections of each other about the line** $y = x$. Furthermore, if f^{-1} is the inverse of the function f, then the inverse of f^{-1} is f itself.

In Figure 59(b), we have sketched the graphs of the functions from Example 7 on the same coordinate axes to demonstrate this relationship.

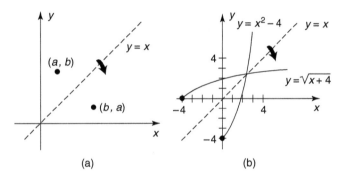

Figure 59   Graphs of Inverse Functions as Reflections about $y = x$

Warning

Although the notation f^{-1} for the inverse of f may have come from x^{-1}, the notation for the multiplicative inverse of x, it is important to avoid the possible confusion with the fact that

$$x^{-1} = \frac{1}{x}$$

a. In general,

$$f^{-1}(x) \neq \frac{1}{f(x)}$$

For example, if $g(x) = x - 1$, then

$$g^{-1}(x) \neq \frac{1}{x - 1}$$

In fact, using the methods of this section, we can show that

$$g^{-1}(x) = x + 1$$

b. The inverse function notation is *not* to be thought of as a power.

c. To avoid additional confusion, we may write

$$\frac{1}{f(x)} = [f(x)]^{-1}$$

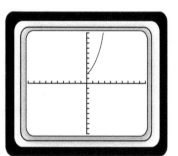

Graphing Calculator Power User's Corner

Graphing Inverse Functions

If your graphing calculator has a parametric grapher, you can graph inverse relations by following the steps listed below for $f(x) = x^2 - 4$, $x \geq 0$. These steps can be modified for other functions.

1. Set the WINDOW values to $-5 \leq X \leq 5$, $-5 \leq Y \leq 5$ and $0 \leq T \leq 5$.

2. To display $y = f(x) = x^2 - 4$, GRAPH

$$x = t \quad \text{and} \quad y = t^2 - 4$$

3. To display the inverse function $y = f^{-1}(x)$, or equivalently, $x = f(y)$, GRAPH

$$x = t^2 - 4 \quad \text{and} \quad y = t$$

4. To display (a portion of) the line $y = x$, GRAPH

$$x = t \quad \text{and} \quad y = t$$

Using the DRAW feature, you may be able to DRAW INVERSE for a given function.

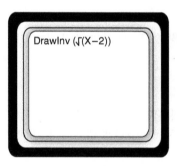

Exercise Set 3.5

In Exercises 1–10, $f(x) = x^2 + 1$ and $g(x) = x - 2$. Determine the following:

1. $(f + g)(x)$
2. $(f + g)(2)$
3. $(f - g)(x)$
4. $(f - g)(3)$
5. $(f \cdot g)(x)$
6. $(f \cdot g)(-1)$
7. $\left(\dfrac{f}{g}\right)(x)$
8. $\left(\dfrac{f}{g}\right)(-2)$
9. the domains of f and of g
10. the domains of $\dfrac{f}{g}$ and of $\dfrac{g}{f}$

In Exercises 11–18, $f(x) = 2x + 1$ and $g(x) = 2x^2 + x$. Determine the following:

11. $(f \circ g)(x)$
12. $(g \circ f)(x)$
13. $(f \circ g)(2)$
14. $(g \circ f)(3)$
15. $(f \circ g)(x + 1)$
16. $(f \circ f)(-2)$
17. $(g \circ f)(x - 1)$
18. $(g \circ g)(x)$

In Exercises 19–24, $f(x) = x^2 + 4$ and $g(x) = \sqrt{x + 2}$. Determine the following:

19. $(f \circ g)(x)$
20. $(g \circ f)(x)$

21. $(f \circ f)(-1)$

22. the domain of $(f \circ g)(x)$

23. the domain of $(g \circ f)(x)$

24. the domain of $(g \circ g)(x)$

In Exercises 25–28, determine $(f \circ g)(x)$ and $(g \circ f)(x)$.

25. $f(x) = x - 1, \quad g(x) = x + 2$

26. $f(x) = \sqrt{x + 1}, \quad g(x) = x + 2$

27. $f(x) = \dfrac{1}{x + 1}, \quad g(x) = \dfrac{1}{x - 1}$

28. $f(x) = \dfrac{x + 1}{x - 1}, \quad g(x) = x$

In Exercises 29–38, write the given function $h(x)$ as a composite of two functions f and g so that $h(x) = (f \circ g)(x)$. (There may be more than one answer.)

29. $h(x) = x^2 + 3$

30. $h(x) = \dfrac{1}{x + 2}$

31. $h(x) = (3x + 2)^8$

32. $h(x) = (x^3 + 2x^2 + 1)^{15}$

33. $h(x) = (x^3 - 2x^2)^{1/3}$

34. $h(x) = \left(\dfrac{x^2 + 2x}{x^3 - 1}\right)^{3/2}$

35. $h(x) = |x^2 - 4|$

36. $h(x) = |x^2 + x| - 4$

37. $h(x) = \sqrt{4 - x}$

38. $h(x) = \sqrt{2x^2 - x + 2}$

In Exercises 39–44, verify that $g = f^{-1}$ for the given functions f and g by showing that $f[g(x)] = x$ and $g[f(x)] = x$.

39. $f(x) = 2x + 4, \quad g(x) = \dfrac{1}{2}x - 2$

40. $f(x) = 3x - 2, \quad g(x) = \dfrac{1}{3}x + \dfrac{2}{3}$

41. $f(x) = 2 - 3x, \quad g(x) = -\dfrac{1}{3}x + \dfrac{2}{3}$

42. $f(x) = x^3, \quad g(x) = \sqrt[3]{x}$

43. $f(x) = \dfrac{1}{x}, \quad g(x) = \dfrac{1}{x}$

44. $f(x) = \dfrac{1}{x - 2}, \quad g(x) = \dfrac{1}{x} + 2$

In Exercises 45–52, find $f^{-1}(x)$. Sketch the graphs of $y = f(x)$ and $y = f^{-1}(x)$ on the same coordinate axes.

45. $f(x) = 2x + 3$

46. $f(x) = 3x - 4$

47. $f(x) = 3 - 2x$

48. $f(x) = \dfrac{1}{2}x + 1$

49. $f(x) = \dfrac{1}{3}x - 5$

50. $f(x) = 2 - \dfrac{1}{5}x$

51. $f(x) = x^3 + 1$

52. $f(x) = \dfrac{1}{x + 1}$

53. Determine which functions are one-to-one.

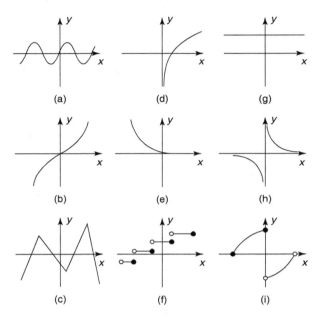

(a) (d) (g)

(b) (e) (h)

(c) (f) (i)

54. Modify the example in the Graphing Calculator Power User's Corner to display

 a. $y = 3x + 5$ and its inverse in the viewing rectangle $-10 \leq X \leq 10, -10 \leq Y \leq 10$ with $-10 \leq T \leq 10$.

 b. $y = x^5 + 4$ and its inverse in the viewing rectangle $-10 \leq X \leq 10, -10 \leq Y \leq 10$ with $-10 \leq T \leq 10$.

In Exercises 55–62, use the horizontal line test to determine whether the given function is a one-to-one function.

55. $f(x) = 2x - 1$

56. $f(x) = 3 - 5x$

57. $f(x) = x^2 - 2x + 1$

58. $f(x) = x^2 + 4x + 4$

59. $f(x) = -x^3 + 1$

60. $f(x) = x^3 - 2$

61. $f(x) = \begin{cases} 2x & \text{if} & x \leq -1 \\ x^2 & \text{if} & -1 < x \leq 0 \\ 3x - 1 & \text{if} & x > 0 \end{cases}$

62. $f(x) = \begin{cases} x^2 - 4x + 4 & \text{if} & x \leq 2 \\ x & \text{if} & x > 2 \end{cases}$

63. Prove that a one-to-one function can have at most one inverse function. (*Hint*: Assume that the functions g and h are both inverses of the function f. Show that $g(x) = h(x)$ for all real values x in the range of f.)

64. Prove that the linear function $f(x) = ax + b$ is a one-to-one function if $a \neq 0$, and is not a one-to-one function if $a = 0$.

65. Find the inverse of the linear function $f(x) = ax + b$, $a \neq 0$.

66. Find two restrictions of the function $f(x) = |x + 3|$ that would allow it to have an inverse. Find the two inverses corresponding to these restrictions.

67. The boiling point of toluene is 230° on the Fahrenheit scale and 110° on the Celsius scale. The freezing point of toluene is $-139°F$ and $-95°C$.

    a. Express degrees Celsius C as a function of degrees Fahrenheit F.

    b. Express degrees Fahrenheit F as a function of degrees Celsius C, by finding the inverse of the expression found in part (a).

68. The number of pairs q of sneakers manufactured in a day is a function of the number of working sewing machines m. A certain sneaker manufacturer finds the relationship to be as follows: $q = f(m) = 32m$. The total revenue r from selling these sneakers can be defined by: $r = g(q) = 30q$.

    a. Find $(g \circ f)(m)$.

    b. Interpret $(g \circ f)(m)$.

69. The number of computers n a computer firm is willing to produce is a function of the price p_c it can get for selling each unit. This relationship is called the supply equation, and it is given as $n = f(p_c) = 20p_c - 5000$ for this computer manufacturer. The price per computer p_c is a function of the price of microchips p_m given as $p_c = g(p_m) = \frac{4000}{p_m}$.

    a. Find $(f \circ g)(p_m)$.

    b. Interpret $(f \circ g)(p_m)$.

70. The Jazzy Jewel Company designs and manufactures gold earrings. The company's fixed costs, those independent of the level of production, are given by $C_F = f(p) = 12,500$. The variable costs, those directly related to the level of production, are a function of the price p of gold, and are given by $C_V = g(p) = 12p$.

    a. Find $(f + g)(p)$.

    b. Interpret $(f + g)(p)$.

71. The Pirates Baseball Club Store's total costs C_T is a function of the number of items n stocked in the store, and is given by $C_T = f(n) = 5500 + 2.5n$. The revenue R earned by the Pirates Store is given by $R = g(n) = 22.5n$.

    a. Find $(g - f)(n)$.

    b. What relationship does $(g - f)(n)$ define?

    c. Find $(g - f)500)$ and $(g - f)(250)$. Explain your results.

    d. Find the value of n that makes $(g - f)(n) = 0$.

    e. What information is gained by the Pirates Baseball Club Store by knowing the result of part (d)?

72. A ball is thrown off a cliff above a lake. At any time t in seconds, the distance d the ball is above the surface of the lake can be described by $r = f(t) = 112 + 96t + 16t^2$. The depth of the lake directly below the ball can be described by $d = g(t) = 1000 - 10t^2$.

    a. Find $(f + g)(t)$.

    b. Interpret $(f + g)(t)$.

    c. How many feet above the bottom of the lake is the ball after 4 seconds?

    d. When does the ball hit the water?

    e. How many feet above the bottom of the lake is the top of the cliff?

 73. Enter the function as shown.

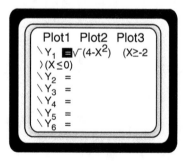

Now using the DRAW menu, select Draw Inverse and look at the graph of the inverse function. How would inverse differ if we graphed over the interval $0 \leq x \leq 2$ instead?

Applications

1. The regular price of a book is x dollars. Let $f(x) = x - 10$ and $g(x) = 0.7x$.

a. If the regular price of a math book is $98.00. Find $f(98)$ and $g(98)$. Please interpret your answers.

b. Describe what functions $f(x)$ and $g(x)$ model in terms of the price of the book.

c. Find $(f \circ g)(x)$ and describe the model in terms of the price of the book.

d. Repeat part (b) for $(g \circ f)(x)$.

e. Which composite function models a greater discount on the book, $(f \circ g)(x)$ or $(g \circ f)(x)$? Explain your answer.

2. Curry College Student Center organized a T-shirt sale event to raise money for the tsunami victims in Japan. They ordered T-shirts from BuyTShirts.com with each T-shirt costing $5 and $60 for the delivery charge. Curry College Student Center decided to sell each T-shirt at $8.

a. What is the cost function?

b. What is the revenue function?

c. What is the profit function?

d. Find the breakeven point and explain your answer.

e. If 450 T-shirts were ordered and sold, find the amount of money that we collected for tsunami victims in Japan.

f. Sketch the profit function. Find and interpret the x-intercept and the y-intercept.

3. The number of pairs of jeans Q manufactured in a day is a function of the number of working sewing machines m. Great Jeans manufacturer finds the relationship to be as follows: $Q = f(m) = 25m$. The total revenue R from selling these pairs of jeans can be defined by: $R = g(Q) = 35Q$.

a. Interpret the functions $f(m)$ and $g(Q)$.

b. If the manufacturer has 40 sewing machines, find the number of pairs of jeans the company can produce in a day?

c. Use your answer from part (b), find the total revenue by selling these pairs of jeans.

d. Find and interpret $(g \circ f)(40)$.

e. Find and interpret $(g \circ f)(m)$.

f. Find $(f \circ g)(m)$ as an expression of a function.

g. Can you explain the meaning of $(f \circ g)(m)$ to the CEO of Great Jeans? Explain your answer.

4. The formula $F = f(C) = \frac{9}{5}C + 32$ is used to convert from C degrees Celsius to F degrees Fahrenheit. The formula $C = g(F) = \frac{5}{9}(F - 32)$ is used to convert from F degrees Fahrenheit to C degrees Celsius. Show that these two functions are inverse functions.

5. A couple planning their anniversary party has found that the cost to hire a caterer for the reception depends on the number of guests attending. If 50 people attend, the cost per person will be $25. For each person less than 50, the cost will increase by $4. Assume that no more than 50 people will attend. Let x represent the number less than 50 who do not attend. For example, if 42 attend, $x = 8$.

a. Write a function defined by $N(x)$ giving the number of guests.

b. Write a function defined by $G(x)$ giving the cost per guest.

c. What is the total cost if 40 people attend?

d. Write a function which models the total cost of the anniversary party.

6. A book author invests her royalties in two accounts for one year.

a. The first account pays 5% simple interest. If she invests x dollars in this account, write an expression for y_1 in terms of x, where y_1 represents the amount of interest earned.

b. She invests in the second account $800 less than she invested in the first account. The second account pays 3% simple interest. Write an expression for y_2, where y_2 represents the amount of interest earned from the second account.

c. What does $y_1 + y_2$ represent?

d. How much interest will she receive if $2000 is invested in the first account?

3.6 Direct and Inverse Variation

Direct Variation

There are two functional relationships that occur so frequently that they are given distinct names: direct and inverse variation. We say that two positive quantities *vary directly* if an increase in one causes a proportional increase in the other. In the table

x	1	2	3	4
y	3	6	9	12

we see that an increase in x causes a proportional increase in y. If we look at the ratios $\frac{y}{x}$, we see that

$$\frac{y}{x} = \frac{3}{1} = \frac{6}{2} = \frac{9}{3} = \frac{12}{4} = 3$$

or $y = 3x$. The ratio $\frac{y}{x}$ remains constant for all values of $x \neq 0$ and $y \neq 0$. This is an example of the principle of **direct variation**. This principle may be extended to include all real numbers through the following definition.

Principle of Direct Variation
If y varies directly as x, then $y = kx$ for some constant k.

As another example, when we say that y varies directly as the square of x, we mean that $y = kx^2$ for some constant k. The constant k is called the **constant of variation**.

Example 1   Direct Variation
Suppose that y varies directly as the cube of x and that $y = 24$ when $x = -2$. Write the appropriate equation, solve for the constant of variation k and use this k to relate the variables.

Solution
From the principle of direct variation, we know that the functional relationship is

$$y = kx^3 \qquad \text{for some constant } k$$

Substituting the values $y = 24$ and $x = -2$, we have

$$24 = k(-2)^3 = -8k$$
$$k = -3$$

Thus,

$$y = -3x^3$$

a. If P varies directly as the square of V, and $P = 64$ when $V = 16$, find the constant of variation.

b. The circumference C of a circle varies directly as the radius r. If $C = 25.13$ when $r = 4$, express C as a function of r, that is, use the constant of variation to relate the variables C and r.

Answers

a. $\dfrac{1}{4}$ b. $C = 6.2825r$

Inverse Variation

Two positive quantities are said to *vary inversely* if an increase in one causes a proportional decrease in the other In the table

x	1	2	3	4
y	24	12	8	6

we see that an increase in x causes a proportional decrease in y. If we look at the product xy, we see that

$$xy = 1 \cdot 24 = 2 \cdot 12 = 3 \cdot 8 = 4 \cdot 6 = 24$$

or

$$y = \frac{24}{x}$$

In general, the principle of **inverse variation** may be extended to include all real numbers as follows.

Principle of Inverse Variation

If y varies inversely as x, then $y = \dfrac{k}{x}$ for some constant k.

Once again, k is called the constant of variation.

Example 2   Inverse Variation

Suppose that y varies inversely as x^2 and that $y = 10$ when $x = 10$. Write the appropriate equation, solve for the constant of variation k and use this k to relate the variables.

Solution

The functional relationship is

$$y = \frac{k}{x^2} \qquad \text{for some constant } k$$

Substituting $y = 10$ and $x = 10$, we have

$$10 = \frac{k}{(10)^2} = \frac{k}{100}$$

$$k = 1000$$

Thus,

$$y = \frac{1000}{x^2}$$

✔ Progress Check

If v varies inversely as the cube of w, and $v = 2$ when $w = -2$, find the constant of variation.

Answer

-16

Joint Variation

An equation of variation can involve more than two variables. We say that a quantity *varies jointly* as two or more other quantities if it varies directly as their product.

Example 3   Joint Variation

Express the following statement as an equation: P varies jointly as R, S and the square of T.

Solution

Since P must vary directly as RST^2, we have $P = kRST^2$ for some constant k.

Example 4   Joint Variation and Word Problems

A snow removal firm finds that the annual profit P varies jointly as the number of available plows p and the square of the total inches of snowfall s and inversely as the price per gallon of gasoline g. If the profit is $15,000 when the snowfall is 6 inches, 5 plows are used, and the price of gasoline is $1.50 per gallon, express the profit P as a function of s, p and g.

Solution

We are given that

$$P = k\frac{ps^2}{g}$$

for some constant k. To determine k, we substitute $P = 15,000$, $p = 5$, $s = 6$ and $g = 1.5$. Thus,

$$15,000 = k\frac{(5)(6)^2}{1.5} = 120k$$

$$k = \frac{15,000}{120} = 125$$

Thus

$$P = 125\frac{ps^2}{g}$$

Exercise Set 3.6

1. In the following table, y varies directly with x.

x	2	3	4	6	8	12		
y	8	12	16	24			80	120

  a. Find the constant of variation.

  b. Write an equation showing that y varies directly with x.

  c. Fill in the blanks of the table.

2. In the accompanying table, y varies inversely with x.

x	1	2	3	6	9	12	15	18		
y	6	3	2	1	$\frac{2}{3}$				$\frac{1}{4}$	$\frac{1}{10}$

  a. Find the constant of variation.

  b. Write an equation showing that y varies inversely with x.

  c. Fill in the blanks of the table.

3. If y varies directly as x, and $y = -\frac{1}{4}$ when $x = 8$,

  a. find the constant of variation;

  b. find y when $x = 12$.

4. If C varies directly as the square of s, and $C = 12$ when $s = 6$,

  a. find the constant of variation;

  b. find C when $s = 9$.

5. If s varies directly as the square of t, and $s = 10$ when $t = 10$,

  a. find the constant of variation;

  b. find s when $t = 5$.

6. If V varies as the cube of T, and $V = 16$ when $T = 4$,

  a. find the constant of variation;

  b. find V when $T = 6$.

7. If y varies inversely as x, and $y = -\frac{1}{2}$ when $x = 6$,

  a. find the constant of variation;

  b. find y when $x = 12$.

8. If V varies inversely as the square of p, and $V = \frac{2}{3}$ when $p = 6$,

  a. find the constant of variation;

  b. find V when $p = 8$.

9. If K varies inversely as the cube of r, and $K = 8$ when $r = 4$,

  a. find the constant of variation;

  b. find K when $r = 5$.

10. If T varies inversely as the cube of u, and $T = 2$ when $u = 2$,

  a. find the constant of variation;

  b. find T when $u = 5$.

11. If M varies directly as the square of r and inversely as the square of s, and $M = 4$ when $r = 4$ and $s = 2$,

  a. write the appropriate equation relating M, r and s;

  b. find M when $r = 6$ and $s = 5$.

12. If f varies jointly as u and v, and $f = 36$ when $u = 3$ and $v = 4$,

  a. write the appropriate equation connecting f, u and v;

  b. find f when $u = 5$ and $v = 2$.

13. If T varies jointly as p and the cube of v, and inversely as the square of u, and $T = 24$ when $p = 3$, $v = 2$ and $u = 4$,

    a. write the appropriate equation connecting T, p, v and u;

    b. find T when $p = 2$, $v = 3$ and $u = 36$.

14. If A varies jointly as the square of b and the square of c, and inversely as the cube of d, and $A = 18$ when $b = 4$, $c = 3$ and $d = 2$,

    a. write the appropriate equation relating A, b, c and d;

    b. find A when $b = 9$, $c = 4$ and $d = 3$.

15. The distance s an object falls from rest in t seconds varies directly as the square of t. If an object falls 144 feet in 3 seconds,

    a. how far does it fall in 5 seconds?

    b. how long does it take to fall 784 feet?

16. In a certain state the income tax paid by a person varies directly as the income. If the tax is $20 per month when the monthly income is $1600, find the tax due when the monthly income is $900.

17. The resistance R of a conductor varies inversely as the area A of its cross section. If $R = 20$ ohms when $A = 8$ square centimeters, find R when $A = 12$ square centimeters.

18. The pressure P of a certain enclosed gas varies directly as the temperature T and inversely as the volume V. Suppose that 300 cubic feet of gas exert a pressure of 20 pounds per square foot when the temperature is 500 K (absolute temperature measured on the Kelvin scale). What is the pressure of this gas when the temperature is lowered to 400 K and the volume is increased to 500 cubic feet?

19. The intensity of illumination I from a source of light varies inversely as the square of the distance d from the source. If the intensity is 200 candlepower when the source is 4 feet away,

    a. what is the intensity when the source is 6 feet away?

    b. how close should the source be to provide an intensity of 50 candlepower?

20. The weight of a body in space varies inversely as the square of its distance from the center of the earth. If a body weighs 400 pounds on the surface of the earth, how much does it weigh 1000 miles from the surface of the earth? Assume that the radius of the earth is 4000 miles.

21. The equipment cost of a printing job varies jointly as the number of presses and the number of hours that the presses are run. When 4 presses are run for 6 hours, the equipment cost is $1200. If the equipment cost for 12 hours of running is $3600, how many presses are being used?

22. The current I in a wire varies directly as the electromotive force E and inversely as the resistance R. In a wire whose resistance is 10 ohms, a current of 36 amperes is obtained when the electromotive force is 120 volts. Find the current produced when $E = 220$ volts and $R = 30$ ohms.

23. The illumination from a light source varies directly as the intensity of the source and inversely as the square of the distance from the source. If the illumination is 50 candlepower per square foot on a screen 2 feet away from a light source whose intensity is 400 candlepower, what is the illumination 4 feet away from a source whose intensity is 3840 candlepower?

24. If f varies directly as u and inversely as the square of v, what happens to f if both u and v are doubled?

25. The intensity of light from a point source varies inversely with the square of the distance from the source.

    a. Express the equation of intensity I as a function of distance d.

    b. If the intensity 5.5 meters from the source is 3.80 watts per square meter, what is the intensity 4 meters from the source?

26. Hooke's Law says that the distance a spring is stretched varies directly as the weight of the object attached to the spring. A 5-kilogram weight stretches a spring 35 centimeters.

    a. Find the constant of variation.

b. If a 3-kilogram weight is attached to the spring, how far will the spring be stretched?

27. Some economists theorize that the Dow Jones Industrial Average (an index of stock prices) varies inversely as the price of oil. The Dow Jones Average was 2520 when the price of oil was $18.50 per barrel. After Iraq invaded Kuwait in 1990, the price of oil increased by $13.50 per barrel. What should the Dow Jones Industrial Average be if this theory is correct?

28. The amount of pollution emitted into the air in a particular city varies directly with the number of cars driven in that city. If 35,000 cars cause 1988 tons of pollutants, how many cars would cause 2644.04 tons of pollutants to enter the atmosphere?

29. The volume V of gas varies directly as the temperature T and inversely as the pressure P. The volume of a particular gas is 245 cubic centimeters when the temperature is 56°F and the pressure is 25 kilograms per cubic centimeter.

   a. Find the pressure of the gas when the volume is 210 cubic centimeters and the temperature is 45°F.

   b. Find the temperature of the gas when the pressure is 40 kilograms per cubic centimeter and the volume is 305 cubic centimeters.

30. Sociologists developed a model to determine the average number of telephone calls per day between two cities. The model states that the average number of phone calls varies jointly with the population P_1 in one city and the population P_2 in the other city, and inversely as the square of the distance between the two cities.

   a. Write the equation of variation.

   b. The population of Philadelphia is 1,642,900 and the population of Pittsburgh is 387,490. The distance between the two cities is 300 miles. The average

number of phone calls per day between these two cities is 10,200. Find the constant of variation.

   c. The population of Miami Beach is 373,940. The distance from Miami Beach to Jacksonville, Florida, is 350 miles and the population of Jacksonville is 309,860. Find the average number of phone calls per day between the two cities, if the constant of variation is the same as that found for part (b).

31. The load L that a beam supports varies jointly with its width w and with the square of its length l, and inversely as its depth d.

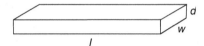

   a. Write the equation of variation.

   b. A 200 pound weight hangs safely from the center of a beam with dimensions 5 feet long by 3 inches wide by 4 inches deep. Find the constant of variation if all dimensions are measured in feet.

   c. What size weight would hang safely from a beam with dimensions 5 feet long by 6 inches wide by 2 inches deep?

   d. What is the effect on the load the beam can support if the width is doubled and the depth is halved?

   e. What is the effect on the load the beam can support if the length is doubled?

32. The intelligence quotient (IQ) varies directly as a person's mental age and varies inversely as a person's chronological age.

   a. Write the equation of variation.

   b. A child with 125 IQ has a mental age of 15 and a chronological age of 12. Find the constant of variation.

   c. If a 14-year-old child has an IQ of 135, what is the child's mental age?

Terms and Symbols

abscissa	coordinate axes	distance formula
Cartesian coordinate system	coordinates of a point	domain
composite function	decreasing function	$(f \circ g)(x)$
constant function	dependent variable	$f[g(x)]$
constant of variation	direct variation	function

$f(x)$

$f^{-1}(x)$

general first-degree equation

graph of a function

graph of an equation in two variables

horizontal line test

horizontal shift

image

increasing function

independent variable

inverse function

inverse variation

joint variation

line

linear function

midpoint formula

one-to-one function

ordered pair

ordinate

origin

parabola

piecewise-defined function

point–slope form

polynomial function

quadrant

quadratic function

range

rectangular coordinate system

reflection

slope

slope–intercept form

solution of an equation in two variables

symmetry

symmetry with respect to the origin

symmetry with respect to the x-axis

symmetry with respect to the y-axis

symmetry with respect to $y = x$

turning point

vertical line test

vertical shift

x-axis

x-coordinate

x-intercept

y-axis

y-coordinate

y-intercept

Key Ideas for Review

Topic	Key Idea
Rectangular Coordinate System	In a rectangular coordinate system, every ordered pair of real numbers (a, b) corresponds to a point in the plane, and every point in the plane corresponds to an ordered pair of real numbers.
Distance Formula	The distance $\overline{PQ}$ between points $P(x_1, y_1)$ and $Q(x_2, y_2)$ is given by the distance formula $$\overline{PQ} = \sqrt{(x_2 - x_1)^2 + (y_2 - y_1)^2}$$
Midpoint Formula	The coordinates (x_m, y_m) of the midpoint M of the line segment with endpoints $P(x_1, y_1)$ and $Q(x_2, y_2)$ are given by $$x_m = \frac{x_1 + x_2}{2} \qquad y_m = \frac{y_1 + y_2}{2}$$
Graphs of Equations	An equation in two variables can be graphed by plotting points that satisfy the equation and joining the points to form a smooth curve.
Functions	A function is a rule that assigns exactly one element y of a set Y to each element x of a set X. The domain is the set of inputs, and the range is the set of outputs.
Domain	The domain of a function is the set of all real numbers for which the function is defined. Beware of division by zero and of even roots of negative numbers.
Range	The range of a function is the set of all outputs corresponding to the domain of that function.
Various Definitions	A function may be defined by an equation. However, sometimes a function may be defined by a table, a chart or several equations. Moreover, not every equation defines a function.

Topic	Key Idea
Substitution	Function notation gives the definition of the function and also the value or expression at which to evaluate the function. If the function f is defined by $f(x) = x^2 + 2x$, then the notation $f(3)$ denotes the result of replacing the independent variable x by 3 wherever it appears: $$f(x) = x^2 + 2x$$ $$f(3) = 3^2 + 2(3) = 15$$
Vertical Line Test	A graph represents a function if and only if no vertical line meets the graph in more than one point.
Graphs	To graph $f(x)$, just graph $y = f(x)$.
Vertical Shift	If $p > 0$, the graph of $y = f(x) + p$ shifts the graph of $y = f(x)$ up p units, and the graph of $y = f(x) - p$ shifts the graph of $y = f(x)$ down p units.
Horizontal Shift	If $p > 0$, the graph of $y = f(x - p)$ shifts the graph of $y = f(x)$ p units to the right, and the graph of $y = f(x + p)$ shifts the graph of $y = f(x)$ p units to the left.
Reflection	The graph of $y = -f(x)$ is the reflection about the x-axis of the graph $y = f(x)$.
Piecewise Definition	The graph of a function can have holes or gaps, and can be defined in "pieces."
Increasing, Decreasing, Constant	As we move from left to right, the graph of an increasing function rises, whereas the graph of a decreasing function falls. The graph of a constant function neither rises nor falls; it is horizontal.
Polynomials	Polynomials in one variable are all functions and have "smooth" curves as their graphs.
Line	The graph of the linear function $f(x) = ax + b$ is a line.
Slope	Any two points on a line can be used to find its slope m: $$m = \frac{y_2 - y_1}{x_2 - x_1}$$
Rising and Falling	Positive slope indicates that a line is rising; negative slope indicates that a line is falling.
Horizontal and Vertical	The slope of a horizontal line is 0; the slope of a vertical line is undefined.
Point–Slope Form	The point–slope form of a line is $y - y_1 = m(x - x_1)$.
Slope–Intercept Form	The slope–intercept form of a line is $y = mx + b$.
Horizontal and Vertical Forms	The equation of the horizontal line through the point (a, b) is $y = b$; the equation of the vertical line through the point (a, b) is $x = a$.
Graphs	The graphs of the linear function $f(x) = ax + b$ and the general first-degree equation $Ax + By + C = 0$ are always lines if A and B are not both zero.
Parallel	Parallel lines have the same slope.

Topic	Key Idea
Perpendicular	The slopes of perpendicular lines are negative reciprocals of each other, with the exception of horizontal and vertical lines.
Algebra of Functions	Functions can be combined by the usual operations of addition, subtraction, multiplication and division.
Composition	A composite function is a function of a function.
One-to-One	We say a function is one-to-one if every element of the range corresponds to precisely one element of the domain.
Horizontal Line Test	No horizontal line meets the graph of a one-to-one function in more than one point.
Inverse Function	The inverse f^{-1} of a function reverses the correspondence defined by the function f. The domain of f becomes the range of f^{-1}, and the range of f becomes the domain of f^{-1}.
Properties	A function f and its inverse f^{-1} satisfy $$f^{-1}[f(x)] = x \quad \text{for all } x \text{ in the domain of } f$$ $$f[f^{-1}(y)] = y \quad \text{for all } y \text{ in the range of } f$$
One-to-One	The inverse of a function f is defined only if f is one-to-one.
Graph	The graphs of a function and its inverse are reflections of one another about the line $y = x$.
Inverse	The inverse of the inverse of a function is the function itself.
Variation	Direct and inverse variation are functional relationships.
Functional Forms	We say that y varies directly as x if $y = kx$ for some constant k; we say that y varies inversely as x if $y = \frac{k}{x}$ for some constant k.
Joint Variation	Joint variation is a term for direct variation involving more than two quantities.

Review Exercises

Solutions to exercises whose numbers are in **bold** are in the Solutions section in the back of the book.

1. Find the distance between the points $(-4, -6)$ and $(2, -1)$.

2. Find the length of the longest side of the triangle whose vertices are $A(3, -4)$, $B(-2, -6)$ and $C(-1, 2)$.

In Exercises 3 and 4, sketch the graph of the given equation by forming a table of values.

3. $y = 1 - |x|$ 4. $y = \sqrt{x - 2}$

In Exercises 5 and 6, analyze the given equation for symmetry with respect to the x-axis, y-axis and origin.

5. $y^2 = 1 - x^3$ 6. $y^2 = \dfrac{x^2}{x^2 - 5}$

In Exercises 7 and 8, state if the graph determines y to be a function of x.

7.

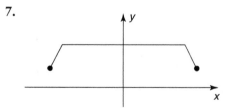

8.

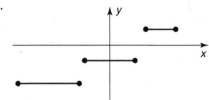

In Exercises 9 and 10 determine the domain of the given function.

9. $f(x) = \sqrt{3x - 5}$

10. $f(x) = \dfrac{x}{x^2 + 2x + 1}$

11. If $f(x) = \sqrt{x - 1}$, find a real number whose image is 15.

12. If $f(t) = t^2 + 1$, find all real numbers whose image is 10.

In Exercises 13–22, determine appropriate WINDOW values and GRAPH the given functions on your graphing calculator.

13. $y = 5x - 4$

14. $y = 3x^3 + 2$

15. $y = x - x^2$

16. $y = |x - x^2|$

17. $y = x - 3$

18. $y = |x - 3|$

19. $y = \dfrac{|x - 3|}{x - 3}$

20. $y = 2\sqrt{x} + 7$

21. $y = 2\sqrt{x + 7}$

22. $y = \dfrac{5}{x^2 + 1}$

In Exercises 23–25, $f(x) = x^2 - x$. Evaluate the following.

23. $f(-3)$

24. $f(y - 1)$

25. $\dfrac{f(2 + h) - f(2)}{h}$

Exercises 26–29 refer to the function f defined by

$$f(x) = \begin{cases} x - 1 & \text{if} \quad x \le -1 \\ x^2 & \text{if} \quad -1 < x \le 2 \\ -2 & \text{if} \quad x > 2 \end{cases}$$

26. Sketch the graph of the function f.

27. Determine where the function f is increasing, decreasing and constant.

28. Evaluate $f(-4)$.

29. Evaluate $f(4)$.

In Exercises 30–35, sketch the indicated graph, where the graph of $y = f(x)$ is

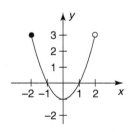

30. $y = f(x) + 3$

31. $y = f(x + 1)$

32. $y = -f(x)$

33. $y = |f(x)|$

34. $y = 2f(x)$

35. $y = \frac{1}{2}f(x) - 1$

In Exercises 36–41, the points A and B have coordinates $(-4, -6)$ and $(-1, 3)$, respectively.

36. Find the slope of the line through A and B.

37. Find an equation of the line through the points A and B.

38. Find an equation of the line through A that is parallel to the y-axis.

39. Find an equation of the horizontal line through B.

40. Find an equation of the line through A that is parallel to the line $4x - y - 3 = 0$.

41. Find an equation of the line through B that is perpendicular to the line $2y + x - 5 = 0$.

In Exercises 42–47, $f(x) = x + 1$ and $g(x) = x^2 - 1$. Determine the following:

42. $(f + g)(x)$

43. $(f \cdot g)(-1)$

44. $\left(\dfrac{f}{g}\right)(x)$

45. the domain of $\left(\dfrac{f}{g}\right)(x)$

46. $(g \circ f)(x)$

47. $(f \circ g)(2)$

In Exercises 48–51, $f(x) = \sqrt{x} - 2$ and $g(x) = x^2$. Determine the following.

48. $(f \circ g)(x)$

49. $(g \circ f)(x)$

50. $(f \circ g)(-2)$

51. $(g \circ f)(-2)$

In Exercises 52 and 53, $f(x) = 2x + 4$ and $g(x) = \frac{x}{2} - 2$.

52. Prove that f and g are inverse functions of each other.

53. Sketch the graphs of $y = f(x)$ and $y = g(x)$ on the same coordinate axes.

54. If R varies directly as q, and if $R = 20$ when $q = 5$, find R when $q = 40$.

55. If S varies inversely as the cube of t, and if $S = 8$ when $t = -1$, find S with $t = -2$.

56. P varies jointly as q and r and inversely as the square of t, and $P = -3$ when $q = 2$, $r = -3$ and $t = 4$. Find P when $q = -1$, $r = \frac{1}{2}$ and $t = 4$.

57. Jim has $10,000 to invest. He invests x dollars in tax-free municipal bonds yielding 8.5%. He invests 3 times

the amount he invested in the bonds in certificates of deposit earning 9%. Jim puts the remainder of the money in a savings account at an interest rate of 5.25%.

a. Express Jim's earned interest as a function of x.

b. How much total interest does Jim earn if he invests $3000 in certificates of deposit?

58. A well-known college uses students' SAT scores to predict their grade point averages (GPA) at the end of their first year of college. The following table gives some representative SAT scores and GPAs from the linear model the college uses.

SAT	950	975	1050
GPA	2.00	2.10	2.40

a. Express the GPA as a function of SAT scores.

b. Find the inverse function of part (a).

c. What score would a student have to get on the SATs so that the student's GPA would be 4.00?

59. One gram of water (H_2O) is made up of one part hydrogen (H) and eight parts oxygen (O).

a. Express the number of grams of hydrogen needed to form water as a function of the number of grams w of water.

b. Express the number of grams of oxygen needed to form water as a function of the number of grams w of water.

c. How much hydrogen and how much oxygen are needed to form 315 grams of water?

60. Ohm's Law states that the resistance R in ohms of a conductor varies directly as the voltage V in volts and inversely as the current I in amperes. Electrical power P in watts varies jointly as the current I and the voltage V. Assume the constants of variation are equal to one.

a. 120 volts operates a 1000-watt hairdryer. How much current does it draw and what is its resistance?

b. In the United States the standard voltage is 120 volts, whereas in European countries the standard is 240 volts. Hairdryers produced in the United States now have a switch permitting the use of this appliance in foreign countries. How much current does the hairdryer in part (a) draw in England and what is its resistance?

c. The resistance of a light bulb is 240 ohms. The standard voltage required to light the light bulb is 120 volts. How much current does it draw and what is the power of the light bulb?

Review Test

1. Find the perimeter of the triangle whose vertices are $(2, 5)$, $(-3, 1)$ and $(-3, 4)$.

2. Use symmetry to assist in sketching the graph of the equation $y = 2x^2 - 1$.

3. Analyze the equation $y = \frac{1}{x^3}$ for symmetry with respect to the axes and origin.

4. Determine the domain of the function
$$f(x) = \frac{1}{\sqrt{x} - 1}$$

5. If $f(x) = \sqrt{x - 1}$, find a real number whose image is 4.

6. If $f(x) = 2x^2 + 3$, find $f(2t)$.

Exercises 7–10 refer to the function f defined by

$$f(x) = \begin{cases} 0 & \text{if} \quad x < -2 \\ |x| & \text{if} \quad -2 \le x \le 3 \\ x^2 - x & \text{if} \quad x > 3 \end{cases}$$

7. Determine where the function f is increasing, decreasing and constant.

8. Evaluate $f(-5)$.

9. Evaluate $f(-2)$.

10. Sketch the graph of $y = \frac{1}{2}f(x + 1)$.

11. Find an equation of the line through the points $(-3, 5)$ and $(-5, 2)$.

12. Find an equation of the vertical line through the point $(-3, 4)$.

13. Find the slope m and y-intercept b of the line whose equation is $2y - x = 4$.

14. Find an equation of the line through the point $(4, -1)$ that is parallel to the x-axis.

15. Find an equation of the line that passes through the point $(-2, 3)$ and is perpendicular to the line
$$y - 3x - 2 = 0$$

In Exercises 16–18, $f(x) = \frac{1}{x-1}$ and $g(x) = x^2$. Find the following.

16. $(f - g)(2)$

17. $\left(\dfrac{g}{f}\right)(x)$

18. $(g \circ f)(3)$

19. Prove that $f(x) = -3x + 1$ and $g(x) = -\frac{1}{3}(x - 1)$ are inverse functions of each other.

20. If h varies directly as the cube of r, and $h = 2$ when $r = -\frac{1}{2}$, find h when $r = 4$.

21. T varies jointly as a and the square of b and inversely as the cube of c, and $T = 64$ when $a = -1$, $b = \frac{1}{2}$ and $c = 2$. Find T when $a = 2$, $b = 4$ and $c = -1$.

Cumulative Review Exercises: Chapters 1–3

In Exercises 1–5, determine if each expression is a polynomial.

1. $\sqrt{2}x^2 + 3x + \pi$

2. $2x^2 + \dfrac{3}{x} + 1$

3. $5x^2 + 3\sqrt{x} + 4$

4. $2x^2 + \dfrac{x}{3} + 1$

5. $-\dfrac{3}{4}$

In Exercises 6–8, simplify the given expressions.

6. $\sqrt[4]{a^8 b^6}$

7. $\dfrac{3}{7 - \sqrt{x}}$

8. $\left(\dfrac{a^2}{b^6}\right)^{1/2}\left(\dfrac{a^5}{b^{5/4}}\right)^{2/5}$

In Exercises 9 and 10, perform the indicated operations.

9. $\dfrac{3 - x}{x^3 + x} - \dfrac{x^2}{x^2 + 1}$

10. $\left(\dfrac{x^2 - 9}{2x^2 + 3x - 2}\right)\left(\dfrac{2x - 1}{3 - x}\right)$

11. Solve for u and v: $(5 - u) + (7v + 2)i = 10 + 9i$.

In Exercises 12–14, perform the indicated operations.

12. $(3 - 2i)^2$

13. $(2 + 4i)(3 - 5i)$

14. $(2 + i)^4(3 - i)^2$

In Exercises 15–18, simplify the expression and write the answer using only positive exponents.

15. $x^{5/2}(x^{-2/3} - 1)$

16. $\sqrt{12} - \sqrt{75} + 2\sqrt{27}$

17. $\dfrac{2}{x^2 - x} - \dfrac{2x}{x - 1}$

18. $\dfrac{x^{-2} + 1}{x^{-1} - 3}$

In Exercises 19 and 20, factor completely.

19. $3x^3 + x^2 - 2x$

20. $(x - 1)^{2/3} + 2(x - 1)^{5/3}$

21. Rationalize the denominator:
$$\dfrac{2}{\sqrt{x} - \sqrt{2}}$$

In Exercises 22–25, solve the inequality.

22. $3x - 2 \leq x + 3$

23. $|1 - 2h| > 2$

24. $2t^2 - 5t \geq 12$

25. $|x^2 - 3| \leq 2$

In Exercises 26 and 27, find the domain of the function.

26. $\dfrac{1}{\sqrt{2x - 1}}$

27. $\dfrac{x}{x^2 - 1}$

28. Find the length of the hypotenuse of the right triangle whose vertices are $(-2, 2)$, $(4, 2)$ and $(-2, -3)$.

29. Given $f(t) = 1 - t^2$,
   a. find $f(2a - 1)$.
   b. find all real numbers whose image is -15.
   c. find $\dfrac{f(t + h) - f(t)}{h}$

30. The function G is defined by
$$G(x) = \begin{cases} \frac{1}{2} & \text{if} & x < -2 \\ x & \text{if} & -2 \leq x \leq 2 \\ -x^2 & \text{if} & x > 2 \end{cases}$$
   a. Find $G(0)$.
   b. Find $G(-3)$.
   c. Graph $G(x)$.

31. A chemist has several mixtures, each containing alcohol. She has x liters of mixture A with 5% alcohol, y liters of mixture B with 7% alcohol and z liters of mixture C with $3\frac{1}{2}$% alcohol. Write an expression representing the total number of liters of alcohol in the three mixtures.

In Exercises 32–42, solve for x.

32. $2x^2 - x - 3 = 0$

33. $2x^2 - x + 19 = 15$

34. $\sqrt{x} + 12 = x$

35. $\dfrac{3 - 5x}{x + 2} = 4$

36. $6x^2 + 5x - 4 = 0$

37. $(3 - x)^2 - 16 = 0$

38. $x - \sqrt{-1 - 5x} = -3$

39. $-5 \le 1 - 4x \le 9$

40. $\left| \dfrac{x - 3}{2} \right| \ge 10$

41. $x^2 - 3x - 10 \le 0$

42. $\dfrac{3}{x - 2} \ge 1$

In Exercises 43 and 44, find the equation of the specified line.

43. The line is horizontal and passes through $(2, -1)$.

44. The line is perpendicular to $x = 4y + 1$ and passes through $(\frac{1}{2}, 2)$.

45. Given the points $A(3, -2)$ and $B(-1, 2)$, find

    a. the slope of the line through the points A and B.

    b. an equation of the line through the points A and B.

    c. an equation of the line through B parallel to the y-axis.

    d. an equation of the line through the point $C(-4, -1)$ that is perpendicular to the line AB.

46. The hypotenuse of a right triangle has a length of 20 inches. If one leg of the triangle is 3 times the other leg, what is the length of the shortest side of the triangle?

47. Find the intercepts of the parabola $f(x) = -3x^2 - x + 2$.

48. Find the equation of the line whose x- and y-intercepts are both a.

49. Ron borrows $12,000 from his father (who does not charge interest) to buy a new car. He determines that if he increases his monthly payment by $50, he will have 8 fewer payments. What is Ron's new monthly payment, and how long will it take him to satisfy his debt?

50. Four towns are located as shown in the figure below. The lines connecting the points on the graph represent the roads between the four towns. Jack lives in Hometown and has to go to Workville everyday. He can choose either to go through town A, Route 1, or town B, Route 2. If he chooses to drive to Workville using Route 1, his average speed is 50 mph. His average speed using Route 2 is 30 mph. Which route should he choose so that he arrives at Workville in a minimum amount of time?

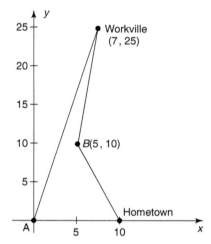

51. $P(x)$ represents the profit function of the Quark Textbook Company for sales of x copies of a book on advanced physics, where

$$P(x) = \begin{cases} \frac{1}{10}x^2 - 20x & \text{if} \quad 0 \le x \le 300 \\ -\frac{1}{10}x^2 + 120x - 24{,}000 & \text{if} \quad 300 < x \le 1000 \end{cases}$$

    a. What is the domain of $P(x)$?

    b. Sketch the graph of $P(x)$.

    c. Using the graph, determine:

       i. the range of $P(x)$

       ii. the number of books that maximizes $P(x)$

       iii. the maximum profit

    d. How many books does the Quark Textbook Company have to sell so that the company begins to make a profit?

52. The heat loss per hour through a glass window varies jointly as the area (A) of the window and the temperature difference (t_d) between the inside and outside temperatures, and varies inversely as the thickness (T) of the window.

a. A window measares 2 feet by 3 feet and is $\frac{1}{24}$ feet thick. The inside temperature is 68°F, and the outside temperature is 38°F. Find the constant of variation if 2592 calories of heat are conducted in 1 hour through the window.

b. The same window can conduct 3888 calories through it in 1 hour. What is the temperature difference?

Writing Exercises

1. Given the equation $y - y_1 = m(x - x_1)$, discuss how you would find the y-intercept.

2. Discuss how to use symmetry in sketching the graph of a function.

3. If we know the symmetries of the graph of a function that has an inverse, discuss the symmetries of the graph of the inverse function.

4. Discuss the relationship between the domain of $\frac{f}{g}$ with the domains of f and g.

5. Discuss in words the meaning of the following: The graph of a function is symmetric with respect to the x-axis, the y-axis or the origin.

Chapter 3 Project

At the beginning of this chapter, we mentioned a function that relates the number of times a cricket chirps in one minute to the outside temperature in degrees Fahrenheit. Here is that function (you have seen it several times!).

$$f(n) = \frac{n}{4} + 40$$

What would the temperature be if you heard 36 chirps in one minute? 52? Use your graphing calculator to set up a TABLE, pairing the inputs (number of chirps) with the outputs (temperature) for 10 values of n.

For this chapter's project, look back at the following Exercises:

- Section 3.2, Exercise 50

- Section 3.4, Exercises 75, 76, and 77

- Section 3.5, Exercise 73

Put these results together with your table, and answer the following question:

In your own words, explain how the concepts of *function, line, slope,* and *inverse* can be used to describe and predict phenomenon in the world around us.

Mathematics and biology go together well! The same could be said for physics, chemistry, or just about any branch of science. The concept of function is crucial to understanding how scientists model the real world with mathematics.

Explore the connections between mathematics and biology further at http://archives.math.utk.edu/mathbio/.

http://archives.math .utk.edu/mathbio/

Polynomial Functions

http://www.amstat.org,
http://www.awm-math
.org/, http://fcit.usf.edu
/math/websites
/general.html

The United States Postal Service allows a package to have a combined length and girth of up to 130 inches. (The girth is the perimeter around the widest part of the package.) Suppose I created a package by cutting squares out of the sides of a rectangle of cardboard, then folding up the sides. How big should the squares be to give me the largest possible volume? How big should they be to maximize the volume and the combined length and girth? (You will be asked to answer these questions in this chapter's project.) The solutions can be found using polynomials (in this case, cubic or degree three polynomials).

The facts about package volume discussed here suggest how useful mathematics is in many careers, including packaging. Are you fascinated by numbers, patterns, and statistics? Learn more about them (and some careers in mathematics) at http://www.amstat.org, http://www.awm-math.org/, and http://fcit.usf.edu/math/websites/general.html.

In Section 3.3 we observed that the polynomial function

$$f(x) = ax + b \tag{1}$$

is called a linear function and that the polynomial function

$$g(x) = ax^2 + bx + c, \quad a \neq 0 \tag{2}$$

is called a quadratic function. To facilitate the study of polynomial functions in general, we will use the notation

$$P(x) = a_n x^n + a_{n-1} x^{n-1} + \cdots + a_1 x + a_0, \quad a \neq 0 \tag{3}$$

to represent a **polynomial function of degree n,** where n is a nonnegative integer. Note that the subscript k of the coefficient a_k is the same as the exponent in x^k. In general, the coefficients a_k may be real or complex numbers. Although this chapter will focus on real values for a_k, we will indicate which results hold true when the coefficients a_k are complex numbers.

If $a \neq 0$ in Equation (1), we set the polynomial function equal to zero and obtain the linear equation

$$ax + b = 0$$

which has precisely one solution,

$$x = -\frac{b}{a}$$

If we set the polynomial function in Equation (2) equal to zero, we have the quadratic equation

$$ax^2 + bx + c = 0, \quad a \neq 0$$

which has the two solutions given by the quadratic formula,

$$x = \frac{-b \pm \sqrt{b^2 - 4ac}}{2a}, \quad a \neq 0$$

If we set the polynomial function in Equation (3) equal to zero, we have the **polynomial equation of degree n**

$$a_n x^n + a_{n-1} x^{n-1} + \cdots + a_1 x + a_0 = 0, \quad a_n \neq 0 \tag{4}$$

In this chapter, we study methods of finding solutions to Equation (4). Any complex number satisfying Equation (4) is called a *solution*, or **root**, of the polynomial equation $P(x) = 0$. Such values are also called the **zeros** of the polynomial $P(x)$.

Mathematicians, curious about polynomials, have considered many questions in this area. For example:

• Does a polynomial always have a zero?

• What is the total number of zeros of a polynomial of degree n?

• How many of the zeros of a polynomial are real numbers?

• What can one say about the zeros of a polynomial if all its coefficients are integers?

• Is there a relationship between the zeros and the factors of a polynomial?

• Can we find a formula for expressing the zeros of a polynomial in terms of the coefficients of the polynomial?

We will explore some of these questions in the course of this chapter.

4.1   Quadratic Functions and Their Graphs

A function of the form

$$f(x) = ax^2 + bx + c \tag{1}$$

where a, b and c are real numbers and $a \neq 0$, is called a **quadratic function**. By **completing the square**, it is always possible to rewrite Equation (1) in the form

$$f(x) = a(x - h)^2 + k \tag{2}$$

where h and k are constants. We demonstrate this process with a few examples.

Example 1   Completing the Square
Write the quadratic function

$$f(x) = 2x^2 - 4x - 1$$

in the form of Equation (2).

Solution
We complete the square in a manner analogous to that used in Section 2.3 for solving quadratic equations. Here, we will factor out the coefficient a of x^2, complete the square and balance the equation as follows.

$$f(x) = 2(x^2 - 2x \quad) - 1 \qquad \text{Factor out 2.}$$
$$= 2(x^2 - 2x + 1) - 1 - 2 \qquad \text{Complete the square and balance.}$$
$$= 2(x - 1)^2 - 3$$

which is in the form of Equation (2) with $a = 2$, $h = 1$ and $k = -3$.

✔ Progress Check

Write each quadratic function f in the form $f(x) = a(x - h)^2 + k$.

a. $f(x) = -3x^2 - 12x - 13$ b. $f(x) = 2x^2 - 2x + 3$

Answers

a. $f(x) = -3(x + 2)^2 - 1$ b. $f(x) = 2\left(x - \dfrac{1}{2}\right)^2 + \dfrac{5}{2}$

Warning

Be careful to balance the equation properly when completing the square. In Example 1, we wrote

$$f(x) = 2(x^2 - 2x \quad) - 1$$
$$= 2(x^2 - 2x + 1) - 1 - 2$$

We added $+1$ to the expression in parentheses that, due to the factor 2 in front of the parentheses, adds $+2$ to $f(x)$. We must balance by subtracting 2 as shown.

In Example 1 we completed the square to show that

$$f(x) = 2x^2 - 4x - 1 = 2(x - 1)^2 - 3$$

From Section 3.3, we know that this is the graph of the **parabola** $f(x) = 2x^2$ shifted 3 units downward and 1 unit to the right. In general, the graph of Equation (2) is that of the parabola $f(x) = ax^2$ shifted k units vertically and h units horizontally. Thus, the graph of Equation (2) is a parabola opening from the point (h, k), which is called the **vertex** of the parabola. If $a > 0$, the **parabola opens upward** from the vertex; if $a < 0$, the **parabola opens downward**. We can summarize these results in this way.

Graph of $f(x) = ax^2 + bx + c$

The quadratic function

$$f(x) = ax^2 + bx + c, \quad a \neq 0$$

can be written in the form

$$f(x) = a(x - h)^2 + k$$

where h and k are constants. The graph is a parabola with vertex at (h, k), opening upward if $a > 0$ and downward if $a < 0$.

Example 2   Graphing Quadratic Functions

Sketch the graphs of the following functions.

a. $f(x) = 2x^2 + 4x - 1$ b. $f(x) = -2x^2 + 4x$

Solution

a. Completing the square in x, we have

$$f(x) = 2x^2 + 4x - 1$$
$$= 2(x^2 + 2x \quad) - 1$$
$$= 2(x^2 + 2x + 1) - 1 - 2$$
$$= 2(x + 1)^2 - 3$$

which is in the form $f(x) = a(x - h)^2 + k$ with $a = 2$, $h = -1$ and $k = -3$. The vertex of the parabola is at $(-1, -3)$, and the graph opens upward as shown in Figure 1(a).

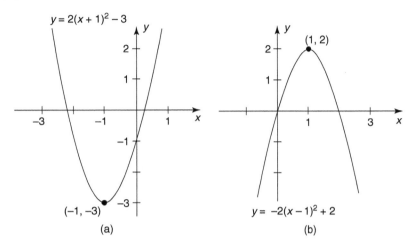

Figure 1   Graphs of Quadratic Equations

b. Completing the square,

$$\begin{aligned}
f(x) &= -2x^2 + 4x \\
&= -2(x^2 - 2x \quad) \\
&= -2(x^2 - 2x + 1) + 2 \\
&= -2(x - 1)^2 + 2
\end{aligned}$$

Here, $a = -2$, $h = 1$ and $k = 2$. The vertex of the parabola is at $(1, 2)$, and the parabola opens downward as shown in Figure 1(b).

Intercepts and Roots

Since the graph of the quadratic function of Equation (1) is the graph of the equation

$$y = ax^2 + bx + c, \quad a \neq 0$$

the graph intersects the x-axis at those points where $y = 0$. The x-intercepts are those points where

$$y = 0$$

implying that

$$ax^2 + bx + c = 0$$

The y-intercept is that point where $x = 0$, implying that $y = c$.

Intercepts of the Parabola

The x-intercepts of the parabola

$$f(x) = ax^2 + bx + c, \quad a \neq 0$$

are the real roots of the quadratic equation

$$ax^2 + bx + c = 0$$

and are given by the quadratic formula. The y-intercept has coordinates $(0, c)$.

The discriminant of the quadratic equation tells us the number of real roots, and therefore, the number of **x-intercepts of the parabola.** Thus, there can be two different real roots, a **double root** or two complex roots. These graphs are shown in Figure 2 for the case when $a > 0$.

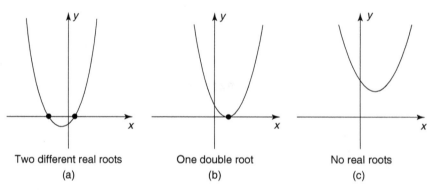

| Two different real roots | One double root | No real roots |
| (a) | (b) | (c) |

Figure 2 Roots, Intercepts and Graphs of Quadratic Functions when $a > 0$

Example 3   Graphing Parabolas

Find the vertex and all intercepts of each of the following parabolas. Sketch the graph.

a. $f(x) = -x^2 + 3x - 2$ b. $f(x) = x^2 + 1$ c. $f(x) = x^2 + 2x + 1$

Solution

a. To find the vertex, we must complete the square

$$f(x) = -x^2 + 3x - 2 = -\left(x - \frac{3}{2}\right)^2 + \frac{1}{4}$$

The vertex is at $\left(\frac{3}{2}, \frac{1}{4}\right)$ and the parabola opens downward. Setting $y = f(x) = 0$, we see that

$$x^2 - 3x + 2 = 0$$

$$(x - 1)(x - 2) = 0$$

and the x-intercepts occur at $x = 1$ and $x = 2$. Finally, the y-intercept is $y = f(0) = -2$. The graph is shown in Figure 3(a).

b. Since

$$f(x) = x^2 + 1 = (x - 0)^2 + 1$$

the vertex is at (0, 1) and the parabola opens upward. To find the x-intercepts, we set $y = f(x) = 0$ so that

$$x^2 + 1 = 0$$

Since this quadratic equation has no real roots, there are no x-intercepts. To find the y-intercept, we set $x = 0$ and find that $y = f(0) = 1$. See Figure 3(b) for the graph.

c. Completing the square,

$$f(x) = x^2 + 2x + 1 = (x + 1)^2 + 0$$

The vertex is at the point $(-1, 0)$ and the parabola opens upward. Setting $f(x) = 0$, we see that

$$x^2 + 2x + 1 = (x + 1)^2 = 0$$

so that $x = -1$ is the only x-intercept. Finally, we set $x = 0$ and find that $y = f(0) = 1$ is the y-intercept. See Figure 3(c).

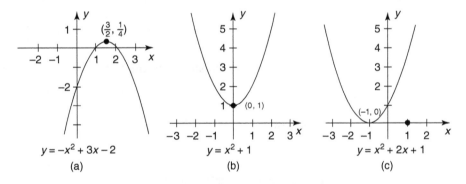

$$y = -x^2 + 3x - 2$$
(a)

$$y = x^2 + 1$$
(b)

$$y = x^2 + 2x + 1$$
(c)

Figure 3   Graphs of Quadratic Functions

Maximum and Minimum Values

We know that the graph of the function

$$f(x) = ax^2 + bx + c, \qquad a \neq 0$$

is a parabola that opens from its vertex. If $a > 0$, the graph opens upward and the function takes on its **minimum** value at the vertex (See Figure 4(a).); if $a < 0$, the graph opens downward and the function takes on its **maximum** value at the vertex (See Figure 4(b).). Using the method for completing the square, we can find the coordinates of the vertex (h, k) from the general equation.

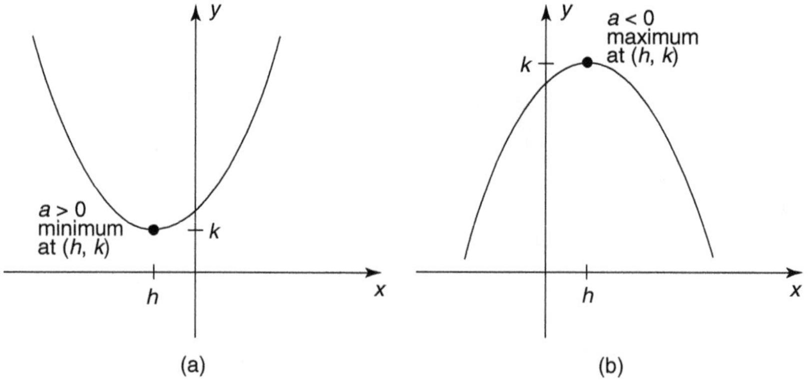

Figure 4   Maximum and Minimum for $f(x) = ax^2 + bx + c$

$$f(x) = ax + bx + c$$
$$= a\left(x^2 + \frac{b}{a}x + \qquad\right) + c$$
$$= a\left(x^2 + \frac{b}{a}x + \left(\frac{b}{2a}\right)^2\right) + c - a\left(\frac{b}{2a}\right)^2$$
$$= a\left(x + \frac{b}{2a}\right)^2 + \left(c - \frac{b^2}{4a}\right)$$

Since this last expression is of the form

$$f(x) = a(x - h)^2 + k$$

we see that

$$h = -\frac{b}{2a}$$

Therefore, the vertex has coordinates

$$\left(-\frac{b}{2a}, f\left(-\frac{b}{2a}\right)\right)$$

The maximum or minimum value of the quadratic function

$$f(x) = ax^2 + bx + c, \quad a \neq 0$$

occurs at the vertex where

$$x = -\frac{b}{2a}$$

It is a maximum value if $a < 0$ and a minimum value if $a > 0$. The maximum or minimum value is

$$f\left(-\frac{b}{2a}\right)$$

Example 4   Maximum and Minimum Values of Quadratic Functions

Find the maximum or minimum value of the function $f(x) = -x^2 + 3x - 2$.

Solution

For this quadratic function, $a = -1$, $b = 3$, and the vertex occurs at $x = -\frac{b}{2a} = \frac{3}{2}$. Since $a < 0$, the curve opens downward and the function attains a maximum value at the vertex. We find this maximum value by evaluating $f(x)$ when $x = \frac{3}{2}$, namely, $f(\frac{3}{2}) = \frac{1}{4}$. Conclusion: the maximum value of the function is $\frac{1}{4}$ and occurs when $x = \frac{3}{2}$. (See Figure 3(a).)

✔ Progress Check

Given the function $f(x) = 2x^2 + x - 1$. Determine

a. if f has a maximum or minimum value;

b. the value of x at which the maximum or minimum occurs;

c. the maximum or minimum value of f.

Answers

a. minimum   b. $-\frac{1}{4}$ c. $-\frac{9}{8}$

Example 5   Maximum and Minimum in Word Problems

A rectangular region with one side against an existing building is to be fenced in. If 100 feet of fencing material are available, what dimensions will maximize the area of the region? What is the maximum area?

Solution

In Figure 5, we indicate the lengths of the two parallel sides by x. Since we have 100 feet of material available, the length of the remaining side must be $100 - 2x$. The area A is a function of x and is given by

$$A(x) = x(100 - 2x) = -2x^2 + 100x$$

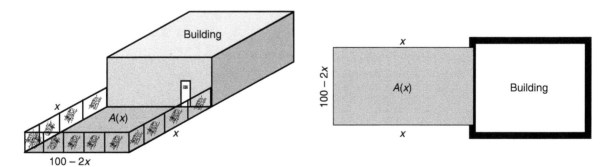

Figure 5   Diagram for Example 5

This quadratic function has a maximum (Why?) that is assumed when $x = -\frac{b}{2a} = 25$. The dimensions of the three sides are 25, 25 and 50 feet, and the maximum area is 1250 square feet.

Example 6   Maximum and Minimum in Word Problems
Find two numbers whose sum is 18 and whose product is a maximum.

Solution
If one of the numbers is x, then the other number must be $18 - x$. The product P is a function of x such that

$$P(x) = x(18 - x) = -x^2 + 18x$$

The function has a maximum (Why?) at $x = -\frac{b}{2a} = 9$. The two numbers are 9 and 9, and the product is 81.

Example 7   Maximum and Minimum in Word Problems
A corporate vice-president finds that the cost C in dollars to produce and sell x units of the company's product is approximated by the function

$$C(x) = 3x^2 - 30x + 3000$$

If each unit sells for \$300, find the number of units manufactured and sold that will maximize profit.

Solution
Since each unit sells for \$300, the revenue R from selling x units is

$$R(x) = 300x$$

The profit P is revenue minus cost, that is,

$$\begin{aligned} P(x) &= R(x) - C(x) \\ &= 300x - (3x^2 - 30x + 3000) \\ &= -3x^2 + 330x - 3000 \end{aligned}$$

Since P is a quadratic function and its leading coefficient is negative, P attains a maximum where $x = -\frac{b}{2a} = -\frac{330}{-6} = 55$. The company maximizes its profit if it manufactures and sells 55 units. (Verify that the maximum profit is \$6075.)

Example 8   Applied Maximum and Minimum
Which point on the graph of the function $f(x) = \sqrt{x}$ is closest to the point $(2, 0)$?

Solution
In Figure 6, we use the symbol d to denote the distance from the point $(2, 0)$ to a point $P(x, y)$ on the graph of $y = \sqrt{x}$. By the distance formula, we can write

$$d = \sqrt{(x - 2)^2 + (y - 0)^2} = \sqrt{x^2 - 4x + 4 + y^2}$$

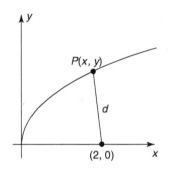

Figure 6 Diagram for Example 8 where $f(x) = \sqrt{x}$

Since point $P(x, y)$ lies on the graph of $y = \sqrt{x}$, we can substitute $\sqrt{x}$ for y and write d as a function of the variable x alone.

$$d(x) = \sqrt{x^2 - 4x + 4 + x} = \sqrt{x^2 - 3x + 4}$$

Since the square root function is an increasing function, d is minimum when d^2 is minimum, that is, the same value of x that provides a minimum for d provides a minimum for $d^2 = x^2 - 3x + 4$. This minimum occurs where $x = -\frac{b}{2a} = \frac{3}{2}$. The corresponding value of y is

$$y = \sqrt{x} = \sqrt{\frac{3}{2}} = \frac{\sqrt{6}}{2}$$

Therefore, the point we seek has coordinates $\left(\frac{3}{2}, \frac{\sqrt{6}}{2}\right)$.

Exercise Set 4.1

In Exercises 1–10, write the quadratic function f in the form $f(x) = a(x - h)^2 + k$. Then, determine appropriate WINDOW values, and GRAPH the quadratic function on your graphing calculator.

1. $f(x) = x^2 - 6x + 10$
2. $f(x) = -x^2 - 2x - 3$
3. $f(x) = -2x^2 + 4x - 5$
4. $f(x) = 3x^2 + 12x + 14$
5. $f(x) = 2x^2 + 6x + 5$
6. $f(x) = -4x^2 + 4x$
7. $f(x) = -x^2 - x$
8. $f(x) = 3x^2 + 18x + 9$
9. $f(x) = -2x^2 + 5$
10. $f(x) = -\frac{1}{2}x^2 + 2x + 2$

In Exercises 11–18, find the vertex and all intercepts of the parabola. Sketch the graph. Then, determine appropriate WINDOW values, and check your answer using your graphing calculator.

11. $f(x) = 2x^2 - 4x$
12. $f(x) = -x^2 - 2x + 3$
13. $f(x) = -4x^2 + 4x - 1$
14. $f(x) = x^2 + 4x + 4$
15. $f(x) = \frac{1}{2}x^2 + 2x + 4$
16. $f(x) = -2x^2 + 2x - \frac{5}{2}$
17. $f(x) = -\frac{1}{2}x^2 + 3x - 4$
18. $f(x) = x^2 - x + 1$

In Exercises 19–26, use your graphing calculator to GRAPH the given functions in the default viewing rectangle. What is the relationship between the linear factors of the quadratic function and the x-intercepts of the graph?

19. $y = (x + 1)(x - 2)$
20. $y = -(x + 1)(x - 2)$
21. $y = x(x + 5)$
22. $y = (x + 5)^2$
23. $y = (x - 3)(x - 7)$
24. $y = 2(x - 3)(x - 7)$
25. $y = 0.3(x - 3)(x - 7)$
26. $y = -0.1(x - 5)(x + 5)$

In Exercises 27–30, the graphs represent quadratic functions of the form $f(x) = (x - r_1)(x - r_2)$. The graphs are drawn in the viewing rectangle $-10 \le X \le 10$ and $-20 \le Y \le 20$ with XSCL = 1 and YSCL = 5. For each function

a. Determine r_1 and r_2.

b. Write the function in the form $f(x) = ax^2 + bx + c$.

c. Use your graphing calculator to compare the graph of the function you found in part (b) with the graph shown below to verify your answer.

27.

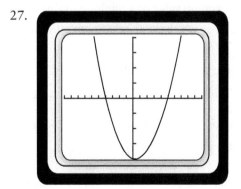

28.

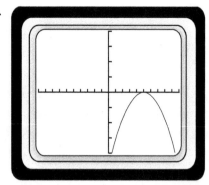

29.

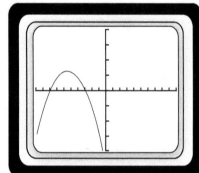

30.

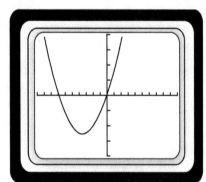

In Exercises 31–38, you are given a quadratic function. Determine

    a. if f has a maximum value or a minimum value;

    b. the value of x at which the maximum or minimum occurs;

    c. the maximum or minimum value of f.

31. $f(x) = 3x^2 - 2x + 4$ 32. $f(x) = -x^2 - x - 4$

33. $f(x) = -2x^2 - 5$ 34. $f(x) = 2x^2 + 3x + 2$

35. $f(x) = x^2 + 5x$ 36. $f(x) = -4x^2 + 3$

37. $f(x) = 2x^2 - \frac{1}{2}x - \frac{3}{2}$ 38. $f(x) = \frac{2}{3}x^2 + x - 1$

39. Find two positive numbers such that their sum is 20 and their product is a maximum.

40. Find two positive numbers such that their sum is 100 and their product is a maximum.

41. Find two numbers whose sum is 50 and the sum of the squares of the numbers is a minimum.

42. Find two numbers such that their sum is 20 and the sum of their squares is a minimum.

43. Which point on the graph of the function $f(x) = \sqrt{x}$ is closest to the point $(1, 0)$?

44. A rectangle has a perimeter of 100 meters. What are the dimensions of the sides if the area is a maximum?

45. A farmer has 1000 feet of fencing material with which to enclose a rectangular field that borders on a straight stream. If the farmer does not enclose the side bordering on the stream, what are the dimensions of the field of maximum area?

46. Suppose that 320 feet of fencing are available to enclose a rectangular field and that one side of the field must be given double fencing. What are the dimensions of the rectangle that will yield the largest possible area?

47. A rectangle has a perimeter of 40 feet. What are the dimensions of the sides if the square of its diagonal is a minimum?

48. A piece of wire 20 inches long is to be cut into two pieces, one of which will be bent into a circle and the other into a square. How long should each piece be to minimize the sum of the areas?

49. A ball is thrown up from the ground with an initial velocity of 80 feet per second. The height s in feet can be expressed as a function of time t in seconds by

$$s(t) = 80t - 16t^2$$

When does the ball reach its maximum height and what is the maximum height?

50. At a rate of $40 per room, a 100-room motel is fully occupied each night. For each $1 increase in the room rate, 2 fewer rooms are rented. What increase in room rate will maximize revenue?

51. A movie theater finds that 200 people attend each performance at the current rate of $4 and that attendance decreases by 10 persons for each 25 cent increase in price. What increase yields the greatest gross revenue?

Applications 4.1

1. The equation $P = -0.002t^2 + 0.096t + 9.15$ models the approximate number (in millions) of female college students in the United States for the academic years 2000 to 2006, with $t = 0$ representing year 2000.

   a. Sketch the graph of the function.

   b. Find the positive t-intercepts. Please explain your answer. How do you think about this mathematical model?

   c. Find the P-intercepts. What does it represent?

2. The quarterly profit of Canton Realty depends on the amount of money x spent on advertising per quarter according to the model $P(x) = -\frac{1}{5}x^2 + 8x + 25$, $(0 \le x \le 40)$, where $P(x)$ and x are measured in thousands of dollars.

   a. Sketch the graph of the function.

   b. What is the Canton Realty's profit when the quarterly adverting budget is $10,000?

   c. How much does Canton Realty have to spend on advertise to maximize its' profit? What is the maximized profit?

3. The geometric form of the Gateway Arch in St. Louis was set by mathematical equations provided to Saarinen by Hannskarl Bandel. To capture the height and the width of the Gateway Arch, a simplified model is given by $H(x) = -0.006349(x^2 - 630x)$, where $H(x)$ and x are measured in feet.

   a. Sketch the graph of the simple model.

   b. Using the simple model, find the width of the Gateway Arch.

   c. Using the simple model, find the height of the Gateway Arch.

4. The Royal Gorge Bridge is the world's highest suspension bridges—hanging 956 feet high and spanning a quarter mile (1320 feet) across the Arkansas River. Assume that the cables are parabolic in shape and are suspended from the tops of the towers. The cables touch the road surface at the center of the bridge. (Assume that the road is level.)

   a. Find a mathematical model which describes the shape of the cables.

   b. Find the height of the cables at a point 100 feet from the center.

4.2   Graphs of Polynomial Functions of Higher Degree

We have already shown that the graph of the first-degree polynomial function

$$P(x) = ax + b$$

is always a line, and the graph of the second-degree polynomial function

$$P(x) = ax^2 + bx + c, \qquad a \ne 0$$

is always a parabola. However, for $n > 2$, the graph of the polynomial function

$$P(x) = a_nx^n + a_{n-1}x^{n-1} + \cdots + a_1x + a_0, \qquad a_n \ne 0$$

is much more difficult to describe. Nevertheless, it is still possible to make some useful observations concerning the shape and nature of the graph of a polynomial of degree greater than 2.

Continuity and the Intermediate Value Theorem

We begin by exploring what the graph of a polynomial function can and cannot "do." The graphs in Figure 7 illustrate "typical" polynomials.

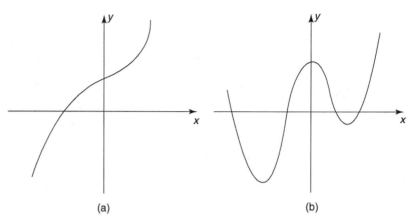

Figure 7   Graphs of Polynomial Functions

Continuity, Smoothness and Corners

- The graph of a polynomial function is **continuous**, which means that there are no "breaks" or "holes." (The graph can be drawn without lifting the pencil from the paper.)

- The graph of a polynomial function is **smooth**; it has no "corners" (also called **cusps**). In particular, no segment of the graph of a polynomial function of degree greater than 1 is a line.

Graphing Calculator Alert

The properties of continuity and smoothness will not be evident on your graphing calculator display. You must train your eye to properly *interpret* the calculator display as a continuous, smooth graph (when the function is continuous and smooth). For example, consider the graphing calculator representations of the graphs in Figures 7(a) and 7(b) as shown in Figures 8(a) and 8(b), respectively.

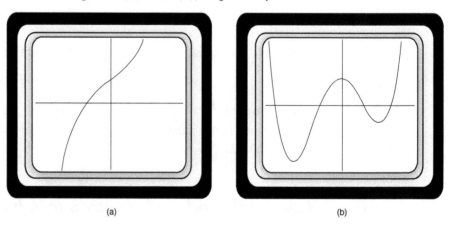

Figure 8   Graphing Calculator Graphs of Polynomial Functions

The labels accompanying the graphs in Figure 9 explain why each of these graphs cannot be that of a polynomial function.

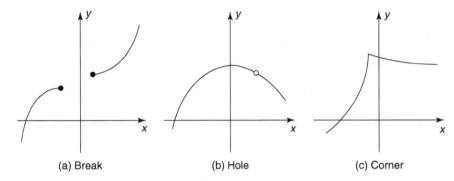

(a) Break   (b) Hole   (c) Corner

Figure 9   Graphics of Non-Polynomial Functions

The property of continuity has enabled us to plot points on the graph of a polynomial function and then to connect these points. In Figure 10, on the graph of $y = P(x)$, to get from the point $A(a, P(a))$ to $B(b, P(b))$, the graph must pass through every y-coordinate between $P(a)$ and $P(b)$. This result is formally known as the Intermediate Value Theorem for Polynomial Functions.

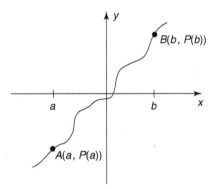

Figure 10   Intermediate Value Theorem
for Polynomial $y = P(x)$

Intermediate Value Theorem for Polynomial Functions
If $a < b$ and P is a polynomial function such that $P(a) \neq P(b)$, then P takes on every value between $P(a)$ and $P(b)$ in the interval $[a, b]$.

This theorem is useful in finding the roots of the polynomial equation $P(x) = 0$. As shown in Figure 10, if we can find values a and b such that $P(a)$ and $P(b)$ are opposite in sign, then there must be at least one value c in the interval $[a, b]$ where $P(c) = 0$. This shows that there is at least one real root c such that $a < c < b$.

Turning Points

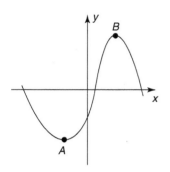

Figure 11   Locating Turning Points

In Figure 11, *A* and B, called **turning points**, are those points at which the graph changes "direction," from rising to falling or from falling to rising. If we knew the number and location of the turning points of a polynomial graph, it would make it easier to sketch that graph. We shall give only a partial answer to these problems.

Turning Points

The graph of a polynomial function of degree n has at most $n - 1$ turning points.

The polynomial function whose graph is shown in Figure 10 has no turning points. Therefore, the degree of this polynomial must be at least 1. Since the graph in Figure 11 has two turning points, the degree of this polynomial must be at least 3. Observe that the degree of the polynomial associated with Figure 7(b) must be at least 4.

Behavior for Large $|x|$

We can factor x^n out of

$$P(x) = a_n x^n + a_{n-1} x^{n-1} + \cdots + a_1 x + a_0$$

to obtain

$$P(x) = x^n \left(a_n + \frac{a_{n-1}}{x} + \frac{a_{n-2}}{x^2} + \cdots + \frac{a_1}{x^{n-1}} + \frac{a_0}{x^n} \right), \qquad x \neq 0$$

When the equation is written this way, it is possible to see how $P(x)$ behaves when $|x|$ assumes large values. (Observe that this may happen when x is positive or when x is negative.) Consider the expression

$$\frac{a_{n-k}}{x}$$

where k is a positive integer and a_{n-k} is a constant. As $|x|$ becomes larger and larger, this expression gets closer and closer to zero. So, for sufficiently large values of $|x|$, we can ignore the contribution of all terms of the form a_{n-k}/x^k. The term that remains is $a_n x^n$. In summary,

---

For large values of $|x|$, the polynomial function

$$P(x) = a_n x^n + a_{n-1} x^{n-1} + \cdots + a_1 x + a_0, \qquad a_n \neq 0$$

is dominated by its leading term $a_n x^n$.

We can make practical use of this last result. In Figures 12(a) and 12(b), we have sketched the graphs of polynomial functions of degrees 3 and 4, respectively. Note that as $|x|$ increases, the **"ends" of the graph** of the third-degree polynomial function extend indefinitely in opposite directions, whereas the ends of the graph of the fourth-degree polynomial function extend indefinitely in the same direction.

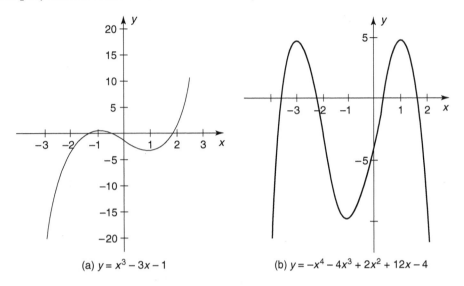

(a) $y = x^3 - 3x - 1$ (b) $y = -x^4 - 4x^3 + 2x^2 + 12x - 4$

Figure 12 Polynomial Functions of Odd and Even Degree

Consider any polynomial function of odd degree. Since the leading term $a_n x^n$ is of odd degree, this term assumes opposite signs for positive and negative values of x. When $|x|$ is large, this term dominates, hence the polynomial assumes opposite signs for positive and negative values of x. Therefore, one end of the graph extends upward and the other downward.

If a polynomial has even degree, its leading term is also of even degree. Therefore, this term assumes the same sign for positive and negative values of x. When $|x|$ is large, this term dominates, so that the polynomial assumes the same sign for positive and negative values of x. Thus, the ends of the graph both extend upward or both extend downward.

Graphs of Polynomial Functions
The graph of the polynomial function

$$P(x) = a_n x^n + a_{n-1} x^{n-1} + \cdots + a_1 x + a_0, \qquad a_n \neq 0$$

has these characteristics.

- If n is odd and $a_n > 0$, the graph extends upward if $|x|$ is large and $x > 0$, and extends downward if $|x|$ is large and $x < 0$, that is, the "right end" extends upward and the "left end" extends downward; if $a_n < 0$, the behavior is reversed.

- If n is even and $a_n > 0$, the graph extends upward at both ends; if $a_n < 0$, the graph extends downward at both ends.

Example 1 Determining Behavior for Large $|x|$

Without sketching the graph, determine the behavior of the graph of each of the following polynomial functions for large values of $|x|$.

a. $P(x) = -3x^5 + 26x^2 - 5$

b. $P(x) = -\dfrac{1}{2}x^6 + 209x^3 + 16x + 2$

Solution

a. We need only concern ourselves with the lead term, $-3x^5$. Since the degree is odd and the lead coefficient is negative, the right end of the graph extends downward and the left end of the graph extends upward.

b. Since this is a polynomial of degree 6, the degree is even and the graph moves in the same direction at both ends. The negative lead coefficient indicates that both ends extend downward. ■

Polynomials in Factored Form

Given a polynomial function of degree n, we now know that the graph: (a) is continuous; (b) is smooth; (c) has at most $n - 1$ turning points; and (d) behaves in a predictable manner at the ends. We need some additional guidance to discover what happens when $|x|$ is not too large. We shall only consider polynomials that can be written as a product of linear factors. In this case, we are able to find the x-intercepts and to determine where the graph of the polynomial lies above the x-axis and where it lies below the x-axis. The following example illustrates the procedure.

Example 2 Using Intercepts in Graphing

Sketch the graph of the polynomial

$$P(x) = x^3 + x^2 - 6x$$

Solution

Factoring, we find that

$$P(x) = x(x^2 + x - 6)$$
$$= x(x + 3)(x - 2)$$

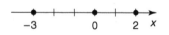

Figure 13 x-intercepts of $P(x) = x^3 + x^2 - 6x$

Since $P(x) = 0$ at $x = 0$, $x = -3$ and $x = 2$, these values are the x-intercepts of $P(x)$. We indicate these values on the real number line as shown in Figure 13.

We now utilize the Critical Value Method, which was presented in Section 2.5. (Specifically, refer to Example 10 of that section, which dealt with polynomial inequalities.) The x-intercepts presented above play the same role as the critical values. We consider the four intervals

$$(-\infty, -3), (-3, 0), (0, 2) \text{ and } (2, \infty)$$

The polynomial $P(x)$ always has the same sign, provided the values of x are restricted to any one of these intervals. Thus, we can think of each interval as corresponding to part (if not all) of a solution set to some polynomial inequality. We choose a test point in each interval to determine the sign of the polynomial in that interval. To repeat, all test points within the same interval produce the same sign.

From interval $(-\infty, -3)$, choose test point $x = -4$. Since $P(-4) < 0$, $P(x) < 0$ for all points in $(-\infty, -3)$. From $(-3, 0)$, choose test point $x = -1$. Since $P(-1) > 0$, $P(x) > 0$ for all points in $(-3, 0)$. Choosing $x = 1$ from $(0, 2)$ implies that $P(1) < 0$, thus $P(x) < 0$ for all points in $(0, 2)$. Finally, choosing $x = 3$ from $(2, \infty)$ yields that $P(x) > 0$ for all points in $(2, \infty)$. We summarize these results in Figure 14. Plotting a few points, we obtain the graph shown in Figure 15. (Check that the right end extends upward and the left end extends downward from the analysis of $P(x)$ for large $|x|$.)

Figure 14 Sign of $P(x)$ in Given Intervals

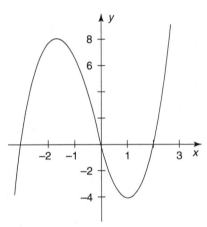

Figure 15 Graph of $P(x) = x^3 + x^2 - 6x$

Warning

The sign of $P(x)$ in adjacent intervals does *not* always change from positive to negative or from negative to positive.

Consider the polynomial $P(x) = x^2$. This has only one x-intercept, $x = 0$. Thus, there are two intervals to examine: $(-\infty, 0)$ and $(0, \infty)$. For test point $x = -1$ from $(-\infty, 0)$, $P(-1) > 0$ and hence $P(x) > 0$ for all points in $(-\infty, 0)$. For test point $x = 1$ from $(0, \infty)$, $P(1) > 0$ and hence $P(x) > 0$ for all points in $(0, \infty)$.

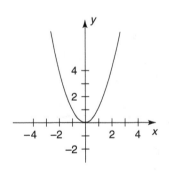

Figure 16 Graph of $P(x) = x^2$

The graph of $P(x) = x^2$ is shown in Figure 16.

Since we know that polynomials are continuous, if $P(x)$ is a polynomial with $P(a)$ and $P(b)$ of opposite sign where $a < b$, then $P(x)$ must have at least one x-intercept in the interval (a, b). Let r be such an x-intercept, that is, $P(r) = 0$, where $a < r < b$. Thus, r is a root of the equation $P(x) = 0$ with $a < r < b$.

Example 3   Looking for Roots in Intervals

Show that the equation $x^3 + 2x^2 + 5x + 1 = 0$ has a root in the interval $[-1, 0]$

Solution

Let $P(x) = x^3 + 2x^2 + 5x + 1$. Since $P(-1) = -3 < 0$ and $P(0) = 1 > 0$, $P(-1)$ and $P(0)$ are of opposite sign. Therefore, $P(x)$ has at least one x-intercept in $(-1, 0)$. Hence, the equation $x^3 + 2x^2 + 5x + 1 = 0$ must have at least one root in the interval $[-1, 0]$.

We have found the x-intercepts of a polynomial by putting the polynomial into factored form. We may also reverse the procedure, that is, we may construct a polynomial in factored form from a given set of x-intercepts.

Example 4   Using x-Intercepts to Form a Polynomial

Find a polynomial whose x-intercepts are 2, 4 and -1.

Solution

If a polynomial has a factor of $x - 2$, then it has an intercept of 2. Similarly, if a polynomial has factors $x - 4$ and $x + 1$, then it has x-intercepts of 4 and -1. Therefore, the polynomial

$$P(x) = (x - 2)(x - 4)(x + 1)$$

has x-intercepts 2, 4 and -1. (Find another polynomial with the same x-intercepts.)

Graphing Calculator Power User's Corner

Graphing Polynomial Functions

Your graphing calculator is a powerful tool for graphing polynomial functions. However, you must take care to include all of the important features of the function in your graph. For polynomials, these important features include the intercepts, the turning points of the functions and the behavior of the function when $|x|$ is very large. It is frequently impossible to show all of this behavior in one viewing rectangle. The examples below show how several viewing rectangles can be used to provide complete information about a polynomial function.

Example 5   Graphing Polynomials with a Graphing Calculator

Graph the function $y = 11x^3 - x - 5$ using the following information:

a. $-10 \leq X \leq 10$, $-10 \leq Y \leq 10$, XSCL = 1 and YSCL = 1

b. $-1 \leq X \leq 1$, $-6 \leq Y \leq -4$, XSCL = 1 and YSCL = 1

c. $-100 \leq X \leq 100$, $-11{,}000{,}000 \leq Y \leq 11{,}000{,}000$, XSCL = 10 and YSCL = 1{,}000{,}000

Solution

a.

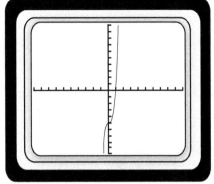

Observe that the *x*-intercept is approximately 0.808, and the *y*-intercept is -5.

b.

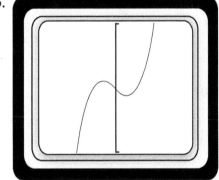

We see that the coordinates of the turning points are *approximately* (0.174, -5.116) and (-0.174, -4.884). Observe that these turning points are "hidden" in the default viewing rectangle.

c.

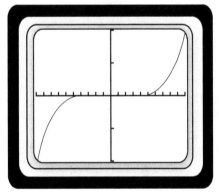

This viewing rectangle shows the behavior of *y* when $|x|$ is large.

It is important to note that the values you obtain when using TRACE on your graphing calculator are *approximate*. It is often necessary to ZOOM-IN to obtain more accurate results. Although the coordinates in the text are correct, they do not necessarily correspond to any values obtained when using the TRACE command.

Example 6   Graphing Polynomials with a Graphing Calculator

Graph the function $y = 2x^5 - 11x^4 + 20x^2 - 3$ using the following information:

a. $-10 \le X \le 10$, $-10 \le Y \le 10$, XSCL = 1 and YSCL = 1

b. $-10 \le X \le 10$, $-500 \le Y \le 100$, XSCL = 1 and YSCL = 100

c. $-100 \le X \le 100$, $-2 \cdot 10^{10} \le Y \le 2 \cdot 10^{10}$, XSCL = 10 and YSCL = 10^{10}

Solution

a.

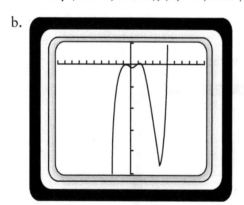

Observe that the x-intercepts are approximately -1.155, -0.408, 0.405, 1.537 and 5.121. (The x-intercept 5.121 may not be displayed on some graphing calculators.) The y-intercept is -3. The coordinates of the turning points are approximately $(1.101, 8.316)$, $(0, -3)$ and $(-0.871, 4.839)$.

b.

We see that the largest x-intercept is approximately 5.121 and the coordinates of the turning point are approximately $(4.170, -459.5)$.

c.

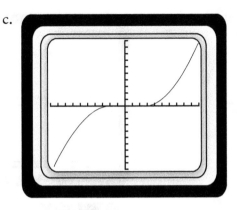

This viewing rectangle shows the behavior of y when $|x|$ is large.

Exercise Set 4.2

In Exercises 1–8, show that the equation has a root in the given interval.

1. $2x^4 - x^3 + 2x - 2 = 0$ $[-2, -1]$

2. $3x^3 - 2x^2 + 5x + 4 = 0$ $[-1, 0]$

3. $x^5 - 3x^3 + x^2 - 3 = 0$ $[1, 2]$

4. $-x^4 + 3x^2 + 5 = 0$ $[2, 3]$

5. $x^6 - 3x^3 + x^2 - 2 = 0$ $[1, 2]$

6. $2x^5 - x^4 + 3x^2 - 6 = 0$ $[1, 2]$

7. $-2x^3 - x^2 + 3x - 4 = 0$ $[-2, -1]$

8. $2x^4 - 3x^3 + x^2 - 1 = 0$ $[-1, 0]$

 In Exercises 9–16, without sketching, determine the behavior of the graph of the given polynomial function for large values of $|x|$. Use the letters U and D to indicate whether the graph extends upward or downward. Then, GRAPH $y = P(x)$ and $y =$ leading term of $P(x)$ together in each of the following viewing rectangles: (a) $-10 \leq X \leq 10$ and $-100 \leq Y \leq 100$; (b) $-10 \leq X \leq 10$ and $-10{,}000 \leq Y \leq 10{,}000$; and (c) $-10 \leq X \leq 10$ and $-100{,}000 \leq Y \leq 100{,}000$. For each $P(x)$ determine which viewing rectangle most clearly shows the polynomial function behaving like its leading term.

In Exercises 17–22, determine the x-intercepts and the intervals where $P(x) > 0$ and $P(x) < 0$. Sketch the graph of $P(x)$. Then, determine appropriate WINDOW values and

Polynomial Function	Leading Term	Large Values of $\lvert x \rvert$, $x > 0$	Large Values of $\lvert x \rvert$, $x < 0$
9. $P(x) = x^7 - 175x^3 + 23x^2$			
10. $P(x) = -3x^8 + 22x^4 + 3$			
11. $P(x) = -8x^3 + 17x^2 - 15$			
12. $P(x) = 14x^{12} - 5x^{11} + 3x - 1$			
13. $P(x) = -5x^{10} + 16x^7 + 5$			
14. $P(x) = 2x^5 - 11x^4 - 12x^3$			
15. $P(x) = 4x^8 - 10x^6 + x^3 - 8$			
16. $P(x) = -3x^9 + 6x^6 - 2x^5 + x$			

GRAPH $P(x)$ on your graphing calculator. Be sure your graph shows the important features of each function.

17. $P(x) = (x - 3)(2x - 1)(x + 2)$

18. $P(x) = (2 - x)(x - 4)(x + 1)$

19. $P(x) = 2x^3 + 3x^2 - 5x$

20. $P(x) = x^4 - 5x^2 + 4$

21. $P(x) = x^4 - x^3 - 6x^2$

22. $P(x) = (2x + 5)(x - 1)(x + 1)(x - 3)$

In Exercises 23–28 determine a polynomial equation whose roots include the given values.

23. $2, -4, 4$

24. $5, -5, 1, -1$

25. $-1, -2, -3$

26. $-3, \sqrt{2}, -\sqrt{2}$

27. $4, 1 \pm \sqrt{3}$

28. $1, 2, 2 \pm \sqrt{2}$

 In Exercises 29–33, use your graphing calculator to GRAPH the given function in the indicated viewing rectangle. Set the XSCL and YSCL values appropriately. Also, find the x- and y-intercepts.

29. $y = (x - 1)(x + 3)(x - 5)$
    $-10 \leq X \leq 10$ and $-30 \leq Y \leq 30$

30. $y = -(x + 8)(x - 2)$
    $-10 \leq X \leq 10$ and $-10 \leq Y \leq 25$

31. $y = -x(x - 5)(x + 5)(x + 8)$
    $-10 \leq X \leq 10$ and $-300 \leq Y \leq 600$

32. $y = (x + 20)(x + 10)(x - 5)$
    $-25 \leq X \leq 10$ and $-1250 \leq Y \leq 600$

33. $y = (x - 10)(x + 30)(x - 50)$
    $-100 \leq X \leq 100$ and $-30,000 \leq Y \leq 30,000$

In Exercises 34 and 35, we present graphs representing polynomial functions that are the product of linear factors. Graphs are drawn in the viewing rectangle $-10 \leq X \leq 10$ and $-500 \leq Y \leq 500$ with XSCL = 1 and YSCL = 100.

   a. Write the function as a product of linear factors.

   b. Use your graphing calculator to compare the graph of the function you found in part (a) with the graph shown below to verify your answer.

34.

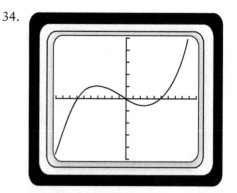

35.

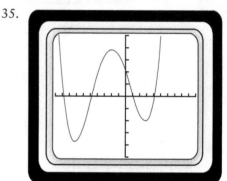

36. Construct a polynomial function to model the situation described in the chapter opener. A square piece of cardboard measuring 60 inches on a side is made into a rectangular box by cutting identical squares from the four corners, then folding up the flaps. Let x represent the length of the side of each discarded square. Write a formula for the volume of the box in terms of x. Put your formula in standard form.

37. Refer to Exercise 36. Graph your volume function, and select an appropriate viewing window. Find the maximum value of the function. What is the volume of the largest box that could be constructed in this way, and how large must the discarded squares be to obtain that volume?

38. The Post Office allows a package to have a maximum value of 130 inches for the sum of the length and girth. (The girth is the distance around the package.) Does the package of maximum volume which you have designed in Exercise 37 meet this requirement? Suppose you first cut one end from the original square of cardboard, leaving a rectangle measuring 60 inches by 40 inches. Repeat Exercises 36 and 37 for this situation. Would this package satisfy the postal requirement?

Applications 4.2

1. The number of enterprise instant messaging (IM) accounts is projected to grow according to the function $N(t) = 0.13t^3 + 2.96t^2 + 11.37t + 60$ $(0 \le t \le 8)$, where $N(t)$ is measured in millions and t in years, with $t = 0$ corresponding to 2005.

   a. Sketch the graph of the function.

   b. How many IM accounts were there in 2006?

   c. What is the number of IM accounts expected to be in 2012?

2. Based on records from 2001 through 2006, sewage services paid for by households in 60 Boston–area communities that use an average of 90,000 gallons of water a year is given by $C(t) = 2.16t^3 + 40t + 756$ $(0 \le t \le 6)$, where $C(t)$ is measured in dollars/year and t in years, with $t = 0$ corresponding to 2001.

   a. What was the average amount paid by a household in 2001 for water and sewage services?

   b. If the trend continued, what was the average amount in 2008?

3. Based on CNN data, President Obama's approval rating from December 2010 to May 2011 can be modeled as $P(t) = 1.25t^3 - 8.68t^2 + 15.07t + 45.4$ $(0 \le t \le 6)$, where $P(t)$ is measured in percentage and t in months, where $t = 0$ represents December 2010.

   a. Sketch the graph of the function.

   b. Use the model to predict Obama's approval rating in June of 2011.

4. The average percent of the labor force that is unemployed from 2004 to 2011 can be modeled as $P(t) = -0.073t^3 + 0.934t^2 - 2.447t + 5.824$ $(0 \le t \le 7)$, where $P(t)$ is measured in percentage and t in years, where $t = 0$ represents 2004.

   a. Sketch the graph of the function.

   b. Use the model to predict the percent of unemployed in 2012.

   c. Can you use this model to predict the percent of unemployed in 2015? Explain your answer as precisely as you can.

4.3   Polynomial Division and Synthetic Division

Polynomial Division

To find the zeros of a polynomial, it is necessary to divide the polynomial by a second polynomial. There is a procedure for polynomial division that parallels the long-division process of arithmetic. In arithmetic, if we divide an integer p by an integer $d \ne 0$, we obtain a quotient q and a remainder r, so we can write

$$\frac{p}{d} = q + \frac{r}{d} \tag{1}$$

where

$$0 \le r < d \tag{2}$$

This result can also be written in the form

$$p = qd + r \tag{3}$$

For example,

$$\frac{7284}{13} = 560 + \frac{4}{13}$$

or

$$7284 = (560)(13) + 4$$

In the long-division process for polynomials, we divide the dividend $P(x)$ by the divisor $D(x) \neq 0$ to obtain a quotient $Q(x)$ and a remainder $R(x)$. We then have

$$\frac{P(x)}{D(x)} = Q(x) + \frac{R(x)}{D(x)} \qquad (4)$$

where $R(x) = 0$ or where

$$\text{degree of } R(x) < \text{degree of } D(x) \qquad (5)$$

This result can also be written as

$$P(x) = Q(x)D(x) + R(x) \qquad (6)$$

Note that Equations (1) and (4) have the same form, as do Equations (3) and (6). Equation (2) requires that the remainder be less than the divisor, and the analogous requirement for polynomials in Equation (5) is that the *degree* of the remainder be less than the degree of the divisor.

We illustrate the long-division process for polynomials with an example.

Example 1   Polynomial Division
Divide $3x^3 - 7x^2 + 1$ by $x - 2$.

Solution

Polynomial Division

Step 1. Arrange the terms of both polynomials by descending powers of x. If a power is missing, write the term with a zero coefficient.	*Step 1.* $$x - 2 \overline{)3x^3 - 7x^2 + 0x + 1}$$
Step 2. Divide the first term of the dividend by the first term of the divisor. The answer is written above the first term of the dividend.	*Step 2.* $$\begin{array}{r} 3x^2 \\ x - 2 \overline{)3x^3 - 7x^2 + 0x + 1} \end{array}$$
Step 3. Multiply the divisor by the quotient obtained in *Step 2* and then subtract the product.	*Step 3.* $$\begin{array}{r} 3x^2 \\ x - 2 \overline{)3x^3 - 7x^2 + 0x + 1} \\ \underline{3x^3 - 6x^2 } \\ -x^2 + 0x + 1 \end{array}$$
Step 4. Repeat *Steps 2* and *3* until the remainder is zero or the degree of the remainder is less than the degree of the divisor.	*Step 4.* $$\begin{array}{r} 3x^2 - x - 2 = Q(x) \\ x - 2 \overline{)3x^3 - 7x^2 + 0x + 1} \\ \underline{3x^3 - 6x^2 } \\ -x^2 + 0x + 1 \\ \underline{-x^2 + 2x } \\ -2x + 1 \\ \underline{-2x + 4} \\ -3 = R(x) \end{array}$$
Step 5. Write the answer in the form of Equation (4) or Equation (6).	*Step 5.* $$\begin{aligned} P(x) &= 3x^3 - 7x^2 + 1 \\ &= \underbrace{(3x^2 - x - 2)}_{Q(x)} \underbrace{(x - 2)}_{D(x)} \underbrace{-3}_{R(x)} \end{aligned}$$

✔ Progress Check

Divide $4x^2 - 3x + 6$ by $x + 2$.

Answer

$4x - 11 + \dfrac{28}{x + 2}$

Synthetic Division

Our work in this chapter will frequently require division of a polynomial by a first-degree polynomial $x - r$, where r is a constant. Fortunately, there is a shortcut called **synthetic division** that simplifies this task. To demonstrate synthetic division, we do Example 1 again, writing only the coefficients.

$$
\begin{array}{r}
3 \;\; -1 \;\; -2 \qquad\quad \\
-2 \overline{)3 \;\; -7 \;\;\; 0 \;\;\; 1} \\
3 \;\; -6 \qquad\qquad \\
\overline{-1 \;\;\; 0 \;\;\; 1} \\
-1 \;\;\; 2 \qquad \\
\overline{-2 \;\;\; 1} \\
-2 \;\;\; 4 \\
\overline{-3}
\end{array}
$$

Note that the boldface numerals are duplicated. We can use this to our advantage and simplify the process as follows.

$$
\begin{array}{r|rrrr}
-2 & 3 & -7 & 0 & 1 \\
   &   & -6 & 2 & 4 \\
\hline
   & 3 & -1 & -2 & -3
\end{array}
$$

coefficients   remainder
of the
quotient

In the third row we copied the leading coefficient (3) of the dividend, multiplied it by the divisor (-2) and wrote the result (-6) in the second row under the next coefficient. The numbers in the second column were subtracted to obtain $-7 - (-6) = -1$. The procedure is repeated until the third row is of the same length as the first row.

Since subtraction is more apt to produce errors than is addition, we can modify this process slightly. If the divisor is $x - r$, we write r instead of $-r$ in the box and use addition in each step instead of subtraction. Repeating our example, we have

$$
\begin{array}{r|rrrr}
2 & 3 & -7 & 0 & 1 \\
  &   & 6 & -2 & -4 \\
\hline
  & 3 & -1 & -2 & -3
\end{array}
$$

From Equations (5) and (6), we see that

$$P(x) = Q(x)D(x) + R(x)$$

where

$$\text{degree of } R(x) < \text{degree of } D(x)$$

Since we are only considering cases where the divisor $D(x)$ has degree 1, then the remainder $R(x)$ must have degree 0, that is, $R(x)$ is a constant.

Example 2　Synthetic Division
Divide $4x^3 - 2x + 5$ by $x + 2$ using synthetic division.

Solution

Synthetic Division

Step 1. If the divisor is $x - r$, write r in the box. Arrange the coefficients of the dividend by descending powers of x, supplying a zero coefficient for every missing power.

Step 2. Copy the leading coefficient in the third row.

Step 3. Multiply the last entry in the third row by the number in the box and write the result in the second row under the next coefficient. Add the numbers in that column.

Step 4. Repeat *Step 3* until there is an entry in the third row for each entry in the first row. The last number in the third row is the remainder; the other numbers are the coefficients of the quotient in descending order.

Step 1.
$$-2|\quad 4\quad 0\ -2\quad 5$$

Step 2.
$$-2|\quad 4\quad 0\ -2\quad 5$$
$$4$$

Step 3.
$$-2|\quad 4\quad 0\ -2\quad 5$$
$$\quad\ -8$$
$$4\ -8$$

Step 4.
$$-2|\quad 4\quad 0\ -2\quad 5$$
$$\quad\ -8\ 16\ -28$$
$$4\ -8\ 14|-23$$

$$\frac{4x^3 - 2x + 5}{x + 2} = 4x^2 - 8x + 14 - \frac{23}{x + 2}$$

✔ Progress Check

Use synthetic division to obtain the quotient $Q(x)$ and the constant remainder R when $2x^4 - 10x^2 - 23x + 6$ is divided by $x - 3$.

Answer

$Q(x) = 2x^3 + 6x^2 + 8x + 1;\quad R = 9$

Warning

a. Synthetic division can be used only when the divisor of the polynomial is a linear factor. Do not forget to write a zero for the coefficient of each missing term.

b. When dividing by $x - r$, place r in the box. For example, when the divisor is $x + 3$, place -3 in the box, since $x + 3 = x - (-3)$. Similarly, when the divisor is $x - 3$, place $+3$ in the box, since $x - 3 = x - (+3)$.

Exercise Set 4.3

In Exercises 1–10, use polynomial division to find the quotient $Q(x)$ and the remainder $R(x)$ when the first polynomial is divided by the second polynomial.

1. $x^2 - 7x + 12, \quad x - 5$

2. $x^2 + 3x + 3, \quad x + 2$

3. $2x^3 - 2x, \quad x^2 + 2x - 1$

4. $3x^3 - 2x^2 + 4, \quad x^2 - 2$

5. $3x^4 - 2x^2 + 1, \quad x + 3$

6. $x^5 - 1, \quad x^2 - 1$

7. $2x^3 - 3x^2, \quad x^2 + 2$

8. $3x^3 - 2x - 1, \quad x^2 - x$

9. $x^4 - x^3 + 2x^2 - x + 1, \quad x^2 + 1$

10. $2x^4 - 3x^3 - x^2 - x - 2, \quad x - 2$

In Exercises 11–20, use synthetic division to find the quotient $Q(x)$ and the constant remainder R when the first polynomial is divided by the second polynomial.

11. $x^3 - x^2 - 6x + 5, \quad x + 2$

12. $2x^3 - 3x^2 - 4, \quad x - 2$

13. $x^4 - 81, \quad x - 3$

14. $x^4 - 81, \quad x + 3$

15. $3x^3 - x^2 + 8, \quad x + 1$

16. $2x^4 - 3x^3 - 4x - 2, \quad x - 1$

17. $x^5 + 32, \quad x + 2$

18. $x^5 + 32, \quad x - 2$

19. $6x^4 - x^2 + 4, \quad x - 3$

20. $8x^3 + 4x^2 - x - 5, \quad x + 3$

4.4   The Remainder and Factor Theorems

The Remainder Theorem

From our work with the division process, we may surmise that division of a polynomial $P(x)$ by $x - r$ results in a quotient $Q(x)$ and a constant remainder R such that

$$P(x) = (x - r) \cdot Q(x) + R$$

Since this identity holds for all real values of x, it must hold when $x = r$. Consequently,

$$P(r) = (r - r) \cdot Q(r) + R$$
$$= 0 \cdot Q(r) + R$$

or

$$P(r) = R$$

We have proved the Remainder Theorem.

> **Remainder Theorem**
> If a polynomial $P(x)$ is divided by $x - r$, the remainder is $P(r)$.

Example 1 Applying the Remainder Theorem

Determine the remainder when $P(x) = 2x^3 - 3x^2 - 2x + 1$ is divided by $x - 3$.

Solution

By the Remainder Theorem, the remainder is $R = P(3)$. We then have

$$R = P(3) = 2(3)^3 - 3(3)^2 - 2(3) + 1 = 22$$

We can verify this result by using synthetic division.

$$
\begin{array}{r|rrrr}
3 & 2 & -3 & -2 & 1 \\
  &   & 6 & 9 & 21 \\
\hline
  & 2 & 3 & 7 & \mathbf{22}
\end{array}
$$

The numeral in boldface is the remainder, so we have verified that $R = 22$.

✔ Progress Check

Determine the remainder when $3x^2 - 2x - 6$ is divided by $x + 2$ using both the method of substitution and the method of synthetic division.

Answer
10

Factor Theorem

Assume that a polynomial $P(x)$ can be written as a product of polynomials.

$$P(x) = D(x)Q(x)$$

where both $D(x)$ and $Q(x)$ are of degree greater than 0. Since $D(x) \neq 0$,

$$\frac{P(x)}{D(x)} = \frac{D(x)Q(x)}{D(x)} = Q(x)$$

and we have the following definition.

> The polynomial $D(x)$ is a **factor of a polynomial** $P(x)$ if division of $P(x)$ by $D(x)$ results in a remainder of zero.

We can now combine this rule and the Remainder Theorem to prove the Factor Theorem.

Factor Theorem
A polynomial $P(x)$ has a factor $x - r$ if and only if $P(r) = 0$.

If $x - r$ is a factor of $P(x)$, then division of $P(x)$ by $x - r$ must result in a remainder of zero. By the Remainder Theorem, the remainder is $P(r)$, and hence $P(r) = 0$. Conversely, if $P(r) = 0$, then the remainder is zero and $P(x) = (x - r)Q(x)$ for some polynomial $Q(x)$ of degree one less than that of $P(x)$. By definition, $x - r$ is then a factor of $P(x)$.

Example 2 Applying the Factor Theorem

Show that $x + 2$ is a factor of

$$P(x) = x^3 - x^2 - 2x + 8$$

Solution

By the Factor Theorem, $x + 2 = x - (-2)$ is a factor if $P(-2) = 0$. Using synthetic division to evaluate $P(-2)$,

$$
\begin{array}{r|rrrr}
-2 & 1 & -1 & -2 & 8 \\
   &   & -2 & 6 & -8 \\
\hline
   & 1 & -3 & 4 & 0
\end{array}
$$

we see that $P(-2) = 0$. Alternatively, we can evaluate

$$P(-2) = (-2)^3 - (-2)^2 - 2(-2) + 8 = 0$$

We conclude that $x + 2$ is a factor of $P(x)$.

✔ Progress Check
Show that $x - 1$ is a factor of $P(x) = 3x^6 - 3x^5 - 4x^4 + 6x^3 - 2x^2 - x + 1$.

Summary

The following are equivalent statements for polynomial function $P(x)$ and real number r.

- r is a zero of $P(x)$.

- $x = r$ is a *root* of the equation $P(x) = 0$.

- $P(r) = 0$ (Remainder Theorem)

- $x - r$ is a *factor* of $P(x)$.   (Factor Theorem)

- r is an x-intercept of the graph of the function $y = P(x)$.

Exercise Set 4.4

In Exercises 1–6, use the Remainder Theorem and synthetic division to find $P(r)$.

1. $P(x) = x^3 - 4x^2 + 1, \quad r = 2$

2. $P(x) = x^4 - 3x^2 - 5x, \quad r = -1$

3. $P(x) = x^5 - 2, \quad r = -2$

4. $P(x) = 2x^4 - 3x^3 + 6, \quad r = 2$

5. $P(x) = x^6 - 3x^4 + 2x^3 + 4, \quad r = -1$

6. $P(x) = x^6 - 2, \quad r = 1$

In Exercises 7–12, use the Remainder Theorem to determine the remainder when $P(x)$ is divided by $x - r$.

7. $P(x) = x^3 - 2x^2 + x - 3, \quad x - 2$

8. $P(x) = 2x^3 + x^2 - 5, \quad x + 2$

9. $P(x) = -4x^3 + 6x - 2, \quad x - 1$

10. $P(x) = 6x^5 - 3x^4 + 2x^2 + 7, \quad x + 1$

11. $P(x) = x^5 - 30, \quad x + 2$

12. $P(x) = x^4 - 16, \quad x - 2$

In Exercises 13–20, use the Factor Theorem to decide whether or not the first polynomial is a factor of the second polynomial.

13. $x - 2, \quad x^3 - x^2 - 5x + 6$

14. $x - 1, \quad x^3 + 4x^2 - 3x + 1$

15. $x + 2, \quad x^4 - 3x - 5$

16. $x + 1, \quad 2x^3 - 3x^2 + x + 6$

17. $x + 3, \quad x^3 + 27$

18. $x + 2, \quad x^4 + 16$

19. $x + 2, \quad x^4 - 16$

20. $x - 3, \quad x^3 + 27$

In Exercises 21–26, determine whether the given value of x is a root of the given polynomial equation.

21. $x^3 - 3x + 2 = 0, \quad x = -2$

22. $3x^2 - x + 1 = 0, \quad x = 2$

23. $-2 + x + 2x^2 - x^3 = 0, \quad x = -1$

24. $3x^2 + 2x - 1 = 0, \quad x = \dfrac{1}{3}$

25. $2x^2 + 4x - 1 = 0, \quad x = \dfrac{3}{2}$

26. $x^3 + 27 = 0, \quad x = -3$

In Exercises 27–32, determine all zeros of the polynomial function f.

27. $f(x) = (x + 1)(x - 2)$

28. $f(x) = (x - 1)^2(x + 3)$

29. $f(x) = (1 - x)(2x - 1)$

30. $f(x) = (2 - x)(x + 2)(1 + x)$

31. $f(x) = (1 - 2x)^2(1 + 2x)$

32. $f(x) = x^3(x - 2)^2$

In Exercises 33–36, use synthetic division to determine the value of k or r as requested.

33. Determine the values of r for which division of $x^2 - 2x - 1$ by $x - r$ has a remainder of 2.

34. Determine the values of r for which
$$\frac{x^2 - 6x - 1}{x - r}$$
has a remainder of -9.

35. Determine the values of k for which $x - 2$ is a factor of $x^3 - 3x^2 + kx - 1$.

36. Determine the values of k for which $2k^2x^3 + 3kx^2 - 2$ is divisible by $x - 1$.

37. Use the Factor Theorem to show that $x - 2$ is a factor of $P(x) = x^8 - 256$.

38. Use the Factor Theorem to show that $P(x) = 2x^4 + 3x^2 + 2$ has no factor of the form $x - r$, where r is a real number.

39. Use the Factor Theorem to show that $x - y$ is a factor of $x^n - y^n$, where n is a natural number.

40. *Mathematics in Writing:* Explain in your own words how and why the remainder theorem works to find a function value. Investigate whether the remainder theorem still yields correct function values when the input is a complex number. (If your graphing calculator has an i key, you can perform the operations very quickly!)

Chapter 4 ■ Polynomial Functions 265

4.5 Factors and Zeros

Complex Numbers and Their Properties

We introduced the complex number system in Section 1.8. We then used this number system in Section 2.3 to provide solutions to quadratic equations. Recall that $z = a + bi$ is said to be a complex number where a and b are real numbers, and the imaginary unit $i = \sqrt{-1}$ has the property that $i^2 - 1$. We say that $a + bi$ is the *algebraic form* of z. We defined fundamental operations with complex numbers in the following way.

Equality: $a + bi = c + di$ if $a = c$ and $b = d$

Addition: $(a + bi) + (c + di) = (a + c) + (b + d)i$

Multiplication: $(a + bi)(c + di) = (ac - bd) + (ad + bc)i$

Conjugate: The conjugate of $a + bi$ is $a - bi$

Division: $\dfrac{a + bi}{c + di} = \dfrac{ac + bd}{c^2 + d^2} + \dfrac{bc - ad}{c^2 + d^2}i, \quad c^2 + d^2 \neq 0$

With this background, we can now explore further properties of the complex number system.

If we let $z = a + bi$, it is customary to write the conjugate $a - bi$ as $\bar{z}$. We will need the following properties of complex numbers and their conjugates.

Properties of Complex Conjugates

If z and w are complex numbers, then

1. $\bar{z} = \bar{w}$ if and only if $z = w$

2. $\bar{z} = z$ if and only if z is a real number

3. $\overline{z+w} = \bar{z} + \bar{w}$

4. $\overline{z \cdot w} = \bar{z} \cdot \bar{w}$

5. $\overline{z^n} = \bar{z}^n$, n a positive integer

To prove Properties 1–5, let $z = a + bi$ and $w = c + di$. Properties 1 and 2 follow directly from the definition of equality of complex numbers. To prove Property 3, we note that $z + w = (a + c) + (b + d)i$. Then, by the definition of a complex conjugate,

$$\overline{z+w} = (a + c) - (b + d)i$$
$$= (a - bi) + (c - di)$$
$$= \bar{z} + \bar{w}$$

Properties 4 and 5 can be proved in a similar manner, although a proof of Property 5 requires the use of mathematical induction, a method to be discussed in a later chapter.

Example 1   Properties of Complex Conjugates

If $z = 1 + 2i$ and $w = 3 - i$, verify that

a. $\overline{z+w} = \overline{z} + \overline{w}$ 　　　　 b. $\overline{z \cdot w} = \overline{z} \cdot \overline{w}$ 　　　　 c. $\overline{z^2} = \overline{z}^2$

Solution

a. $z + w = (1 + 2i) + (3 - i)$ 　　　 $\overline{z} = 1 - 2i$

$\quad\quad\quad = 4 + i$ 　　　　　　　　　 $\overline{w} = 3 + i$

$\overline{z + w} = 4 - i$ 　　　　　　　　 $\overline{z} + \overline{w} = (1 - 2i) + (3 + i)$

$\quad\quad\quad\quad\quad\quad\quad\quad\quad\quad\quad = 4 - i$

Thus, $\overline{z+w} = \overline{z} + \overline{w}$.

b. $z \cdot w = (1 + 2i)(3 - i) = 5 + 5i$ 　　 $\overline{z} = 1 - 2i$

$\overline{z \cdot w} = 5 - 5i$ 　　　　　　　　　 $\overline{w} = 3 + i$

$\quad\quad\quad\quad\quad\quad\quad\quad\quad\quad\quad \overline{z} \cdot \overline{w} = (1 - 2i)(3 + i)$

$\quad\quad\quad\quad\quad\quad\quad\quad\quad\quad\quad\quad\quad = 5 - 5i$

Thus, $\overline{z \cdot w} = \overline{z} \cdot \overline{w}$.

c. $z^2 = (1 + 2i)(1 + 2i)$ 　　　　　 $\overline{z}^2 = (1 - 2i)(1 - 2i)$

$\quad\quad = -3 + 4i$ 　　　　　　　　　　 $\quad = -3 - 4i$

$\overline{z^2} = -3 - 4i$

Thus, $\overline{z^2} = \overline{z}^2$.

📟 Graphing Calculator Alert

Your graphing calculator may be able to "handle" operations involving complex numbers. Check for an "i" key. The answers may be displayed in the standard form $a + bi$. Even an operation like finding the conjugate may be available. Check your graphing calculator manual for details. The manual may be available online at the manufacturer's website.

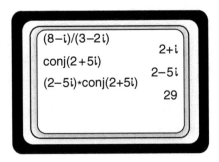

✔ **Progress Check**

If $z = 2 + 3i$ and $w = \frac{1}{2} - 2i$, verify that

a. $\overline{z+w} = \overline{z} + \overline{w}$ b. $\overline{z \cdot w} = \overline{z} \cdot \overline{w}$ c. $\overline{z^2} = \overline{z}^2$ d. $\overline{w^3} = \overline{w}^3$

Factor Theorem

By using the Factor Theorem, we can show that there is a close relationship between the factors and the zeros of the polynomial $P(x)$. By definition, r is a zero of $P(x)$ is equivalent to $P(r) = 0$. But the Factor Theorem tells us that $P(r) = 0$ is equivalent to $x - r$ being a factor of $P(x)$. This leads to the following alternative statement of the Factor Theorem.

Factor Theorem
A polynomial $P(x)$ has a zero at $x = r$ if and only if $x - r$ is a factor of $P(x)$.

Example 2   Application of the Factor Theorem
Find a polynomial $P(x)$ of degree 3 whose zeros are -1, 1 and -2.

Solution
By the Factor Theorem, $x + 1$, $x - 1$ and $x + 2$ are factors of $P(x)$. The product

$$P(x) = (x + 1)(x - 1)(x + 2) = x^3 + 2x^2 - x - 2$$

is a polynomial of degree 3 with the desired zeros. Note that multiplying $P(x)$ by any nonzero real number results in another polynomial with the same zeros. For example, the polynomial

$$5 \cdot P(x) = 5x^3 + 10x^2 - 5x - 10$$

also has -1, 1 and -2 as its zeros. Thus, the answer is not unique.

✔ **Progress Check**
Find a polynomial $P(x)$ of degree 3 whose zeros are 2, 4 and -3.

Answer
$x^3 - 3x^2 - 10x + 24$

We began this chapter with the question, "Does a polynomial always have a zero?" The answer was supplied by Carl Friedrich Gauss (1777–1855) at age 22 in his doctoral dissertation. The importance of this theorem is reflected in its title.

The Fundamental Theorem of Algebra—Part 1

Every polynomial $P(x)$ of degree $n \geq 1$ has at least one zero among the complex numbers.

Note that the zero guaranteed by this theorem may be a real number since the real numbers are a subset of the complex number system. Furthermore, we may now see why it was necessary to create the complex numbers. No system beyond the complex numbers is required. (The proof of this theorem is beyond the scope of this text.)

In order to determine how many zeros a polynomial of degree n has, we must consider the following theorem.

Linear Factor Theorem

A polynomial $P(x)$ of degree $n \geq 1$ can be written as the product of n linear factors:

$$P(x) = a(x - r_1)(x - r_2) \cdots (x - r_n)$$

Note that a is the leading coefficient of $P(x)$ and that $r_1, r_2, \ldots, r_n$ may be complex numbers.

To prove this theorem, we first note that the Fundamental Theorem of Algebra guarantees the existence of a zero r_1. By the Factor Theorem, $x - r_1$ is a factor, and consequently,

$$P(x) = (x - r_1)Q_1(x) \tag{1}$$

where $Q_1(x)$ is a polynomial of degree $n - 1$. If $n - 1 \geq 1$ then $Q_1(x)$ must have a zero r_2. Thus,

$$Q_1(x) = (x - r_2)Q_2(x)$$

where $Q_2(x)$ is of degree $n - 2$. Substituting in Equation (1) for $Q_1(x)$, we have

$$P(x) = (x - r_1)(x - r_2)Q_2(x)$$

This process is repeated n times until $Q_n(x) = a$ is of degree 0. Hence,

$$P(x) = a(x - r_1)(x - r_2) \cdots (x - r_n) \tag{2}$$

Since a is the leading coefficient of the polynomial on the right side of Equation (2), it must also be the leading coefficient of $P(x)$.

Example 3   Application of the Linear Factor Theorem

Find the polynomial $P(x)$ of degree 3 that has the zeros -2, i and $-i$, and satisfies $P(1) = -3$.

Solution

Since -2, i and $-i$ are zeros of $P(x)$, we may write

$$P(x) = a(x + 2)(x - i)(x + i)$$

To find the constant a, we use the condition $P(1) = -3$.

$$P(1) = -3 = a(1 + 2)(1 - i)(1 + i) = 6a$$

$$a = -\frac{1}{2}$$

Therefore,

$$P(x) = -\frac{1}{2}(x + 2)(x - i)(x + i)$$

Multiplicity of a Zero

Recall that the zeros of a polynomial need not be different from one another. The polynomial

$$P(x) = x^2 - 2x + 1$$

can be written in factored form as

$$P(x) = (x - 1)(x - 1)$$

This shows that the zeros of $P(x)$ are 1 and 1. Since a zero is associated with a factor, and a factor may be repeated, we may have repeated zeros. If the factor $x - r$ appears k times, we say that r is a **zero of multiplicity** k.

We now establish an alternative form of the Fundamental Theorem of Algebra.

The Fundamental Theorem of Algebra—Part 2

If $P(x)$ is a polynomial of degree $n \geq 1$ then $P(x)$ has precisely n zeros among the complex numbers when a zero of multiplicity k is counted k times.

We can prove this theorem as follows: If we write $P(x)$ in the form of Equation (2), we see that $r_1, r_2, \ldots, r_n$ are zeros of the polynomial $P(x)$, hence there exist n zeros. If there is an additional zero r that is different from the zeros $r_1, r_2, \ldots, r_n$, then $r - r_1$, $r - r_2, \ldots, r - r_n$ are all different from 0. Substituting r for x in Equation (2) yields

$$P(r) = a(r - r_1)(r - r_2) \cdots (r - r_n)$$

which cannot equal 0, since the product of nonzero numbers cannot equal 0. Thus, r_1, $r_2, \ldots, r_n$ are zeros of $P(x)$ and there are no other zeros. We conclude that $P(x)$ has precisely n zeros.

Example 4 Polynomials in Factored Form

Find all zeros of the polynomial

$$P(x) = \left(x - \frac{1}{2}\right)^3 (x + i)(x - 5)^4$$

Solution

The distinct zeros of the polynomial are $\frac{1}{2}$, $-i$ and 5. Furthermore, $\frac{1}{2}$ is a zero of multiplicity 3, $-i$ is a zero of multiplicity 1 and 5 is a zero of multiplicity 4. ■

If we know that r is a zero of $P(x)$, we can write

$$P(x) = (x - r)Q(x)$$

We can then determine $Q(x)$ as the quotient

$$Q(x) = \frac{P(x)}{x - r}$$

This means that the degree of $Q(x)$ is one less than the degree of $P(x)$. Furthermore, if r_1 is a zero of $Q(x)$, then

$$P(r_1) = (r_1 - r)Q(r_1) = (r_1 - r) \cdot 0 = 0$$

Therefore, r_1 is also a zero of $P(x)$. We call $Q(x)$ the **quotient polynomial,** or **deflated polynomial,** of $P(x)$. Sometimes $Q(x) = 0$ is referred to as the **deflated equation** of the polynomial equation $P(x) = 0$.

Example 5 Finding Zeros of Polynomials

If 4 is a zero of the polynomial $P(x) = x^3 - 8x^2 + 21x - 20$, find the other zeros.

Solution

Since 4 is a zero of $P(x)$, $x - 4$ is a factor of $P(x)$. Therefore,

$$P(x) = (x - 4)Q(x)$$

To find the quotient polynomial, we compute

$$Q(x) = \frac{P(x)}{x - 4}$$

by synthetic division.

$$
\begin{array}{r|rrrr}
4 & 1 & -8 & 21 & -20 \\
  &   & 4 & -16 & 20 \\
\hline
  & 1 & -4 & -5 & 0
\end{array}
$$

$\underbrace{\qquad\qquad}_{\substack{\text{coefficients} \\ \text{of } Q(x)}}$ $\overset{|}{\underset{\text{remainder}}{}}$

The deflated equation is

$$x^2 - 4x + 5 = 0$$

Using the quadratic formula, we find the roots of the deflated equation to be $2 + i$ and $2 - i$. Therefore, the zeros of $P(x)$ are 4, $2 + i$ and $2 - i$.

✔ **Progress Check**

If -2 is a zero of the polynomial $P(x) = x^3 - 7x - 6$, find the remaining zeros.

Answer

$-1, 3$

Example 6 **Finding Zeros and Factors of Polynomials**

If -1 is a zero of multiplicity 2 of $P(x) = x^4 + 4x^3 + 2x^2 - 4x - 3$, find the remaining zeros and write $P(x)$ as a product of linear factors.

Solution

Since -1 is a double zero of $P(x)$, then $(x + 1)^2$ is a factor of $P(x)$. Therefore,

$$P(x) = (x + 1)^2 Q(x)$$

or

$$P(x) = (x^2 + 2x + 1)Q(x)$$

Using polynomial division, we divide both sides of this equation by $x^2 + 2x + 1$ to obtain

$$Q(x) = \frac{x^4 + 4x^3 + 2x^2 - 4x - 3}{x^2 + 2x + 1}$$

$$= x^2 + 2x - 3$$

$$= (x - 1)(x + 3)$$

The roots of the deflated equation $Q(x) = 0$ are 1 and -3, and these are the remaining zeros of $P(x)$. By the Linear Factor Theorem,

$$P(x) = (x + 1)^2(x - 1)(x + 3)$$

✔ **Progress Check**

If -2 is a zero of multiplicity 2 of $P(x) = x^4 + 4x^3 + 5x^2 + 4x + 4$, write $P(x)$ as a product of linear factors.

Answer

$P(x) = (x + 2)(x + 2)(x + i)(x - i)$

Conjugate Zeros

From the quadratic formula, if a quadratic equation with real coefficients has a complex root $a + bi$, $b \neq 0$, then the conjugate $a - bi$ is the other root. The following theorem extends this result to a polynomial of degree n with real coefficients.

Conjugate Zeros Theorem

If $P(x)$ is a polynomial of degree $n \geq 1$ with real coefficients, and if $a + bi$, $b \neq 0$, is a zero of $P(x)$, then the complex conjugate $a - bi$ is also a zero of $P(x)$.

To prove the Conjugate Zeros Theorem, we let $z = a + bi$ and make use of the Properties of Complex Conjugates developed earlier in this section. We may write

$$P(x) = a_n x^n + a_{n-1} x^{n-1} + \cdots + a_1 x + a_0$$

Since z is a zero of $P(x)$,

$$a_n z^n + a_{n-1} z^{n-1} + \cdots + a_n z + a_0 = 0$$

From Property 1, we may take the conjugate of both sides of the equation to obtain

$$\overline{a_n z^n + a_{n-1} z^{n-1} + \cdots + a_1 z + a_0} = \overline{0} = 0$$

Properties 3 and 4 state that we may distribute the conjugate to sums and products respectively.

$$\overline{a_n z^n} + \overline{a_{n-1} z^{n-1}} + \cdots + \overline{a_1 z} + \overline{a_0} = 0$$

$$\overline{a_n}\,\overline{z^n} + \overline{a_{n-1}}\,\overline{z^{n-1}} + \cdots + \overline{a_1}\,\overline{z} + \overline{a_0} = 0$$

Since $a_0, a_1, \ldots, a_n$ are all real numbers, we know that $\overline{a_0} = a_0$, $\overline{a_1} = a_1$, $\ldots$, $\overline{a_n} = a_n$. Finally, using Property 5, we obtain

$$a_n \overline{z}^n + a_{n-1} \overline{z}^{n-1} + \cdots + a_1 \overline{z} + a_0 = 0$$

which establishes that $\overline{z}$ is a zero of $P(x)$.

Example 7   Application of the Conjugate Zeros Theorem

Find a polynomial $P(x)$ with real coefficients of degree 3, whose zeros include -2 and $1 - i$.

Solution

Since $1 - i$ is a zero of $P(x)$, it follows from the Conjugate Zeros Theorem that $1 + i$ is also a zero of $P(x)$. By the Factor Theorem, $x + 2$, $x - (1 - i)$ and $x - (1 + i)$ are factors of $P(x)$. Therefore,

$$\begin{aligned}
P(x) &= (x + 2)[x - (1 - i)][x - (1 + i)] \\
&= (x + 2)(x^2 - 2x + 2) \\
&= x^3 - 2x + 4
\end{aligned}$$

✔ **Progress Check**

Find a polynomial $P(x)$ with real coefficients of degree 4, whose zeros include i and $-3 + i$.

Answer

$P(x) = x^4 + 6x^3 + 11x^2 + 6x + 10$

The following is a corollary of the Conjugate Zeros Theorem.

A polynomial $P(x)$ of degree $n \geq 1$ with real coefficients can be written as a product of linear and quadratic factors with real coefficients, where the quadratic factors have no real zeros.

By the Linear Factor Theorem, we may write

$$P(x) = a(x - r_1)(x - r_2) \cdots (x - r_n)$$

where $r_1, r_2, \ldots, r_n$ are the n zeros of $P(x)$. Some of these zeros may not be real numbers. Since the multiplicity of conjugate zeros must be the same (Why?), a complex zero $a + bi$, $b \neq 0$, may be paired with its conjugate $a - bi$ to provide the quadratic factor

$$[x - (a + bi)][x - (a - bi)] = x^2 - 2ax + a^2 + b^2 \tag{3}$$

which has real coefficients. Thus, a *quadratic* factor with real coefficients results from each pair of complex conjugate zeros; a *linear* factor with real coefficients results from each real zero. Furthermore, the discriminant of the quadratic factor in Equation (3) is $-4b^2$, which is always negative. Thus, this quadratic factor could never have real zeros.

Polynomials with Complex Coefficients

Although the definition of a polynomial, given at the beginning of this chapter, permits the coefficients to be complex numbers, we have limited our examples to polynomials with real coefficients. For completeness, we point out that both the Linear Factor Theorem and the Fundamental Theorem of Algebra hold for polynomials with complex coefficients.

On the other hand, the Conjugate Zeros Theorem may not hold if the polynomial $P(x)$ has complex coefficients. To see this, consider the polynomial

$$P(x) = x - (2 + i)$$

which has a complex coefficient and has the zero $2 + i$. The conjugate $\overline{2 + i} = 2 - i$ is *not* a zero of $P(x)$. Therefore, the Conjugate Zeros Theorem fails to apply.

Example 8   Polynomials with Complex Coefficients

Find a polynomial $P(x)$ of degree 2 with complex coefficients that has the zeros -1 and $1 - i$.

Solution

Since -1 is a zero of $P(x)$, $x + 1$ is a factor. Similarly, $x - (1 - i)$ is also a factor of $P(x)$. We can then write

$$P(x) = (x + 1)[x - (1 - i)]$$
$$= x^2 + ix - 1 + i$$

which is a polynomial of degree 2 with complex coefficients with the required zeros.   ■

Exercise Set 4.5

In Exercises 1–6, multiply by the conjugate and simplify.

1. $2 - i$

2. $3 + i$

3. $3 + 4i$

4. $2 - 3i$

5. $-4 - 2i$

6. $5 + 2i$

In Exercises 7–15, perform the indicated operations and write the answer in the form $a + bi$.

7. $\dfrac{2 + 5i}{1 - 3i}$

8. $\dfrac{1 + 3i}{2 - 5i}$

9. $\dfrac{3 - 4i}{3 + 4i}$

10. $\dfrac{4 - 3i}{4 + 3i}$

11. $\dfrac{3 - 2i}{2 - i}$

12. $\dfrac{2 - 3i}{3 - i}$

13. $\dfrac{2 + 5i}{3i}$

14. $\dfrac{5 - 2i}{-3i}$

15. $\dfrac{4i}{2 + i}$

In Exercises 16–21, find the reciprocal and write the answer in the form $a + bi$.

16. $3 + 2i$

17. $4 + 3i$

18. $\dfrac{1}{2} - i$

19. $1 - \dfrac{1}{3}i$

20. $-7i$

21. $-5i$

22. Prove that the multiplicative inverse of the complex number $a + bi$, a and b not both 0 is

$$\dfrac{a}{a^2 + b^2} - \dfrac{b}{a^2 + b^2}i$$

23. If z and w are complex numbers, prove that

$$\overline{z \cdot w} = \overline{z} \cdot \overline{w}$$

24. If z is a complex number, verify that $\overline{z^2} = \overline{z}^2$ and $\overline{z^3} = \overline{z}^3$.

In Exercises 25–30, find a polynomial $P(x)$ of lowest degree that has the indicated zeros.

25. $2, -4, 4$

26. $5, -5, 1, -1$

27. $-1, -2, -3$

28. $-3, \sqrt{2}, -\sqrt{2}$

29. $4, 1 \pm \sqrt{3}$

30. $1, 2, 2 \pm \sqrt{2}$

In Exercises 31–34, find the polynomial $P(x)$ of lowest degree that has the indicated zeros and satisfies the given condition.

31. $\dfrac{1}{2}, \dfrac{1}{2}, -2$; $P(2) = 3$

32. $3, 3, -2, 2$; $P(4) = 12$

33. $\sqrt{2}, -\sqrt{2}, 4$; $P(-1) = 5$

34. $\dfrac{1}{2}, -2, 5$; $P(0) = 5$

In Exercises 35–42, find the roots of the equation $P(x) = 0$. Then, determine appropriate WINDOW values and GRAPH $y = P(x)$ on your graphing calculator.

35. $(x - 3)(x + 1)(x - 2) = 0$

36. $(x - 3)(x^2 - 3x - 4) = 0$

37. $(x + 2)(x^2 - 16) = 0$

38. $(x^2 - x)(x^2 - 2x + 5) = 0$

39. $(x^2 + 3x + 2)(2x^2 + x) = 0$

40. $(x^2 + x + 4)(x - 3)^2 = 0$

41. $(x - 5)^3(x + 5)^2 = 0$

42. $(x + 1)^2(x + 3)^4(x - 2) = 0$

In Exercises 43–46, find a polynomial that has the indicated zeros and no others.

43. -2 of multiplicity 3

44. 1 of multiplicity 2, -4 of multiplicity 1

45. $\frac{1}{2}$ of multiplicity 2, -1 of multiplicity 2

46. -1 of multiplicity 2,   0 and 2 each of multiplicity 1

In Exercises 47–52, use the given root(s) to help in finding the remaining roots of the equation.

47. $x^3 - 3x - 2 = 0$; -1

48. $x^3 - 7x^2 + 4x + 24 = 0$;   3

49. $x^3 - 8x^2 + 18x - 15 = 0$;   5

50. $x^3 - 2x^2 - 7x - 4 = 0$; -1

51. $x^4 + x^3 - 12x^2 - 28x - 16 = 0$; -2 (double root)

52. $x^4 - 2x^2 + 1 = 0$;   1 (double root)

In Exercises 53–60, use your graphing calculator to GRAPH the given polynomial functions in the viewing rectangle $-10 \le X \le 10$ and $-100 \le Y \le 100$.

53. $y = (x + 2)(x - 3)$

54. $y = (x + 2)(x - 3)^2$

55. $y = (x + 2)(x - 3)^3$

56. $y = (x + 2)^2(x - 3)$

57. $y = (x + 2)^3(x - 3)$

58. $y = (x + 2)^2(x - 3)^2$

59. $y = (x + 2)^3(x - 3)^2$

60. $y = (x + 2)^3(x - 3)^3$

In Exercises 61–68, predict the shape of the following polynomial functions near $x = -2$ and near $x = 3$. Determine appropriate values for YMIN and YMAX when $-10 \le X \le 10$. Use your graphing calculator to GRAPH the functions to verify your predictions.

61. $y = (x + 2)(x - 3)^4$

62. $y = (x + 2)(x - 3)^5$

63. $y = (x + 2)^4(x - 3)$

64. $y = (x + 2)^4(x - 3)^2$

65. $y = (x + 2)^4(x - 3)^3$

66. $y = (x + 2)^4(x - 3)^4$

67. $y = (x + 2)^4(x - 3)^5$

68. $y = (x + 2)^5(x - 3)^5$

In Exercises 69–74, find a polynomial that has the indicated zeros and no others.

69. $1 + 3i, -2$

70. $1, -1, 2 - i$

71. $1 + i, 2 - i$

72. $-2, 3, 1 + 2i$

73. -2 is a root of multiplicity 2, $3 - 2i$

74. 3 is a triple root, $-i$

In Exercises 75–80, use the given root(s) to help in writing the given equation as a product of linear and quadratic factors with real coefficients.

75. $x^3 - 7x^2 + 16x - 10 = 0$; $3 - i$

76. $x^3 + x^2 - 7x + 65 = 0$; $2 + 3i$

77. $x^4 + 4x^3 + 13x^2 + 18x + 20 = 0$; $-1 - 2i$

78. $x^4 + 3x^3 - 5x^2 - 29x - 30 = 0$; $-2 + i$

79. $x^5 + 3x^4 - 12x^3 - 42x^2 + 32x + 120 = 0$;
    $-3 - i, -2$

80. $x^5 - 8x^4 + 29x^3 - 54x^2 + 48x - 16 = 0$; $2 + 2i, 2$

81. Write a polynomial $P(x)$ with complex coefficients that has the zero $a + bi$, $b \ne 0$, and that does not have $a - bi$ as a zero.

82. Prove that a polynomial equation of degree 4 with real coefficients has four real roots, two real roots or no real roots.

83. Prove that a polynomial equation of odd degree with real coefficients has at least one real root.

84. Prove that conjugate roots of a polynomial equation with real coefficients have the same multiplicity.

85. *Zeros and Extreme Values:* If you go on to study calculus, you will learn that the zeros of one function can often be used to find the maximum or minimum values of another function. For instance, the zeros of

$$12x^2 - 480x + 3600$$

can be used to find the answer to Exercise 37 in Section 4.2.

a. Find the zeros.

b. What is the relationship between the zeros of this function and the maximum value of the volume?

c. What is the significance of the second zero of the quadratic function?

Applications 4.5

1. The total cost of a book (in dollars) is given by $C(x) = 3x^3 - 6x^2 + 108x + 11$, where x is the demand for the book.

   a. Sketch the graph of the function.

   b. Find the value of x that gives a total cost of $628.

   c. If the demand function is given by
   $p(x) = -x^2 + 10x + 330$, find the value of x that gives the profit of $910.

2. Based on records from 2001 through 2006, sewage services paid for by households in 60 Boston–area communities that use an average of 90,000 gallons of water a year is given by $C(t) = 2.16t^3 + 40t + 756$ $(0 \le t \le 6)$, where $C(t)$ is measured in dollars/year and t in years, with $t = 0$ corresponding to 2001.

   a. What was the average amount paid by a household in 2003 for water and sewage services?

   b. If the trend continued, what was the average amount in 2007?

   c. When will the average amount reach $934.32?

3. The tuition at Curry College from 2007 to 2011 is given in the following table.

Year	2007	2008	2009	2010	2011
Tuition($)	24,500	25,600	27,000	29,000	30,700

A third degree polynomial mathematical model giving the approximate tuition over the period in the question is given by $T(t) = -50t^3 + 428.57t^2 + 635.71t + 24,517.14$ where t is measured in years, with $t = 0$ corresponding to 2007.

   a. Sketch the graph of the function and the given data on the same set of axes.

   b. Assuming that the projection held and the trend continued, what will be Curry College tuition in 2012?

   c. Can you use this model to predict Curry College tuition in 2017? Explain your answer.

   d. When will the tuition reach $32,960?

4.6   Real, Complex and Rational Zeros

In this section we will restrict our investigation to polynomials with real coefficients. Our objective is to obtain some information concerning the number of positive real zeros and the number of negative real zeros of such polynomials.

If the terms of a polynomial with real coefficients are written in descending order, then a **variation in sign** occurs whenever two successive terms have opposite signs. In determining the number of variations in sign, we ignore terms with zero coefficients. The polynomial.

$$4x^5 - 3x^4 - 2x^2 + 1$$

has two variations in sign. The French mathematician René Descartes (1596–1650), who provided us with the foundations of analytic geometry, also gave us a theorem relating the nature of the real zeros of polynomials to the variations in sign. The proof of Descartes's Theorem is outlined in Exercises 45–50.

> **Descartes's Rule of Signs**
>
> If $P(x)$ is a polynomial with real coefficients and a nonzero constant term, then
>
> a. the number of positive zeros is equal to the number of variations in sign of $P(x)$ less some nonnegative even number that could be 0;
>
> b. the number of negative zeros is equal to the number of variations in sign of $P(-x)$ less some nonnegative even number that could be 0.

If it is determined that a polynomial of degree n has r real zeros, then the remaining $n - r$ zeros must consist of groups of conjugate pairs of complex numbers. Therefore, we see that $n - r$ must be an even number, possibly 0.

To apply Descartes's Rule of Signs to the polynomial

$$P(x) = 3x^5 + 2x^4 - x^3 + 2x - 3$$

we first note that there are three variations in sign as indicated. Thus, either there are three positive zeros or there is one positive zero. Next, we form $P(-x)$,

$$P(-x) = 3(-x)^5 + 2(-x)^4 - (-x)^3 + 2(-x) - 3$$
$$= -3x^5 + 2x^4 + x^3 - 2x - 3$$

This can also be obtained by changing the signs of the coefficients of the odd-power terms. We see that $P(-x)$ has two variations in sign, and conclude that $P(x)$ has either two negative zeros or no negative zeros. We summarize our results in Table 1.

Table 1   Analyzing the Nature of Zeros

$P(x) = 3x^5 + 2x^4 - x^3 + 2x - 3$			
Possible Positive Zeros	Possible Negative Zeros	Possible Complex Zeros	Total Number of Zeros
3	2	0	5
1	0	4	5
1	2	2	5

Example 1   Application of Descartes's Rule of Signs

Use Descartes's Rule of Signs to analyze the roots of the equation

$$2x^5 + 7x^4 + 3x^2 - 2 = 0$$

Solution

Since

$$P(x) = 2x^5 + 7x^4 + 3x^2 - 2$$

has one variation in sign, there is precisely one positive zero. We calculate $P(-x)$ to be

$$P(-x) = -\underbrace{2x^5 + 7x^4 + 3x^2}_{} - 2$$

There are two variations in sign, so $P(x)$ has either two negative zeros or no negative zeros. Since $P(x)$ has five zeros, the possibilities are

one positive zero, two negative zeros, two complex zeros

one positive zero, zero negative zeros, four complex zeros

✔ Progress Check

Use Descartes's Rule of Signs to analyze the nature of the roots of the equation

$$x^6 + 5x^4 - 4x^2 - 3 = 0$$

Answer
one positive root, one negative root, four complex roots

Rational Zeros

When the coefficients of a polynomial are all integers, it is possible to search systematically for the *rational* zeros using the following theorem.

Rational Zero Theorem

If the coefficients of the polynomial

$$P(x) = a_n x^n + a_{n-1} x^{n-1} + \cdots + a_1 x + a_0, \qquad a_n \neq 0$$

are all integers and $\frac{p}{q} \neq 0$ is a rational zero reduced to lowest terms, then

a. p is a factor of the constant term a_0, and

b. q is a factor of the leading coefficient a_n.

Proof of Rational Zero Theorem

Since $\frac{p}{q}$ is a zero of $P(x)$, $P\left(\frac{p}{q}\right) = 0$. Thus,

$$a_n\left(\frac{p}{q}\right)^n + a_{n-1}\left(\frac{p}{q}\right)^{n-1} + \cdots + a_1\left(\frac{p}{q}\right) + a_0 = 0 \tag{1}$$

Multiplying Equation (1) by q^n, we have

$$a_n p^n + a_{n-1} p^{n-1} q + \cdots + a_1 p q^{n-1} + a_0 q^n = 0 \tag{2}$$

or

$$a_np^n + a_{n-1}p^{n-1}q + \cdots + a_1pq^{n-1} = -a_0q^n \tag{3}$$

Taking the common factor p out of the left-hand side of Equation (3) yields

$$p(a_np^{n-1} + a_{n-1}p^{n-2}q + \cdots + a_1q^{n-1}) = -a_0q^n$$

After dividing by p, we obtain

$$a_np^{n-1} + a_{n-1}p^{n-2}q + \cdots + a_1q^{n-1} = \frac{-a_0q^n}{p} \tag{4}$$

Since $a_1, a_2, \ldots, a_n$, p and q are all integers, the left-hand side of Equation (4) is an integer, hence, the right-hand side is also an integer. Since $\frac{p}{q}$ is assumed to be reduced to lowest terms, p and q have no factors in common. Therefore, p must be a factor of a_0, proving part (a).

We can also rewrite Equation (2) in the form

$$q(a_{n-1}p^{n-1} + a_{n-2}p^{n-2}q + \cdots + a_1pq^{n-2} + a_0q^{n-1}) = -a_np^n$$

An argument similar to the preceding one now establishes part (b).

Example 2   Rational Roots of a Polynomial Equation

Find the rational roots of the equation

$$8x^4 - 2x^3 + 7x^2 - 2x - 1 = 0$$

Solution

If $\frac{p}{q}$ is a rational root reduced to lowest terms, then p is a factor of 1 and q is a factor of 8. We can now list the possibilities:

possible numerators: ± 1 (the factors of 1)

possible denominators: $\pm 1, \pm 2, \pm 4, \pm 8$ (the factors of 8)

possible rational roots: $\pm 1, \pm\dfrac{1}{2}, \pm\dfrac{1}{4}, \pm\dfrac{1}{8}$

If $P(x) = 8x^4 - 2x^3 + 7x^2 - 2x - 1$, we see that $P(1) \neq 0$ and $P(-1) \neq 0$. Therefore, 1 and -1 are not roots. We may also use synthetic division to test if the other candidates are roots. Trying $\frac{1}{2}$ we have

$$
\begin{array}{r|rrrrr}
\tfrac{1}{2} & 8 & -2 & 7 & -2 & -1 \\
 &   & 4 & 1 & 4 & 1 \\
\hline
 & 8 & 2 & 8 & 2 & 0 \\
\end{array}
$$

which demonstrates that $\frac{1}{2}$ is a root. Similarly,

$$
\begin{array}{r|rrrrr}
-\tfrac{1}{4} & 8 & -2 & 7 & -2 & -1 \\
 &   & -2 & 1 & -2 & 1 \\
\hline
 & 8 & -4 & 8 & -4 & 0 \\
\end{array}
$$

which shows that $-\frac{1}{4}$ is also a root. Verify that none of the other possible rational roots produce a zero remainder.

✔ **Progress Check**

Find the rational roots of the equation

$$9x^4 - 12x^3 + 13x^2 - 12x + 4 = 0$$

Answer

$\dfrac{2}{3}, \dfrac{2}{3}$

We can combine the Rational Zero Theorem and the quotient polynomial to give us more powerful methods of finding the zeros of a polynomial.

Example 3 Rational Roots and Deflated Equations

Find the rational roots of the equation

$$8x^5 + 12x^4 + 14x^3 + 13x^2 + 6x + 1 = 0$$

Solution

Since the coefficients of the polynomial are all integers, we may use the Rational Zero Theorem to list the possible rational roots:

> possible numerators: ±1   (the factors of 1)
>
> possible denominators: ±1, ±2, ±4, ±8   (the factors of 8)
>
> possible rational roots: $\pm 1, \pm\dfrac{1}{2}, \pm\dfrac{1}{4}, \pm\dfrac{1}{8}$

If $P(x) = 8x^5 + 12x^4 + 14x^3 + 13x^2 + 6x + 1$, we see that $P(1) \neq 0$, $P(-1) \neq 0$ and $P(\frac{1}{2}) \neq 0$. Therefore 1, -1 and $\frac{1}{2}$ are not roots. Testing $-\frac{1}{2}$ by synthetic division yields

$$
\begin{array}{r|rrrrrr}
-\frac{1}{2} & 8 & 12 & 14 & 13 & 6 & 1 \\
  &   & -4 & -4 & -5 & -4 & -1 \\
\hline
  & 8 & 8 & 10 & 8 & 2 & 0
\end{array}
$$

coefficients of quotient polynomial

Since the remainder is 0, $-\frac{1}{2}$ is a root. We now consider the deflated equation

$$8x^4 + 8x^3 + 10x^2 + 8x + 2 = 0$$

which has the same roots as

$$4x^4 + 4x^3 + 5x^2 + 4x + 1 = 0$$

While 1, -1 and $\frac{1}{2}$ have been eliminated, we must still try $-\frac{1}{2}$ once again.

$$
\begin{array}{r|rrrrr}
-\frac{1}{2} & 4 & 4 & 5 & 4 & 1 \\
  &   & -2 & -1 & -2 & -1 \\
\hline
  & 4 & 2 & 4 & 2 & 0
\end{array}
$$

coefficients of quotient polynomial

Focus on Solving Polynomial Equations

Cardan's Formula
Cardano provided this formula for one root of the cubic equation:

$$x^3 + bx + c = 0$$

$$x = \sqrt[3]{\sqrt{\frac{b^3}{27} + \frac{c^2}{4}} - \frac{c}{2}}$$
$$- \sqrt[3]{\sqrt{\frac{b^3}{27} + \frac{c^2}{4}} + \frac{c}{2}}$$

Try this formula for:
$$x^3 - x = 0$$
$$x^3 - 1 = 0$$
$$x^3 - 3x + 2 = 0$$

The quadratic formula provides us with the solutions of a polynomial equation of the second degree. How about polynomial equations of the third degree? of the fourth degree? of the fifth degree?

The search for formulas expressing the roots of polynomial equations in terms of the coefficients of the equations intrigued mathematicians for hundreds of years. A method for finding the roots of polynomial equations of degree 3 was published around 1535 and is known as Cardan's formula despite the possibility that Geronimo Cardano (also known as Cardan) stole the result from his friend Nicolo Tartaglia. Shortly afterward, a method that is attributed to Ferrari was published for solving polynomial equations of degree 4.

The next 250 years were spent in seeking formulas for the roots of polynomial equations of degree 5 or higher—without success. Finally, early in the nineteenth century, the Norwegian mathematician N. H. Abel and the French mathematician Evariste Galois proved that *no such formulas exist*. Galois's work on this problem was completed a year before his death in a duel at age 20. His proof, using the new concepts of group theory, was so advanced that his teachers wrote it off as being unintelligible gibberish.

Observe that $-\frac{1}{2}$ is a root once again. This illustrates an important point: A rational root may be a multiple root! Applying the same technique to the resulting deflated equation

$$4x^3 + 2x^2 + 4x + 2 = 0$$

which has the same roots as

$$2x^3 + x^2 + 2x + 1 = 0$$

$$
\begin{array}{r|rrrr}
-\frac{1}{2} & 2 & 1 & 2 & 1 \\
 & & -1 & 0 & -1 \\
\hline
 & 2 & 0 & 2 & 0 \\
\end{array}
$$

$$\underbrace{}$$

coefficients of quotient polynomial

The final deflated equation is

$$2x^2 + 2 = 0 \quad \text{or} \quad x^2 + 1 = 0$$

which has the roots $\pm i$. Thus, the original equation has the rational roots

$$-\frac{1}{2}, -\frac{1}{2}, -\frac{1}{2}$$

Since the original equation had real coefficients, we could have used Descartes's Rule of Signs before trying different possible roots. We would have discovered that there are no positive real roots and 1, 3 or 5 negative real roots.

✔ Progress Check
Find all zeros of the polynomial

$$P(x) = 9x^4 - 3x^3 + 16x^2 - 6x - 4$$

Answer
$\dfrac{2}{3}, -\dfrac{1}{3}, \pm\sqrt{2}i$

Example 4   Rational Zeros and Quotient Polynomials

Write the polynomial

$$P(x) = 3x^4 + 2x^3 + 2x^2 + 2x - 1$$

as a product of linear and quadratic factors with real coefficients such that the quadratic factors have no real zeros.

Solution

Since the coefficients of the polynomial are all integers, we may use the Rational Zero Theorem to obtain

$$\text{possible numerators: } \pm 1 \quad \text{(factors of 1)}$$
$$\text{possible denominators: } \pm 1, \pm 3 \quad \text{(factors of 3)}$$
$$\text{possible rational zeros: } \pm 1, \pm\frac{1}{3}$$

Next, we note that $P(x)$ has real coefficients so that Descartes's Rule of Signs applies. There is one positive zero and one or three negative zeros. (Why?) If the positive zero is rational, it must be 1 or $\frac{1}{3}$. Since $P(1) \neq 0$, we evaluate $P(\frac{1}{3})$ using synthetic division.

$$
\begin{array}{r|rrrrr}
\frac{1}{3} & 3 & 2 & 2 & 2 & -1 \\
 & & 1 & 1 & 1 & 1 \\
\hline
 & 3 & 3 & 3 & 3 & 0
\end{array}
$$

$$\underbrace{\qquad\qquad\qquad\qquad}$$

coefficients of quotient polynomial

Therefore, $\frac{1}{3}$ is a zero, and the deflated equation is

$$Q_1(x) = 3x^3 + 3x^2 + 3x + 3 = 0$$

which has the same roots as

$$Q_2(x) = x^3 + x^2 + x + 1 = 0$$

Since any zero of $Q_2(x)$ is also a zero of $P(x)$, and since we have removed the only positive zero, $Q_2(x)$ cannot have any positive zeros. (Verify that $Q_2(x)$ has no positive zeros and one or three negative zeros.) Since $Q_2(-1) = 0$, -1 is a zero. Using synthetic division, we obtain

Focus on Transcendental Numbers

A real number that is a root of some polynomial equation with *integer* coefficients is said to be *algebraic*. We see that $\frac{2}{3}$ is algebraic since it is the root of the equation $3x - 2 = 0$. (Verify that all rational numbers are algebraic.) Also, $\sqrt{2}$ is algebraic since it satisfies the equation $x^2 - 2 = 0$. (Verify that the nth root of any positive integer is algebraic, where n is a positive integer.)

To show that a real number r is *not* algebraic, we must demonstrate that there is no polynomial equation with integer coefficients that has r as one of its roots. Although this appears to be an impossible task, it was performed in 1844 when Joseph Liouville exhibited specific examples of such numbers, called *transcendental* numbers. Subsequently, Georg Cantor (1845–1918), provided a more general proof of the existence of transcendental numbers.

The number π is a transcendental number; it is not a root of any polynomial equation with integer coefficients.

$$
\begin{array}{r|rrrr}
-1 & 1 & 1 & 1 & 1 \\
   &   & -1 & 0 & -1 \\
\hline
   & 1 & 0 & 1 & 0
\end{array}
$$

$\underbrace{}$
coefficients of quotient polynomial

Therefore, we have the deflated equation

$$x^2 + 1 = 0$$

which has no real roots. (Why?) Thus,

$$P(x) = 3x^4 + 2x^3 + 2x^2 + 2x - 1 = 3\left(x - \frac{1}{3}\right)(x + 1)(x^2 + 1)$$

In Chapter 1 we discussed number systems and said that numbers such as $\sqrt{2}$ and $\sqrt{3}$ were irrational. The Rational Zero Theorem provides a direct means of verifying that this is indeed so.

Example 5 Application of the Rational Zero Theorem
Prove that $\sqrt{3}$ is not a rational number.

Solution
If we let $x = \sqrt{3}$, then $x^2 = 3$ or $x^2 - 3 = 0$. Let $P(x) = x^2 - 3$. By the Rational Zero Theorem, the only possible rational zeros of $P(x)$ are ± 1 and ± 3. Using substitution, we see that none of these numbers is a zero of $P(x)$, implying that $P(x)$ has *no* rational zeros. Since $P(\sqrt{3}) = 0$, $\sqrt{3}$ is a zero, hence, $\sqrt{3}$ cannot be a rational number.

Graphing Calculator Power User's Corner

Analyzing Roots

We can combine the theory presented in this section with the power of the graphing calculator to obtain an efficient method for determining the nature of the roots of polynomials. Let us consider the function

$$P(x) = 2x^5 + 7x^4 + 3x^2 - 2$$

from Example 1. Using Descartes's Rule of Signs, we know that $P(x)$ has one positive root and either zero negative roots or two negative roots. Furthermore, the Rational Zero Theorem tells us that the only possible rational roots of $P(x)$ are ± 1, ± 2 and $\pm\frac{1}{2}$. We graph $P(x)$ in the default viewing rectangle as shown in Figure 17. We see that $P(x)$ has one positive root between 0 and 1, and two negative roots, one between 0 and -1, the other between -3 and -4. Thus, the only possible rational roots of $P(x)$ are $\pm\frac{1}{2}$. Using a calculator or synthetic division, we verify that neither $\pm\frac{1}{2}$ is a root of $P(x)$. Thus, we conclude that $P(x)$ has three irrational roots and two complex roots. We will approximate the irrational roots in Section 4.7.

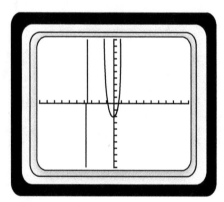

Figure 17 Graph of $y = 2x^5 + 7x^4 + 3x^2 - 2$, $-10 \leq X \leq 10$, $-10 \leq Y \leq 10$, XSCL = 1, YSCL = 1

Exercise Set 4.6

In Exercises 1–12, use Descartes's Rule of Signs to analyze the nature of the roots of the given equation. List all possibilities.

1. $3x^4 - 2x^3 + 6x^2 + 5x - 2 = 0$

2. $2x^6 + 5x^5 + x^3 - 6 = 0$

3. $x^6 + 2x^4 + 4x^2 + 1 = 0$

4. $3x^3 - 2x + 2 = 0$

5. $x^5 - 4x^3 + 7x - 4 = 0$

6. $2x^3 - 5x^2 + 8x - 2 = 0$

7. $5x^3 + 2x^2 + 7x - 1 = 0$

8. $x^5 + 6x^4 - x^3 - 2x - 3 = 0$

9. $x^4 - 2x^3 + 5x^2 + 2 = 0$

10. $3x^4 - 2x^3 - 1 = 0$

11. $x^8 + 7x^3 + 3x - 5 = 0$

12. $x^7 + 3x^5 - x^3 - x + 2 = 0$

In Exercises 13–22, use the Rational Zero Theorem to find all rational roots of the given equation.

13. $x^3 - 2x^2 - 5x + 6 = 0$

14. $3x^3 - x^2 - 3x + 1 = 0$

15. $6x^4 - 7x^3 - 13x^2 + 4x + 4 = 0$

16. $36x^4 - 15x^3 - 26x^2 + 3x + 2 = 0$

17. $5x^6 - x^5 - 5x^4 + 6x^3 - x^2 - 5x + 1 = 0$

18. $16x^4 - 16x^3 - 29x^2 + 32x - 6 = 0$

19. $4x^4 - x^3 + 5x^2 - 2x - 6 = 0$

20. $6x^4 + 2x^3 + 7x^2 + x + 2 = 0$

21. $2x^5 - 13x^4 + 26x^3 - 22x^2 + 24x - 9 = 0$

22. $8x^5 - 4x^4 + 6x^3 - 3x^2 - 2x + 1 = 0$

In Exercises 23–30, use the Rational Zero Theorem and quotient polynomials to find all roots of the given equation.

23. $4x^4 + x^3 + x^2 + x - 3 = 0$

24. $x^4 + x^3 + x^2 + 3x - 6 = 0$

25. $5x^5 - 3x^4 - 10x^3 + 6x^2 - 40x + 24 = 0$

26. $12x^4 - 52x^3 + 75x^2 - 16x - 5 = 0$

27. $6x^4 - x^3 - 5x^2 + 2x = 0$

28. $2x^4 - \frac{3}{2}x^3 + \frac{11}{2}x^2 + \frac{23}{2}x + \frac{5}{2} = 0$

29. $2x^4 - x^3 - 28x^2 + 30x - 8 = 0$

30. $12x^4 + 4x^3 - 17x^2 + 6x = 0$

In Exercises 31–36, use Descartes's Rule of Signs, the Rational Zero Theorem and quotient polynomials to find all roots of the given equation.

31. $x^4 - 6x^3 + 10x^2 - 6x + 9 = 0$

32. $2x^4 - 3x^3 + 5x^2 - 6x + 2 = 0$

33. $x^4 - 6x^2 + 8 = 0$

34. $x^4 - 4x^3 + 7x^2 - 6x + 2 = 0$

35. $4x^4 + 4x^3 - 3x^2 - 4x - 1 = 0$

36. $x^5 + x^4 - 7x^3 - 11x^2 - 8x - 12 = 0$

In Exercises 37–40, find the integer value(s) of k for which the given equation has rational roots, and find the roots. (*Hint:* Use synthetic division.)

37. $x^3 + kx^2 + kx + 2 = 0$

38. $x^4 - 4x^3 - kx^2 + 6kx + 9 = 0$

39. $x^4 - 3x^3 + kx^2 - 4x - 1 = 0$

40. $x^3 - 4kx^2 - k^2x + 4 = 0$

41. If $P(x)$ is a polynomial with real coefficients that has one variation in sign, prove that $P(x)$ has exactly one positive zero.

42. If $P(x)$ is a polynomial with integer coefficients and the leading coefficient is $+1$ or -1, prove that the rational zeros of $P(x)$ are all integers and are factors of the constant term.

43. Prove that $\sqrt{5}$ is not a rational number.

4.7 Approximation of the Zeros of Polynomial Functions

There are many techniques available for approximating the real zeros of polynomial functions. We shall discuss two methods that are suitable as an introduction to this topic. They will require the use of a calculator.

Evaluating a Polynomial

The methods we will present require the evaluation of the polynomial $P(x)$ many times. The streamlined form of synthetic division is useful, especially when combined with a calculator. (If you have access to a programmable calculator or a computer, you may wish to write a program to evaluate $P(x)$.)

There is a way to rewrite a polynomial that is well suited for computer use. We illustrate this scheme, referred to as **nested form,** using a general third-degree polynomial.

$$P(x) = a_3x^3 + a_2x^2 + a_1x + a_0$$
$$= [(a_3x + a_2)x + a_1]x + a_0$$

where the innermost parentheses are evaluated first. This particular form is valuable since it reduces the number of operations needed to evaluate $P(x)$. (Verify that there are three fewer multiplications needed in this example using nested form.) This nesting technique can be extended to a polynomial of any degree.

Example 1   Nested Form
Write in nested form: $P(x) = 2x^4 - x^3 + 4x^2 - 3x - 8$

Solution
Following the scheme outlined above, and remembering to evaluate the parentheses from innermost to outermost, we have

$$P(x) = \{[(2x - 1)x + 4]x - 3\}x - 8$$

The nested form of polynomial evaluation works well in conjunction with the memory facility of most scientific calculators. To evaluate the polynomial of Example 1 for a given value of x, say $x = 3.45$, you would follow this outline:

$$3.45 \boxed{\text{STO}} \; 2 \; \boxed{\times} \; \boxed{\text{RCL}} \; \boxed{-} \; 1 \; \boxed{=}$$
$$\boxed{\times} \; \boxed{\text{RCL}} \; \boxed{+} \; 4 \; \boxed{=}$$
$$\boxed{\times} \; \boxed{\text{RCL}} \; \boxed{-} \; 3 \; \boxed{=}$$
$$\boxed{\times} \; \boxed{\text{RCL}} \; \boxed{-} \; 8 \; \boxed{=}$$

Approximating Roots by Successive Digits

Suppose we seek a real root of the polynomial equation $P(x) = 0$, and we can find values a and b such that $P(a)$ and $P(b)$ are of opposite sign. We can deduce from the Intermediate Value Theorem that there must be at least one value c in the interval (a, b) where $P(c) = 0$. Thus, c is a real root and $a < c < b$. Our problem is to get a better estimate for c.

Consider the following example with the equation

$$P(x) = 2x^4 + 4x^3 - x^2 - 10x - 10 = 0$$

Since $P(0) < 0$ and $P(3) > 0$, there must be at least one root in the interval $(0, 3)$. Let us form Table 2.

Table 2 $P(x)$ in the Interval [0, 3]

x	0	1	2	3
$P(x)$	-10	-15	30	221

Since $P(1)$ is negative and $P(2)$ is positive, there is a root in the interval $(1, 2)$. To improve our estimate, we start at $x = 1$ and increase x by tenths to form Table 3. Note that we only record the *sign* of $P(x)$. Also, we stop as soon as we record a change in sign. Since $P(1.5)$ is negative and $P(1.6)$ is positive, we isolate the root in the interval $(1.5, 1.6)$.

Table 3 $P(x)$ in the Interval [1, 2]

x	1.0	1.1	1.2	1.3	1.4	1.5	1.6	1.7	1.8	1.9	2.0
$P(x)$	−	−	−	−	−	−	+				

The process just illustrated may be repeated any number of times, providing another decimal place of accuracy at each stage. We take this one stage further as shown in Table 4.

Table 4 $P(x)$ in the Interval [1.5, 1.6]

x	1.50	1.51	1.52	1.53	1.54	1.55	1.56	1.57	1.58	1.59	1.60
$P(x)$	−	−	−	−	−	−	−	−	−	+	

At this point we can conclude that there is a root in the interval $(1.58, 1.59)$, and thus the first three digits of the root are 1.58.

✔ **Progress Check**

Use the method of successive digits to find the root of the equation

$$x^3 + x^2 - 3x - 3 = 0$$

in the interval $[1, 2]$ accurate to two decimal places.

Answer
1.73

Approximating Roots by Bisection

Many of the sophisticated methods for approximating roots require a knowledge of calculus and are not suitable for this text. There is, however, a technique known as **bisection** that does not require calculus, and can be of use in many circumstances.

Suppose we are told that the polynomial equation

$$P(x) = x^4 + x^3 - 5x^2 - 6x - 6 = 0$$

has a root in the interval [2, 3]. We *bisect* the interval and evaluate the polynomial at the endpoints and midpoint of the interval [2, 3] and find

$$P(2) < 0 \qquad P(2.5) > 0 \qquad P(3) > 0$$

By the Intermediate Value Theorem, we have isolated the root in the interval (2, 2.5). Repeating the process, we find that

$$P(2) < 0 \qquad P(2.25) < 0 \qquad P(2.5) > 0$$

which narrows the interval containing the root to (2.25, 2.5). We can repeat this process until we obtain a result of desired accuracy.

It is not necessarily clear that one method is better than the other in all situations. However, the method of bisection is well suited for computer usage. It is a technique for finding approximate solutions that can be applied to a large variety of problems.

✔ Progress Check

Find a root of the equation $x^5 + x^4 + x + 2 = 0$ in the interval $[-2, -1]$ to two decimal places by the method of bisection.

Answer
-1.27

Graphing Calculator Power User's Corner

Approximating Roots

The zoom-in capability of the graphing calculator provides another method for approximating the real roots of functions. Returning to Example 1 in Section 4.6, consider $P(x) = 2x^5 + 7x^4 + 3x^2 - 2$. We saw in that section that $P(x)$ has three irrational roots (one positive and two negative) and two complex roots.

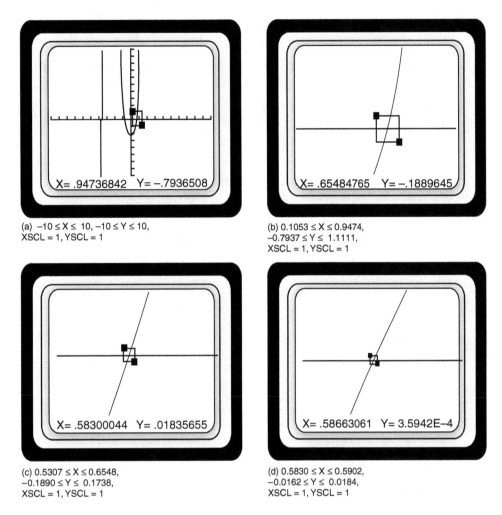

(a) $-10 \le X \le 10, -10 \le Y \le 10,$
XSCL = 1, YSCL = 1

(b) $0.1053 \le X \le 0.9474,$
$-0.7937 \le Y \le 1.1111,$
XSCL = 1, YSCL = 1

(c) $0.5307 \le X \le 0.6548,$
$-0.1890 \le Y \le 0.1738,$
XSCL = 1, YSCL = 1

(d) $0.5830 \le X \le 0.5902,$
$-0.0162 \le Y \le 0.0184,$
XSCL = 1, YSCL = 1

Figure 18   Graph of $y = 2x^5 + 7x^4 + 3x^2 - 2$

There are several ways to ZOOM-IN on most graphing calculators:

1. We can ZOOM-IN "manually" by resetting the WINDOW values.

2. We can ZOOM-IN "automatically" by setting "zoom factors."

3. We can ZOOM-IN using a ZOOM BOX.

You should experiment with each of these methods. The graphs in Figure 18 illustrate the ZOOM BOX method for the positive root of $P(x)$. You will most likely obtain slightly different coordinates on your graphing calculator.

If we continue the ZOOM-IN process, we find that, to seven decimal places,

$$x_1 = 0.5865959$$
$$x_2 = -0.6195154$$
$$x_3 = -3.6092550$$

The ZOOM-IN method provides a quick way to find rough approximations to the roots of functions. However, it is tedious if you desire a high degree of accuracy. A numerical method, such as the bisection method, can be programmed into your calculator, enabling you to obtain accurate approximations to roots more efficiently.

Your graphing calculator may be able to tell you the zeros. It will ask for a "left bound" and a "right bound." You need to enter these values; your calculator will give you the value of the zero between these two numbers. For the example below, -1 was entered as the left bound, and 1 as the right bound. See how the answer compares with the one we found using ZOOM.

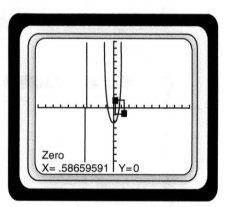

Zero
X= .58659591   Y=0

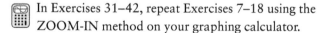

Exercise Set 4.7

In Exercises 1–6, write the polynomial in nested form.

1. $3x^3 - 2x^2 + 5x - 1$ 2. $-x^4 - 3x^2 + 4$

3. $x^5 + 2x^4 - 2x - 3$ 4. $2x^4 - x^3 + x + 7$

5. $2x^4 - x^2 + x + 4$ 6. $x^6 - 2x^5 - x^3 + 1$

In Exercises 7–18, find a root of the polynomial equation in the stated interval by the method of successive digits to two decimal places.

7. $2x^4 - x^3 + 2x - 2 = 0$ $[-2, -1]$

8. $3x^3 - 2x^2 + 5x + 4 = 0$ $[-1, 0]$

9. $x^5 - 3x^3 + x^2 - 3 = 0$ $[1, 2]$

10. $-x^4 + 3x^2 + 5 = 0$ $[2, 3]$

11. $x^6 - 3x^3 + x^2 - 2 = 0$ $[1, 2]$

12. $2x^5 - x^4 + 3x^2 - 6 = 0$ $[1, 2]$

13. $-2x^3 - x^2 + 3x - 4 = 0$ $[-2, -1]$

14. $2x^4 - 3x^3 + x^2 - 1 = 0$ $[-1, 0]$

15. $2x^5 - 3x^2 - 5 = 0$ $[1, 2]$

16. $2x^3 + 3x^2 - 2x + 4 = 0$ $[-3, -2]$

17. $2x^5 - x^4 + x^2 - 3 = 0$ $[1, 2]$

18. $2x^3 - 2x^2 + 3x - 2 = 0$ $[0, 1]$

In Exercises 19–30, repeat Exercises 7–18 using the method of bisection.

In Exercises 31–42, repeat Exercises 7–18 using the ZOOM-IN method on your graphing calculator.

Terms and Symbols

bisection method	minimum	smooth
completing the square	multiplicity of a zero	synthetic division
complex conjugate	nested form	turning point
continuous function	parabola	variation in sign
cusp	parabola opening downward	vertex of a parabola
deflated equation	parabola opening upward	x-intercept of a parabola
deflated polynomial	polynomial equation of degree n	$\bar{z}$
double root	polynomial function of degree n	zero of a polynomial
"ends" of a graph	quadratic function	zero of multiplicity k
factor of a polynomial	quotient polynomial	
maximum	root of an equation	

Key Ideas for Review

Topic	Key Idea
Quadratic Functions and Graphs	The quadratic function $$f(x) = ax^2 + bx + c = 0, \quad a \neq 0$$ can be written in the form $$f(x) = a(x - h)^2 + k$$ where h and k are constants. The graph is a parabola with vertex at (h, k), opening upward if $a > 0$ and downward if $a < 0$.
x-intercepts	The discriminant of the quadratic function is $b^2 - 4ac$.

$b^2 - 4ac$	x-intercepts
positive	2
zero	1
negative	0

Topic	Key Idea
Maximum, Minimum	The maximum or minimum of a quadratic function occurs at $$x = -\frac{b}{2a}$$
Polynomial Functions	The polynomial function of degree n has the form $$P(x) = a_n x^n + a_{n-1} x^{n-1} + \cdots + a_1 x + a_0, \quad a_n \neq 0$$
Zeros and Roots	The zeros of the polynomial function $P(x)$ are the roots of the polynomial equation $P(x) = 0$.
Graphs	The graph of a polynomial function of degree n is continuous, smooth and has at most $n - 1$ turning points.
Intermediate Value Theorem	If P is a polynomial function and $a < b$ with $P(a) \neq P(b)$, then P assumes every value between $P(a)$ and $P(b)$ in the interval $[a, b]$.

Topic	Key Idea
Lead Term Dominance	For large values of $|x|$, a polynomial function is dominated by its lead term, that is, the lead term determines the sign of the function.
"Ends" of a Graph	For a polynomial of odd degree, the "ends" of the graph extend indefinitely in opposite directions. For a polynomial of even degree, both ends of the graph extend upward or both extend downward.
Polynomial Division	Polynomial division results in a quotient and a remainder, both of which are polynomials. The degree of the remainder is less than the degree of the divisor.
Synthetic Division	Synthetic division is a quick way to divide a polynomial by a first-degree polynomial $x - r$, where r is a real constant.
Remainder Theorem	If a polynomial $P(x)$ is divided by $x - r$, the remainder is $P(r)$.
Factor Theorem	A polynomial $P(x)$ has a zero at $x = r$ if and only if $x - r$ is a factor of $P(x)$.
Fundamental Theorem of Algebra	If $P(x)$ is a polynomial of degree $n \geq 1$, then $P(x)$ has precisely n zeros among the complex numbers when a zero of multiplicity k is counted k times.
Deflated Equation	If r is a real root of polynomial equation $P(x) = 0$, then the roots of $$Q(x) = \frac{P(x)}{x - r} = 0$$ are the other roots of $P(x) = 0$.
Conjugate Zeros Theorem	If $a + bi$, $b \neq 0$, is a zero of the polynomial $P(x)$ with real coefficients, then the conjugate of $a + bi$, $\overline{a + bi} = a - bi$, is also a zero of $P(x)$.
Descartes's Rule of Signs	If $P(x)$ is a polynomial with real coefficients and a nonzero constant term, then a. the number of positive zeros equals the number of variations in sign of $P(x)$ less some nonnegative even number that could be zero; b. the number of negative zeros equals the number of variations in sign of $P(-x)$ less some nonnegative even number that could be zero.
Rational Zero Theorem	If $\frac{p}{q}$ is a rational zero in lowest terms of the polynomial $P(x)$ with integer coefficients, then p is a factor of the constant term a_0 of $P(x)$, and q is a factor of the leading coefficient a_n of $P(x)$.
Listing Possible Rational Zeros	If $P(x)$ has integer coefficients, then the Rational Zero Theorem enables us to list all possible rational zeros of $P(x)$. Recall that r is a zero if and only if $P(r) = 0$.
Polynomials Using Nested Form	An example of nested form for the fourth-degree polynomial $$P(x) = a_4x^4 + a_3x^3 + a_2x^2 + a_1x + a_0$$ is $$P(x) = \{[(a_4x + a_3)x + a_2]x + a_1\}x + a_0$$ The latter (nested) form generally requires fewer arithmetic operations to evaluate $P(x)$ than does the former.
Approximating Roots	The methods of successive digits or bisection can be used to approximate the roots of a polynomial equation.

Review Exercises

Solutions to exercises whose numbers are in **bold** are in the Solutions section in the back of the book.

In Exercises 1 and 2, find the vertex and all intercepts of the parabola.

1. $f(x) = -x^2 - 4x$

2. $f(x) = x^2 - 5x + 7$

In Exercises 3 and 4, determine (a) if f has a maximum or minimum value; (b) the value of x at which the maximum or minimum occurs; (c) the maximum or minimum value of f.

3. $f(x) = 2x^2 - x + 1$

4. $f(x) = -x^2 - 3x - 1$

In Exercises 5 and 6, determine the behavior of the graph of the given polynomial function for large values of $|x|$.

5. $P(x) = -2x^5 + 27x^2 + 100$

6. $P(x) = 4x^3 - 10{,}000$

In Exercises 7 and 8, use synthetic division to find the quotient $Q(x)$ and the constant remainder R when the first polynomial is divided by the second polynomial.

7. $2x^3 + 6x - 4, \quad x - 1$

8. $x^4 - 3x^3 + 2x - 5, \quad x + 2$

In Exercises 9 and 10, use synthetic division to find $P(2)$ and $P(-1)$.

9. $P(x) = 7x^3 - 3x^2 + 2$

10. $P(x) = x^5 - 4x^3 + 2x$

In Exercises 11 and 12, use the Factor Theorem to show that the second polynomial is a factor of the first polynomial.

11. $2x^4 + 4x^3 + 3x^2 + 5x - 2, \quad x + 2$

12. $2x^3 - 5x^2 + 6x - 2, \quad x - \dfrac{1}{2}$

In Exercises 13–15, write the given quotient in the form $a + bi$.

13. $\dfrac{3 - 2i}{4 + 3i}$

14. $\dfrac{2 + i}{-5i}$

15. $\dfrac{-5}{1 + i}$

In Exercises 16–18, write the reciprocal of the given complex number in the form $a + bi$.

16. $1 + 3i$

17. $-4i$

18. $2 - 5i$

In Exercises 19–21, find a polynomial of lowest degree that has the indicated zeros.

19. $-3, -2, -1$

20. $3, \pm\sqrt{-3}$

21. $-2, \pm\sqrt{3}, 1$

In Exercises 22–24, find a polynomial that has the indicated zeros and no others.

22. $\dfrac{1}{2}$ of multiplicity 2, -1 of multiplicity 2

23. $i, -i$, each of multiplicity 2

24. -1 of multiplicity 3, 3 of multiplicity 1

In Exercises 25–27, use the given root to assist in finding the remaining roots of the equation.

25. $2x^3 - x^2 - 13x - 6 = 0; \quad -2$

26. $x^3 - 2x^2 - 9x + 4 = 0; \quad 4$

27. $2x^4 - 15x^3 + 34x^2 - 19x - 20 = 0; \quad -\dfrac{1}{2}$

In Exercises 28–31, use Descartes's Rule of Signs to determine the maximum number of positive and negative real roots of the given equation.

28. $x^4 - 2x - 1 = 0$

29. $x^5 - x^4 + 3x^3 - 4x^2 + x - 5 = 0$

30. $x^3 - 5 = 0$

31. $3x^4 - 2x^2 + 1 = 0$

In Exercises 32–34, find all the rational roots of the given equation.

32. $6x^3 - 5x^2 - 33x - 18 = 0$

33. $6x^4 - 7x^3 - 19x^2 + 32x - 12 = 0$

34. $x^4 + 3x^3 + 2x^2 + x - 1 = 0$

In Exercises 35 and 36, find all roots of the given equation.

35. $6x^3 + 15x^2 - x - 10 = 0$

36. $2x^4 - 3x^3 - 10x^2 + 19x - 6 = 0$

Review Test

1. Find the vertex and intercepts of the parabola whose equation is $y = 3x^2 - 2x + 1$. Find the maximum or minimum value on the graph of the parabola.

Exercises 2 and 3 refer to the polynomial function

$$P(x) = -2x^9 + 3x^6 + 200$$

2. Describe the behavior of the graph of $P(x)$ for large values of $|x|, x > 0$.

3. Describe the behavior of the graph of $P(x)$ for large values of $|x|, x < 0$.

4. Find the quotient and remainder when $2x^4 - x^2 + 1$ is divided by $x^2 + 2$.

5. Use synthetic division to find the quotient and remainder when $3x^4 - x^3 - 2$ is divided by $x + 2$.

6. If $P(x) = x^3 - 2x^2 + 7x + 5$, use synthetic division to find $P(-2)$.

7. Determine the remainder when $4x^5 - 2x^4 - 5$ is divided by $x + 2$.

8. Use the Factor Theorem to show that $x - 3$ is a factor of $2x^4 - 9x^3 + 9x^2 + x - 3$.

In Exercises 9 and 10, find a polynomial of lowest degree that has the indicated zeros.

9. $-2, 1, 3$

10. $-1, 1, 3 \pm \sqrt{2}$

In Exercises 11 and 12, find the roots of the given equation.

11. $(x^2 + 1)(x - 2) = 0$

12. $(x + 1)^2(x^2 - 3x - 2) = 0$

In Exercises 13–15, find a polynomial that has the indicated zeros and no others.

13. -3 of multiplicity 2, 1 of multiplicity 3

14. $-\dfrac{1}{4}$ of multiplicity 2, i, $-i$, 1

15. $i, 1 + i$

In Exercises 16 and 17, use the given root to help in finding the remaining roots of the equation.

16. $4x^3 - 3x + 1 = 0$, -1

17. $x^4 - x^2 - 2x + 2 = 0$,   1

18. If $2 + i$ is a root of $x^3 - 6x^2 + 13x - 10 = 0$, write the equation as a product of linear and quadratic factors with real coefficients.

In Exercises 19 and 20, determine the maximum number of roots of specified type for the given equation.

19. $2x^5 - 3x^4 + 1 = 0$;   positive real roots

20. $3x^4 + 2x^3 - 2x^2 - 1 = 0$;   negative real roots

In Exercises 21 and 22, find all rational roots of the given equation.

21. $6x^3 - 17x^2 + 14x + 3 = 0$

22. $2x^5 - x^4 - 4x^3 + 2x^2 + 2x - 1 = 0$

23. Find all roots of the equation

$$3x^4 + 7x^3 - 3x^2 + 7x - 6 = 0$$

Writing Exercises

1. Make up a word problem which uses a quadratic function and requires finding a maximum value.

2. Discuss under what conditions a polynomial function has a maximum (minimum).

3. When using the method of bisection for approximating the root of a polynomial, one has to decide when

to stop the procedure. Describe criteria which can be used to make this decision.

4. Given a polynomial, describe a procedure for determining the number and type of roots (real, complex, rational, irrational). Justify each step in your explanation.

Chapter 4 Project

Cubic polynomials can be used to model volumes, as you saw in this chapter (Section 4.2, Exercises 36–38; Section 4.5, Exercises 85–86). You also took a look ahead to see how the zeros of polynomials can sometimes be used to find the maximum (or minimum) values of other polynomials. Review those exercises now.

Make sketches that show the method described in those exercises. Label them carefully.

Now, set up a general volume function for packages constructed in this way, which have the maximum allowable value for the sum of length and girth, according to postal requirements. Use L and W to represent the length and width of the original cardboard rectangle. Let x represent the length of the side of each discarded square, as before. Start by explaining in your own words why

$$(L - 2x) + 2(W - 2x) + 2x = 130 \tag{1}$$

Simplify this formula.

Suppose you always start with a square of cardboard, so that $L = W$. Replace L with W in formula (1), then solve for x. Write a volume function for a package designed in this way. (The independent variable for this function will be W. You may simply substitute your expression which gives x in terms of W for x in the volume formula you derived in Section 4.2, Exercise 36.)

Interpret this polynomial, using any of the techniques you have learned in this chapter. What is the largest possible volume of a package designed to meet these specifications?

Rational, Exponential, and Logarithmic Functions

http://www.dcs
.warwick.ac.uk/bshm/
resources.html

How does a business make decisions about how many units of their products to produce in order to make a profit? Suppose you were a manufacturer of graphing calculators. Your **fixed** or start-up **cost** is, let's say, $10,000. Before you produce a single calculator, you are already spending money! Now let's assume each calculator costs you $50 to manufacture. What is the average cost to you of producing your first 100 calculators? What formula will give you the average cost of the first x calculators?

The formula you need is a rational function of x. Take a look at this chapter's project, at the end of the chapter. The intersecting worlds of business, finance, and economics generally all rely upon mathematics, and especially the mathematics of functions. Investigate the history of functions and the rest of mathematics at a site hosted by the British Society for the History of Mathematics, http://www.dcs.warwick.ac.uk/bshm/resources.html.

In this chapter, we are going to investigate two types of relationships. The first is derived from the polynomial functions considered in Chapter 3. Specifically, we will study a function that is the quotient of two polynomials. Although sums, differences and products of two polynomials still produce polynomials, quotients in general tend to be more complicated. Additionally, we will examine the various curves that arise when one considers the intersection of a plane and a cone. These curves will be the graphs of an important class of relationships that are not necessarily functions.

In 1637, the French philosopher and scientist, René Descartes, developed an idea that combined the techniques of algebra with those of geometry. He created a new field of study called **analytic geometry,** an area in which one can apply the methods and equations of algebra to the solution of problems in geometry and also obtain geometric representations of algebraic equations. In Chapter 3, we observed some applications of these methods in deriving the distance and midpoint formulas. Analytic geometry is also well suited to the study of conic sections, since geometry plays such an important role here as well.

5.1   Rational Functions and Their Graphs

We can apply our knowledge of polynomial functions to the study of a function of the form

$$f(x) = \frac{P(x)}{Q(x)}$$

where $P(x)$ and $Q(x)$ are polynomials and $Q(x) \neq 0$. This is called a **rational function.** (You may recall that a *rational number* is the quotient of two integers.) We will assume that the polynomials $P(x)$ and $Q(x)$ have no common factors, and we will call such a rational function **irreducible.** (Show that $P(x)$ and $Q(x)$ have no common zeros.) We will also assume that $Q(x)$ is of degree 1 or higher. (If $Q(x)$ were of degree 0, it would actually be a constant, hence $f(x)$ would be a polynomial.)

Domain and Intercepts

Since $P(x)$ and $Q(x)$ are polynomials, they are both defined for all real values of x. The function f can have "problems" only where the denominator is zero. Consequently, the domain of f consists of all real numbers except those for which $Q(x) = 0$.

To find the y-intercepts of the function f, set x equal to 0 and evaluate $y = f(0)$. Should $Q(0) = 0$, then $f(0)$ is undefined and there are no y-intercepts. ($f(x)$ has at most one y-intercept.)

To find the x-intercepts, we note that $y = f(x)$ can be 0 only if the numerator $P(x)$ is zero. Therefore, the x-intercepts correspond to the roots of the polynomial equation $P(x) = 0$. Since we have assumed that f is irreducible, if r is such that $P(r) = 0$, then $Q(r) \neq 0$. In other words, $P(x)$ and $Q(x)$ have no common zeros.

Example 1 Domain and Intercepts

Find the domain and intercepts of each irreducible rational function.

a. $f(x) = \dfrac{x + 1}{x - 1}$ b. $g(x) = \dfrac{x^3 + 2x^2 - 3x}{x^2 - 4}$ c. $h(x) = \dfrac{x^2 - 9}{x^2 + 1}$

Solution

a. The denominator is 0 when $x = 1$. Thus, the domain of f is the set of all real numbers except $x = 1$.

   To find the y-intercept, we set $x = 0$ and find $y = f(0) = -1$. To find the x-intercepts, we set the numerator equal to 0 and find that $y = f(x) = 0$ when $x = -1$. Summarizing, the y-intercept is $(0, -1)$, and the x-intercept is $(-1, 0)$.

b. The denominator is 0 when $x = 2$ and when $x = -2$. The domain of g is then the set of all real numbers except $x = \pm 2$.

   To find the y-intercept, we set $x = 0$ and find $y = g(0) = 0$. To find the x-intercepts, we set the numerator equal to 0 and find that

$$x^3 + 2x^2 - 3x = 0$$

$$x(x^2 + 2x - 3) = 0$$

$$x(x - 1)(x + 3) = 0$$

   has the solutions $x = 0$, $x = 1$ and $x = -3$. Summarizing, the y-intercept is $(0, 0)$, and the x-intercepts are $(0, 0)$, $(1, 0)$ and $(-3, 0)$.

c. Since the denominator $x^2 + 1$ can never be zero (Why?), the domain of h is the set of all real numbers.

   To find the y-intercept, we set $x = 0$ and find $y = h(0) = -9$. To find the x-intercepts, we set the numerator $x^2 = 9 - 0$ and find that $x = \pm 3$. Summarizing, the y-intercept is $(0, -9)$, and the x-intercepts are $(3, 0)$ and $(-3, 0)$. ∎

✔ Progress Check

Find the domain and intercepts of each rational function.

a. $S(x) = \dfrac{x - 3}{2x^2 - 3x - 2}$ b. $T(x) = \dfrac{5}{x^4 + x^2 + 5}$

Answers

a. *Domain:* all real numbers except $x = -\frac{1}{2}$, $x = 2$; y-intercept: $(0, \frac{3}{2})$; x-intercept: $(3, 0)$.

b. *Domain:* all real numbers; y-intercept: $(0, 1)$; no x-intercept.

Graphing $\dfrac{k}{x}$ and $\dfrac{k}{x^2}$

We begin the study of graphs of rational functions by considering examples in which the numerator is a constant.

x	$y = \frac{1}{x}$
$\frac{1}{1000}$	1000
$\frac{1}{100}$	100
$\frac{1}{10}$	10
1	1
2	$\frac{1}{2}$
4	$\frac{1}{4}$

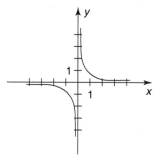

Figure 1 Graph of $y = \dfrac{1}{x}$

x	$y = \frac{1}{x^2}$
$\frac{1}{1000}$	1,000,000
$\frac{1}{100}$	10,000
$\frac{1}{10}$	100
1	1
2	$\frac{1}{4}$
4	$\frac{1}{16}$

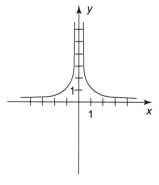

Figure 2 Graph of $y = \dfrac{1}{x^2}$

Example 2   Rational Functions with Constant Numerators

Sketch the graph of the function

$$f(x) = \frac{1}{x}$$

Solution

Domain: The denominator is 0 when $x = 0$. Thus, the domain of f is the set of all real numbers except $x = 0$.

Intercepts: There are no x-intercepts or y-intercepts.

Symmetry: The graph of f is symmetric with respect to the origin since the equation remains unchanged when x and y are replaced by $-x$ and $-y$, respectively. Therefore, we only need to plot those points corresponding to positive values of x. We sketch the graph of $y = \frac{1}{x}$ as shown in Figure 1.

Example 3   Rational Functions with Constant Numerators

Sketch the graph of the function

$$f(x) = \frac{1}{x^2}$$

Solution

Domain: The denominator is 0 when $x = 0$. Thus, the domain of f is the set of all real numbers except $x = 0$.

Intercepts: There are no x-intercepts or y-intercepts.

Symmetry: The graph of f is symmetric with respect to the y-axis since the equation remains unchanged when x is replaced by $-x$. Therefore, we only need consider positive values of x. We sketch the graph of $y = \frac{1}{x^2}$ as shown in Figure 2.

Asymptotes

The graphs in Figure 1 and Figure 2 illustrate an important concept: the graphs appear to approach specific horizontal and vertical lines without ever touching them. Such lines play an important role in the graphs of many functions, and we may define them in the following intuitive way.

> A line is said to be an **asymptote** of a graph if the graph gets closer and closer to the line as we move farther and farther out along the line.

Note the behavior of the graphs in Figures 1 and 2 as x gets closer and closer to 0. Both graphs approach the y-axis, and we say that the line $x = 0$ (the y-axis) is a **vertical asymptote** for each graph. Similarly, as $|x|$ gets extremely large, both graphs approach the x-axis, and we say that the line $y = 0$ (the x-axis) is a **horizontal asymptote** for each graph.

Example 4   Using Asymptotes in Graphing

Sketch the graph of the rational function

$$F(x) = \frac{1}{(x - 1)}$$

Solution
If we compare $F(x) = \frac{1}{x-1}$ with the function from Example 2, $f(x) = \frac{1}{x}$, we see that

$$F(x) = f(x - 1)$$

From Section 3.3, we may observe that the graph of $F(x)$ is that of $f(x)$ shifted 1 unit to the right, as shown in Figure 3. Note that the vertical asymptote has also been shifted or *translated* 1 unit to the right. (Shifting the graph to the right or left leaves the horizontal asymptote unchanged.)

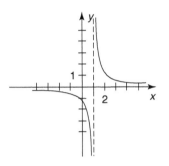

Figure 3   Graph of
$F(x) = \dfrac{1}{x - 1}$

Example 5   Using Asymptotes in Graphing

Sketch the graph of the rational function

$$F(x) = \frac{3}{(x + 2)^2}$$

Solution
If we compare

$$F(x) = \frac{3}{(x + 2)^2}$$

with the function from Example 3, $f(x) = \frac{1}{x^2}$, we see that

$$F(x) = 3f(x + 2)$$

From Section 3.3, we may observe that the graph of $F(x)$ is that of $f(x)$ shifted 2 units to the left and stretched by a factor of 3, as shown in Figure 4. Note that the vertical asymptote has also been translated 2 units to the left.

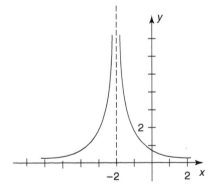

Figure 4   Graph of $F(x) = \dfrac{3}{(x + 2)^2}$

Since the asymptotes play an important role in graphing rational functions, it is useful to find a procedure for locating them. The graphs in each of the preceding figures of this chapter indicate that the functions *increase without bound*, **approaching ∞,** or *decrease without bound*, **approaching –∞,** as the curve approaches a vertical asymptote. Note that in these cases, the absolute value of the denominator of the quotient gets closer and closer to 0. The following theorem provides the means for finding all vertical asymptotes.

Vertical Asymptote Theorem
The graph of the rational function

$$f(x) = \frac{P(x)}{Q(x)}$$

has a vertical asymptote at $x = r$ if r is a real root of $Q(x)$ but not of $P(x)$.

Example 6   Vertical Asymptotes
Find the vertical asymptotes of the function

$$f(x) = \frac{2}{x^3 - 2x^2 - 3x}$$

Solution
Factoring the denominator, we have

$$f(x) = \frac{2}{x(x + 1)(x - 3)}$$

Therefore, $x = 0$, $x = -1$ and $x = 3$ are the vertical asymptotes of $f(x)$.   ■

To find the horizontal asymptotes of a function, we must examine the behavior of that function as x approaches ∞ and as x approaches –∞, that is, as $|x|$ *increases without bound*. Recall the expression

$$\frac{k}{x^n}$$

where k is a constant and n is a positive integer. This expression becomes very small as $|x|$ becomes very large. In other words, $\frac{k}{x^n}$ approaches 0 as $|x|$ approaches ∞.

Example 7   Horizontal Asymptotes
Find the horizontal asymptotes of the function

$$f(x) = \frac{2}{x^3 - 2x^2 - 3x}$$

Solution
If we factor out x^3 from the denominator, we have

$$f(x) = f(x) = \frac{2}{x^3\left(1 - \dfrac{2}{x} - \dfrac{3}{x^2}\right)} = \left(\frac{2}{x^3}\right)\left(\frac{1}{1 - \dfrac{2}{x} - \dfrac{3}{x^2}}\right)$$

As $|x|$ approaches ∞, the terms $\frac{2}{x^3}$, $-\frac{2}{x}$ and $-\frac{3}{x^2}$ approach 0. Therefore, $f(x)$ approaches 0 as $|x|$ approaches ∞, and hence $y = 0$ is the only horizontal asymptote. ■

Example 8   Using Asymptotes in Graphing

Sketch the graph of the function

$$f(x) = \frac{2}{x^3 - 2x^2 - 3x}$$

Solution

Since we can write

$$f(x) = \frac{2}{x(x + 1)(x - 3)}$$

we determine that the critical values of $f(x)$ are -1, 0 and 3. (See the Critical Value Method in Section 2.5)

Solution by the Critical Value Method

Interval	Test Point	Substitution	Sign
$x < -1$	$x = -2$	$f(-2) < 0$	$-$
$-1 < x < 0$	$x = -\frac{1}{2}$	$f(-\frac{1}{2}) > 0$	$+$
$0 < x < 3$	$x = 1$	$f(1) < 0$	$-$
$x > 3$	$x = 4$	$f(4) > 0$	$+$

These results are summarized as follows.

$$
\begin{array}{ccccc}
- & | & + & | & - & | & + \\
 & \bullet & & \bullet & & \bullet & \\
 & -1 & & 0 & & 3 &
\end{array}
$$

If $x < -1$ and x approaches -1, then $f(x)$ approaches $-\infty$. If $-1 < x < 0$ and x approaches -1, then $f(x)$ approaches ∞. Using a similar analysis at each point corresponding to a vertical asymptote, we may draw the following partial graphs of $f(x)$ as shown in Figure 5. From Example 7, we have that $y = 0$ is the horizontal asymptote. Combining this observation with the portions of the graph of $f(x)$ sketched in Figure 5 leads to the graph of $f(x)$ sketched in Figure 6.

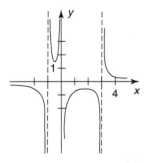

Figure 6   Graph of
$f(x) = \dfrac{2}{x(x + 1)(x - 3)}$

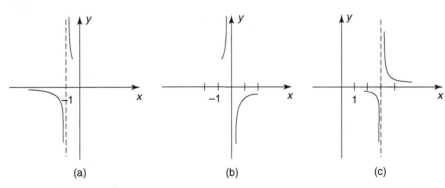

(a)   (b)   (c)

Figure 5   Partial Graphs of $f(x) = \dfrac{2}{x(x + 1)(x - 3)}$

Example 9   Horizontal Asymptotes

Find the horizontal asymptotes of the function

$$f(x) = \frac{2x^2 - 5}{3x^2 + 2x - 4}$$

Solution

We illustrate the steps of the procedure.

Horizontal Asymptotes

Step 1. Factor out the highest power of x found in the numerator, and factor out the highest power of x found in the denominator.	*Step 1.* $$f(x) = \frac{x^2\left(2 - \dfrac{5}{x^2}\right)}{x^2\left(3 + \dfrac{2}{x} - \dfrac{4}{x^2}\right)}$$
Step 2. Since we are interested in large values of $|x|$, we may cancel common factors in the numerator and denominator.	*Step 2.* $$f(x) = \frac{2 - \dfrac{5}{x^2}}{3 + \dfrac{2}{x} - \dfrac{4}{x^2}}, \quad x \neq 0$$
Step 3. As $|x|$ increases, terms of the form $\frac{k}{x^n}$ approach 0 and may be ignored.	*Step 3.* The terms $-\frac{5}{x^2}, \frac{2}{x}$ and $-\frac{4}{x^2}$ approach 0 as $|x|$ approaches ∞.
Step 4. If $f(x)$ approaches some number c, then $y = c$ is a horizontal asymptote. Otherwise, there is no horizontal asymptote.	*Step 4.* Ignoring these terms, we have $y = \frac{2}{3}$ as the horizontal asymptote.

Example 10   Horizontal Asymptotes

Find the horizontal asymptotes of the function

$$f(x) = \frac{2x^3 + 3x - 2}{x^2 + 5}$$

Solution

Factoring, we have

$$f(x) = \frac{x^3\left(2 + \dfrac{3}{x^2} - \dfrac{2}{x^3}\right)}{x^2\left(1 + \dfrac{5}{x^2}\right)}$$

$$= \frac{x\left(2 + \dfrac{3}{x^2} - \dfrac{2}{x^3}\right)}{1 + \dfrac{5}{x^2}}, \quad x \neq 0$$

As $|x|$ increases, the terms $\frac{3}{x^2}, -\frac{2}{x^3}$ and $\frac{5}{x^2}$ approach zero and can be ignored. Therefore, as $|x|$ increases, $f(x)$ approaches $2x$. However, as $|x|$ approaches ∞, $f(x)$ does not approach some number c. In fact, $|y|$ approaches ∞ as $|x|$ approaches ∞. Thus, there is no horizontal asymptote.

The following theorem can be proved by utilizing the procedure of Example 9.

Horizontal Asymptote Theorem
The graph of the rational function

$$f(x) = \frac{P(x)}{Q(x)}$$

has a horizontal asymptote if the degree of $P(x)$ is less than or equal to the degree of $Q(x)$.

Note that the graph of a rational function may have many vertical asymptotes but at most one horizontal asymptote. A more specific version of the Horizontal Asymptote Theorem can be found in Exercises 28 and 29.

✔ **Progress Check**
Determine the horizontal asymptote of the graph of each function.

a. $f(x) = \dfrac{x - 1}{2x^2 + 1}$

b. $g(x) = \dfrac{4x^2 - 3x + 1}{-3x^2 + 1}$

c. $h(x) = \dfrac{3x^3 - x + 1}{2x^2 - 1}$

Answers
a. $y = 0$ b. $y = -\dfrac{4}{3}$ c. no horizontal asymptote

Sketching Graphs

We now summarize the information that can be gathered in preparation for sketching the graph of a rational function:

- symmetry with respect to the axes and the origin

- x-intercepts, y-intercepts

- vertical asymptotes

- horizontal asymptotes

- brief table of values including points near the vertical asymptotes

Example 11   Graphing Rational Functions

Sketch the graph of

$$f(x) = \frac{x^2}{x^2 - 1}$$

Solution

Symmetry: Replacing x with $-x$ results in the same equation, establishing symmetry with respect to the y-axis.

Intercepts: Setting $x = 0$, we obtain the y-intercept $y = 0$. Setting $y = f(x) = 0$ yields the x-intercept $x = 0$. Therefore, the point $(0, 0)$ is both the x- and y-intercept.

Vertical asymptotes: Setting the denominator equal to zero, we find that $x = 1$ and $x = -1$ are vertical asymptotes of the graph of f.

Horizontal asymptotes: We note that

$$f(x) = \frac{x^2}{x^2\left(1 - \dfrac{1}{x^2}\right)} = \frac{1}{1 - \dfrac{1}{x^2}}, \qquad x \neq 0$$

As $|x|$ gets larger and larger, $\frac{1}{x^2}$ approaches 0 and the values of $f(x)$ approach 1. Thus, $y = 1$ is the horizontal asymptote.

We determine the critical values of $f(x)$ to be 0 and ± 1. Our analysis of the behavior of $f(x)$ in the various intervals yields

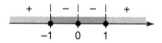

Following the technique used in Example 8 and plotting a few points, we sketch the graph in Figure 7.

x	y
$\frac{1}{2}$	-0.33
$\frac{3}{4}$	-1.29
$\frac{5}{4}$	2.78
$\frac{3}{2}$	1.80
2	1.33

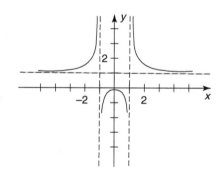

Figure 7   Graph of $f(x) = \dfrac{x^2}{x^2 - 1}$

✔ Progress Check

Find the horizontal and vertical asymptotes, and the x- and y-intercepts. Sketch the graph of the function

$$f(x) = \frac{x^2 - x - 6}{x^2 - 2x}$$

Answer

The horizontal asymptote is $y = 1$. The vertical asymptotes are $x = 0$ and $x = 2$. There is no y-intercept, and the x-intercepts are $(3, 0)$ and $(-2, 0)$. We sketch the graph of $f(x)$ in Figure 8.

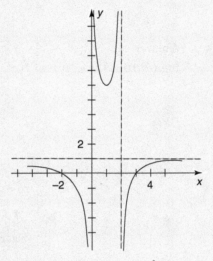

Figure 8   Graph of $f(x) = \dfrac{x^2 - x - 6}{x^2 - 2x}$

Reducible Rational Functions

We conclude this section with an example of a **reducible** rational function, that is, one in which the numerator and denominator have a factor in common other than a constant. Reducible rational functions are often used to illustrate functions that have "holes" in their graphs. Such functions are not continuous at these holes.

Example 12   Graphing Reducible Rational Functions

Sketch the graph of the function

$$f(x) = \frac{x^2 - 1}{x - 1}$$

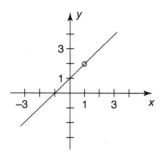

Figure 9   Graph of
$$f(x) = \frac{x^2 - 1}{x - 1}$$

Solution

We observe that

$$f(x) = \frac{x^2 - 1}{x - 1} = \frac{(x + 1)(x - 1)}{x - 1} = x + 1, \quad x \neq 1$$

Thus, the graph of the function $f(x)$ coincides with the line $y = x + 1$, with the exception that $f(x)$ is undefined at $x = 1$. We sketch the graph of $f(x)$ in Figure 9.

✔ Progress Check

Sketch the graph of the function

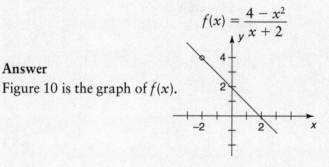

Answer

Figure 10 is the graph of $f(x)$.

Figure 10   Graph of $f(x) = \dfrac{4 - x^2}{x + 2}$

In discussing graphs and their asymptotes, we did not consider the possibility of an *oblique*, or *slanted*, asymptote. This is an asymptote that is neither horizontal nor vertical. A rational function has an oblique asymptote if the degree of the numerator is one more than the degree of the denominator.

Example 13   **Finding Oblique Asymptotes**

Find the oblique asymptote of

$$f(x) = \frac{x^2 - x}{x + 1}$$

Solution

Since the

degree of the numerator − degree of the denominator = 2 − 1 = 1

there is an oblique asymptote. After we perform the division, we obtain

$$f(x) = \frac{x^2 - x}{x + 1} = x - 2 + \frac{2}{x + 1}$$

As $|x|$ gets larger and larger, $\frac{2}{x+1}$ approaches 0 and $f(x)$ gets closer and closer to its oblique asymptote, the line

$$y = x - 2$$

as shown in the following figure.

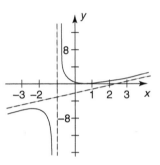

⌨ Graphing Calculator Power User's Corner

Graphing Rational Functions

Rational functions present several challenges to users of graphing calculators. It is important to be knowledgeable about these functions to properly interpret the display on your graphing calculator.

For example, graphs of rational functions sometimes seem to be "swallowed up" by the x-axis, as in the graphs of $f(x) = \frac{1}{x}$ and $g(x) = \frac{1}{x^2}$ shown in the default viewing rectangle in Figure 11. This lack of detail is due to the plotting mechanism of the calculator. When $|y|$ becomes very close to zero, the calculator plots the function *on* the x-axis instead of *near* the x-axis. Hence, these points become "invisible" to the user. One way to see more detail is to shift the graphs up 1 unit, that is, graph $y = \frac{1}{x} + 1$ and $y = \frac{1}{x^2} + 1$. (Graph the functions $f(x) = \frac{1}{x}$ and $g(x) = \frac{1}{x^2}$ in the EQUAL viewing rectangle and note any difference.)

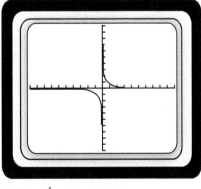

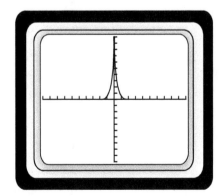

(a) $f(x) = \frac{1}{x}$, $-10 \leq X \leq 10$, $-10 \leq Y \leq 10$, XSCL = 1, YSCL = 1

(b) $g(x) = \frac{1}{x^2}$, $-10 \leq X \leq 10$, $-10 \leq Y \leq 10$, XSCL = 1, YSCL = 1

Figure 11   Graphs of Rational Functions

Vertical asymptotes pose the greatest difficulty for the graphing calculator. Consider the function

$$f(x) = \frac{x^2}{x^2 - 1}$$

from Example 11 shown in the two viewing rectangles of Figure 12. The asymptotes seem to be included in the graph in the default viewing rectangle. This happens because the calculator has not tried to evaluate $f(x)$ at $x = \pm 1$ and does not "know" that the function is undefined for these values. In the process of connecting the points that have been plotted, the calculator seems to draw the asymptotes. Graphing in a "point plotting" mode eliminates the asymptotes in this viewing rectangle, but it does not necessarily result in a better representation.

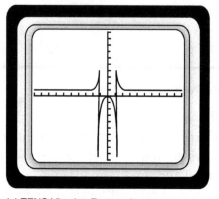 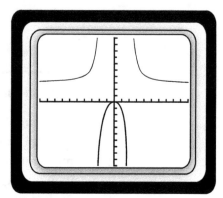

(a) TENS Viewing Rectangle,
XSCL = 1, YSCL = 1

(b) EQUAL Viewing Rectangle,
XSCL = 1, YSCL = 1

Figure 12   Graph of $f(x) = \dfrac{x^2}{x^2 - 1}$

For this example, the EQUAL viewing rectangle presents a good representation of the function without drawing the asymptotes. It is the responsibility of the user to determine that this function has vertical asymptotes at $x = \pm 1$. However, the function

$$g(x) = \frac{x^2}{x^2 - 7}$$

has vertical asymptotes at $x = \pm\sqrt{7}$. Yet, there is no viewing rectangle that displays this function without graphing the asymptotes.

Finally, consider rational functions with "holes" in their graphs, such as Example 12, where

$$f(x) = \frac{x^2 - 1}{x - 1}$$

As shown in Figure 13(a), graphing this function in the default viewing rectangle does not indicate the "hole" at the point $(1, 2)$ because the calculator does not attempt to plot a point for $x = 1$. However, in Figure 13(b), we see that using the EQUAL viewing rectangle does produce a visible "hole" in the graph.

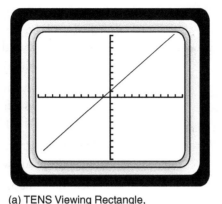

(a) TENS Viewing Rectangle,
XSCL = 1, YSCL = 1

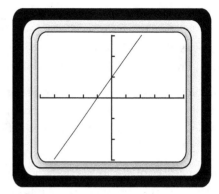

(b) EQUAL Viewing Rectangle,
XSCL = 1, YSCL = 1

Figure 13   Graph of $f(x) = \dfrac{x^2 - 1}{x - 1}$

Although the graphing calculator is helpful in determining the graph of a rational function, a careful analysis of the behavior of the function is necessary to obtain a correct and complete representation.

Exercise Set 5.1

In Exercises 1–6, determine the domain and intercepts of the given function.

1. $f(x) = \dfrac{x^2}{x - 1}$

2. $f(x) = \dfrac{x - 1}{x^2 + x - 2}$

3. $g(x) = \dfrac{x^2 + 1}{x^2 - 2x}$

4. $g(x) = \dfrac{x^2 + 2}{x^2 - 2}$

5. $F(x) = \dfrac{x^2 - 3}{x^2 + 3}$

6. $T(x) = \dfrac{3x + 2}{2x^3 - x^2 - x}$

In Exercises 7–21, determine the vertical and horizontal asymptotes of the graph of the given function. Sketch the graph. Then, determine appropriate WINDOW values, and check your answer using your graphing calculator. Choose the viewing rectangle carefully to obtain a correct and complete representation of the function. Be sure that your viewing rectangle is large enough to indicate the asymptotic behavior of the functions. You may not always be able to show all of the important behavior of the function in one viewing rectangle. (See the Graphing Calculator Power User's Corner in Section 4.2.)

7. $f(x) = \dfrac{1}{x - 4}$

8. $f(x) = \dfrac{-2}{x - 3}$

9. $f(x) = \dfrac{3}{x + 2}$

10. $f(x) = \dfrac{-1}{(x - 1)^2}$

11. $f(x) = \dfrac{1}{(x + 1)^2}$

12. $f(x) = \dfrac{-1}{x^2 + 1}$

13. $f(x) = \dfrac{x + 2}{x - 2}$

14. $f(x) = \dfrac{x}{x + 2}$

15. $f(x) = \dfrac{2x^2 + 1}{x^2 - 4}$

16. $f(x) = \dfrac{x^2 + 1}{x^2 + 2x - 3}$

17. $f(x) = \dfrac{x^2 + 2}{2x^2 - x - 6}$

18. $f(x) = \dfrac{x^2 - 1}{x + 2}$

19. $f(x) = \dfrac{x^2}{4x - 4}$

20. $f(x) = \dfrac{x - 1}{2x^3 - 2x}$

21. $f(x) = \dfrac{x^3 + 4x^2 + 3x}{x^2 - 25}$

In Exercises 22–27, determine the domain and sketch the graph of the reducible function. Furthermore, determine appropriate WINDOW values, and check your answer using your graphing calculator. Choose the viewing rectangle carefully to display the "holes." (Select the x-values from some multiple of the EQUAL viewing rectangle and choose appropriate y-values.)

22. $f(x) = \dfrac{x^2 - 25}{2x - 10}$

23. $f(x) = \dfrac{2x^2 - 8}{x + 2}$

24. $f(x) = \dfrac{2x^2 + 2x - 12}{3x - 6}$

25. $f(x) = \dfrac{x^2 + 2x - 8}{2x^2 - 8x + 8}$

26. $f(x) = \dfrac{x + 2}{x^2 - x - 6}$ 27. $f(x) = \dfrac{2x}{x^2 + x}$

In Exercises 28 and 29, $f(x) = \dfrac{P(x)}{Q(x)}$ is an irreducible rational function. Provide a proof for the stated theorem.

28. If the polynomials $P(x)$ and $Q(x)$ are of the same degree, then there is a horizontal asymptote $y = k$, where k is the ratio of the leading coefficients of $P(x)$ and $Q(x)$.

29. If the degree of $P(x)$ is less than the degree of $Q(x)$, then there is a horizontal asymptote at $y = 0$.

30. Suppose you are a manufacturer of graphing calculators. Your fixed or start-up cost is $10,000. Each calculator costs you $50 to manufacture.

    a. What is the average cost to you of producing your first 100 calculators?

    b. What formula will give you the average cost of the first x calculators?

31. The average cost of producing n units of a product is given by

    $$A(n) = \frac{C(n)}{n}$$

    Given the cost function

    $$C(n) = 0.01n^3 - 0.1n^2 + 100n + 1000$$

    find

    a. The average cost of producing n units.

    b. The average cost of a function of x, if the number of units produced is $n = x - 2$.

     c. GRAPH the average cost formulas you found in parts a and b, and use the graphs to determine when the cost is increasing or decreasing. (You will need to find an appropriate viewing WINDOW.)

Applications 5.1

1. On the website http://reviews.cnet.com/green-tech/tv-power-efficiency/ the average yearly cost for electricity on watching a 50-inch TV for a common household is $64 in 2009. Mike paid $1699.00 for his 50 inch TV as a birthday gift to himself in 2009.

    a. Determine the total cost for Mike's TV that last 2 years, 5 years, and 10 years. Assume the only costs associated with the TV are its purchase cost, $30 per month on cable, and electricity.

    b. Determine the annual cost for Mike's TV that last 2 years, 5 years, and 10 years. Assume the only costs associated with the TV are its purchase cost, $30 per month on cable, and electricity.

    c. Develop a function that gives the annual cost of Mike's TV as a function of the number of years Mike owns the TV.

    d. Sketch the graph of the function in part (c). What is an appropriate window?

    e. Determine the asymptotes of the function in part (c).

    f. Explain the meaning of the horizontal asymptote in terms of the cost of the TV.

2. Research showed that the concentration of a drug in the blood stream t hours after it is injected is given by $C(t) = \frac{0.25t}{t^2 + 0.81}$, where C is measured in micrograms and t is measured in minutes.

    a. Sketch the graph of the function over the first hour after the drug was injected. Label axes clearly.

    b. Determine when the maximum amount of the drug is in the body and the amount at that time. (Use your graphing calculator to trace the point.)

    c. Explain, within the context of the problem, the shape of the graph between injecting the drug ($t = 0$) and the maximum point. What does the shape of the graph communicate between the maximum point and the three hours after injecting the drug?

    d. Find the asymptotes of the function. What is the meaning of the asymptotes within the content of the problem?

3. There are a lot of uncertainties about the Gulf oil spill (CNNMoney.com). But one thing is clear: In addition to the intangible loss of wildlife, it's going to cost BP a lot of money. The cost C (in billions of dollars) of removing p percent amount spilled oil is given by $C(p) = \frac{90p}{100 - p}$. (This math model is also called the Cost-Benefit model.)

    a. Sketch the graph of the function.

    b. Find the cost to remove 10%, 35%, and 75% of the spilled oil.

    c. Find the asymptote(s) of the function.

    d. What happens if the company does try to remove 100 percent of the spilled oil? Will the company be successful at doing so, or will the attempt end in failure, that is, will it be too expensive for the BP company?

4. Tracy was planning to drive from Boston to Fundy Bay National Park, a total of 754 miles, in July 2011.

   a. How long will the trip take if Tracy averages 30 miles per hour?

   b. How long will the trip take if Tracy averages 70 miles per hour?

   c. Determine a function which describes the time it takes to make this trip as a function of Tracy's driving speed. Identify the meaning of the variables.

   d. Graph the function. Find asymptote(s).

   e. What does this graph tell you about the time it will take Tracy to travel depending on the speed of the car? Explain your answer.

5.2   The Circle

The conic sections provide us with an opportunity to illustrate the power of analytic geometry. We shall see that a geometric figure defined as a set of points can often be described analytically by an algebraic equation. Furthermore, we can start with an algebraic equation and use graphing procedures to study the properties of the curve, as well as the equation.

First, consider how the term "conic section" originates. If we pass a plane though a cone at various angles, as shown in Figure 14, the intersections are called **conic sections**. In exceptional cases, the intersection of a plane and a cone may be a point, a line or a pair of lines.

We begin with the geometric definition of a circle.

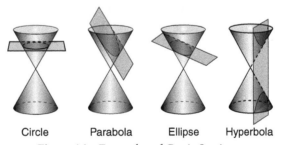

Circle   Parabola   Ellipse   Hyperbola
Figure 14   Examples of Conic Sections

Definition of a Circle
A **circle** is the set of all points in a plane that are at a given distance from a fixed point in the plane. The fixed point is called the **center** of the circle and the given distance is called the **radius**.

Recall from Section 3.1 the formula for the length d of the line segment joining points $P_1(x_1, y_1)$ and $P_2(x_2, y_2)$ as

$$d = \sqrt{(x_2 - x_1)^2 + (y_2 - y_1)^2}$$

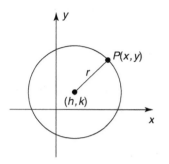

Figure 15 Deriving the Equation of a Circle

Using the methods of analytic geometry, we place the center at a point (h, k) as shown in Figure 15. If $P(x, y)$ is a point on the circle, then by the distance formula, the distance from P to the center (h, k) is

$$\sqrt{(x - h)^2 + (y - k)^2}$$

Since this distance is equal to the radius r, we can write

$$\sqrt{(x - h)^2 + (y - k)^2} = r$$

or

$$(x - h)^2 + (y - k)^2 = r^2$$

Since $P(x, y)$ is any point on the circle, we say that

Standard Form of the Equation of a Circle

$$(x - h)^2 + (y - k)^2 = r^2$$

is the standard form of the equation of the circle with center (h, k) and radius r.

Note the special case of

$$x^2 + y^2 = r^2$$

which is the equation of the circle of radius r, centered at the origin.

Example 1 Finding the Equation of a Circle
Write the equation of the circle with center at $(2, -5)$ and radius 3.

Solution
Substituting $h = 2$, $k = -5$ and $r = 3$ into the equation

$$(x - h)^2 + (y - k)^2 = r^2$$

yields

$$(x - 2)^2 + (y + 5)^2 = 9$$

Example 2 Finding the Center and Radius of a Circle
Find the center and radius of the circle whose equation is

$$(x + 1)^2 + (y - 3)^2 = 4$$

Solution
If we compare this equation with the standard form

$$(x - h)^2 + (y - k)^2 = r^2$$

we have

$$h = -1 \quad k = 3 \quad r = 2$$

The center is at $(-1, 3)$, and the radius is 2.

> **✔ Progress Check**
>
> Find the center and radius of the circle whose equation is
>
> $$\left(x - \frac{1}{2}\right)^2 + (y + 5)^2 = 15$$
>
> **Answer**
> center $(\frac{1}{2}, -5)$, radius $\sqrt{15}$

General Form

If we are given the equation of a circle in the general form

$$Ax^2 + Ay^2 + Dx + Ey + F = 0, \quad A \neq 0$$

in which the coefficients of x^2 and y^2 are the same, we may rewrite the equation in standard form. The process involves completing the square in each variable.

Recall from Section 2.3 that if we have the expression

$$x^2 + dx$$

we add $(\frac{d}{2})^2$ to form

$$x^2 + dx + \frac{d^2}{4} = \left(x + \frac{d}{2}\right)^2$$

For example, starting with the expressions

$$x^2 + 4x \quad \text{and} \quad y^2 - 10y$$

we complete the squares in this way:

$$x^2 + 4x + 4 = (x + 2)^2 \quad \text{and} \quad y^2 - 10y + 25 = (y - 5)^2$$

Example 3 Standard Form of the Equation of a Circle
Write the equation of the circle $2x^2 + 2y^2 - 12x + 16y - 31 = 0$ in standard form.

Solution
Grouping the terms in x and y and factoring produces

$$2(x^2 - 6x) + 2(y^2 + 8y) = 31$$

Completing the square in both x and y, we have

$$2(x^2 - 6x + 9) + 2(y^2 + 8y + 16) = 31 + 18 + 32$$
$$2(x - 3)^2 + 2(y + 4)^2 = 81$$

Note that the quantities 18 and 32 were added to the right-hand side to maintain equality. The last equation can be written as

$$(x - 3)^2 + (y + 4)^2 = \frac{81}{2}$$

This is the standard form of the equation of the circle with center at $(3, -4)$ and radius

$$r = \sqrt{\frac{81}{2}} = \frac{9\sqrt{2}}{2}$$

✔ **Progress Check**
Write the equation of the circle $4x^2 + 4y^2 - 8x + 4y = 103$ in standard form, and determine the center and radius.

Answer
$(x - 1)^2 + (y + \frac{1}{2})^2 = 27$, center $(1, -\frac{1}{2})$, radius $3\sqrt{3}$

Example 4   Standard Form of the Equation of a Circle
Write the equation $3x^2 + 3y^2 - 6x + 15 = 0$ in standard form.

Solution
Regrouping, we have

$$3(x^2 - 2x) + 3y^2 = -15$$

We then complete the square in x and y:

$$3(x^2 - 2x + 1) + 3y^2 = -15 + 3$$
$$3(x - 1)^2 + 3y^2 = -12$$
$$(x - 1)^2 + y^2 = -4$$

Since $r^2 = -4$ is impossible, the graph of the equation is not a circle. (Note that the left-hand side of the equation in standard form is a sum of squares and hence nonnegative. However, the right-hand side is negative.) Thus, there are no real values of x and y that satisfy the equation. This is an example of an equation that does not have a graph.

Example 5   Standard Form of the Equation of a Circle
Find an equation of the circle that has its center at $C(-1, 2)$ and that passes through the point $P(3, 4)$.

Solution
Since the distance from the center to any point on the circle determines the radius, we can use the distance formula to find

$$r = \overline{PC} = \sqrt{20}$$

Then we can write the equation of the circle in standard form as

$$(x + 1)^2 + (y - 2)^2 = 20$$

✔ Progress Check

Write the equation $x^2 + y^2 - 12y + 36 = 0$ in standard form, and analyze its graph.

Answer

The standard form is $x^2 + (y - 6)^2 = 0$. The equation is that of a "circle" with center at $(0, 6)$ and radius 0. The "circle" is actually the point $(0, 6)$.

 Graphing Calculator Power User's Corner

Graphing Circles

For these graphs, it is worthwhile to use WINDOW values that are multiples of the EQUAL viewing rectangle. They will produce "better shaped" circles.

To display the circle $(x - h)^2 + (y - k)^2 = r^2$ on your graphing calculator, graph $y = \sqrt{r^2 - (x - h)^2} + k$ and $y = -\sqrt{r^2 - (x - h)^2} + k$. For example, we display in Figure 16

$$(x + 1)^2 + (y - 3)^2 = 4$$

that is, we GRAPH

$$y = \sqrt{(4 - (x + 1)^2)} + 3 \quad \text{and} \quad y = -\sqrt{(4 - (x + 1)^2)} + 3$$

in the viewing rectangle that is two times the EQUAL viewing rectangle. (Compare this with the default viewing rectangle.)

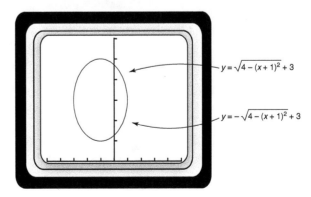

Figure 16   Graph of $(x + 1)^2 + (y - 3)^2 = 4$, XSCL = 2, YSCL = 2

To display the circle $Ax^2 + Ay^2 + Dx + Ey + F = 0$ on your graphing calculator, use the quadratic formula to solve for y and GRAPH

$$y = \frac{-E \pm \sqrt{E^2 - 4A(Ax^2 + Dx + F)}}{2A}$$

For example, we display in Figure 17

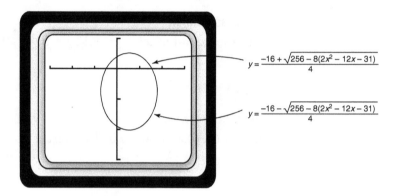

Figure 17   Graph of $2x^2 + 2y^2 - 12x + 16y - 31 = 0$, XSCL = 4, YSCL = 4

$$2x^2 + 2y^2 - 12x + 16y - 31 = 0$$

that is, we GRAPH

$$y = \frac{-16 + \sqrt{256 - 8(2x^2 - 12x - 31)}}{4}$$

and

$$y = \frac{-16 - \sqrt{256 - 8(2x^2 - 12x - 31)}}{4}$$

in the viewing rectangle that is four times the EQUAL viewing rectangle. (Compare this with the default viewing rectangle.)

Your calculator may have a DRAW feature which will enable you to draw a circle by entering the vertex and the radius, as below:

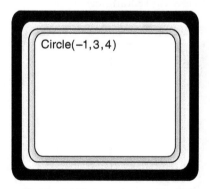

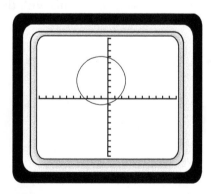

Graph of $(x + 1)^2 + (y - 3)^2 = 4$

Exercise Set 5.2

In Exercises 1–8, find an equation of the circle with center at (h, k) and radius r.

1. $(h, k) = (2, 3)$, $r = 2$

2. $(h, k) = (-3, 0)$, $r = 3$

3. $(h, k) = (-2, -3)$, $r = \sqrt{5}$

4. $(h, k) = (2, -4)$, $r = 4$

5. $(h, k) = (0, 0)$, $r = 3$

6. $(h, k) = (0, -3)$, $r = 2$

7. $(h, k) = (-1, 4)$, $r = 2\sqrt{2}$

8. $(h, k) = (2, 2)$, $r = 2$

In Exercises 9–16, find the center and radius of the circle with the given equation. Then, determine appropriate WINDOW values and GRAPH the circle on your graphing calculator.

9. $(x - 2)^2 + (y - 3)^2 = 16$

10. $(x + 2)^2 + y^2 = 9$

11. $(x - 2)^2 + (y + 2)^2 = 4$

12. $\left(x + \dfrac{1}{2}\right)^2 + (y - 2)^2 = 8$

13. $(x + 4)^2 + \left(y + \dfrac{3}{2}\right)^2 = 18$

14. $x^2 + (y - 2)^2 = 4$

15. $\left(x - \dfrac{1}{3}\right)^2 + y^2 = -\dfrac{1}{9}$

16. $(x - 1)^2 + \left(y - \dfrac{1}{2}\right)^2 = 3$

In Exercises 17–24, write the equation of each given circle in standard form, and determine the center and radius if it exists. Then, determine appropriate WINDOW values and GRAPH the circle on your graphing calculator.

17. $x^2 + y^2 + 4x - 8y + 4 = 0$

18. $x^2 + y^2 - 2x + 6y - 15 = 0$

19. $2x^2 + 2y^2 - 6x - 10y + 6 = 0$

20. $2x^2 + 2y^2 + 8x - 12y - 8 = 0$

21. $2x^2 + 2y^2 - 4x - 5 = 0$

22. $4x^2 + 4y^2 - 2y + 7 = 0$

23. $3x^2 + 3y^2 - 12x + 18y + 15 = 0$

24. $4x^2 + 4y^2 + 4x + 4y - 4 = 0$

In Exercises 25–36, write the given equation in standard form, and determine if the graph of the equation is a circle, a point or neither.

25. $x^2 + y^2 - 6x + 8y + 25 = 0$

26. $x^2 + y^2 + 4x + 6y + 5 = 0$

27. $x^2 + y^2 + 3x - 5y + 7 = 0$

28. $x^2 + y^2 - 4x - 6y - 13 = 0$

29. $2x^2 + 2y^2 - 12x - 4 = 0$

30. $2x^2 + 2y^2 + 4x - 4y + 25 = 0$

31. $2x^2 + 2y^2 - 6x - 4y - 2 = 0$

32. $2x^2 + 2y^2 - 10y + 6 = 0$

33. $3x^2 + 3y^2 + 12x - 4y - 20 = 0$

34. $x^2 + y^2 + x + y = 0$

35. $4x^2 + 4y^2 + 12x - 20y + 38 = 0$

36. $4x^2 + 4y^2 - 12x - 36 = 0$

37. Find the area of the circle whose equation is
$$x^2 + y^2 - 2x + 4y - 4 = 0$$

38. Find the circumference of the circle whose equation is
$$x^2 + y^2 - 6x + 8 = 0$$

39. Show that the circles whose equations are
$$x^2 + y^2 - 4x + 9y - 3 = 0$$
and
$$3x^2 + 3y^2 - 12x + 27y - 27 = 0$$
are concentric.

40. Find an equation of the circle that has its center at $(3, -1)$ and passes through the point $(-2, 2)$.

41. Find an equation of the circle that has its center at $(-5, 2)$ and passes through the point $(-3, 4)$.

42. The two points $(-2, 4)$ and $(4, 2)$ are the endpoints of the diameter of a circle. Write the equation of the circle in standard form.

43. The two points $(3, 5)$ and $(7, -3)$ are the endpoints of the diameter of a circle. Write the equation of the circle in standard form.

Exercises 44 and 45 relate to the Graphing Calculator Power User's Corner on "Graphing Circles."

44. Why are the circles not round in the default viewing rectangle? Can you always find a viewing rectangle to make a circle appear round, and if so, how? If not, why not?

45. Why do the top and bottom halves of the circles not meet in some viewing rectangles? Can you always find a viewing rectangle to make them meet, and if so, how? If not, why not?

46. Use simultaneous equations to determine the equation of the circle passing through the points $(1, 2)$, $(-1, 2)$ and $(0, 3)$, given that the general form of a circle is

$$Ax^2 + Ay^2 + Dx + Ey + F = 0, \quad A \neq 0$$

47. Convert your solution to Exercise 46 to standard form, and state the center and radius of the circle.

48. Find the equation of the path of a satellite in a circular orbit 250,000 miles above a planet whose radius is 75,000 miles.

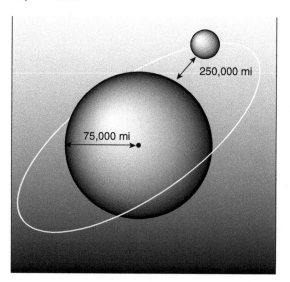

5.3   The Parabola

We begin our study of the parabola with the geometric definition

---

Definition of a Parabola
A **parabola** is the set of all points in a plane that are equidistant from a given point and a given line, both in the plane. The given point is called the **focus** and the given line is called the **directrix**.

In Figure 18, all points P_i on the parabola are equidistant from the focus F and the directrix D, that is, $\overline{P_iF} = \overline{P_iQ_i}$. The line through the focus that is perpendicular to the directrix is called the **axis of the parabola**. This line is also called the **axis of symmetry** since the parabola is symmetric with respect to it. The point V in Figure 18, where the parabola intersects its axis, is called the **vertex** of the parabola. The vertex is the point from which the parabola opens. Note that the vertex is the point on the parabola that is closest to the directrix.

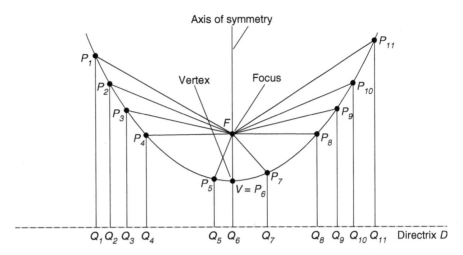

Figure 18   Directrix, Focus, Vertex, and Axis of a Parabola

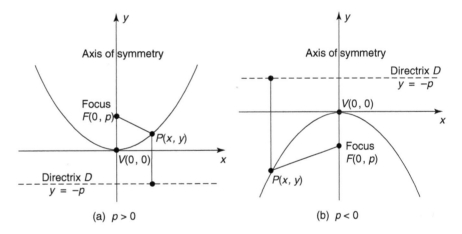

Figure 19   Deriving the Equation of a Parabola

We can apply the methods of analytic geometry to find an equation of a parabola. For a parabola with a vertical axis, choose that axis to be the y-axis, and take the origin as its vertex, as shown in Figure 19. Since the vertex is on the parabola, it is equidistant from the focus and the directrix. Thus, if the coordinates of the focus F are $(0, p)$, then the equation of the directrix is $y = -p$. We let $P(x, y)$ be any point on the parabola, and we equate the distance from P to the focus F with the distance from P to the directrix D. Using the distance formula,

$$\overline{PF} = \overline{PQ}$$

$$\sqrt{(x - 0)^2 + (y - p)^2} = \sqrt{(x - x)^2 + (y + p)^2}$$

Squaring both sides,

$$x^2 + y^2 - 2py + p^2 = y^2 + 2py + p^2$$

$$x^2 = 4py$$

We have obtained one form of the equation of the parabola.

Standard Form of the Equation of a Parabola with Vertical Axis and Vertex $(0, 0)$

$$x^2 = 4py$$

The focus is at $(0, p)$.

Conversely, it can be shown that the graph of the equation $x^2 = 4py$ is a parabola. Note that substituting $-x$ for x leaves the equation unchanged, verifying symmetry with respect to the y-axis. If $p > 0$, the parabola opens upward as shown in Figure 19(a), whereas if $p < 0$, the parabola opens downward, as shown in Figure 19(b).

Example 1   Finding Some Characteristics of a Parabola

Determine the focus and directrix of the parabola $x^2 = 8y$, and sketch its graph.

Solution

The equation of the parabola is of the form

$$x^2 = 4py = 8y$$

so $p = 2$. The equation of the directrix is $y = -p = -2$, and the focus is at $(0, p) = (0, 2)$. Since $p > 0$, the parabola opens upward. The graph of the parabola is shown in Figure 20.

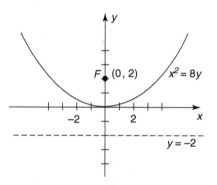

Figure 20   Graph of $x^2 = 8y$

✔ Progress Check

Determine the focus and directrix of the parabola $x^2 = -3y$.

Answer

focus at $(0, -\frac{3}{4})$, directrix $y = \frac{3}{4}$

Example 2   Finding the Equation of a Parabola

Find the equation of the parabola with vertex at $(0, 0)$ and focus at $(0, -\frac{3}{2})$.

Focus on Devices with a Parabolic Shape

The properties of the parabola are used in the design of some important devices. For example, by rotating a parabola about its axis, we obtain a *parabolic reflector*, a shape used in the headlight of an automobile. The light source (the bulb) is placed at the focus of the parabola. The headlight is coated with a reflecting material, and the rays of light bounce back in lines that are parallel to the axis of the parabola, permitting a headlight to disperse light in front of the automobile where it is needed.

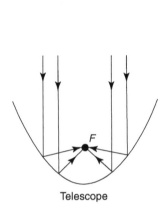

Telescope

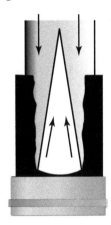

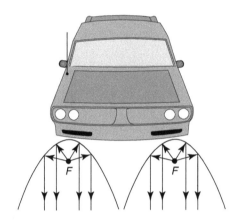

A reflecting telescope reverses the use of these same properties. Here, the rays of light from a distant star, which are nearly parallel to the axis of the parabola, are reflected by the mirror to the focus. The eyepiece is placed at the focus, where the rays of light are gathered.

Solution

Since the focus is at $(0, p)$, we have $p = -\frac{3}{2}$. The equation of the parabola is

$$x^2 = 4py = 4\left(-\frac{3}{2}y\right) = -6y$$

✔ Progress Check

Find the equation of the parabola with vertex at $(0, 0)$ and focus at $(0, 3)$.

Answer

$x^2 = 12y$

If we place the parabola as shown in Figure 21, we can proceed as we did for a parabola with a vertical axis and vertex $(0, 0)$ to obtain the following result.

> **Standard Form of the Equation of a Parabola with Horizontal Axis and Vertex (0, 0)**
>
> $$y^2 = 4px$$
>
> The focus is at $(p, 0)$.

Note that substituting $-y$ for y leaves this equation unchanged, verifying symmetry with respect to the x-axis. If $p > 0$, the parabola opens to the right as shown in Figure 21(a), but if $p < 0$, the parabola opens to the left as shown in Figure 21(b).

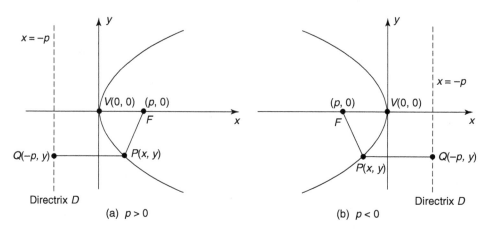

Figure 21   Deriving the Equation of a Parabola

Example 3   Finding the Equation of a Parabola

Find the equation of the parabola with vertex at $(0, 0)$ and directrix $x = \frac{1}{2}$.

Solution

The directrix is $x = -p$, so $p = -\frac{1}{2}$. The equation of the parabola is then

$$y^2 = 4px = -2x$$

Example 4   Finding the Equation of a Parabola

Find the equation of the parabola that has its axis as the x-axis, its vertex at $(0, 0)$ and passes through the point $(-2, 3)$.

Solution

Since the axis of the parabola is the x-axis, the equation of the parabola is $y^2 = 4px$. The parabola passes through the point $(-2, 3)$, so the coordinates of this point must satisfy the equation of the parabola. Thus,

$$y^2 = 4px$$
$$(3)^2 = 4p(-2)$$
$$4p = -\frac{9}{2}$$

Table 1   Standard Forms of the Equation of a Parabola with Vertex (h, k)

Equation	Axis	Directrix	Direction of Opening
$(x - h)^2 = 4p(y - k)$	$x = h$	$y = k - p$	Up if $p > 0$ Down if $p < 0$
$(y - k)^2 = 4p(x - h)$	$y = k$	$x = h - p$	Right if $p > 0$ Left if $p < 0$

and the equation of the parabola is

$$y^2 = 4px = -\frac{9}{2}x$$

✔ **Progress Check**

Find the equation of the parabola that has its axis as the y-axis, its vertex at $(0, 0)$ and passes through the point $(1, -2)$.

Answer

$$x^2 = -\frac{1}{2}y$$

Vertex at (h, k)

It is also possible to determine an equation of a parabola when the vertex is at some arbitrary point (h, k). The form of the equation depends on whether the axis of the parabola is parallel to the x-axis or to the y-axis. The situations are summarized in Table 1. Note that if the point (h, k) is the origin, then $h = k = 0$, and we arrive at the equations we derived previously. Thus, in all cases, the sign of the constant p determines the direction in which the parabola opens. Furthermore, an equation of a parabola can always be written in one of the standard forms shown in Table 1.

Note that these changes in the equations of the parabola are similar to the change that occurs in the equation of the circle when the center is moved from the origin to a point (h, k). In both cases, x is replaced by $x - h$ and y is replaced by $y - k$.

Example 5   Finding Some Characteristics of a Parabola

Determine the vertex, axis and the direction in which the parabola opens.

$$\left(x - \frac{1}{2}\right)^2 = -3(y + 4)$$

Solution

Comparison of the equation with the standard form

$$(x - h)^2 = 4p(y - k)$$

yields $h = \frac{1}{2}$, $k = -4$, $p = -\frac{3}{4}$. The axis of the parabola is found by setting the square term equal to 0.

$$\left(x - \frac{1}{2}\right)^2 = 0$$

$$x = \frac{1}{2}$$

Thus, the vertex is at $(h, k) = (\frac{1}{2}, -4)$, the axis is $x = \frac{1}{2}$ and the parabola opens downward since $p < 0$.   ■

✔ Progress Check

Determine the vertex, axis and the direction in which the parabola opens.

$$3(y + 1)^2 = 12\left(x - \frac{1}{3}\right)$$

Answer

vertex $(\frac{1}{3}, -1)$, axis $y = -1$, opens to the right

---

Example 6   Finding Some Characteristics of a Parabola

Locate the vertex and the axis of symmetry of each of the given parabolas. Sketch the graph.

a. $x^2 + 2x - 2y - 3 = 0$ b. $y^2 - 4y + x + 1 = 0$

Solution

a. We complete the square in x:

$$x^2 + 2x = 2y + 3$$
$$x^2 + 2x + 1 = 2y + 3 + 1$$
$$(x + 1)^2 = 2(y + 2)$$

The vertex of the parabola is at $(-1, -2)$ and the axis is $x = -1$ as shown in Figure 22(a).

b. We complete the square in y:

$$y^2 - 4y = -x - 1$$
$$y^2 - 4y + 4 = -x - 1 + 4$$
$$(y - 2)^2 = -(x - 3)$$

The vertex of the parabola is at (3, 2) and the axis is $y = 2$ as shown in Figure 22(b).

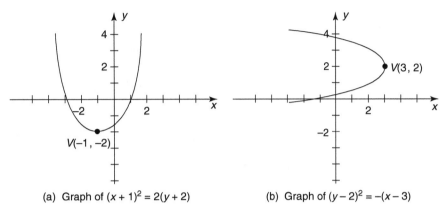

(a) Graph of $(x + 1)^2 = 2(y + 2)$ (b) Graph of $(y - 2)^2 = -(x - 3)$

Figure 22 Graphs for Example 6

✔ **Progress Check**

Write the equation of the parabola in standard form. Locate the vertex and the axis, and sketch the graph.

a. $y^2 - 2y - 2x - 5 = 0$ b. $x^2 - 2x + 2y - 1 = 0$

Answers

a. $(y - 1)^2 = 2(x + 3)$, vertex $(-3, 1)$, axis $y = 1$. The graph is shown in Figure 23(a).

b. $(x - 1)^2 = -2(y - 1)$, vertex $(1, 1)$, axis $x = 1$. The graph is shown in Figure 23(b).

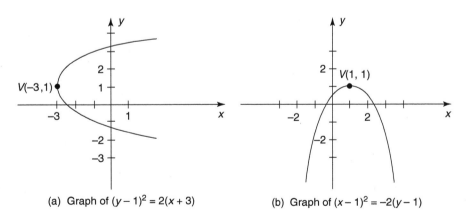

(a) Graph of $(y - 1)^2 = 2(x + 3)$ (b) Graph of $(x - 1)^2 = -2(y - 1)$

Figure 23 Graphs for Progress Check

Graphing Calculator Power User's Corner

Graphing Parabolas

To display the parabola $(x - h)^2 = 4p(y - k)$ on your graphing calculator, GRAPH $y = \frac{k + (x - h)^2}{4p}$. To display the parabola $Ax^2 + Dx + Ey + F = 0$ on your graphing calculator, GRAPH $y = -\frac{Ax^2 + Dx + F}{E}$.

To display the parabola $(y - k)^2 = 4p(x - h)$ on your graphing calculator, GRAPH $y = \sqrt{4p(x - h)} + k$ and $y = -\sqrt{4p(x - h)} + k$. To display the parabola $Cy^2 + Dx + Ey + F = 0$ on your graphing calculator, use the quadratic formula to solve for y and GRAPH

$$y = \frac{-E + \sqrt{E^2 - 4C(Dx + F)}}{2C}$$

and

$$y = \frac{-E - \sqrt{E^2 - 4C(Dx + F)}}{2C}$$

For example, to display $y^2 - 2y - 2x - 5 = 0$, GRAPH

$$y = \frac{2 + \sqrt{4 - 4(-2x - 5)}}{2}$$

and

$$y = \frac{2 - \sqrt{4 - 4(-2x - 5)}}{2}$$

Compare the graphs of this parabola in the default viewing rectangle and the EQUAL viewing rectangle.

Exercise Set 5.3

In Exercises 1–8, determine the focus and directrix of the given parabola, and sketch the graph.

1. $x^2 = 4y$

2. $x^2 = -4y$

3. $y^2 = 2x$

4. $y^2 = -\frac{3}{2}x$

5. $x^2 + 5y = 0$

6. $2y^2 - 3x = 0$

7. $y^2 - 12x = 0$

8. $x^2 - 9y = 0$

In Exercises 9–20, determine the equation of the parabola that has its vertex at the origin and satisfies the given conditions.

9. Focus at $(1, 0)$

10. Focus at $(0, -3)$

11. Directrix $x = -\frac{3}{2}$

12. Directrix $y = \frac{5}{2}$

13. Axis is the y-axis, and the parabola passes through the point $(4, -2)$.

14. Axis is the x-axis, and the parabola passes through the point $(2, 1)$.

15. Axis is the x-axis and $p = -\frac{5}{4}$.

16. Axis is the y-axis and $p = 2$.

17. Focus at $(-1, 0)$ and directrix $x = 1$.

18. Focus at $(0, -\frac{5}{2})$ and directrix $y = \frac{5}{2}$.

19. Axis is the x-axis, and the parabola passes through the point $(4, 2)$.

20. Axis is the y-axis, and the parabola passes through the point $(2, 4)$.

In Exercises 21–24, determine in which direction each parabola opens.

21. $4x^2 + y = 0$

22. $4x^2 - y = 0$

23. $2x + y^2 = 0$

24. $2x - 5y^2 = 0$

In Exercises 25–38, write the equation in standard form. Determine the vertex, axis and the direction in which each parabola opens. Determine appropriate WINDOW values, and GRAPH the parabola on your graphing calculator.

25. $x^2 - 2x - 3y + 7 = 0$

26. $x^2 + 4x + 2y - 2 = 0$

27. $y^2 - 8y + 2x + 12 = 0$

28. $y^2 + 6y - 3x + 12 = 0$

29. $x^2 - x + 3y + 1 = 0$

30. $y^2 + 2y - 4x - 3 = 0$

31. $y^2 - 10y - 3x + 24 = 0$

32. $x^2 + 2x - 5y - 19 = 0$

33. $x^2 - 3x - 3y + 1 = 0$

34. $y^2 + 4y + x + 3 = 0$

35. $y^2 + 6y + \frac{1}{2}x + 7 = 0$

36. $x^2 + 2x - 3y + 19 = 0$

37. $x^2 + 2x + 2y + 3 = 0$

38. $y^2 - 6y + 2x + 17 = 0$

In Exercises 39–44, determine the vertex, axis and the direction in which each parabola opens. Sketch the graph. Determine appropriate WINDOW values, and check your answer using your graphing calculator.

39. $x^2 - 4x - 2y + 2 = 0$

40. $y^2 + 2x - 4y + 6 = 0$

41. $2x^2 + 16x + y + 34 = 0$

42. $2x^2 - y + 3 = 0$

43. $y^2 + 2x + 2 = 0$

44. $y^2 + 3x - 2y - 5 = 0$

45. A stuntman has agreed to perform his famous human cannonball routine for the "Greatest Show in the Galaxy" carnival. The stuntman determines that his path will follow the parabola $y = 40x - x^2$, with the units measured in feet. His assistant has a 30 square foot circular net to catch his landing. The assistant places the net so that its center is 45 feet from the cannon.

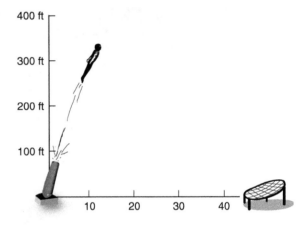

a. Sketch the path the stuntman will travel.

b. Determine if the net will "catch" the stuntman.

46. Consider a large parabolic reflector in the shape of a headlight used by a construction crew late at night. The lamp is designed in such a way that its light source is placed at the focus of the parabola, which lies $3\frac{1}{4}$ inches from its vertex. Suppose the lamp is to be $16\frac{1}{8}$ inches deep.

a. Sketch a graph of the parabola.

b. How wide will the reflector be?

c. How far will the rim of the lamp be from the light source?

47. A police helicopter has a searchlight that is designed so that its light source lies at the focal point of a parabolic reflector that is 6 inches from its vertex. Suppose the searchlight is designed to be 25 inches deep.

a. Find the width of the searchlight.

b. How far will the light source be from the rim of the searchlight?

48. A cable from a suspension bridge in the shape of a parabola hangs from two 75-feet towers, which are 650 feet apart. The lowest part of the cable hangs 17 feet from the roadway of the bridge.

a. Assume that the bridge cable will be supported by vertical beams. How long should such a support beam be if it is located 125 feet from the center of the span of the bridge?

b. Determine the length of vertical supporting beams for the bridge cable, if they are to be placed (i) 75 feet, (ii) 200 feet or (iii) 300 feet from the center of the cable.

650 ft

17 ft

Applications 5.3

1. The Gladesville Bridge in Sydney, Australia, was the longest single span concrete arched bridge in the world when it was constructed in 1964. The shape of the arch is almost parabolic.

   a. Please view the picture of the bridge at http://en.wikipedia.org/wiki/Gladesville_Bridge.

   b. If the function $y = -x^2$ describes the shape of the bridge, please explain the meaning of the negative sign.

   c. Find the vertex of the function. Where is the vertex located on the bridge?

d. Find the focus of the function. Where is the focus located? Explain your answer.

e. Sketch the graph of the function, the vertex, and the focus.

2. Tracy's family has a parabolic antenna, which has a cross-section of width 12 meters and depth of 2 meters.

   a. Sketch the graph of the antenna and label the vertex of the function.

   b. Where should a receiver be placed for the best reception?

3. A ping-pong ball was dropped and the equation $y = H(t) = -0.15t^2 + 2.804t - 0.514$ can be used to find where the ball will be at any time during the motion.

   a. Sketch the graph of the function.

   b. Find when the ball will reach its maximum height.

   c. What is the maximum height?

4. A 23-year-old British Stuntman was killed after a safety net failed during his "human cannonball" routine at an Easter Monday (April 26, 2011) daredevil show in southern England. A stuntman determines that his path will follow the parabola $y = H(x) = 60x - x^2$, where x is measured in feet.

   a. Sketch the graph of the stuntman's path.

   b. Find the location where the stuntman landed.

   c. Find the highest point where the stuntman could reach.

   d. His assistant has a 30 square foot circular net to catch his landing. The center of the net was placed 45 feet from the cannon. Determine if the net will "catch" the stuntman.

5.4 Translation of Axes

In Figure 24, two sets of coordinate axes are displayed There is the standard x- and y-coordinate axes with origin O, and there is another set of coordinate axes, x' and y', that are parallel to the x-axis and y-axis, respectively.

Consider shifting the x-axis vertically to the x'-axis and shifting the y-axis horizontally to the y'-axis. This process is called **translation of axes,** and we say that the x- and y-axes have been translated.

A point P in the plane has coordinates (x, y) with respect to the xy-coordinate system and (x', y') with respect to the $x'y'$-coordinate system. Suppose that O', the origin

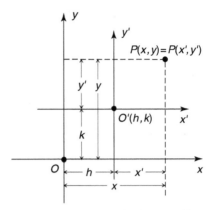

Figure 24 Deriving the Formulas for Translation of Axes

of the $x'y'$ system, has coordinates (h, k) in the xy system. We can obtain the following formulas relating x to x' and y to y'.

Translation of Axes Formulas

$$x' = x - h \quad \text{and} \quad y' = y - k$$

Example 1   Using the Formulas for Translation of Axes

The origin O' of the $x'y'$-coordinate system is at $(-2, 4)$.

a. Express x' and y' in terms of x and y, respectively.

b. Find the $x'y'$-coordinates of the point P whose xy-coordinates are $(4, -6)$.

Solution

a. Substituting $h = -2$ and $k = 4$, we obtain the translation formulas

$$x' = x + 2 \quad y' = y - 4$$

b. Substituting $x = 4$ and $y = -6$ yields

$$x' = 4 + 2 = 6 \quad y' = -6 - 4 = -10$$

The $x'y'$-coordinates of P are $(6, -10)$

✔ Progress Check

The origin O' of the $x'y'$-coordinate system is at $(-1, -2)$.

a. Express x and y in terms of x' and y', respectively.

b. Find the xy-coordinates of the point P whose $x'y'$-coordinates are $(3, -3)$.

Answers

a. $x = x' - 1, y = y' - 2$ b. $(2, -5)$

We can use the translation formulas to transform equations given in the xy-coordinate system to equations in the $x'y'$-coordinate system, and vice versa. For example, in the $x'y'$ system, the equation of the circle with center at O' and radius r is

$$(x')^2 + (y')^2 = r^2$$

Substituting the translation formulas

$$x' = x - h \quad \text{and} \quad y' = y - k$$

we find that the equation of this circle in xy-coordinates is

$$(x - h)^2 + (y - k)^2 = r^2$$

which is precisely the standard form of the equation of the circle with center at (h, k) and radius r, as discussed in Section 5.2.

Example 2 Analyzing and Sketching a Conic Section
Discuss and sketch the graph of the equation

$$x^2 - 4x + y^2 + 2y + 1 = 0$$

Solution
We group the terms in x and the terms in y

$$(x^2 - 4x \quad) + (y^2 + 2y \quad) = -1$$

Completing the square in each variable

$$(x^2 - 4x + 4) + (y^2 + 2y + 1) = -1 + 4 + 1 = 4$$

(Note that the equation is balanced by adding $4 + 1$ to the right-hand side.) We then have

$$(x - 2)^2 + (y + 1)^2 = 4$$

which is the equation of a circle with center at $(2, -1)$ and radius 2. In terms of the $x'y'$ coordinate system with origin O' at $(2, -1)$, the equation becomes

$$(x')^2 + (y')^2 = 4$$

We see that the equation and analysis are simplified by translating the axes to the point $(h, k) = (2, -1)$ as shown in Figure 25.

The technique of translation of axes can be applied to each of the conic sections. The results can be summarized as shown in Table 2. If we write the equation of a conic section in standard form, we can perform a translation of axes to the origin $O'(h, k)$ and then analyze and sketch the graph in the simplified form relative to the $x'y'$-coordinate system.

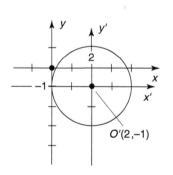

Figure 25 Graph of $x^2 - 4x + y^2 + 2y + 1 = 0$

Example 3 Analyzing and Sketching a Conic Section
Sketch the graph of the equation

$$x^2 - 4x - 4y - 4 = 0$$

Table 2   Standard Forms of Conic Sections

Conic Section	Standard Form	Characteristics	Example
Circle	$(x - h)^2 + (y - k)^2 = r^2$	Center: (h, k) Radius: r	$(x - 2)^2 + (y + 4)^2 = 25$ Center: $(2, -4)$ Radius: 5
Parabola	$(x - h)^2 = 4p(y - k)$ or $(y - k)^2 = 4p(x - h)$	Vertex: (h, k) Axis: $x = h$ Directrix: $y = k - p$ $p > 0$: Opens up $p < 0$: Opens down Vertex: (h, k) Axis: $y = k$ Directrix: $x = h - p$ $p > 0$: Opens right $p < 0$: Opens left	$(x + 1)^2 = 2(y - 3)$ Vertex: $(-1, 3)$ Axis: $x = -1$ Directrix: $y = \dfrac{5}{2}$ Opens up $(y + 4)^2 = -4(x + 5)$ Vertex: $(-5, -4)$ Axis: $y = -4$ Directrix: $x = -4$ Opens left

Solution

Write the equation as

$$(x^2 - 4x \quad) = 4y + 4$$

and complete the square in x.

$$(x^2 - 4x + 4) = 4y + 4 + 4$$
$$(x - 2)^2 = 4y + 8 = 4(y + 2)$$

Letting

$$x' = x - 2 \quad \text{and} \quad y' = y + 2$$

we obtain

$$(x')^2 = 4y'$$

In the $x'y'$-coordinate system, this is seen to be the equation of a parabola with vertex at $O'(2, -2)$ and $p = 1$. The graph is sketched in Figure 26.

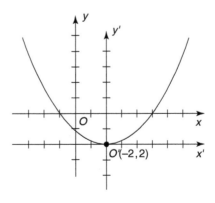

Figure 26   Graph of $x^2 - 4x - 4y - 4 = 0$

✔ Progress Check

Show that the graph of the equation

$$y^2 + 4y - 6x + 22 = 0$$

is a parabola.

Graphing Calculator Power User's Corner

Graphing General Conic Sections

The most general equation for a conic section is

$$Ax^2 + Bxy + Cy^2 + Dx + Ey + F = 0$$

The *Bxy* term causes a rotation of the graph of the conic section. We can rewrite this equation to see that it is a quadratic in *y*:

$$Cy^2 + (Bx + E)y + (Ax^2 + Dx + F) = 0$$

(This is of the form $ay^2 + by + c = 0$ with $a = C$, $b = Bx + E$, and $c = Ax^2 + Dx + F$.) We can use the quadratic formula to solve this equation for *y*.

For example, to display the graph of the conic section

$$2x^2 - 4xy + 5y^2 - 6x - y - 100 = 0$$

rewrite the equation as

$$5y^2 + (-4x - 1)y + (2x^2 - 6x - 100) = 0$$

and solve for *y*

$$y = \frac{(4x + 1) \pm \sqrt{(-4x - 1)^2 - 20(2x^2 - 6x - 100)}}{10}$$

As shown in Figure 38, we GRAPH

$$y = \frac{4x + 1 + \sqrt{(-4x - 1)^2 - 20(2x^2 - 6x - 100)}}{10}$$

and

$$y = \frac{4x + 1 - \sqrt{(-4x - 1)^2 - 20(2x^2 - 6x - 100)}}{10}$$

in the viewing rectangle that is three times the EQUAL viewing rectangle. Note that the shape of an ellipse or hyperbola may be distorted if the viewing rectangle is not proportionally scaled. Unfortunately, a proportionally scaled viewing rectangle does not necessarily guarantee an undistorted graph.

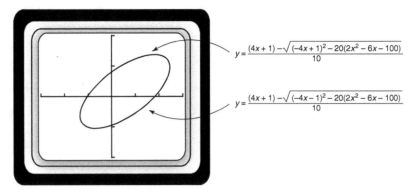

$$y = \frac{(4x+1) - \sqrt{(-4x+1)^2 - 20(2x^2 - 6x - 100)}}{10}$$

$$y = \frac{(4x+1) - \sqrt{(-4x-1)^2 - 20(2x^2 - 6x - 100)}}{10}$$

Figure 27   Graph of $2x^2 - 4xy + 5y^2 - 6x - y - 100 = 0$

Graphing Calculator Challenge

Write a program that will prompt for the values A, B, C, D, E and F, and then GRAPH the conic section $Ax^2 + Bxy + Cy^2 + Dx + Ey + F = 0$. Do not forget to allow for the special case when $C = 0$.

Exercise Set 5.4

In Exercises 1–4, the origin O' of the $x'y'$-coordinate system is at $(-1, 4)$. Find the $x'y'$-coordinates of the point whose xy-coordinates are given.

1. $(0, 0)$
2. $(-2, 1)$
3. $(4, 3)$
4. $(-6, -2)$

In Exercises 5–8, the origin O' of the $x'y'$-coordinate system is at $(-3, 4)$. Find the xy-coordinates of the point whose $x'y'$-coordinates are given.

5. $(0, 0)$
6. $(-2, 1)$
7. $(4, 3)$
8. $(-6, -2)$

In Exercises 9–18, sketch the graph of the given equation. Then, determine appropriate WINDOW values, and check your answer using your graphing calculator.

9. $x^2 + 4x - y + 5 = 0$
10. $2x^2 - 12x + y + 21 = 0$
11. $y^2 + 2x + 15 = 0$

5.5   A Brief Review of Inverse Functions

In Section 3.5, we introduced the concept of an inverse function. Since the exponential and logarithmic functions are inverses of each other, we are presenting a summary of facts concerning inverse functions. We want to keep the properties of inverse functions in mind in order to help us understand the development of the exponential and logarithmic functions.

Recall that we first consider functions that are one-to-one.

A function f is one-to-one if $f(a) = f(b)$ only when $a = b$.

Example 1   One-to-One Functions
Show that $f(x) = \frac{1}{2}x + 1$ is one-to-one.

Solution
Since $f(a) = \frac{1}{2}a + 1$ and $f(b) = \frac{1}{2}b + 1$, we set

$$f(a) = f(b)$$

$$\frac{1}{2}a + 1 = \frac{1}{2}b + 1$$

$$\frac{1}{2}a = \frac{1}{2}b$$

$$a = b$$

Therefore, $f(x)$ is one-to-one.

Example 2   One-to-One Functions
Show that $f(x) = x^2 + 1$ is not one-to-one.

Solution
Setting

$$f(a) = f(b)$$
$$a^2 + 1 = b^2 + 1$$
$$a^2 = b^2$$

However, this does not imply that $a = b$. For example, $2 \neq -2$, yet $f(2) = 5 = f(-2)$. Therefore, $f(x)$ is not one-to-one.

We may determine if a function is one-to-one by examining its graph.

Horizontal-Line Test
If no horizontal line meets the graph of a function in more that one point, then the function is one-to-one.

Example 3   Determining One-to-One Functions
Show that $f(x) = \frac{1}{2}x + 1$ is one-to-one.

Solution

The graph of $f(x) = \frac{1}{2}x + 1$ is shown in Figure 28. Any horizontal line meets $f(x)$ in at most one point. Therefore, $f(x)$ is one-to-one.

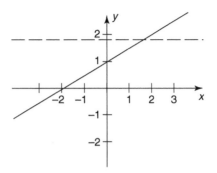

Figure 28   Graph of $f(x) = \dfrac{1}{2}x + 1$

Example 4   Determining One-to-One Functions

Show that $f(x) = x^2 + 1$ is a function but not a one-to-one function.

Solution

The graph of $f(x) = x^2 + 1$ is shown in Figure 2. Note that any vertical line meets $f(x)$ in at most one point, hence $f(x)$ is a function. However, in Figure 29 we see a horizontal line that meets $f(x)$ in two points. Therefore, $f(x)$ is not one-to-one.

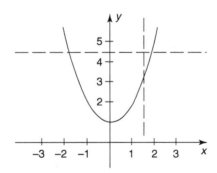

Figure 29   Graph of $f(x) = x^2 + 1$

We now recall the definition of an inverse function.

Inverse Functions

If f is a one-to-one function with domain X and range Y, then the function g with domain Y and range X satisfying

$$g[f(x)] = x \qquad \text{for every } x \text{ in } X$$
$$f[g(y)] = y \qquad \text{for every } y \text{ in } Y$$

is called an **inverse function** of f.

As an alternative, we may write

$$f^{-1}[f(x)] = x \qquad \text{for every } x \text{ in } X$$
$$f[f^{-1}(y)] = y \qquad \text{for every } y \text{ in } Y$$

Equivalently,

$$y = f(x) \text{ and } x = f^{-1}(y) \text{ for every } x \text{ in } X, \text{ every } y \text{ in } Y$$

Example 5   Finding Inverse Functions

Find the inverse function of $f(x) = \frac{1}{2}x + 1$.

Solution

If $f^{-1}(x)$ exists, then $y = f(x)$ implies that $x = f^{-1}(y)$. Let

$$y = \tfrac{1}{2}x + 1$$

Solving for x, we obtain

$$x = 2y - 2$$

and

$$f^{-1}(y) = 2y - 2$$

Writing this as a function of x,

$$f^{-1}(x) = 2x - 2y$$

(Verify that $f^{-1}[f(x)] = x$ and $f[f^{-1}(y)] = y$ for all x in X and all y in Y.)

The graphs of a function and its inverse are **reflections** of each other about the line $y = x$. Furthermore, if f^{-1} is the inverse of the function f, then the inverse of f^{-1} is f itself.

In Figure 30, we draw the graphs of $f(x) = \frac{1}{2}x + 1$ and $f^{-1}(x) = 2x - 2$. Observe that they are reflections of each other about $y = x$.

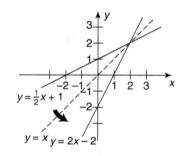

Figure 30   Graphs of Inverse Functions
as Reflections about $y = x$

Exercise Set 5.5

1. Let $F(x) = 2x - 2$. Find

   a. $F^{-1}[F(4)]$ b. $(F \circ F^{-1})(25)$

   c. $F^{-1}[F(y + 1)]$

   d. Refer to the Graphing Calculator Power User's Corner on "Graphing Inverse Functions" in Section 3.5. Set $-10 \le X \le 10$, $-10 \le Y \le 10$, and $-10 \le T \le 10$, and modify that example to GRAPH $y = F(x)$ and its inverse in the same viewing rectangle.

2. Let $f(x) = x^3 + 2x + 3$ and assume the domain of f^{-1} to be the set of all real numbers. Find

   a. $f[f^{-1}(-3)]$ b. $(f^{-1} \circ f)(\sqrt{3})$

   c. $f[f^{-1}(2a - 1)]$

   d. Refer to the Graphing Calculator Power User's Corner on "Graphing Inverse Functions" in Section 3.5. Set $-10 \le X \le 10$, $-10 \le Y \le 10$, and $-10 \le T \le 10$, and modify that example to GRAPH $y = f(x)$ and its inverse in the same viewing rectangle.

In Exercises 3–6, determine whether the given function $f(x)$ is one-to-one. If it is, find its inverse $f^{-1}(x)$, and sketch the graphs of $y = f(x)$ and $y = f^{-1}(x)$ on the same coordinate axes.

3. $f(x) = \sqrt{x}$ 4. $f(x) = |x|$

5. $f(x) = \dfrac{1}{x}$ 6. $f(x) = -1$

7. Let $f(x) = x^3 + 2x + 3$. Find $f^{-1}(3)$.

8. Let $H(x) = 2x^3 + 5x - 2$. Find $H^{-1}(-2)$.

9. A function G is defined by the following table:

x	-10	-5	0	5	10
$G(x)$	17	20	-4	3	10

   a. Is G a one-to-one function? Why?

   b. Find $G^{-1}(3)$.

   c. Find $G^{-1}(-4)$.

   d. Find $G^{-1}(x)$.

10. A function H is defined by the following table.

x	-4	-1	0	2	3
$H(x)$	0	2	-1	0	1

   a. Does H have an inverse? Why?

   b. Find $H(-1)$.

   c. Find $H(1)$.

11. Find two restrictions of the function $f(x) = x^2$ that allow it to have an inverse.

12. Find the inverse function for $f(x) = x^2 + 3$ on $[0, \infty)$.

13. Sketch the inverse function for $f(x) = x^4$ restricted to $(-\infty, 0]$.

14. Let $f(x) = -2x + 5$. Find $f^{-1}(x)$ and then sketch both functions on the same graph.

5.6   Exponential Functions

The function $f(x) = 2^x$ is quite different from any of the functions we have considered thus far. Previously, we defined functions using the basic algebraic operations (addition, subtraction, multiplication, division, powers and roots). However, $f(x) = 2^x$ has a variable in the exponent and does not fall into the class of algebraic functions. Rather, it is our first example of an exponential function.

An **exponential function** has the form

$$f(x) = a^x, \qquad a > 0, \qquad a \neq 1$$

where the real constant a is called the **base,** and the independent variable x may assume any real value.

Graphs of Exponential Functions

x	$y = 2^x$
-4	$\frac{1}{16}$
-3	$\frac{1}{8}$
-2	$\frac{1}{4}$
-1	$\frac{1}{2}$
0	1
1	2
2	4
3	8

To get a better understanding of exponential functions, we shall consider some examples.

Example 1   Graphing an Exponential Function
Sketch the graph of $f(x) = 2^x$.

Solution
Let $y = 2^x$, and make a table of x and y values. After plotting these points, we sketch the smooth curve as shown in Figure 31. Note that the x-axis is a horizontal asymptote, that is, the curve gets closer and closer to the x-axis as x approaches $-\infty$.   ■

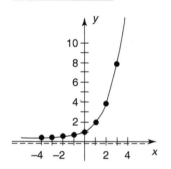

Figure 31   Graph of $y = 2^x$

Observe that when we sketched the graph of $f(x) = 2^x$, we obtained some values of 2^x without giving a complete explanation of our computations. Specifically, we have not explained how to find 2^x when x is irrational. For example, how do we calculate $2^{\sqrt{2}}$? For our purposes, we shall think of $2^{\sqrt{2}}$ as that value that 2^x approaches as x gets closer and closer to $\sqrt{2}$, such as $2^{1.4}$, $2^{1.41}$, $2^{1.414}$, ... A precise definition is given in more advanced mathematics courses, noting that the same laws of exponents hold for irrational exponents as well as for rational exponents.

The exponential function 2^x grows very rapidly for large values of x compared with x^2. For example, if $x = 2$, they both yield the same answer, 4. However, if $x = 20$

$$2^{20} = 1,048,576 \qquad \text{while} \qquad (20)^2 = 400$$

Warning
Previously, we considered functions in which a *variable is raised to a constant power.* It is possible to confuse this with exponential functions in which *a constant is raised to a variable power.* For example,

Exponential Functions	Nonexponential Functions
2^x	x^2
$(10)^x$	x^{10}
$\left(\frac{1}{2}\right)^x$	$x^{1/2}$
$(\sqrt{2})^x$	$x^{\sqrt{2}}$
π^x	x^{π}

x	$y = 2^{-x}$
-3	8
-2	4
-1	2
0	1
1	$\frac{1}{2}$
2	$\frac{1}{4}$
3	$\frac{1}{8}$
4	$\frac{1}{16}$

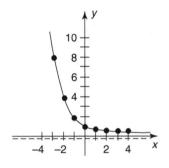

Figure 32 Graph of
$y = \left(\dfrac{1}{2}\right)^x = 2^{-x}$

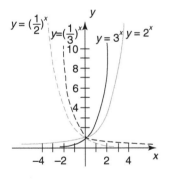

Figure 33 Graph of Various Exponential Functions

Example 2 Graphing an Exponential Function
Sketch the graph of $f(x) = (\frac{1}{2})^x = 2^{-x}$.

Solution
After finding the coordinates of some points, as listed in the table below, we sketch the graph as shown in Figure 32.

Note that the graph of $y = 2^{-x}$ is a reflection about the y-axis of the graph $y = 2^x$.

Properties of Exponential Functions

Consider the graphs of $y = 2^x$, $y = (\frac{1}{2})^x$, $y = 3^x$, and $y = (\frac{1}{3})^x$ all sketched on the same coordinate system as shown in Figure 33. The graphs of $y = (\frac{1}{2})^x$ and $y = (\frac{1}{3})^x$ are typical of the graph of $y = a^x$ where $0 < a < 1$. Similarly, the graph of $y = 2^x$ and $y = 3^x$ are typical of the graph of $y = a^x$ for $a > 1$. We state various properties in Table 3.

Since $f(x) = a^x$ is a one-to-one function, we have the following result.

> If $a^u = a^v$, then $u = v$.

Observe that the graphs of $y = a^x$ and $y = b^x$ intersect only at $x = 0$.

> If $a^u = b^u$ with $a > 0$ and $b > 0$, then $u = 0$ or $a = b$.

Table 3 Properties of the Exponential Function

$$f(x) = a^x, \qquad a > 0, \qquad a \neq 1$$

1. The graph of $f(x) = a^x$ always passes through the points $(0, 1)$ and $(1, a)$.

2. The graph of $f(x) = a^x$ is the reflection about the y-axis of the graph of $f(x) = (\frac{1}{a})^x = a^{-x}$.

3. The graph of $f(x) = a^x$ has the horizontal asymptote $y = 0$.

4. The domain of $f(x) = a^x$ consists of the set of real numbers; the range is the set of positive numbers.

5. $f(x) = a^x$ is increasing if $a > 1$; $f(x) = a^x$ is decreasing if $0 < a < 1$.

6. $f(x) = a^x$ is a one-to-one function since it passes the horizontal-line test.

7. Let $0 < a < b$. If $x > 0$, then $a^x < b^x$; if $x < 0$, then $a^x > b^x$.

Example 3 Solving Exponential Equations

Solve for x.

a. $3^{10} = 3^{5x}$ b. $2^7 = (x - 1)^7$ if $x > 1$ c. $3^{3x} = 9^{x-1}$

Solution

a. Since $a^u = a^v$ implies $u = v$, we have

$$10 = 5x$$
$$x = 2$$

b. Since $a^u = b^u$ with $a > 0$, $b > 0$, and $u \neq 0$ implies $a = b$, we have

$$2 = x - 1$$
$$x = 3$$

c.
$$3^{3x} = 9^{x-1} = (3^2)^{x-1} = 3^{2x-2}$$

Since $a^u = a^v$ implies $u = v$, we have

$$3x = 2x - 2$$
$$x = -2$$

✔ Progress Check

Solve for x.

a. $2^8 = 2^{x+1}$ b. $4^{2x+1} = 4^{11}$ c. $8^{x+1} = 2$

Answers

a. 7   b. 5   c. $-\dfrac{2}{3}$

The Number e

There is an irrational number that was first designated by the letter e by the Swiss mathematician Leonhard Euler (1707–1783). The number e is the value that the expression

$$\left(1 + \frac{1}{m}\right)^m$$

approaches as m gets larger and larger. We will approximate this expression for different values of m, as shown in Table 4.

Table 4 Approximating the Value of e

m	1	2	10	100	1000	10,000	100,000	1,000,000
$\left(1 + \dfrac{1}{m}\right)^m$	2.0	2.25	2.5937	2.7048	2.7169	2.7181	2.71827	2.71828

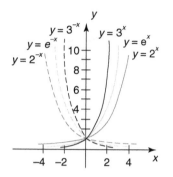

Figure 34 The National Exponential Function with other Exponential Functions

Alternatively, we write the following.

As m approaches ∞, $(1 + \frac{1}{m})^m$ approaches $e \approx 2.71828$.

Although the definition of the number e appears to be rather unnatural, the function $f(x) = e^x$ is called the **natural exponential function**. This function plays a most important role in mathematics.

The graphs of $f(x) = e^x$ and $f(x) = e^{-x}$ are shown in Figure 34. Since $2 < e < 3$, the graph of $y = e^x$ falls between the graphs of $y = 2^x$ and $y = 3^x$.

Graphing Calculator Alert

Graphing calculators and many scientific calculators have a special key to evaluate the function e^x. (Do not use the standard exponent key $\boxed{x^y}$, $\boxed{y^x}$, or $\boxed{\wedge}$ to evaluate these exponential expressions.) The $\boxed{e^x}$ key is usually a shifted or second function key. Use the keystrokes $\boxed{e^x}\,\boxed{1}$ to obtain the value of e.

Using the $\boxed{e^x}$ key, graph the function $y = e^x$ in the default viewing rectangle.

Applications

There are many applications involving the use of exponential functions. We shall consider models associated with business, biology and physics. Specifically, we shall investigate a mechanism for computing compound interest earned on an investment, a model that can represent population growth under most favorable environmental conditions and, finally, a model that simulates the process of radioactive decay.

Compound Interest

Suppose you invest P dollars at an interest rate r that is paid to you at the end of a period of t years. Then, the amount A available to you is calculated by the formula for simple interest:

$$A = P + Prt = P(1 + rt)$$

Most banks, however, advertise that they pay **compound interest**, that is, each successive payment includes interest on the previously accrued interest.

We use Table 5 to explore the effect of annual compounding over a period of 3 years, first with an investment of $100 compounded annually at a rate of 10% and then in general. We discover that the amount of interest paid increases each year, since the principal at the start of the next year has increased. Further, the amount A available at the end of each year suggests the following formula.

$$A = P(1 + r)^t$$

Table 5   Effect of Compound Interest over Three Years

Year	Starting Amount	Ending Amount	Starting Amount	Ending Amount
1	100.00	$100(1 + 0.1) = 110.00$	P	$P(1 + r)$
2	110.00	$110(1 + 0.1) = 121.00$	$P(1 + r)$	$P(1 + r)^2$
3	121.00	$121(1 + 0.1) = 133.10$	$P(1 + r)^2$	$P(1 + r)^3$

Example 4   Compound Interest

Suppose that $5000 is invested at an interest rate of 7.5% compounded annually. Find the value of the investment after 4 years.

Solution

To apply the formula for compound interest, we must express the interest rate as a decimal, that is, $7.5\% = 0.075$.

We are given $P = 5000$, $r = 0.075$, and $t = 4$. Substituting,

$$A = P(1 + r)^t$$
$$= 5000(1 + 0.075)^4 \approx \$6677.35$$

What happens if interest is compounded more frequently than once per year? Many banks advertise that they pay interest compounded semiannually, quarterly or daily. We can modify the compound interest formula to handle any **compounding period,** the time period between successive additions of interest. For example, suppose that compounding takes place semiannually, that is, twice a year at an *annual* rate r. Then, the interest rate applied to each period is assumed to be $\frac{r}{2}$. In addition, if the investment is held for t years, then there are $2t$ compounding periods. The amount available after t years is then

$$A = P\left(1 + \frac{r}{2}\right)^{2t}$$

We may now generalize to the situation where compounding takes place k times per year. The interest rate applied to each period is $\frac{r}{k}$ and there are a total of kt compounding periods. The formula can then be stated the following way:

Compound Interest Formula

If P dollars are invested at an annual interest rate r compounded k times annually, then the amount A available at the end of t years is

$$A = P\left(1 + \frac{r}{k}\right)^{kt}$$

Example 5   Compound Interest

Suppose that $6000 is invested at an annual interest rate of 8%. What will the value of the investment be after 3 years if

a. interest is compounded quarterly?

b. interest is compounded semiannually?

Solution

a. We are given $P = 6000$, $r = 0.08$, $k = 4$ and $t = 3$. Thus,

$$A = P\left(1 + \frac{r}{k}\right)^{kt} = 6000(1 + 0.02)^{12} \approx \$7609.45$$

b. We have $P = 6000$, $r = 0.08$, $k = 2$ and $t = 3$. Therefore

$$A = 6000(1 + 0.04)^6 \approx \$7591.91$$

Note that the interest obtained when compounding quarterly is greater than the interest obtained when compounding semiannually.

✔ Progress Check

Suppose that $5000 is invested at an annual interest rate of 6% compounded semiannually. What is the value of the investment after 12 years?

Answer

$10,163.97

Continuous Compounding

When P, r, and t, are held fixed and the frequency of compounding is increased, the return on the investment is increased. Table 6 displays the approximate increase in the value of an investment at the end of 1 year using various compounding periods.

Table 6   Investment of $P = \$1000$ at Rate $r = 8.0\%$ for One Year

Compounding Period	Compounding Frequency k	Amount A	Additional Interest
annual	1	$1080.00	
quarter	4	$1082.43	$2.43
month	12	$1083.00	$0.57
day	365	$1083.28	$0.28
hour	8760	$1083.29	$0.01

Although the value of the investment increases as we increase the compounding frequency, the additional benefit appears to diminish. In fact, the result in Table 6 is almost the same to two decimal places for daily and hourly compounding. (Show that the amount A continues to increase slightly if we consider more than two decimal places. In fact, show that this increase continues for a compounding period of 1 minute and 1 second.) This observation leads us to suspect that there may be a limiting value that is approached as we increase the compounding frequency. Consider the limit of this compounding process as we let the compounding period approach zero and the compounding frequency get larger and larger. The limit is called **continuous compounding.**

Recall the compound interest formula

$$A = P\left(1 + \frac{r}{k}\right)^{kt}$$

If we let $m = \frac{k}{r}$, we obtain

$$A = P\left(1 + \frac{1}{m}\right)^{mrt} = P\left[\left(1 + \frac{1}{m}\right)^m\right]^{rt}$$

Letting the compounding frequency k become larger and larger is equivalent to letting m get larger and larger. In Section 6.2 we observed that

As m approaches ∞, $\left(1 + \frac{1}{m}\right)^m$ approaches e.

We obtain the following result.

Continuous Compounding
If P dollars are invested at an interest rate r compounded continuously, then the amount A available at the end of t years is

$$A = Pe^{rt} \tag{1}$$

Example 6 Continuous Compounding
Suppose that \$20,000 is invested at an annual interest rate of 7% compounded continuously. What is the value of the investment after 4 years?

Solution
We have $P = 20{,}000$, $r = 0.07$, and $t = 4$. Substituting into Equation (1), we obtain

$$A = Pe^{rt}$$
$$= 20{,}000e^{0.07(4)} = 20{,}000e^{0.28}$$
$$\approx 20{,}000(1.3231)$$
$$= 26{,}462$$

The amount available after 4 years is \$26,462.60.

✔ **Progress Check**

Suppose that $10,000 is invested at an annual interest rate of 10% compounded continuously. What is the value of the investment after 6 years?

Answer

Approximately $18,221

By solving Equation (1) for P, we can determine the principal P that must be invested at continuous compounding to have a certain amount A at some future time.

Example 7   Continuous Compounding

Suppose that a principal P is to be invested at continuous compound interest of 8% per year to yield $10,000 in 5 years. Approximately how much should be invested?

Solution

Using Equation (1) with $A = 10,000$, $r = 0.08$ and $t = 5$, we have

$$A = Pe^{rt}$$

$$10,000 = Pe^{0.08(5)} = Pe^{0.40}$$

$$P = \frac{10,000}{e^{0.40}}$$

$$= 10,000e^{-0.40}$$

$$= 10,000(0.6703)$$

$$= 6703$$

Thus, approximately $6703 should be invested initially.

✔ **Progress Check**

Approximately how much money should a 35-year-old woman invest now at continuous compound interest of 10% per year to obtain the sum of $20,000 upon her retirement at age 65?

Answer

Approximately $996

Exponential Growth

Biologists have observed that under extremely favorable environmental conditions, populations appear to increase following the **exponential growth model**.

Exponential Growth Model

$$Q(t) = q_0 e^{kt}, \qquad q_0 > 0, \qquad k > 0$$

This model predicts the quantity Q (size or biomass) of a population that is present at time t. Both q_0 and k are constants specific to the particular population in question. Note that when $t = 0$, we have

$$Q(0) = q_0 e^0 = q_0$$

which says that q_0 is the initial quantity. (It is customary to use subscript 0 to denote an initial value.) The constant k is called the **growth constant**.

Example 8   Exponential Growth Model—Bacteria in a Culture

The number of bacteria in a culture after t hours is described by the exponential growth model

$$Q(t) = 50e^{0.7t}$$

a. Find the initial number of bacteria q_0 in the culture.

b. How many bacteria are in the culture after 10 hours?

Solution

a. To find q_0 we need to evaluate $Q(t)$ at $t = 0$.

$$Q(0) = 50e^{0.7(0)} = 50e^0 = 50 = q_0$$

Thus, there are initially 50 bacteria in the culture.

b. The number of bacteria in the culture after 10 hours is given by $Q(10)$.

$$Q(10) = 50e^{0.7(10)} = 50e^7 \approx 54{,}832$$

Thus, there are approximately 54,832 bacteria after 10 hours.

✔ Progress Check

The number of bacteria in a culture after t minutes is described by the exponential growth model $Q(t) = q_0 e^{0.005t}$. If there were 100 bacteria present initially, how many bacteria will be present after 1 hour has elapsed?

Answer

Approximately 135

Example 9 **Exponential Growth Model—World Population**

Statistics indicate that the world population, since 1950, has been growing at an average rate of 1.9% per year. According to the 2004 Revision Population Database provided by the United Nations at http://esa.un.org/unpp/, the world population in the year 2000 was approximately 6 billion. Assuming an exponential growth model, find the approximate population of the world in the year 2010.

Solution

We let $k = 1.9\% = 0.019$ and $q_0 = 6$. Then the exponential growth model

$$Q(t) = q_0 e^{kt}$$

becomes

$$Q(t) = 6e^{0.019t}$$

For the year 2010, $t = 10$ and we find that

$$Q(10) = 6e^{0.019(10)} = 6e^{0.19} \approx 7.26$$

Therefore, we project a world population of approximately 7.26 billion persons for the year 2010. (Compare this to the UN prediction of 6.843 billion. Why might the two predictions differ? Look at the website mentioned above; it indicates that the average population growth per year for just the last few years is lower than 1.9%. Also, exponential models for population growth fail to consider many factors that affect population growth.) ▪

Exponential Decay

Radioactive elements decay in a manner that is described by the **exponential decay model**.

Exponential Decay Model

$$Q(t) = q_0 e^{-kt}, \qquad q_0 > 0, \qquad k > 0$$

This model predicts the quantity Q (mass) of a particular radioactive material remaining after time t has elapsed. As in the previous model, q_0 represents the initial quantity. The constant k is called the **decay constant**.

We use the term **half-life** to describe the time it takes for half of the atoms of a radioactive element to break down or decay. Table 7 displays the approximate half-lives of a number of elements. Half-lives can vary from a fraction of a second to billions of years. The long half-life of certain radioactive elements, obtained as by-products of nuclear processes, has caused environmentalists to warn us of the potential hazards of nuclear wastes.

Table 7 **Half-Lives of Radioactive Elements**

Radioactive Element	Half-Life	Radioactive Element	Half-Life
Iridium 198	1 minute	Radon 222	4 days
Polonium 210	4 months	Radium 226	1620 years
Uranium 238	4.5 billion years	Thorium 232	14 billion years

Focus on Radioactivity in the News

On April 25, 1986, a nuclear disaster of unprecedented proportions took place at Chernobyl in the former Soviet Union. A fire occurred within a building housing a nuclear reactor, resulting in an explosion that sent radioactive material into the atmosphere. The air and soil of the surrounding farmlands were seriously contaminated.

Soil tests have indicated the presence of cesium 137, a radioactive element that has a half-life of 37 years. Scientists believe that the level of contamination in the soil must be reduced to 1/125th of its current reading before the region can again be used for farming. This will take 7 half-lives (since $2^7 = 128$) or approximately 259 years.

On September 13, 1988, the *New York Times* headline read

MAJOR RADON PERIL IS DECLARED BY U.S. IN CALL FOR TESTS

Radon, a colorless, invisible gas, is released by the breakdown of uranium in the earth's crust. Outdoors, the gas dissipates rapidly and is considered to be harmless. Indoors, however, it may accumulate to dangerous levels, especially in newer homes that have been constructed very tightly to conserve energy. Since the half-life of radon is only 3.8 days, homes showing high concentrations of radon may be salvaged by the installation of ventilation systems.

Example 10   Exponential Decay Model
A radioactive substance has a decay rate of 5% per hour. If 500 grams are present initially, how much of the substance remains after 4 hours?

Solution
We let $k = 5\% = 0.05$ and $q_0 = 500$. Then the exponential decay model

$$Q(t) = q_0 e^{-kt}$$

becomes

$$Q(t) = 500 e^{-0.05t}$$

After 4 hours,

$$Q(4) = 500 e^{-0.05(4)} = 500 e^{-0.2} \approx 409.37$$

Thus, there remain approximately 409.37 grams of the substance.

Example 11   Exponential Decay Model—Half-Life of Radium 226
Radium 226 has an approximate half-life of 1620 years. Show that the quantity Q of radium 226 present after t years is given by

$$Q(t) = q_0 2^{(-t/1620)}$$

Solution

If q_0 represents the initial quantity, then $\frac{q_0}{2}$ is the quantity present when $t = 1620$. Substituting in the exponential decay model

$$Q(t) = q_0 e^{-kt}$$

$$\frac{q_0}{2} = q_0 e^{-1620k}$$

We can write this last equation as

$$\frac{1}{2} = e^{-1620k}$$

Taking reciprocals, we obtain

$$2 = e^{1620k} = (e^k)^{1620}$$

and so

$$e^k = 2^{(1/1620)}$$

Substituting in the original equation, we have

$$Q(t) = q_0 e^{-kt} = q_0(e^k)^{-t} = q_0 (2^{(1/1620)})^{-t} = q_0 2^{(-t/1620)}$$

✔ Progress Check

The number of grams Q of a certain radioactive substance present after t seconds is given by the exponential decay model $Q(t) = q_0 e^{-0.4t}$. If 200 grams of the substance are present initially, find how much remains after 0.1 minute.

Answer
Approximately 18.14 grams

Exercise Set 5.6

In Exercises 1–12, sketch the graph of the given function f.

1. $f(x) = 4^x$

2. $f(x) = 4^{-x}$

3. $f(x) = 10^x$

4. $f(x) = 10^{-x}$

5. $f(x) = 2^{x+1}$

6. $f(x) = 2^{x-1}$

7. $f(x) = 2^{|x|}$

8. $f(x) = 2^{-|x|}$

9. $f(x) = 2^{2x}$

10. $f(x) = 3^{-2x}$

11. $f(x) = e^{x+1}$

12. $f(x) = e^{-2x}$

Exercises 13–24 refer to Exercises 1–12, respectively. Determine appropriate WINDOW values and GRAPH the functions in Exercises 1–12 on your graphing calculator.

In Exercises 25–32, solve for x.

25. $2^x = 2^3$

26. $2^{x-1} = 2^4$

27. $3^x = 9^{x-2}$

28. $2^x = 8^{x+2}$

29. $2^{3x} = 4^{x+1}$

30. $3^{4x} = 9^{x-1}$

31. $e^{x-1} = e^3$

32. $e^{x-1} = 1$

In Exercises 33–36, solve for a if $a > \frac{1}{2}$ and $x \neq 0$.

33. $(a + 1)^x = (2a - 1)^x$

34. $(2a + 1)^x = (a + 4)^x$

35. $(a + 1)^x = (2a)^x$

36. $(2a + 3)^x = (3a + 1)^x$

In Exercises 37–41, use your calculator to evaluate the following expressions:

37. e^2

38. $6e^{-0.02}$

39. $\dfrac{e^3 + e^{-3}}{2}$

40. $\dfrac{1}{1 + e^{-5}}$

41. $\dfrac{5}{6 - 3e^{-8}}$

 In Exercises 42–44, use a calculator to determine which number is greater.

42. $2^\pi, \pi^2$

43. $3^\pi, \pi^3$

44. e^π, π^e

 45. Use your calculator to evaluate the following expressions.

   a. $500(1 + 0.075)^5$

   b. $500\left(1 + \dfrac{0.075}{2}\right)^{2(5)}$

   c. $500\left(1 + \dfrac{0.075}{4}\right)^{4(5)}$

   d. $500\left(1 + \dfrac{0.075}{12}\right)^{12(5)}$

   e. $500\left(1 + \dfrac{0.075}{365}\right)^{365(5)}$

   f. $500\left(1 + \dfrac{0.075}{365(24)}\right)^{(365)(24)(5)}$

   g. $500e^{0.075(5)}$

   h. What do the computations in parts (a) to (g) represent?

 46. GRAPH $y = (1 + \frac{1}{x})^x$ in the following viewing rectangles to visualize that as $x \to \infty$, $(1 + \frac{1}{x})^x \to 2.71828$.

   a. $-10 \le X \le 10$ $-10 \le Y \le 10$

   b. $-100 \le X \le 100$ $0 \le Y \le 5$

   c. $-1000 \le X \le 1000$ $0 \le Y \le 5$

   d. $-1,000,000 \le X \le 1,000,000$ $0 \le Y \le 5$

47. GRAPH $y = (1 + \frac{1}{x})^x$ in the following viewing rectangles to visualize that as $x \to 0$, $(1 + x)^{1/x} \to 2.71828$.

   a. $-10 \le X \le 10$ $-10 \le Y \le 10$

   b. $-1 \le X \le 1$ $0 \le Y \le 5$

   c. $-0.1 \le X \le 0.1$ $0 \le Y \le 5$

   d. $-0.00001 \le X \le 0.00001$ $0 \le Y \le 5$

(On some graphing calculators you may find that $y = 1$ when x is close to 0. This is a result of the internal round-off error of the calculator.)

48. What point is common to the graph of all exponential functions?

49. What symmetry do you observe when you compare the graph of $y = (\frac{1}{4})^x$ with $y = (\frac{1}{4})^{-x}$?

 50. If \$5000 is invested at 7.8% interest compounded monthly, how much would you have after 54 months?

 51. Find the interest received if \$10,000 is invested at 12.5% for 2 years, compounded continuously.

 52. Suppose we have an investment of \$10,000 that is earning 11.5% interest compounded continuously.

   a. How long would it take to double the initial investment?

   b. How long would it take to triple the initial investment?

   c. What would be the answers to parts (a) and (b) if your initial investment were \$20,000?

 53. If a bacteria colony doubles its number at the end of each day, and there were 10,000 at the end of day 2, find q_0 and the number at the end of a week. Use $Q(t) = q_0 2^{kt}$.

 54. If the half-life of a radioactive substance is 25 minutes, what fraction of the substance remains after 125 minutes? Use $Q(t) = q_0 2^{-kt}$.

 55. The number of bacteria in a culture after t hours is described by the exponential growth model $Q(t) = 200e^{0.25t}$.

   a. What is the initial number of bacteria in the culture?

   b. Find the number of bacteria in the culture after 20 hours.

   c. Complete the following table.

t	1	4	8	10
Q				

 56. The number of bacteria in a culture after t hours is described by the exponential growth model $Q(t) = q_0 e^{0.01t}$. If there were 400 bacteria present initially, how many bacteria will be present after 2 days?

 57. At the beginning of 1975, the world population was approximately 4 billion. Suppose that the population is

described by an exponential growth model, and that the rate of growth is 2% per year. Give the approximate world population by the beginning of the year 2050.

58. The number of grams of potassium 42 present after t hours is given by the exponential decay model $Q(t) = q_0 e^{-0.055t}$. If 400 grams of the substance is present initially, how much remains after 10 hours?

59. A radioactive substance has a decay rate of 4% per hour. If 1000 grams is present initially, how much of the substance remains after 10 hours?

60. An investor purchases a $12,000 savings certificate paying 10% annual interest compounded semiannually. Find the amount received when the savings certificate is redeemed at the end of 8 years.

61. The parents of a newborn infant place $10,000 in an investment that pays 8% annual interest compounded quarterly. What sum is available at the end of 18 years to finance the child's college education?

62. A widow is offered a choice of two investments. Investment A pays 8% annual interest compounded quarterly, and investment B pays 9% compounded annually. Which investment yields a greater return?

63. A firm intends to replace its present computer in 5 years. The treasurer suggests that $25,000 be set aside in an investment paying 12% compounded monthly. What sum will be available for the purchase of the new computer?

64. If $5000 is invested at an annual interest rate of 9% compounded continuously, how much is available after 5 years?

65. If $100 is invested at an annual interest rate of 5.5% compounded continuously, how much is available after 10 years?

66. A principal P is to be invested at continuous compound interest of 9% to yield $50,000 in 20 years. What is the approximate value of P to be invested?

67. A 40-year-old executive plans to retire at age 65. How much should be invested at 12% annual interest compounded continuously to provide the sum of $50,000 upon retirement?

68. Investment A offers 8% annual interest compounded semiannually, and investment B offers 8% annual

interest compounded continuously. If $1000 were invested in each, what would be the approximate difference in value after 10 years?

69. If $1000 is deposited in a savings account that earns interest at an annual rate of 9% compounded continuously, what is the value of the account at the end of 8 years?

70. A trust fund is being set up by a single payment so that at the end of 25 years there will be $100,000 in the fund. If interest is compounded continuously at a rate of 8%, how much should be paid into the fund initially?

71. In the late 1950s, the minimum wage in the United States was approximately $1.95 per hour. Since then, assume that the minimum wage has increased according to the exponential function $y(t) = (1.95)^{t/10}$, where t is the number of years after 1958.

    a. Find the minimum wage in 1975.

    b. How much did the minimum wage increase from 1971 to 1980?

72. An investment of $10,000 earns interest at an annual rate of 10% compounded continuously. After t years, its value S is given by $S = 10,000e^{0.1t}$. Find the value of this investment after 25 years.

73. Write a PROGRAM in your calculator that will enable the user to enter the principal, interest rate, and time for an investment, and will return the value of the investment. You may be able to find such a program at your calculator manufacturer's website.

74. *Mathematics in Writing*: Under what circumstances is an exponential function increasing (rising) or decreasing? Compare Exercise 2 in this section with the following:

$$f(x) = \left(\frac{1}{4}\right)^x$$

What conclusions can you draw?

Applications 5.6

1. The continuous compound interest formula is given by $A = Pe^{rt}$, where P is the principal, r is the annual interest rate compounded continuously, t is time in years, and A is the accumulated amount at the end of t years.

a. Find the accumulated amount after 4 years if $2000 is invested at 5% per year compounded continuously.

b. Find the accumulated amount after 4 years if $2000 is invested at 10% per year compounded continuously.

c. Find a function that models the accumulated amount after 4 years if $2000 is invested at r percent per year compounded continuously.

d. Sketch the graph of the function that you wrote in part (c).

e. Find a function that models the accumulated amount after 4 years if $2000 is invested at 10% per year compounded annually. $(A = P(1 + r)^t)$

f. Find a function that models the accumulated amount after 4 years if $2000 is invested at r percent per year compounded annually? $(A = P(1 + r)^t)$

g. Sketch the graph of the function that you wrote in part (f).

h. Which one of the interests gives you a better deal? Explain your answer carefully.

2. Investment A offers 12% return compounded simply, and investment B offers a 10% return compounded continuously.

a. Which investment has a higher rate of return over a 10 year-year period?

b. Which investment has a higher rate of return over a 20 year-year period?

3. The concentration of a drug in an organ at any time t (in seconds) is given by $d(t) = 0.019(1 - e^{-0.021t})$ where $d(t)$ is measured in grams/cubic centimeter.

a. What is the initial concentration of the drug in the organ?

b. What is the concentration of the drug in the organ after 20 seconds?

c. What will be the concentration of the drug in the long run?

d. Sketch the graph of the function.

4. Tracy's current annual salary is $65,000. Twenty years from now, how much will she need to earn in order to retain her present purchasing power if the rate of inflation over that period is 5% per year?

a. Assume that inflation is continuously compounded.

b. Assume that inflation is compounded annually?

5. The population (in billions) of people of the People's Republic of China is approximately by the function $p(t) = 1.23e^{0.00345t}$ where t is the number of years since 1995.

a. Find the population of China in 2000 and 2011.

b. Predict the population in 2014.

c. Use your graphing calculator to estimate the time when the population reaches 2 billion.

d. Graph the function and label at least two points on the graph.

6. The number of bacteria present after t minutes is given by the formula $n(t) = 200e^{0.3t}$.

a. Find the number of bacteria after 5 minutes.

b. Find the number of bacteria after 10 minutes.

c. Use your graphing calculator to estimate the time when the bacteria population reaches 900?

5.7   Logarithmic Functions

Logarithms as Exponents

We noted in the previous section that the exponential function $f(x) = a^x$, $a > 0$, $a \neq 1$ is a one-to-one function. Therefore, it has an inverse, and it is called the **logarithmic function.** Specifically, if

$$f(x) = a^x$$

then we write the inverse using the notation

$$f^{-1}(x) = \log_a x$$

which is read as "log of x to the base a." Note that the base a of the exponential function becomes the **base** of the corresponding logarithmic function. Thus, if

$$y = a^x$$

we are able to solve this equation for x in terms of y. The solution is

$$x = \log_a y$$

Consider the case where $a = 2$, namely,

$$f(x) = 2^x \qquad \text{and} \qquad f^{-1}(x) = \log_2 x$$

Recall that the range of f is the set of all positive numbers and that $f(x)$ is one-to-one. Thus, for any positive number that we choose, there is a unique point on the graph of $f(x)$ whose y-coordinate is that positive number. For example, if we choose the y-coordinate to be 32, as shown in Figure 35, and we denote the x-coordinate by k, we have that

$$f(k) = 32$$

or equivalently

$$2^k = 32 \tag{1}$$

The x-coordinate k is the *logarithm of 32 to the base 2,* which we write as

$$k = \log_2 32 \tag{2}$$

In this example $k = 5$, that is, $\log_2 32 = 5$.

In other words, if we raise 2 to the exponent 5, we obtain 32. Equivalently, if we raise 2 to the exponent $\log_2 32$, we obtain 32. More generally, $\log_a x$ is the exponent to which a must be raised to obtain x. Equations (1) and (2) demonstrate that a *logarithm is an exponent* and can be generalized to provide the following definition:

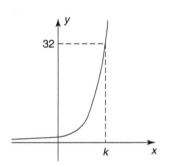

Figure 35 Graph of $y - 2^x$

Logarithmic Function Base *a*

$$y = \log_a x \qquad \text{if and only if} \qquad x = a^y$$

When no base is indicated, the notation **log x** is interpreted to mean $\log_{10} x$ which is also called the **common logarithm.**

Common Logarithm

$$\log x = \log_{10} x$$

The notation **ln** x is used to indicate the logarithm to the base e. Since ln x is the inverse of the natural exponential function e^x, it is called the **natural logarithm**.

Natural Logarithm

$$\ln x = \log_e x$$

The exponential form $x = a^y$ and the logarithmic form $y = \log_a x$ are two ways of expressing the same relationship among x, y, and a. Further, it is always possible to convert one form into the other. A natural question, then, is why create a logarithmic form when we already have an equivalent exponential form. One reason is to allow us to switch an equation from the form $x = a^y$ to a form in which y is a function of x. We will also demonstrate that the logarithmic function has some very useful properties.

Example 1   Logarithmic to Exponential Form
Write in exponential form.

a. $\log_3 9 = 2$ b. $\log_2 \dfrac{1}{8} = -3$ c. $\log_{16} 4 = \dfrac{1}{2}$ d. $\ln 7.39 \approx 2$

Solution
We change from the logarithmic form $\log_a x = y$ to the equivalent exponential form $a^y = x$.

a. $3^2 = 9$ b. $2^{-3} =$ c. $16^{1/2} = 4$ d. $e^2 \approx 7.39$ ■

Example 2   Exponential to Logarithmic Form
Write in logarithmic form.

a. $36 = 6^2$ b. $7 = \sqrt{49}$ c. $= 10^{-2}$ d. $0.1353 \approx e^{-2}$

Solution
Since $y = \log_a x$ if and only if $x = a^y$, the logarithmic forms are

a. $\log_6 36 = 2$ b. $\log_{49} 7 = \dfrac{1}{2}$ c. $\log \dfrac{1}{100} = -2$ d. $\ln 0.1353 \approx -2$

■

✔ Progress Check
Write in logarithmic form.

a. $1000 = 10^3$ b. $6 = 36^{1/2}$ c. $\dfrac{1}{7} = 7^{-1}$ d. $20.09 \approx e^3$

Answers

a. $\log 1000 = 3$ b. $\log_{36} 6 = \dfrac{1}{2}$ c. $\log_7 \dfrac{1}{7} = -1$ d. $\ln 20.09 \approx 3$

Graphs of the Logarithmic Functions

To sketch the graph of the logarithmic function $\log_a x$ we can take advantage of the fact that it is the inverse of the exponential function a^x. We know from our earlier work with inverse functions that the curves are reflections about the line $y = x$. This enables us to sketch the graphs shown in Figure 36 for $a > 1$.

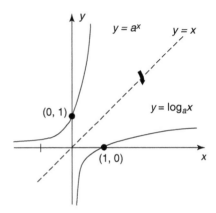

Figure 36   The Logarithmic Function

The graphs in Figure 9 demonstrate that the exponential and logarithmic functions for a base $a > 1$ are both increasing functions. However, the rate of growth for these two functions is dramatically different. The exponential function continues to rise more steeply, accelerating its rate of growth, whereas the logarithmic function continues to flatten out, decelerating its rate of growth.

The next example offers an alternative means for sketching the graph of a logarithmic function.

Example 3   Graphing Logarithmic Functions
Sketch the graph of $y = \log_2 x$.

Solution
To sketch the graph of a logarithmic function, we convert to the equivalent exponential form. Thus, to sketch the graph of $y = \log_2 x$, we form a table of values for the equivalent exponential equation $x = 2^y$.

y	−3	−2	−1	0	1	2	3
$x = 2^y$	$\frac{1}{8}$	$\frac{1}{4}$	$\frac{1}{2}$	1	2	4	8

We can now plot these points and sketch a smooth curve, as shown in Figure 37. Note that the y-axis is a vertical asymptote. We have included the graph of $y = 2^x$ to stress that the graphs of a pair of inverse functions are reflections of each other about the line $y = x$.

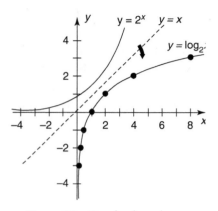

Figure 37   Graph of $y = \log_2 x$

Example 4   Logarithms with Base Less Than 1
Sketch the graphs of $y = \log_3 x$ and $y = \log_{1/3} x$ on the same coordinate axes.

Solution
We could set up a table of values for each function and then sketch the graphs. However, by switching from the logarithmic form

$$y = \log_{1/3} x$$

to the exponential form

$$x = \left(\right)^y = 3^{-y}$$

and then back again to logarithmic form

$$\log_3 x = -y$$

or

$$y = -\log_3 x$$

we can conclude that

$$y = \log_{1/3} x = -\log_3 x$$

This demonstrates that the graph of $y = \log_{1/3} x$ is the reflection of the graph of $y = \log_3 x$ about the x-axis, as shown in Figure 38.

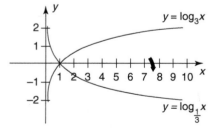

Figure 38   Logarithms with Base Less Than 1

Logarithmic Equations and Calculators

Logarithmic equations can often be solved by changing them into equivalent exponential forms.

Example 5   Solving Logarithmic Equations
Solve for x.

a. $\log_3 x = -2$ b. $\log_x 81 = 4$ c. $\log_5 125 = x$

Solution
a. Using the equivalent exponential form,

$$x = 3^{-2} =$$

b. Changing to the equivalent exponential form,

$$x^4 = 81 = 3^4$$

Since x is the base of a logarithm, $x > 0$. Hence $a^u = b^u$ with $a > 0$, $b > 0$, and $u \neq 0$ implies that

$$x = 3$$

c. In exponential form we have

$$5^x = 125$$

Writing 125 to the base 5, we have

$$5^x = 5^3$$

and since $a^u = a^v$ implies $u = v$, we conclude that

$$x = 3$$

Calculator Alert
Many calculators have keys labeled and , which can be used to calculate the common and natural logarithms, respectively. For example, to compute ln 5.25 you enter

$$5.25$$

and the answer is approximately 1.6582.

Although most scientific calculators have a $\boxed{y^x}$ key, many do not have an $\boxed{e^x}$ key. For those without such a key, we expect that they have an $\boxed{\text{INV}}$ key. Therefore, we can take advantage of the fact that the functions ln x and e^x are a pair of inverse functions to "create" an e^x key. This is done by pressing the two keys $\boxed{\text{INV}}$ $\boxed{\text{In}}$ in succession. For example, to calculate $e^{-0.2}$, you enter

$$0.2 \;\boxed{+/-}\; \boxed{\text{INV}}\; \boxed{\text{In}}$$

and the answer is approximately 0.8187.

Example 6   **Calculators and Logarithms**

a. Solve for x: $\ln x = -0.75$

b. Solve for x: $\log x = 1.25$

c. What do the keystrokes 1 $\boxed{\text{INV}}$ $\boxed{\text{In}}$ produce in the display?

Solution

a. The equivalent exponential form is $x = e^{-0.75}$ and can be found by using the keystrokes

$$0.75 \;\boxed{+/-}\; \boxed{\text{INV}}\; \boxed{\text{In}}$$

and the answer is approximately 0.4724.

b. The equivalent exponential form is $x = 10^{1.25}$ and can be found by using the keystrokes

$$1.25 \;\boxed{\text{INV}}\; \boxed{\text{log}}$$

and the answer is approximately 17.7828. You can verify this result by trying the keystrokes

$$10 \;\boxed{y^x}\; 1.25 \;\boxed{=}$$

c. The keystrokes 1 $\boxed{\text{INV}}$ $\boxed{\text{In}}$ result in computing e^1 or e. This is one way to obtain e in your display for use in further computations.   ■

Logarithmic Identities

If $f(x) = a^x$, then $f^{-1}(x) = \log_a x$. Recall that inverse functions have the property that

$$f[f^{-1}(x)] = x \quad\text{and}\quad f^{-1}[f(x)] = x$$

Substituting $f(x) = a^x$ and $f^{-1}(x) = \log_a x$, we have

$$f[f^{-1}(x)] = x \qquad f^{-1}[f(x)] = x$$
$$f(\log_a x) = x \qquad f^{-1}(a^x) = x$$
$$a^{\log_a x} = x \qquad \log_a a^x = x$$

These two identities are useful in simplifying expressions.

$$a^{\log_a x} = x$$
$$\log_a a^x = x$$

The following pair of identities can be established by converting to the equivalent exponential form.

$$\log_a a = 1$$
$$\log_a 1 = 0$$

Example 7 **Working with Logarithmic Identities**

Evaluate.

a. $8^{\log_8 5}$ b. $\log 10^{-3}$ c. $\log_7 7$ d. $\log_4 1$

Solution

a. 5 b. −3 c. 1 d. 0

✔ **Progress Check**

Evaluate.

a. $\log_3 3^4$ b. $6^{\log_6 9}$ c. $\log_5 1$ d. $\log_8 8$

Answers

a. 4 b. 9 c. 0 d. 1

Properties of Logarithmic Functions

The graph of $y = \log_2 x$ in Figure 10 and the graph of $y = \log_{1/3} x$ in Figure 11 are typical of the graph of $y = \log_a x$ for $a > 1$ and $0 < a < 1$, respectively. We state the following properties in Table 8.

Table 8 Properties of the Logarithmic Function

$$f(x) = \log_a x, \quad a > 0, \quad a \neq 1$$

1. The graph of $f(x) = \log_a x$ always passes through the points $(1, 0)$ and $(a, 1)$ since $\log_a 1 = 0$ and $\log_a a = 1$.

2. The graph of $f(x) = \log_a x$ is the reflection about the x-axis of the graph of $f(x) = \log_{1/a} x$.

3. The domain of $f(x) = \log_a x$ consists of the set of all positive numbers; the range is the set of all real numbers.

4. $f(x) = \log_a x$ is increasing if $a > 1$; $f(x) = \log_a x$ is decreasing if $0 < a < 1$.

5. $f(x) = \log_a x$ is a one-to-one function since it passes the horizontal-line test.

These results are in accord with what we anticipate for a pair of inverse functions. As expected, the domain of the logarithmic function is the range of the corresponding exponential function, and vice versa.

Since $f(x) = \log_a x$ is a one-to-one function, we have the following result.

> If $\log_a u = \log_a v$, then $u = v$.

Observe that the graphs of $y = \log_a x$ and $y = \log_b x$ intersect only at $x = 1$.

> If $\log_a u = \log_b u$, either $u = 1$ or $a = b$.

Example 8 Solving Logarithmic Equations

Solve for x.

a. $\log_5(x + 1) = \log_5 25$ b. $\log_{x-1} 31 = \log_5 31$

Solution

a. Since $\log_a u = \log_a v$ implies $u = v$, then

$$x + 1 = 25$$
$$x = 24$$

b. Since $\log_a u = \log_b u$ and $u \neq 1$, then $a = b$. Hence,

$$x - 1 = 5$$
$$x = 6$$

✔ Progress Check

Solve for x.

a. $\log_x x^2 = \log_2 9$ b. $\log_7 14 = \log_{2x} 14$

Answers

a. $3, -3$ b. $\dfrac{7}{2}$

Summary of Logarithmic Identities and Properties

Identities	Properties
$a^{\log x} = x$	$\log_a u = \log_a v$ implies $u = v$
$\log_a a^x = x$	If $\log_a u = \log_b u$, either $u = 1$ or $a = b$.
$\log_a a = 1$	
$\log_a 1 = 0$	

Focus on Measuring an Earthquake

The Loma Prieta Earthquake of 1989

On October 17, 1989, at 5:04 P.M. a major earthquake with a reading of 7.1 on the Richter scale struck the San Francisco area. Its epicenter was located 75 miles south of San Francisco between Santa Cruz and San Jose. About 63 people died, and damage was estimated to be approximately 6 billion dollars. The earthquake forced the cancellation of the third game of baseball's World Series that was due to start at Candlestick Park in San Francisco at 5:30 P.M.

This earthquake was the fourth worst in U.S. history, as far as loss of life is concerned, since the 1906 San Francisco earthquake (700 dead, 8.3 on the Richter scale), the 1933 Long Beach earthquake (120 dead, 6.3 on the Richter scale), and the 1964 Alaskan earthquake (114 dead, 8.5 on the Richter scale).

On the Richter scale, the magnitude R of an earthquake is defined as

$$R = \log \frac{l}{l_0}$$

where l_0 is a constant that represents a standard intensity and l is the intensity of the earthquake being measured. The Richter scale is a means of measuring a given earthquake against a "standard earthquake" of intensity l_0.

What does 3.0 on the Richter scale mean? Substituting $R = 3$ in the above equation, we have

$$3 = \log \frac{l}{l_0}$$

or, in the equivalent exponential form,

$$1000 = \frac{l}{l_0}.$$

Solving for l,

$$l = 1000 \, l_0$$

which states that an earthquake with a Richter scale reading of 3.0 is $10^3 = 1000$ times as intense as the standard. Therefore, an earthquake registering 8.0 on the Richter scale has an intensity $10^8 = 100,000,000$ times that of the standard.

Based on past experience, the following damages can be expected from an earthquake of various Richter scale readings.

Reading	Damage
2.0	Not noticed
4.5	Some damage in a very limited area
6.0	Hazardous serious damage with destruction of buildings in a limited area
7.0	Felt over a wide area with significant damage
8.0	Great damage
8.7	Maximum recorded

Exercise Set 5.7

In Exercises 1–12, write each equation in exponential form.

1. $\log_2 4 = 2$

2. $\log_5 125 = 3$

3. $\log_9 \dfrac{1}{81} = -2$

4. $\log_{64} 4 = \dfrac{1}{3}$

5. $\ln 20.09 \approx 3$

6. $\ln \dfrac{1}{7.39} \approx -2$

7. $\log_{10} 1000 = 3$

8. $\log_{10} \dfrac{1}{1000} = -3$

9. $\ln 1 = 0$

10. $\log_{10} 0.01 = -2$

11. $\log_3 \dfrac{1}{27} = -3$

12. $\log_{125} \dfrac{1}{5} = -\dfrac{1}{3}$

In Exercises 13–26, write each equation in logarithmic form.

13. $25 = 5^2$

14. $27 = 3^3$

15. $10,000 = 10^4$

16. $\dfrac{1}{100} = 10^{-2}$

17. $\dfrac{1}{8} = 2^{-3}$

18. $\dfrac{1}{27} = 3^{-3}$

19. $1 = 2^0$

20. $1 = e^0$

21. $6 = \sqrt{36}$

22. $2 = \sqrt[3]{8}$

23. $64 = 16^{3/2}$

24. $81 = 27^{4/3}$

25. $\dfrac{1}{3} = 27^{-1/3}$

26. $\dfrac{1}{2} = 16^{-1/4}$

 In Exercises 27–44, solve for x without using a calculator. Verify your answer with a calculator.

27. $\log_5 x = 2$

28. $\log_{16} x = \dfrac{1}{2}$

29. $\log_{25} x = -\dfrac{1}{2}$

30. $\log_{1/2} x = 3$

31. $\ln x = 2$

32. $\ln x = -3$

33. $\ln x = -\dfrac{1}{2}$

34. $\log_4 64 = x$

35. $\log_5 \dfrac{1}{25} = x$ 36. $\log_x 4 = \dfrac{1}{2}$

37. $\log_x \dfrac{1}{8} = -\dfrac{1}{3}$

38. $\log_3 (x - 1) = 2$

39. $\log_5 (x + 1) = 3$

40. $\log_2 (x - 1) = \log_2 10$

41. $\log_{x+1} 24 = \log_3 24$

42. $\log_3 x^3 = \log_3 64$

43. $\log_{x+1} 17 = \log_4 17$

44. $\log_{3x} 18 = \log_4 18$

In Exercises 45–64, evaluate the expression without using a calculator. Verify your answer with a calculator.

45. $3^{\log_3 6}$

46. $2^{\log_2 (2/3)}$

47. $e^{\ln 2}$

48. $e^{\ln (1/2)}$

49. $\log_5 5^3$

50. $\log_4 4^{-2}$

51. $\log_8 8^{1/2}$

52. $\log_{64} 64^{-1/3}$

53. $\log_7 49$

54. $\log_7 \sqrt{7}$

55. $\log_5 5$

56. $\ln e^{x^2}$

57. $\ln 1$

58. $\log_4 1$

59. $\log_2 \dfrac{1}{4}$

60. $\log_{16} 4$

61. $\log 10,000$

62. $e^{\ln(x+1)}$

63. $\ln e^2$

64. $\ln e^{-2/3}$

In Exercises 65–70, use your calculator to evaluate the following expressions.

65. $\log \dfrac{8}{5}$

66. $\dfrac{\ln 8}{5}$

67. $\dfrac{\ln 8}{\ln 5}$

68. $\dfrac{\log 8}{\log 5}$

69. $\dfrac{\log\left(\dfrac{1}{2}\right)}{-0.0006}$

70.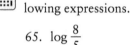

0.015

In Exercises 71–78, sketch the graph of each given function.

71. $f(x) = \log_4 x$

72. $f(x) = \log_{1/2} x$

73. $f(x) = \log 2x$

74. $f(x) = \dfrac{1}{2} \log x$

75. $f(x) = \ln \dfrac{x}{2}$

76. $f(x) = \ln 3x$

77. $f(x) = \log_3 (x - 1)$

78. $f(x) = \log_3 (x + 1)$

In Exercises 79–86, determine the domain of the given function. Also, determine appropriate WINDOW values and GRAPH the given function using your graphing calculator.

79. $f(x) = \ln (1 - x)$

80. $f(x) = \ln (1 - x)^2$

81. $f(x) = \log \dfrac{x}{x - 1}$

82. $f(x) = \log \dfrac{\sqrt{x - 1}}{x}$

83. $f(x) = \ln 2^x$

84. $f(x) = \log e^{-x}$

85. $f(x) = \log(-\sqrt{x})$

86. $f(x) = \ln x^3$

For Exercises 87 and 88, refer to the Graphing Calculator Power User's Corner on "Graphing Inverse Functions" in Section 3.5. Set $-5 \le X \le 5$, $-5 \le Y \le 5$, and $-5 \le T \le 5$, and modify that example accordingly.

87. GRAPH $y = e^x$ and its inverse in the same viewing rectangle. Compare this with the graph of $y = \ln x$.

88. GRAPH $y = 10^x$ and its inverse in the same viewing rectangle. Compare this with the graph of $y = \log x$.

89. The Davis National Bank pays 6% interest compounded quarterly. How long will it take for a deposit to triple in value?

90. Suppose interest is compounded continuously at an annual rate of 5%.

    a. How long will it take for the principal to triple?

    b. How long will it take for the principal to quadruple?

91. If interest is compounded continuously, at what annual rate will a principal of $100 triple in 20 years?

92. Fechner's Logarithmic Law in psychology is used to measure notable changes in sensory response based upon equal increases of a particular sensory stimulus. The law is given by the equation $S = k \log_{10} l$ where S is the magnitude of the sensory experience, l is the physical intensity, and k is a scaling constant. Determine the physical intensity of a sensory experiment if the recorded magnitude of sensation is 0.5005 and the constant $k = 10$.

Exercise 93 refers to the following table of values:

x	0	1	2	3
y	2	6	18	54

93. Plot the points (x, z) where $z = \ln y$.

Applications 5.7

1. The population (in billions) of people of the People's Republic of China is approximately by the function $p(t) = 1.23e^{0.00345t}$ where t is the number of years since 1995.

   a. Find the population of China in 2000 and 2011.

   b. Predict the population in 2014.

   c. Find the time when the population reaches 2 billion.

   d. Graph the function and label at least two points on the graph.

2. The number of bacteria present after t minutes is given by the formula $n(t) = 200e^{0.3t}$.

   a. Find the number of bacteria after 5 minutes.

   b. Find the number of bacteria after 10 minutes.

   c. Find the time when the bacteria population reaches 900?

3. The temperature of a cup of green tea t minutes after it is poured is given by $T(t) = 70 + 100e^{-0.05t}$, where T is measured in degrees Fahrenheit.

   a. What is the temperature of the cup of tea when it was poured?

   b. When will the cup of tea be cool enough to drink, say 110 degrees Fahrenheit?

4. The continuous compound interest formula is given by $A = Pe^{rt}$, where P is the principal, r is the annual interest rate compounded continuously, t is time in years, and A is the accumulated amount at the end of t years.

   a. If you invested $50,000 at an interest rate of 5% compounded continuously in 2000, find the accumulated amount at the end of 2012?

   b. How long does it take to double your money at an interest rate of 5% compounded continuously?

   c. How long does it take to double your money at an interest rate of 10% compounded continuously?

   d. Please check for the Rule of 72 at http://en.wikipedia.org/wiki/Rule_of_72. Explain how this rule was obtained.

5. Halley's law states that the barometric pressure (in inches of mercury) at an altitude of x feet above sea level is approximately given by the equation: $p(x) = 29.9e^{-0.00004x}$, where $x \ge 0$.

   a. If the barometric pressure as measured by a hot-air balloonist is 20 inches of mercury, what is the balloonist's altitude?

   b. Sketch the graph of the function.

5.8   Fundamental Properties of Logarithms

Logarithms are an important computational device because of three fundamental properties. For any positive numbers x and y,

Property 1. $\log_a xy = \log_a x + \log_a y$

Property 2. $\log_a \left(\dfrac{x}{y} \right) = \log_a x - \log_a y$

Property 3. $\log_a x^n = n \log_a x$, n a real number

These properties can be proved by using equivalent exponential forms. To prove the first property, $\log_a xy = \log_a x + \log_a y$, we let

$$\log_a x = u \quad \text{and} \quad \log_a y = v$$

Then the equivalent exponential forms are

$$a^u = x \quad \text{and} \quad a^v = y$$

Multiplying the left-hand and right-hand sides of these equations, respectively, we have

$$a^u a^v = xy$$

or

$$a^{u+v} = xy$$

Substituting a^{u+v} for xy in $\log_a xy$ we have

$$\log_a xy = \log_a a^{u+v}$$
$$= u + v \quad \text{since } \log_a a^x = x$$

Substituting for u and v.

$$\log_a xy = \log_a x + \log_a y$$

Properties 2 and *3* can be established in much the same way.

It is these properties of logarithms that convert the operations of multiplication, division and exponentiation to addition, subtraction and multiplication, respectively. We next demonstrate the use of these properties.

Example 1   Simplifying Logarithmic Expressions
Write in terms of simpler logarithmic forms.

a. $\log_{10} [(225)(478)]$ b. $\log_8 \dfrac{422}{735}$ c. $\log_2 2^5$ d. $\log_a \dfrac{xy}{z}$

Solution
a. $\log_{10}[(225)(478)] = \log_{10} 225 + \log_{10} 478$

b. $\log_8 \dfrac{422}{735} = \log_8 422 - \log_8 735$

c. $\log_2 2^5 = 5 \log_2 2 = 5 \cdot 1 = 5$

d. $\log_a \dfrac{xy}{z} = \log_a x + \log_a y - \log_a z$

✔ **Progress Check**

Write in terms of simpler logarithmic forms.

a. $\log_4[(1.47)(22.3)]$ b. $\log_a \dfrac{x-1}{\sqrt{x}}$

Answers

a. $\log_4 1.47 + \log_4 22.3$ b. $\log_a(x-1) - \dfrac{1}{2}\log_a x$

Example 2   Applying the Properties of Logarithms

Prove that

$$\log_a \frac{1}{x} = -\log_a x$$

Solution

Note that

$$\log_a \frac{1}{x} = \log_a 1 - \log_a x$$

$$\log_a \frac{1}{x} = -\log_a x$$

since $\log_a 1 = 0$.

The result of Example 2 is useful in simplifying logarithmic forms.

Simplifying Logarithms

The next example illustrates rules that speed the handling of logarithmic forms.

Example 3   Simplifying Complex Logarithmic Expressions

Write

$$\log_a \frac{(x-1)^{-2}(y+2)^3}{\sqrt{x}}$$

in terms of simpler logarithmic forms.

Solution

Step 1. Rewrite the expression so that each factor has a positive exponent.	*Step 1.* $$\log_a \frac{(x-1)^{-2}(y+2)^3}{\sqrt{x}}$$ $$= \log_a \frac{(y+2)^3}{(x-1)^2 x^{1/2}}$$
Step 2. Apply *Property 1* and *Property 2* for logarithms of products and quotients. Each factor in the numerator will yield a term with a plus sign. Each facor in the denominator will yield a term with a minus sign.	*Step 2.* $$= \log_a(y+2)^3 - \log_a(x-1)^2 - \log_a x^{1/2}$$
Step 3. Apply *Property 3* to simplify.	*Step 3.* $$= 3\log_a(y+2) - 2\log_a(x-1) - \frac{1}{2}\log_a x$$

✔ **Progress Check**

Simplify

$$\log_a \frac{(2x-3)^{1/2}(y+2)^{-2/3}}{z^4}$$

Answer

$$\frac{1}{2}\log_a(2x-3) - \frac{2}{3}\log_a(y+2) - 4\log_a z$$

Example 4 Applying the Properties of Logarithms

If $\log_a 1.5 = r$, $\log_a 2 = s$, and $\log_a 5 = t$, find the following:

a. $\log_a 7.5$ b. $\log_a \left[(1.5)^3 \sqrt[5]{\dfrac{2}{5}}\right]$

Solution

a. Since

$$7.5 = (1.5)(5)$$

$$\log_a 7.5 = \log_a[(1.5)(5)]$$

$$= \log_a 1.5 + \log_a 5 \qquad \textit{Property 1}$$

$$= r + t \qquad \qquad \text{Substitution}$$

b. Write this as

$$\log_a(1.5)^3 + \log_a\left(\frac{2}{5}\right)^{1/5} \qquad \textit{Property 1}$$

$$= 3\log_a 1.5 + \frac{1}{5}\log_a\frac{2}{5} \qquad \textit{Property 3}$$

$$= 3\log_a 1.5 + \quad[\log_a 2 \quad \frac{1}{5}$$

$$- \log_a 5]\textit{Property 2}$$

$$= 3r + \frac{1}{5}(s - t) \qquad \text{Substitution}$$

✔ Progress Check

If $\log_a 2 = 0.43$ and $\log_a 3 = 0.68$, find the following:

a. $\log_a 18$ b. $\log_a \sqrt[3]{\dfrac{9}{2}}$

Answers

a. 1.79   b. 0.31

Warning

a. Note that

$$\log_a(x + y) \neq \log_a x + \log_a y$$

Property 1 tells us that

$$\log_a(x \cdot y) = \log_a x + \log_a y$$

None of the three properties permits simplification of $\log_a(x + y)$.

b. Note that

$$\log_a x^n \neq (\log_a x)^n$$

By *Property 3*,

$$\log_a x^n = n \log_a x$$

We can also apply the properties of logarithms to combine terms involving logarithms.

Example 5   **Combining Logarithmic Expressions**

Write as a single logarithm.

$$2 \log_a x - 3 \log_a(x + 1) + \log_a \sqrt{x - 1}$$

Solution

$$2 \log_a x - 3 \log_a(x + 1) + \log_a \sqrt{x - 1}$$

$$= \log_a x^2 - \log_a(x + 1)^3 + \log_a \sqrt{x - 1} \qquad \textit{Property 3}$$

$$= \log_a x^2 \sqrt{x - 1} - \log_a(x + 1)^3 \qquad \textit{Property 1}$$

$$= \log_a \frac{x^2 \sqrt{x - 1}}{(x + 1)^3} \qquad \textit{Property 2}$$

✔ Progress Check

Write as a single logarithm.

$$\frac{1}{3} [\log_a(2x - 1) - \log_a(2x - 5)] + 4 \log_a x$$

Answer

$$\log_a x^4 \sqrt[3]{\frac{2x - 1}{2x - 5}}$$

Warning

a. Note that

$$\frac{\log_a x}{\log_a y} \neq \log_a(x - y)$$

Property 2 tells us that

$$\log_a \frac{x}{y} = \log_a x - \log_a y$$

None of the three properties permits simplification of

$$\frac{\log_a x}{\log_a y}$$

b. The expressions

$$\log_a x + \log_b x$$

and

$$\log_a x - \log_b x$$

cannot be simplified. Logarithms with different bases do not readily combine except in special cases.

Change of Base

Sometimes it is convenient to write a logarithm that is given in terms of a base a in terms of another base b, that is, to convert $\log_a x$ to $\log_b x$. (As always, we require a and b to be positive real numbers different from 1.)

To compute $\log_b x$ given $\log_a x$, let $y = \log_b x$. The equivalent exponential form is then

$$b^y = x$$

Taking logarithms to the base a of both sides of this equation, we have

$$\log_a b^y = \log_a x$$

We now apply the fundamental properties of logarithms developed earlier in this section. By *Property 3,*

$$y \log_a b = \log_a x$$

Solving for y,

$$y = \frac{\log_a x}{\log_a b}$$

Since $y = \log_b x$, we have

Change of Base Formula

$$\log_b x = \frac{\log_a x}{\log_a b}, \qquad a > 0, a \neq 1 \qquad b > 0, b \neq 1$$

Example 6   Change of Base

Use the $\boxed{\text{log}}$ key on your calculator to compute $\log_2 27$.

Solution

We use the change of base formula

$$\log_b x = \frac{\log_a x}{\log_a b}$$

with $b = 2$, $a = 10$, and $x = 27$. Then

$$\log_2 27 = \frac{\log 27}{\log 2}$$

The appropriate key sequence is

$$27 \boxed{\text{log}} \boxed{\div} \boxed{2} \boxed{\text{log}} \boxed{=}$$

and the answer is approximately 4.7549.

✔ **Progress Check**

Use the $\boxed{\text{ln}}$ key on your calculator to find:

a. $\log_5 16$

b. $\log_{10} e$

Answers

a. Approximately 1.7227

b. Approximately 0.4343

In Table 9, we summarize the rules we have encountered for manipulating logarithms as well as the common errors to be avoided.

Table 9   Logarithms

Properties	Warnings
$\log_a xy = \log_a x + \log_a y$	$\log_a(x + y) \neq \log_a x + \log_a y$
$\log_a \dfrac{x}{y} = \log_a x - \log_a y$	$\dfrac{\log_a x}{\log_a y} \neq \log_a(x - y)$
$\log_a x^n = n \log_a x$	$\log_a x^n \neq (\log_a x)^n$
$\log_a \dfrac{1}{x} = -\log_a x$	
$\log_b x = \dfrac{\log_a x}{\log_a b}$	

Exercise Set 5.8

In Exercises 1–20, write each expression in terms of simpler logarithmic forms.

1. $\log_{10} [(120)(36)]$

2. $\log_6 \dfrac{187}{39}$

3. $\log_3(3^4)$

4. $\log_3(4^3)$

5. $\log_a(2xy)$

6. $\ln (4xyz)$

7. $\log_a \dfrac{x}{yz}$

8. $\ln \dfrac{2x}{y}$

9. $\ln x^5$

10. $\log_3 y^{2/3}$

11. $\log_a(x^2 y^3)$

12. $\log_a(xy)^3$

13. $\log_a \sqrt{xy}$

14. $\log_a \sqrt[3]{xy^4}$

15. $\ln (x^2 y^3 z^4)$

16. $\log_a(xy^3 z^2)$

17. $\ln (\sqrt{x}\sqrt[3]{y})$

18. $\ln (\sqrt[3]{xy^2}\sqrt[4]{z})$

19. $\log_a \left(\dfrac{x^2 y^3}{z^4}\right)$

20. $\ln \dfrac{x^4 y^2}{z^{1/2}}$

In Exercises 21–30, if $\log 2 \approx 0.30$, $\log 3 \approx 0.47$, and $\log 5 \approx 0.70$, evaluate.

21. $\log 6$

22. $\log \dfrac{2}{3}$

23. $\log 9$

24. $\log \sqrt{5}$

25. $\log 12$

26. $\log \dfrac{6}{5}$

27. $\log \dfrac{15}{2}$

28. $\log 0.3$

29. $\log \sqrt{7.5}$

30. $\log \sqrt[4]{30}$

In Exercises 31–44, write each expression as a single logarithm.

31. $2 \log x + \dfrac{1}{2} \log y$

32. $3 \log_a x - 2 \log_a z$

33. $\dfrac{1}{3} \ln x + \dfrac{1}{3} \ln y$

34. $\dfrac{1}{3} \ln x - \dfrac{2}{3} \ln y$

35. $\frac{1}{3} \log_a x + 2 \log_a y - \frac{3}{2} \log_a z$

36. $\frac{2}{3} \log_a x + 2 \log_a y - 2 \log_a z$

37. $\frac{1}{2}(\log_a x + \log_a y)$

38. $\frac{2}{3}(4 \ln x - 5 \ln y)$

39. $\frac{1}{3}(2 \ln x + 4 \ln y) - 3 \ln z$

40. $\ln x - \frac{1}{2}(3 \ln x + 5 \ln y)$

41. $\frac{1}{2} \log_a(x - 1) - 2 \log_a(x + 1)$

42. $2 \log_a(x + 2) - \frac{1}{2}(\log_a y + \log_a z)$

43. $3 \log_a x - 2 \log_a(x - 1) + \frac{1}{2} \log_a \sqrt[3]{x + 1}$

44. $4 \ln (x - 1) + \frac{1}{2} \ln(x + 1) - 3 \ln y$

The key labeled ⎡ln⎤ on a calculator is used to compute ln $10 \approx 2.3026$, ln $6 \approx 1.7918$, and ln $3 \approx 1.0986$. In Exercises 45–50, use the first value to find the required value.

45. ln $17 \approx 2.8332$; find log 17

46. ln $22 \approx 3.0910$; find $\log_6 22$

47. ln $141 \approx 4.9488$; find $\log_3 141$

48. ln $78 \approx 4.3567$; find $\log_6 78$

49. ln $245 \approx 5.5013$; find log 245

50. ln $7 \approx 1.9459$; find $\log_3 7$

51. Given log $2 \approx 0.301$ and log $3 \approx 0.477$, use the rules of logarithms to find:

    a. log 18   b. $\log \frac{4}{9}$

    c. log 5

52. Use the rules of logarithms to find

    a. $\ln \dfrac{1}{\sqrt{e}}$ b. $\ln 3e - \ln 3$

    c. $e^{(\ln 2 - \ln 3)}$ d. $\log 2 + \log 50$

    e. $e^{-2 \ln 3}$

 In Exercises 53–56, use the change of base equation to evaluate the following logarithms on your calculator:

53. $\log_5 10$ 54. $\log_3 \frac{1}{2}$

55. $\log_2 \sqrt{7}$ 56. $\log_{1/6} 13$

In Exercises 57 and 58, use the change of base equation to graph the following logarithmic functions in the EQUAL viewing rectangle.

57. $y = \log_5 x$ 58. $y = \log_{1/4} x$

5.9 Exponential and Logarithmic Equations

The properties of exponentials and logarithms mentioned in the previous sections can be combined with the following suggestions to solve exponential and logarithmic equations.

> • When solving an exponential equation, consider taking logarithms of both sides of the equation.
>
> • When solving a logarithmic equation, consider forming a single logarithm on one side of the equation, and then converting this equation to the equivalent exponential form.

Example 1   Solving an Exponential Equation

Solve $3^{2x-1} = 17$.

Solution

Consider taking logarithms to the base 10 of both sides of the equation.

$$\log 3^{2x-1} = \log 17$$

Then by *Property 3*,

$$(2x - 1)\log 3 = \log 17$$

$$2x - 1 = \frac{\log 17}{\log 3}$$

$$2x = 1 + \frac{\log 17}{\log 3}$$

$$x = \frac{1}{2} + \frac{\log 17}{2 \log 3}$$

If a numerical value is required, the key sequence

$$17 \boxed{\log} \boxed{\div} \boxed{(} \; 2 \boxed{\times} 3 \boxed{\log} \boxed{)} \boxed{=} \boxed{+} .5 \boxed{=}$$

can be used to obtain the approximate answer 1.7895. If a graphing calculator is used, the keystrokes are

$$1 \boxed{\div} 2 \boxed{+} \boxed{\log} \; 17 \boxed{\div} \boxed{(} \; 2 \boxed{\log} 3 \boxed{)}$$

Note that we could have taken logarithms to *any* base in solving this equation. (Verify that the answer is the same if we had used ln instead of log.)   ■

✔ Progress Check

Solve $2^{x+1} = 3^{2x-3}$ and express your answer in terms of common logarithms.

Answer

$$\frac{\log 2 + 3 \log 3}{2 \log 3 - \log 2}$$

Example 2   Solving an Exponential Equation

Solve the equation $5e^{2-x} = 3$.

Solution
Since the equation contains the base e, we take logarithms to the base e of both sides of the equation.

$$\ln(5e^{2-x}) = \ln\ 3$$
$$\ln 5 + \ln e^{2-x} = \ln 3 \qquad \textit{Property 1}$$
$$2 - x = \ln 3 - \ln 5 \qquad \log_a a^x = x$$
$$= 2 + \ln 5 - \ln 3$$
$$= 2 + \ln \frac{5}{3} \quad \textit{Property 2}$$

If a numerical value is required for x, the key sequence

$$5 \boxed{\div}\ 3 \boxed{=}\ \boxed{\text{ln}}\ 2 \boxed{=}$$

produces the approximation 2.5108. The graphing calculator keystrokes are

$$2 \boxed{+}\ \boxed{\text{ln}}\ \boxed{(}\ 5 \boxed{\div}\ 3 \boxed{)}$$

(Verify the answer using log instead of ln.)

✔ Progress Check
Solve the equation $5 - 2e^{3x-1} = 0$.

Answer
$$\frac{1}{3}\left(1 + \ln \frac{5}{2}\right)$$

Example 3   Solving a Logarithmic Equation
Solve for x: $\log(2x + 8) = 1 + \log(x - 4)$.

Solution
Rewrite the equation in the form

$$\log(2x + 8) - \log(x - 4) = 1$$

We can now apply *Property 2* to form a single logarithm.

$$\log \frac{2x + 8}{x - 4} = 1$$

Converting to the equivalent exponential form, we have

$$\frac{2x + 8}{x - 4} = 10^1 = 10$$
$$2x + 8 = 10x - 40$$
$$x = 6$$

✔ **Progress Check**

Solve $\log x - \dfrac{1}{2} = -\log 3$.

Answer

$\dfrac{\sqrt{10}}{3}$

Example 4   Solving a Logarithmic Equation

Solve for x: $\log_2 x = 3 - \log_2(x + 2)$.

Solution

Rewriting the equation with a single logarithm, we have

$$\log_2 x + \log_2(x + 2) = 3$$

$$\log_2 [x(x + 2)] = 3 \qquad\qquad \text{Why?}$$

$$x(x + 2) = 2^3 = 8 \qquad\qquad \text{Equivalent exponential form}$$

$$x^2 + 2x - 8 = 0$$

$$(x - 2)(x + 4) = 0 \qquad\qquad \text{Factor}$$

$$x = 2 \qquad \text{or} \qquad x = -4$$

The "solution" $x = -4$ must be rejected since the original equation contains $\log_2 x$. Note that the domain of the logarithmic function does not include negative values. ■

✔ **Progress Check**

Solve for x: $\log_3(x - 8) = 2 - \log_3 x$.

Answer

$x = 9$

Example 5   Exponential Growth Model

In a certain country, population is increasing at an annual rate of 2.5%. If we assume an exponential growth model, in how many years will the population double?

Solution

The exponential growth model

$$Q(t) = q_0 e^{0.025t}$$

Focus on Dating the Latest Ice Age

All organic forms of life contain radioactive carbon 14. In 1947, the chemist Willard Libby, who won the Nobel Prize in chemistry in 1960, found that the percentage of carbon 14 in the atmosphere equals the percentage found in the living tissues of all organic forms of life. When an organism dies, it stops replacing carbon 14 in its living tissues. Yet the carbon 14 continues decaying at the rate of 0.012% per year. By measuring the amount of carbon 14 in the remains of an organism, it is possible to estimate fairly accurately when the organism died.

In the late 1940s, radiocarbon dating was used to date the last ice sheet to cover the North American and European continents. Remains of trees in the Two Creeks Forest in northern Wisconsin were found to have lost 74.6% of their carbon 14 content. The remaining carbon 14, therefore, was 25.4% of the original quantity q_0 that was present when the descending ice sheet felled the trees. The accompanying computations use the general equation of an exponential decay model to find the age t of the wood. Conclusion: The latest ice age occurred approximately 11,420 years before the measurements were taken.

$$Q(t) = q_0 e^{-kt}$$
$$0.254 q_0 = q_0 e^{-0.00012t}$$
$$0.254 = e^{-0.00012t}$$
$$\ln 0.254 = \ln e^{-0.00012t}$$
$$-1.3704 \approx -0.00012t$$
$$t \approx 11,420$$

describes the population Q as a function of time t. Since the initial population is $Q(0) = q_0$, we seek the time t required for the population to double or become $2q_0$. We wish to solve the equation

$$Q(t) = 2q_0 = q_0 e^{0.025t}$$

for t. We then have

$$2q_0 = q_0 e^{0.025t}$$
$$2 = e^{0.025t} \qquad \text{Divide by } q_0$$
$$\ln 2 = \ln e^{0.025t} \qquad \text{Take natural logarithms of both sides}$$
$$= 0.025t \qquad \text{Since } \ln e^x = x$$
$$t = \frac{\ln 2}{0.025} \approx \frac{0.6931}{0.025} \approx 27.7$$

or approximately 28 years.

Example 6   Continuous Compounding

A trust fund invests $8000 at an annual interest rate of 8% compounded continuously. How long does it take for the initial investment to grow to $12,000?

Solution

From Section 6.2, we have the equation

$$A = Pe^{rt}$$

where A is the amount available at the end of t years, having initially invested the principal P at a continuously compounded interest rate r. If $A = 12,000$, $P = 8000$, and $r = 8\% = 0.08$, we must find t. Therefore,

$$12,000 = 8000e^{0.08t}$$

$$\frac{12,000}{8000} = e^{0.08t}$$

$$e^{0.08t} = 1.5$$

Taking natural logarithms of both sides, we have

$$0.08t = \ln 1.5$$

$$t = \frac{\ln 1.5}{0.08} \approx \frac{0.4055}{0.08}$$

$$\approx 5.07$$

It takes approximately 5.07 years for the initial $8000 to grow to $12,000. ■

✔ **Progress Check**

The number of bacteria in a culture after t minutes is described by the exponential growth model $Q(t) = q_0e^{0.1t}$. How long does it take for the number of bacteria to double?

Answer

Approximately 6.93 minutes

Exercise Set 5.9

In Exercises 1–31, solve for x.

1. $5^x = 18$

2. $2^x = 24$

3. $2^{x-1} = 7$

4. $3^{x-1} = 12$

5. $3^{2x} = 46$

6. $2^{2x-1} = 56$

7. $5^{2x-5} = 564$

8. $3^{3x-2} = 23.1$

9. $3^{x-1} = 2^{2x-1}$

10. $4^{2x-1} = 3^{2x-3}$

11. $2^{-x} = 15$

12. $3^{-x+2} = 103$

13. $4^{-2x+1} = 12$

14. $3^{-3x+2} = 2^{-x}$

15. $e^x = 18$

16. $e^{x-1} = 2.3$

17. $e^{2x+3} = 30$

18. $e^{-3x+2} = 40$

19. $\log x + \log 2 = 3$

20. $\log x - \log 3 = 2$

21. $\log_x(3 - 5x) = 1$

22. $\log_x(8 - 2x) = 2$

23. $\log x + \log(x - 3) = 1$

24. $\log x + \log(x + 21) = 2$

25. $\log(3x + 1) - \log(x - 2) = 1$

26. $\log(7x - 2) - \log(x - 2) = 1$

27. $\log_2 x = 4 - \log_2(x - 6)$

28. $\log_2(x - 4) = 2 - \log_2 x$

29. $\log_2(x + 4) = 3 - \log_2(x - 2)$

30. $y = \dfrac{e^x + e^{-x}}{2}$

31. $y = \dfrac{e^x - e^{-x}}{2}$

32. Suppose that the world population is increasing at an annual rate of 2%. If we assume an exponential growth model, in how many years will the population double?

33. Suppose that the population of a certain city is increasing at an annual rate of 3%. If we assume an exponential growth model, in how many years will the population triple?

34. The population P of a certain city t years from now is given by

$$P = 20{,}000e^{0.05t}$$

How many years from now will the population be 50,000?

35. Potassium 42 has a decay rate of approximately 5.5% per hour. Assuming an exponential decay model, in how many hours will the original quantity of potassium 42 have been halved?

36. Consider an exponential decay model given by

$$Q = q_0e^{-0.4t}$$

where t is in weeks. How many weeks does it take for Q to decay to $\frac{1}{4}$ of its original amount?

37. How long does it take an amount of money to double if it is invested at a rate of 8% per year compounded semiannually?

38. At what rate of annual interest, compounded semiannually, should a certain amount of money be invested so that it will double in 8 years?

39. The number N of radios that an assembly line worker can assemble daily after t days of training is given by

$$N = 60 - 60e^{-0.04t}$$

After how many days of training does the worker assemble 40 radios daily?

40. The quantity Q in grams of a radioactive substance that is present after t days of decay is given by

$$Q = 400e^{-kt}$$

If $Q = 300$ when $t = 3$, find k, the decay rate.

41. A person on an assembly line produces P items per day after t days of training, where

$$P = 400(1 - e^{-t})$$

How many days of training will it take this person to be able to produce 300 items per day?

42. Suppose that the number N of mopeds sold when x thousands of dollars are spent on advertising is given by

$$N = 4000 + 1000\ln(x + 2)$$

How much advertising money must be spent to sell 6000 mopeds?

In Exercises 43–45, solve for y.

43. $x^2 + x = \ln(y + 1)$

44. $2x + 5 = \frac{1}{2}\ln(y - 3)^4$

45. $\ln x + 3 = \ln(y + 1) + \ln(y - 1)$

Terms and Symbols

a^x	conjugate axis	inverse function
analytic geometry	continuous compounding	irreducible rational function
approaching ∞	decay constant	$\ln x$
approaching $-\infty$	directrix	logarithmic function
asymptote	e	$\log_a x$
asymptotes of a hyperbola	ellipse	$\log x$
axes of ellipse	equation of circle	major axis
axes of hyperbola	equation of ellipse	minor axis
axis of parabola	equation of hyperbola	natural exponential function
axis of symmetry	equation of parabola	natural logarithm
base of exponential function	exponential decay model	one-to-one function
base of logarithmic function	exponential function	parabola
branches of hyperbola	exponential growth model	radius of circle
center of circle	$f^{-1}(x)$	rational function
center of ellipse	foci of ellipse	reducible rational function
center of hyperbola	foci of hyperbola	reflection
change of base	focus of parabola	translation of axes
circle	growth constant	transverse axis
common logarithm	half-life	vertical asymptote
compound interest	horizontal asymptote	vertex of parabola
compounding period	horizontal-line test	vertices of ellipse
conic sections	hyperbola	vertices of hyperbola

Key Ideas for Review

Topic	Key Idea
Horizontal Asymptote	A rational function has a unique horizontal asymptote if the degree of the numerator is less than or equal to the degree of the denominator.
Vertical Asymptote	An irreducible rational function has a vertical asymptote corresponding to each zero of the denominator.
Graphing Rational Functions	Determine the intercepts, symmetry, horizontal and vertical asymptotes of a rational function before attempting to sketch its graph.
Reducible Rational Functions	The graph of a reducible rational function has a "hole" corresponding to each unique common factor of the numerator and denominator.
Analytic Geometry	Analytic geometry applies algebraic techniques to the study of geometry. Theorems from plane geometry can be proved using these methods.
Conic Sections	The conic sections represent the possible intersections of a plane and a cone. In general, a conic section can be a circle, parabola, ellipse or hyperbola. In special cases, these may reduce to a point, a line, two lines or no graph. Each conic section has a geometric definition that can be used to derive a second-degree equation in two variables. The graph of this equation corresponds to that particular conic section.

Topic	Key Idea
Circle	A circle is the set of all points in a plane that are a given distance from a fixed point in the plane. The standard equation is $$(x - h)^2 + (y - k)^2 = r^2$$
Parabola	A parabola is the set of all points in a plane that are equidistant from a given point and a given line, both in the plane. The standard equation is $$(x - h)^2 = 4p(y - k) \quad \text{or} \quad (y - k)^2 = 4p(x - h)$$
Translation of Axes	It is possible to consider a graph of an equation with respect to a new coordinate system with axes x' and y', parallel to the standard x- and y-coordinate axes, respectively. If the origin of the new coordinate system has coordinates (h, k) relative to the standard xy-coordinate system, then the relationships between the two coordinate systems is given by $$x' = x - h \quad \text{and} \quad y' = y - k$$
One-to-One	We say a function is one-to-one if every element of the range corresponds to precisely one element of the domain.
Horizontal Line Test	No horizontal line meets the graph of a one-to-one function in more than one point.
Inverse Function	The inverse of a function, f^{-1}, reverses the correspondence defined by the function f. The domain of f becomes the range of f^{-1}, and the range of f becomes the domain of f^{-1}.
Properties	A function f and its inverse f^{-1} satisfy $$f^{-1}[f(x)] = x \text{ for all } x \text{ in the domain of } f$$ $$f[f^{-1}(y)] = y \text{ for all } y \text{ in the range of } f$$
One-to-One	The inverse of a function f is defined only if f is one-to-one.
Graph	The graphs of a function and its inverse are reflections of each other about the line $y = x$.
Inverse	The inverse of the inverse of a function is the function itself.
Exponential Function	An exponential function has the form $$f(x) = a^x, \quad a > 0, \quad a \neq 1$$
Domain	The domain of $f(x) = a^x$ is the set of all real numbers.
Range	The range of $f(x) = a^x$ is the set of all positive numbers.
Increasing, Decreasing	The graph of $f(x) = a^x$ is increasing if $a > 1$ and decreasing if $0 < a < 1$.
One-to-One	The exponential function is one-to-one.
Equality, Same Base	If $a^x = a^y$, then $x = y$.
Equality, Different Bases	If $a^x = b^x$ with $a > 0$ and $b > 0$, then $x = 0$ or $a = b$.
e	As m approaches ∞, $(1 + \frac{1}{m})^m$ approaches $e \approx 2.71828$.

Topic	Key Idea
Applications	1. Compound Interest $$A = P\left(1 + \frac{r}{k}\right)^{kt}$$ 2. Continuous Compounding $$A = Pe^{rt}$$ 3. Exponential Growth Model $$Q(t) = q_0 e^{kt}, \quad q_0 > 0, \quad k > 0$$ 4. Exponential Decay Model $$Q(t) = q_0 e^{-kt}, \quad q_0 > 0, \quad k > 0$$
Logarithmic Function	The logarithmic function has the form $$f(x) = \log_a x, \quad a > 0, \quad a \neq 1$$ It is the inverse of the exponential function a^x and both functions have base a.
Special Cases	The common logarithm is $\log x = \log_{10} x$, and the natural logarithm is $\ln x = \log_e x$.
Logarithms as Exponents	The logarithmic function $y = \log_a x$ and the exponential form $x = a^y$ are two ways of expressing the same relationship. In short, logarithms are exponents. Consequently, it is always possible to convert one form into the other.
Identities	The following identities are useful in simplifying expressions and in solving equations. $$a^{\log_a x} = x$$ $$\log_a a^x = x$$ $$\log_a a = 1$$ $$\log_a 1 = 0$$
Domain	The domain of $f(x) = \log_a x$ is the set of all positive numbers.
Range	The range of $f(x) = \log_a x$ is the set of all real numbers.
Increasing, Decreasing	The graph of $f(x) = \log_a x$ is increasing if $a > 1$ and decreasing if $0 < a < 1$.
One-to-One	The logarithmic function is one-to-one.
Equality, Same Base	If $\log_a x = \log_a y$, then $x = y$.
Equality, Different Bases	If $\log_a x = \log_b x$, either $x = 1$ or $a = b$.
Fundamental Properties	The fundamental properties of logarithms are as follows, *Property 1.* $\log_a xy = \log_a x + \log_a y$ *Property 2.* $\log_a \frac{x}{y} = \log_a x - \log_a y$ *Property 3.* $\log_a x^n = n \log_a x$
Change of Base	The change of base formula is $$\log_b x = \frac{\log_a x}{\log_a b}$$

Review Exercises

Solutions to exercises whose numbers are in **bold** are in the Solutions section in the back of the book.

In Exercises 1–3, sketch the graph of the given function. Then, determine appropriate WINDOW values, and check your answer using your graphing calculator.

1. $f(x) = \dfrac{x}{x+1}$ 2. $f(x) = \dfrac{x^2}{x+1}$

3. $f(x) = \dfrac{x^2+2}{x^2-1}$

4. Write an equation of the circle whose center is at $(-5, 2)$ and whose radius is 4.

5. Write an equation of the circle whose center is at $(-3, 3)$ and whose radius is 2.

In Exercises 6–11, determine the center and radius of the circle with the given equation.

6. $(x-2)^2 + (y+3)^2 = 9$

7. $\left(x + \dfrac{1}{2}\right)^2 + (y-4)^2 = \dfrac{1}{9}$

8. $x^2 + y^2 + 4x - 6y = -10$

9. $2x^2 + 2y^2 - 4x + 4y = -3$

10. $x^2 + y^2 - 6y + 3 = 0$

11. $x^2 + y^2 - 2x - 2y = 8$

In Exercises 12 and 13, determine the vertex and axis of the given parabola. Sketch the graph.

12. $(y+5)^2 = 4\left(x - \dfrac{3}{2}\right)$ 13. $(x-1)^2 = 2 - y$

In Exercises 14–19, determine the vertex, axis and direction of the given parabola.

14. $y^2 + 3x + 9 = 0$ 15. $y^2 + 4y + x + 2 = 0$

16. $2x^2 - 12x - y + 16 = 0$ 17. $x^2 + 4x + 2y + 5 = 0$

18. $y^2 - 2y - 4x + 1 = 0$ 19. $x^2 + 6x + 4y + 9 = 0$

In Exercises 20 and 21, determine the focus and directrix of the given parabola, and sketch the graph.

20. $x^2 = -\dfrac{2}{3}y$ 21. $3y^2 + 2x = 0$

In Exercises 22 and 23, determine the equation of the parabola with its vertex at the origin that satisfies the given conditions.

22. directrix $y = \dfrac{7}{4}$

23. axis the y-axis; parabola passing through the point $\left(1, \dfrac{5}{2}\right)$

In Exercises 24–29, write the given equation in standard form and determine the intercepts.

24. $9x^2 - 4y^2 = 36$ 25. $9x^2 + y^2 = 9$

26. $5x^2 + 7y^2 = 35$ 27. $9x^2 - 16y^2 = 144$

28. $3x^2 + 4y^2 = 9$ 29. $3y^2 - 5x^2 = 20$

In Exercises 30 and 31 use the intercepts and asymptotes of the hyperbola to sketch the graph.

30. $4x^2 - 4y^2 = 1$ 31. $9y^2 - 4x^2 = 36$

32. Find the equation of the circle with center at the origin and passes through the point $(3, 1)$.

 In Exercises 33–42, identify the conic section whose equation is given. Then, determine appropriate WINDOW values and GRAPH the conic sections on your graphing calculator.

33. $2x^2 - 4x + y = 0$

34. $4y + x^2 - 2x = 1$

35. $x^2 - 2x + y^2 - 4y = -6$

36. $-x^2 - 4x + y^2 + 4 = 0$

37. $y^2 + 2x - 4 = x^2 - 2x$

38. $x^2 - 4x + 2y = 6 + y^2$

39. $2y^2 + 6y - 3x + 2 = 0$

40. $6x^2 - 7y^2 - 5x + 6y = 0$

41. $2x^2 + y^2 + 12x - 2y + 17 = 0$

42. $9x^2 + 4y^2 = -36$

In Exercises 43 and 44, determine whether the given function $f(x)$ is one-to-one. If it is, find its inverse $f^{-1}(x)$, and sketch the graphs of $y = f(x)$ and $y = f^{-1}(x)$ on the same coordinate axes.

43. $f(x) = \dfrac{x}{3} - 2$ 44. $f(x) = \dfrac{|x|}{3} - 2$

45. Sketch the graph of $f(x) = (\frac{1}{3})^x$. Label the point $(-1, f(-1))$.

46. Solve $2^{2x} = 8^{x-1}$ for x.

47. Solve $(2a + 1)^x = (3a - 1)^x$ for a if $a > \frac{1}{3}$ and $x \neq 0$.

48. The amount of $8000 is invested in a certificate paying 12% annual interest compounded semiannually. What amount is available at the end of 4 years?

In Exercises 49–52, write each logarithmic form in exponential form and vice versa.

49. $27 = 9^{3/2}$

50. $\log_{64} 8 = \frac{1}{2}$

51. $\log_2 \frac{1}{8} = -3$

52. $6^0 = 1$

In Exercises 53–56, solve for x.

53. $\log_x 16 = 4$

54. $\log_5 \frac{1}{125} = x - 1$

55. $\ln x = -4$

56. $\log_3(x + 1) = \log_3 27$

In Exercises 57–60, evaluate the given expression.

57. $\log_3 3^5$

58. $\ln e^{-1/3}$

59. $\log_3 \frac{1}{3}$

60. $e^{\ln 3}$

61. Sketch the graph of $f(x) = \log_3 x + 1$.

In Exercises 62–65, write the given expression in terms of simpler logarithmic forms.

62. $\log_a \frac{\sqrt{x-1}}{2x}$

63. $\log_a \frac{x(2-x)^2}{(y+1)^{1/2}}$

64. $\ln[(x + 1)^4(y - 1)^2]$

65. $\log \sqrt[5]{\frac{y^2 z}{z + 3}}$

 In Exercises 66–75, use your calculator to evaluate the following expressions:

66. e^{-5}

67. $\ln \sqrt{2}$

68. $\sqrt[3]{5 - e^3}$

69. $2500 \left(1 + \frac{0.08}{4}\right)^{80}$

70. $2500e^{1.6}$

71. $\frac{\log 5}{\log 2}$

72. $\log_3 4$

73. $e^{5 \ln 2}$

74. 2^e

75. $\log(5 - \pi)$

 76. A father has two sons, Cliff and Joe. Both wish to contribute a portion of their savings to their father's construction firm that they will one day inherit. Cliff and Joe both have different accounts. Cliff originally deposited $8000 in his bank account where 9% interest was compounded quarterly, when he was 12 years old. Joe, however, deposited $7000 in his bank account where 11% interest was compounded semiannually, when he was 14 years old. Who has the potential to contribute more to their father's business if Cliff is now 21 years old and Joe is now 23 years old? By how much?

 77. Veterinary medicine sometimes uses an antibiotic called chloramphenecol to suppress blood cell production. Suppose a patient's red blood cell count drops to 3.0×10^6 RBC/cm³ after therapy with this antibiotic. Assume that cell production can be stimulated at 50 cells exponentially per day, that is, 50^t, t = time measured in days. How long would it be before the patient's count was back to a normal range of 5.0×10^6 RBC/cm³? (Note that red blood cells are produced from bone marrow and not from other blood cells.)

78. The number of bacteria in a certain culture is 320,000 at 4 P.M. At 6 P.M. on the same day, the count is 640,000. Assuming that the population grows exponentially, find the count at 10 P.M. that day.

 79. With reference to Exercise 36, suppose there were 150,000 cells at 4 P.M. and 225,000 at 6 P.M. What will the count be at 2 A.M. the next morning?

80. Lou has $1000 he wishes to invest in a certificate of deposit at bank A. The terms are 5% compounded continuously for 5 years. At bank B the terms are 5.05% compounded semiannually for 5 years. Which is the better investment?

 81. A laboratory medical experiment involves testing the absorption rate of an AIDS antidote drug, once that drug has been injected into the circulatory system. Suppose $C_F = C_0 e^{-kt}$, where C_F = the final concentration, C_0 = the initial concentration, k = a predetermined constant, and t = time measured in minutes.

a. Determine t if $C_F = 1000$ mg, $C_0 = 10,000$ mg, and $k = 2$.

b. Plot C_F for $k = 1, 2, 3$ on the same set of axes, where $t \geq 0$.

Exercises 82 and 83 refer to the following:

Noise is related to the intensity of sound waves as the waves travel through a medium, such as air, water, etc. The intensity I is the energy carried by a wave per unit time, measured in watts per square meter. The loudness B of sound intensity levels is rated on a logarithmic scale and is measured in decibels. The equation relating these variables is

$$B = 10 \log \frac{I}{I_0}$$

where I_0 is the intensity of some reference level, usually taken as the minimum intensity audible to the human ear, 1.0×10^{-12} watts per square meter.

82. What is the loudness level of a radio whose intensity is 1.0×10^{-8} watts per square meter?

83. A single mosquito 1 meter from a person makes a sound close to the threshold of human hearing. What is the loudness level of 1000 mosquitos at such a distance?

Review Test

1. Sketch the graph of the function
$$f(x) = \frac{2x}{x^2 - 1}$$

2. Write an equation of the circle of radius 6 whose center is at $(2, -3)$.

In Exercises 3 and 4, determine the center and radius of the circle.

3. $x^2 + y^2 - 2x + 4y = -1$ 4. $x^2 - 4x + y^2 = 1$

In Exercises 5 and 6, determine the vertex and axis of the parabola. Sketch the graph.

5. $x^2 + 6x + 2y + 7 = 0$ 6. $y^2 - 4x - 4y + 8 = 0$

In Exercises 7 and 8, determine the vertex, axis and the direction in which the parabola opens.

7. $x^2 - 6x + 2y + 5 = 0$ 8. $y^2 + 8y - x + 14 = 0$

In Exercise 9, write the given equation in standard form and determine the intercepts.

9. $x^2 + 4y^2 = 4$

In Exercises 9 and 10, find $f^{-1}(x)$, the inverse of $f(x)$, and sketch the graphs of $y = f(x)$ and $y = f^{-1}(x)$ on the same coordinate axes.

9. $f(x) = -4x + 2$ 10. $f(x) = -\frac{1}{x}$

11. Sketch the graph of $f(x) = 2^{x+1}$. Label the point $(1, f(1))$.

12. Solve $\left(\frac{1}{2}\right)^x = \left(\frac{1}{4}\right)^{2x+1}$

In Exercises 13 and 14, convert from logarithmic form to exponential form or vice versa.

13. $\log_3 \frac{1}{9} = -2$ 14. $64 = 16^{3/2}$

In Exercises 15 and 16, solve for x.

15. $\log_x 27 = 3$ 16. $\log_6\left(\frac{1}{36}\right) = 3x + 1$

In Exercises 17 and 18, evaluate the given expression.

17. $\ln e^{5/2}$ 18. $\log_5 \sqrt{5}$

In Exercises 19 and 20, write the given expression in terms of simpler logarithmic forms.

19. $\log_a \frac{x^3}{y^2 z}$ 20. $\log \frac{x^2\sqrt{2y-1}}{y^3}$

In Exercises 21 and 22, use the value $\log 2 \approx 0.3$ to evaluate the given expression.

21. $\log 5$ 22. $\log 2\sqrt{2}$

In Exercises 23 and 24, write the given expression as a single logarithm.

23. $2 \log x - 3 \log(y + 1)$

24. $\frac{2}{3}[\log_a(x + 3) - \log_a(x - 3)]$

25. The number of bacteria in a culture is described by the exponential growth model

$$Q(t) = q_0 e^{0.02t}$$

Approximately how many hours are required for the number of bacteria to double?

26. Suppose that $500 is invested in a certificate at an annual interest rate of 12% compounded monthly. What is the value of the investment after 6 months?

In Exercises 27 and 28, solve for x.

27. $\log x - \log 2 = 2$

28. $\log_4(x - 3) = 1 - \log_4 x$

In Exercises 29–32, use the values $\log 2 \approx 0.30$, $\log 3 \approx 0.48$, and $\log 7 \approx 0.85$ to evaluate the given expression.

29. $\log 14$

30. $\log 3.5$

31. $\log \sqrt{6}$

32. $\log 0.7$

In Exercises 33–36, write the given expression as a single logarithm.

33. $\dfrac{1}{3} \log_a x - \dfrac{1}{2} \log_a y$

34. $\dfrac{4}{3}$ $[\log x + \log(x - 1)]$

35. $\ln 3x + 2\left(\ln y - \dfrac{1}{2} \ln z\right)$

36. $2 \log_a(x + 2) - \dfrac{3}{2} \log_a(x + 1)$

In Exercises 37 and 38, use the values $\log 32 \approx 1.5$, $\log 8 \approx 0.9$, and $\log 5 \approx 0.7$ to find the requested value.

37. $\log_8 32$

38. $\log_5 32$

39. A substance is known to have a decay rate of 6% per hour. Approximately how many hours are required for the remaining quantity to be half of the original quantity?

In Exercises 40–42, solve for x.

40. $2^{3x-1} = 14$

41. $2 \log x - \log 5 = 3$

42. $\log(2x - 1) = 2 + \log(x - 2)$

Cumulative Review Exercises: Chapters 4–5

1. Given $P(x) = 2x^3 + 5x^2 + 3$,

   a. find $P(-2)$.

   b. find the quotient and remainder when $P(x)$ is divided by $x + 1$.

2. Find all rational roots of the equation

   $$5x^3 - x^2 + 20x - 4 = 0$$

3. The graph of the function

   $$f(x) = 2x^3 - x^2 - 6x + 3$$

   crosses the x-axis at $x = \frac{1}{2}$. Find the other x-intercepts, if any.

4. Given the function

   $$f(x) = \frac{2x^2 + 6x}{x^2 - 9}$$

   a. determine the domain of f.

   b. find all asymptotes of the graph of f.

   c. sketch the graph of f.

   d. Determine appropriate WINDOW values and GRAPH $f(x)$ on your graphing calculator.

In Exercises 5–7, solve for x.

5. $27^{x-1} = 9^{3-x}$

6. $\log_x(2x + 3) = 2$

7. $\log_2(\log_3 x) = 1$

8. A radioactive isotope is known to decay exponentially. If the half-life of the isotope is 5 years, how long will it take for 9 grams to decay to 3 grams?

9. Sketch the graph of $f(x) = 2^x - 1$.

10. If $\log 2 = s$, $\log 3 = t$, and $\log 5 = u$, express the following in terms of s, t, and u:

   a. $\log 18$

   b. $\log \frac{5}{4}$

   c. $\log 1.5$

   d. $\log \sqrt{7.5}$

11. A certificate of deposit is purchased paying interest at the rate of 8% per year, compounded continuously. If the certificate matures in 6 months at a value of $1000, how much was invested initially?

12. Simplify

   $$\ln \frac{x^2 \sqrt{x + 1}}{x - 1}$$

13. Suppose an amount of money P is placed in an account where interest is compounded continuously for 15 years. What interest rate would be necessary in order for the value of the account to quadruple?

14. A $6000 investment is deposited in a local bank where interest is compounded quarterly at a rate of 7%. Find the amount in the account after 4 years. Also, what is the amount of the compound interest earned during the 4 years?

15. A father has an 8-year-old son for whom he is setting up a fund. He wants to have enough money accumulated in the fund to pay for a $20,000 college tuition, to start when his son turns 18. If interest is compounded continuously at an annual rate of 9.2%, how much money should the father initially deposit into the fund?

16. A firm wishes to deposit $75,000 in a bank account for future investment use. The firm estimates it will need 4 times its original deposit to have an effect on the stock market. If the going rate is 8% interest compounded continuously, how long will it take for the original investment to quadruple?

17. Katy will attend a university in the fall. Over the summer she will earn approximately $2000. She wishes to save about half of that for future college expenses. Bond A, maturing in three years, yields an interest rate of 7% compounded continuously and can be purchased for $1000. Bond B, also maturing in three years, yields an interest rate of 9% compounded continuously and can be purchased for $950. Which bond offers Katy the better investment?

18. Newton's law of cooling states that

$$T = (T_0 - T_R)e^{-kt} + T_R$$

where T_0 is the original temperature of the object in question, t is the elapsed time, T_R is the room temperature, k is the constant of decay, and T is the temperature at time t. Suppose a cup of coffee has a temperature of 150° F. It is placed in a room whose temperature is 80°F. If the temperature of the coffee is 90°F 2 hours later, find the constant of decay.

Writing Exercises

1. We define the eccentricity of the ellipse $\dfrac{x^2}{a^2} + \dfrac{y^2}{b^2} = 1$ as $\dfrac{\sqrt{a^2 - b^2}}{a}$. Describe what happens to the shape of this ellipse when its eccentricity varies from 0 to 1.

2. We define the eccentricity of the hyperbola $\dfrac{x^2}{a^2} - \dfrac{y^2}{b^2} = 1$ as $\dfrac{\sqrt{a^2 + b^2}}{a}$. Describe what happens to the shape of this hyperbola when its eccentricity increases.

3. Discuss how circles, parabolas and ellipses are used in everyday life.

4. Suppose you know that the rational function $f(x)$ has the line $y = c$ as a horizontal asymptote. Discuss what can be deduced from this information.

5. Suppose you know that the rational function $f(x)$ has the line $x = c$ as a vertical asymptote. Discuss what can be deduced from this information.

6. The acronym for long-distance radio navigation is LORAN. Research how this system uses hyperbolas to determine the location of ships.

7. Write a brief report illustrating how exponential and logarithmic functions occur in everyday life.

8. Discuss how the invention of logarithms enabled seventeenth century astronomers in Europe to simplify their mathematical computations.

9. Discuss the environmental impact of the exponential growth of the world's population.

10. A newscaster stated that the 1989 earthquake in Southern California, with a reading on the Richter scale of 7.1, was twice as powerful as a subsequent earthquake whose reading on the Richter scale was 3.05. Comment on the newscaster's understanding of the Richter scale.

11. Write a report on Napier's "bones."

12. Suppose you borrow $6000 at simple interest of 5% for one year. The bank gives you $5700. You must repay the loan in one payment when the loan is due.

Explain in words how you would find the true rate of interest.

13. Explain how a slide rule works.

Chapter 5 Project 1

In 1865 in Memphis, TN, there was an earthquake that measured 5.0 on the Richter scale. Memphis is part of a region that the United States Geological Survey refers to as the New Madrid Seismic Zone. Many buildings in this part of the country were never designed with large earthquakes in mind, but seismologists consider the likelihood of a large earthquake in this region within the next 50 years to be high. Tennessee schools have had Earthquake Awareness Week since 1995. (This information comes from http://www.cusec.org/.)

What is the likelihood of a large earthquake in your area? What precautions exist, if any, against the possibility of damage or loss of life from seismic activity?

For this project, first refer back to Exercises 96 and 97 in Section 6.3, and Exercises 59, 60, and 61 in Section 6.4. On your graphing calculator, display the graph of $y = \log x$ and set the viewing window large enough so that you can TRACE a point on the graph all the way up to $y = 9.0$. What is the range of x values? Write a brief essay comparing this graph to the Richter scale and describing how the y values are related to the x values. (*Hint:* The independent variable represents the ratio I/S.)

Copy your graph, and label the points on the graph which give information about the earthquakes in Bolivia, Indonesia, Memphis, Alaska, and Japan.

Chapter 5 Project 2

To determine how many of each item to produce, how many should sell, and how much to charge, businesses must make use of functions which model cost, revenue, and profit. The independent variable for these functions could be the number of units produced. We could then express the profit as a difference function, an algebraic combination of cost and revenue (see Section 3.5 to review the algebra of functions).

What is the profit function? Review Section 5.1, Exercises 30 and 31. Suppose the revenue function for producing graphing calculators is

$$R(x) = 120x$$

and the cost is given by

$$C(x) = 50x + 10,000$$

where R and C are in dollars and x represents the number of graphing calculators produced. Assume that every calculator produced sells (a very favorable assumption!).

Answer the following questions:

- How much does each calculator sell for?

- What is the average cost function? What does its graph look like? Why?

- What is the average profit function?

- Set up a TABLE in your graphing calculator, with one column for the number of calculators produced, one for the cost, one for revenue, and the last column for profit. Use increments of 100 units.

- Is the average profit function an algebraic combination of the average revenue and average cost function? Why or why not?

CHAPTER 6

Systems of Equations and Inequalities

Mathematics students become accustomed to seeing equations. However, if you look at the world around you, you rarely see equations! What you do see is relationships which can be modeled by equations. One way to do this is by polynomial curve fitting. This is a process whereby we find the equation of a polynomial which passes through any point we are given (perhaps these points represent paired data, like heights and weights). The process of finding an equation in standard form for a polynomial that passes through a given set of points requires that we solve a system of equations. You will get some practice doing this in this chapter's project.

Continue your investigation of mathematics on the Web by checking out the following site: www.cut-the-knot.org/.

Many problems in business and engineering require the solution of systems of equations and inequalities. In fact, systems of linear equations and inequalities occur with such frequency that mathematicians and computer scientists have devoted considerable energy to devising methods for their solution. With the aid of large-scale computers, it is possible to solve systems involving thousands of equations or inequalities, containing thousands of variables.

www.cut-the-knot.org/

We begin with the study of the methods of substitution and elimination, methods that are applicable to all types of systems. We then introduce graphical methods for solving systems of linear inequalities and apply this technique to linear programming problems, a type of optimization problem.

6.1   Systems of Equations in Two Unknowns

Consider the following problem.

> A pile of 9 coins consists of nickels and quarters. If the total value of the coins is $1.25, how many of each type of coin are there?

Although we could solve this problem using the methods discussed in Chapter 2, we are going to focus on a somewhat different approach. Let

$$x = \text{the number of nickels}$$

and

$$y = \text{the number of quarters}$$

The requirements can then be expressed as

$$x + y = 9$$
$$5x + 25y = 125$$

This is an example of a **system of equations,** and we seek values of x and y that satisfy *both* equations. If $x = a$ and $y = b$ satisfy both equations, then the ordered pair (a, b) is called a **solution** of the system. Thus,

$$x = 5 \quad \text{and} \quad y = 4$$

or equivalently

$$(5, 4)$$

is a solution, since substituting into the above system yields

$$5 + 4 = 9$$
$$5(5) + 25(4) = 125$$

Solving by Substitution

If we can use one of the equations of a system to express one variable in terms of the other variable, then we can *substitute* this expression into the other equation.

Example 1   Solving by Substitution

Solve the system of equations.

$$x^2 + y^2 = 25$$
$$x + y = -1$$

Solution

From the second equation we have

$$y = -1 - x$$

Substituting this expression for y into the first equation, we obtain

$$x^2 + (-1 - x)^2 = 25$$
$$x^2 + 1 + 2x + x^2 = 25$$
$$2x^2 + 2x - 24 = 0$$
$$x^2 + x - 12 = 0$$
$$(x + 4)(x - 3) = 0$$

which yields $x = -4$ and $x = 3$. Substituting these values for x in the second equation, we obtain the corresponding values of y.

$$x = -4: \quad -4 + y = -1 \quad x = 3: \quad 3 + y = -1$$
$$y = 3 \qquad\qquad\qquad y = -4$$

Thus, $x = -4, y = 3$ and $x = 3, y = -4$ are solutions of the system of equations.   ■

Solving by Graphing

The coordinates of every point on the graph of an equation must satisfy that equation. If we sketch the graphs of a pair of equations on the same coordinate axes, it follows that the *points of intersection* must satisfy *both* equations. Thus, we have a graphical means of solving a system of equations.

Consider the equations of Example 1. The graph of the first equation is a circle of radius 5, centered at the origin. The graph of the second equation is a line. We sketch both curves on the same set of axes, as shown in Figure 1. Note the solutions $(-4, 3)$ and $(3, -4)$ are the points of intersection of these graphs.

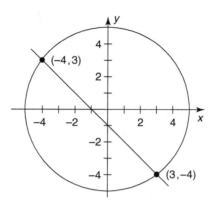

Figure 1 Diagram for Example 1

Graphing Calculator Alert

A graphical representation on your calculator provides *approximate* solutions to a system of equations. Greater accuracy can be achieved by using the ZOOM-IN process described in Section 4.7. Your graphing calculator can probably find the point of intersection for you. Check out the example below.

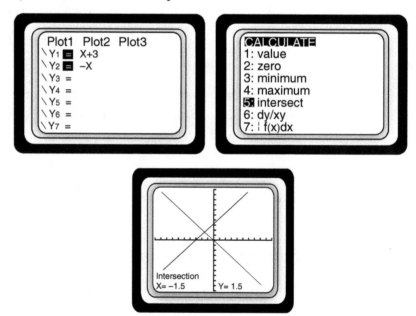

Warning

The expression for x or y obtained from an equation *must not be substituted into the same equation*. From the first equation of the system

$$x + 2y = -1$$
$$3x^2 + y = 2$$

we obtain

$$x = -1 - 2y$$

Substituting in the *same* equation results in

$$(-1 - 2y) + 2y = -1$$
$$-1 = -1$$

The substitution $x = -1 - 2y$ must be made into the *second* equation.

✔ **Progress Check**

Solve the system of equations.

a. $x^2 + 3y^2 = 12$ b. $x^2 + y^2 = 34$
   $x + 3y = 6$ $x - y = 2$

Answers

a. $x = 3, y = 1; x = 0, y = 2$ b. $x = -3, y = -5; x = 5, y = 3$

It is also possible for a system of equations to have no solution or an infinite number of solutions. The following terminology is used to distinguish these situations.

Consistent and Inconsistent Systems

- A **consistent** system of equations has one or more solutions.

- An **inconsistent** system of equations has no solutions.

Example 2   **Consistent and Inconsistent Systems**

Solve the system of equations.

a. $x^2 - 2x - y + 3 = 0$ b. $x + 4y = 10$
   $x + y - 1 = 0$ $-2x - 8y = -20$

Solution

a. Solving the second equation for y, we have

$$y = 1 - x$$

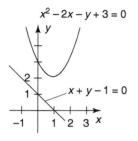

Figure 2   Diagram for Example 2(a)

and substituting in the first equation yields

$$x^2 - 2x - (1 - x) + 3 = 0$$

$$x^2 - x + 2 = 0$$

Since the discriminant of this quadratic equation is negative, the equation has no real roots. But any solution of the system of equations must satisfy this quadratic equation. We can therefore conclude that the system is inconsistent. The graphs of the equations are a parabola and a line that do not intersect, as shown in Figure 2.

b. Solving the first equation for x, we have

$$x = 10 - 4y$$

and substituting in the second equation gives

$$-2(10 - 4y) - 8y = -20$$

$$-20 + 8y - 8y = -20$$

$$-20 = -20$$

The substitution procedure has resulted in an identity, indicating that any solution of the first equation also satisfies the second equation. Since there are an infinite number of ordered pairs (a, b) with $x = a$ and $y = b$ satisfying the first equation, the system is consistent. (Verify that the graphs of these two equations are identical.)   ■

✔ **Progress Check**
Solve by substitution.

a. $3x^2 - y^2 = 7$

    $-9x + 3y = -2$

b. $-5x + 2y = -4$

    $\dfrac{5}{2}x - y = 2$

Answers
a. no solution

b. any point on the line $-5x + 2y = -4$

Systems of Linear Equations

A system consisting only of equations that are of the first degree in x and y is called a **system of linear equations**, or simply a **linear system**. When we graph a linear system of two equations on the same set of coordinate axes, there are three possibilities:

Consistent and Inconsistent Systems

1. The two lines intersect at a point, as shown in Figure 3(a). The system is consistent and has a unique solution, namely, the point of intersection.

2. The two equations are different forms of the same line, as shown in Figure 3(b). The system is consistent and has an infinite number of solutions, namely, all points on the line.

3. The two lines are parallel, as shown in Figure 3(c). Since the lines do not intersect, the system is inconsistent and has no solution.

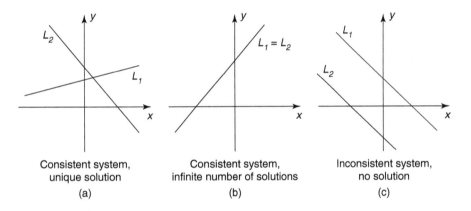

Figure 3   Possible Graphs for a Pair of Linear Equations

Solving by Elimination

The method of elimination seeks to combine the equations of a system in such a way as to *eliminate* one of the unknowns.

Example 3   Solving by Elimination

Solve the system

$$x + y = 9$$
$$5x + 25y = 125$$

Solution

Method of Elimination

Step 1. Multiply each equation by a constant so that the coefficients of either x or y differ only in sign.	*Step 1.* Multiply the first equation by -5 and the second equation by 1 so that the coefficients of x are -5 and 5: $$\begin{aligned} -5x - 5y &= -45 \\ 5x + 25y &= 125 \end{aligned}$$
Step 2. Add the equations. At least one unknown has been "eliminated" in the resulting equation.	*Step 2.* $\qquad\qquad 20y = 80$
Step 3. Solve the resulting equation in one unknown, if possible.	*Step 3.* $\qquad\qquad y = 4$
Step 4. Substitute into either of the *original* equations to solve for the second unknown.	*Step 4.* Substitute $y = 4$ into the first equation of the original system: $$x + y = 9$$ $$x + 4 = 9$$ $$x = 5$$
Step 5. Check in both equations.	*Step 5.* Verify that the solution $$x = 5, \quad y = 4$$ satisfies $$x + y = 9$$ $$5 + 4 = 9 \ ✔$$ $$5x + 25y = 125$$ $$5(5) + 25(4) = 25 + 100 = 125 \ ✔$$

Example 4   Solving by Elimination

Solve the system.

$$4x^2 + 9y^2 = 36$$
$$-9x^2 + 18y^2 = 4$$

Solution

Method of Elimination

Step 1. Multiply each equation by a constant so that the coefficients of either x or y differ only in sign.	*Step 1.* Multiply the first equation by -2 and the second equation by 1 so that the coefficients of y are -18 and 18: $$\begin{aligned} -8x^2 - 18y^2 &= -72 \\ -9x^2 + 18y^2 &= 4 \\ \hline -17x^2 &= -68 \end{aligned}$$
Step 2. Add the equations. At least one unknown has been "eliminated" in the resulting equation.	*Step 2.*
Step 3. Solve the resulting equation in one unknown, if possible.	*Step 3.* $$x^2 = 4$$ $$x = \pm 2$$
Step 4. Substitute into either of the *original* equations to solve for the second unknown.	*Step 4.* Substitute $x = 2$ in the first equation of the original system: $$4x^2 + 9y^2 = 36$$ $$4(2)^2 + 9y^2 = 36$$ $$y = \pm\frac{2}{3}\sqrt{5}$$ Substituting $x = -2$ yields the same values for y.
Step 5. Check in both equations.	*Step 5.* Verify that the solutions $$x = 2, \quad y = \frac{2}{3}\sqrt{5}$$ $$x = 2, \quad y = -\frac{2}{3}\sqrt{5}$$ $$x = -2, \quad y = \frac{2}{3}\sqrt{5}$$ $$x = -2, \quad y = -\frac{2}{3}\sqrt{5}$$ satisfy both equations.

The graphs of these equations (ellipse and hyperbola) are shown in Figure 4.

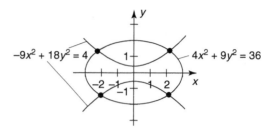

Figure 4   Graph for Example 4

Example 5   Solving by Elimination

Solve the system.

a. $2x^2 - 3y^2 = 9$ b. $5x + 6y = 4$
       $x^2 + y^2 = 4$ $-10x - 12y = -8$

Solution

a.   Adding -2 times the second equation to the first equation yields

$$-5y^2 = 1 \quad \text{or} \quad y^2 = -\frac{1}{5}$$

Since this equation has no real solutions, the graphs of the given system do not intersect, and the system is inconsistent, as shown in Figure 5.

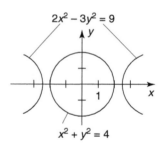

Figure 5   Graph for Example 5(a)

b. Multiplying the first equation by 2, we have

$$
\begin{array}{r}
10x + 12y = 8 \\
-10x - 12y = -8 \\
\hline
0x + 0y = 0
\end{array}
$$

We conclude that the equations represent the same line and that the solution set consists of all points on the line $5x + 6y = 4$.

✔ Progress Check

Solve by elimination.

a. $x - y = 2$
$3x - 3y = -6$

b. $4x + 6y = 3$
$-2x - 3y = -\dfrac{3}{2}$

c. $x^2 - 4x + y^2 - 4y = 1$
$x^2 - 4x \qquad + \ y = -5$

Answers

a. no solution

b. all points on the line $4x + 6y = 3$

c. $x = 2, y = -1$ (The parabola is tangent to the circle.)

Exercise Set 6.1

In Exercises 1–10, find approximate solutions of the given system by graphing.

1. $x + y = 1$
$x - y = 3$

2. $x - y = 1$
$x + y = 5$

3. $3x - y = 4$
$6x - 2y = -8$

4. $x^2 + 4y^2 = 32$
$x + 2y = 0$

5. $xy = -4$
$4x - y = 8$

6. $4x^2 + y^2 = 4$
$x^2 - y^2 = 9$

7. $4x^2 + 9y^2 = 72$
$4x - 3y^2 = 0$

8. $2y^2 - x^2 = -1$
$4y^2 + x^2 = 25$

9. $x^2 + y^2 = 1$
$y^2 - 3x^2 = 5$

10. $3x^2 + 8y^2 = 21$
$x^2 + 4y^2 = 10$

In Exercises 11–20, solve the system of equations by the method of substitution.

11. $x + y = 1$
$x - y = 3$

12. $x + 2y = 8$
$3x - 4y = 4$

13. $x^2 + y^2 = 13$
$2x - y = 4$

14. $x^2 + 4y^2 = 32$
$x + 2y = 0$

15. $y^2 - x = 0$
$y - 4x = -3$

16. $xy = -4$
$4x - y = 8$

17. $x^2 - 2x + y^2 = 3$
$2x + y = 4$

18. $4x^2 + y^2 = 4$
$x - y = 3$

19. $xy = 1$
$x - y + 1 = 0$

20. $\dfrac{1}{2}x - \dfrac{3}{2}y = 4$
$\dfrac{3}{2}x + y = 1$

In Exercises 21–30, solve the system of equations by the method of elimination.

21. $x + 2y = 1$
    $5x + 2y = 13$

22. $x - 4y = -7$
    $2x + 3y = -8$

23. $25y^2 - 16x^2 = 400$
    $9y^2 - 4x^2 = 36$

24. $x^2 - y^2 = 3$
    $x^2 + y^2 = 5$

25. $2x^2 + 3y^2 = 30$
    $x - y^2 = -1$

26. $x^2 + y^2 + 2y = 9$
    $y - 2x = 4$

27. $2x + y = 4$
    $-6x - 3y = -8$

28. $2x + 3y = -2$
    $-3x - 5y = 4$

29. $y^2 - x^2 = -5$
    $3y^2 + x^2 = 21$

30. $x^2 + 4y^2 = 25$
    $4x^2 + y^2 = 25$

In Exercises 31–42, determine whether the system is consistent or inconsistent. If the system is consistent, find all the solutions.

31. $2x + 2y = 6$
    $3x + 3y = 6$

32. $2x + y = 2$
    $3x - y = 8$

33. $y^2 - 8x^2 = 9$
    $y^2 + 3x^2 = -31$

34. $4y^2 + 3x^2 = 24$
    $3y^2 - 2x^2 = 35$

35. $3x + 3y = 9$
    $2x + 2y = -6$

36. $x - 4y = -7$
    $2x - 8y = -4$

37. $3x - y = 18$
    $\frac{3}{2}x - \frac{1}{2}y = 9$

38. $2x + y = 6$
    $x + \frac{1}{2}y = 3$

39. $x^2 - 3xy - 2y - 2 = 0$
    $x - y - 2 = 0$

40. $3x^2 + 8y^2 = 20$
    $x^2 + 4y^2 = 10$

41. $2x - 2y = 4$
    $x - y = 8$

42. $2x - 3y = 8$
    $4x - 6y = 16$

Applications 6.1

1. The sum of the number of calories in a Big Mac and a Big N' Tasty from McDonald's is 1000. The difference in the number of calories in the hamburgers is 80. We know that Big Mac has the larger number of calories, how many calories are in each hamburger?

2. The average monthly combined cost of food and gasoline for the Gallagher family is $1560. If they spend five times as much for food as they do for gasoline, what is the average monthly cost of each?

3. Tracy bought 156 pieces of candy to give away on Halloween. She bought two kinds of candy, paying $0.25 apiece for one kind and $$0.20 a piece for the other. If she spent $36.20 for the candy, how many pieces of each kind did she buy?

4. A combined total of $20,000 is invested in two bonds that pay 4% and 5.5% simple interest. The annual interest is $920. How much is invested in each band?

5. Sherry has job offers from Boch Toyota and Herb Ford to sell cars. Boch Toyota offers her $35,000 per year plus 5% of her yearly sales. Herb Ford offers her $45,000 per year plus 2% of her yearly sales. How much must Sherry earn in yearly sales for the offer from Herb Ford to be the better offer?

6. Sharon local publishing company publishes *Sharon Weekly*. The production and setup costs are $50,000, and the cost of producing each newspaper is $1.25. Each newspaper sells for $2.50. Assume that x newspapers are published and sold.

   a. Write the total cost function and the revenue function.

b. Graph both functions from part (a) on the same coordinate plane.

c. How many newspapers must be sold to break even?

7. Suppose you are setting up a small business and have invested $5000 to produce an item that will sell for $5.99. If each unit can be produced for $2.00, how many unites must you sell to break even?

8. You have 300 feet of fencing to enclose two corrals of equal size. The combined area of the corrals is 500 square feet. Find the dimensions of each corral.

9. A hotel has 150 rooms. Those with kitchen facilities rent for $120 per night and those without kitchen facilities rent for $90 per night. On a night when the hotel was completely occupied, revenue was $15,900. How many of each type of room does the hotel have?

6.2   Applications: Word Problems

In the beginning of the previous section, we saw that it is possible to formulate and solve a word problem using two variables and a system of linear equations rather than one variable and a single linear equation. We now consider a number of word problems using this approach. (For additional practice, see Section 2.2 and try to formulate and solve those problems using two variables and a system of linear equations.)

Example 1   Applying Linear Systems
If 3 sulfa pills and 4 penicillin pills cost 69 cents, and 5 sulfa pills and 2 penicillin pills cost 73 cents, what is the cost of each type of pill?

Solution
Using two variables, we let

$$x = \text{the cost in cents of each sulfa pill}$$
$$y = \text{the cost in cents of each penicillin pill}$$

Then

$$3x + 4y = 69$$
$$5x + 2y = 73$$

We multiply the second equation by -2 and add to eliminate y.

$$
\begin{array}{r}
3x + 4y = 69 \\
-10x - 4y = -146 \\
\hline
-7x = -77 \\
x = 11
\end{array}
$$

Substituting into the first equation, we have

$$3(11) + 4y = 69$$
$$4y = 36$$
$$y = 9$$

Thus, each sulfa pill costs 11 cents, and each penicillin pill costs 9 cents.

Example 2   Applying Linear Systems

Swimming downstream, a swimmer can cover 2 kilometers in 15 minutes. The return trip upstream requires 20 minutes. What is the rate of the swimmer and of the current in kilometers per hour? (The rate of the swimmer is the swimmer's speed if there was no current.)

Solution

Let

$$x = \text{the rate of the swimmer in kilometers per hour}$$

$$y = \text{the rate of the current in kilometers per hour}$$

For swimming downstream, the rate of the current is added to the rate of the swimmer, so $x + y$ is the rate downstream. On the other hand, $x - y$ is the rate for swimming upstream. We display the information we have in the table, expressing time in hours.

Swimming	Rate	× Time	= Distance
Downstream	$x + y$	$\frac{1}{4}$	$\frac{1}{4}(x + y)$
Upstream	$x - y$	$\frac{1}{3}$	$\frac{1}{3}(x - y)$

Since distance upstream = distance downstream = 2 kilometers,

$$\frac{1}{4}(x + y) = 2$$
$$\frac{1}{3}(x - y) = 2$$

or equivalently,

$$x + y = 8$$
$$x - y = 6$$

Solving, we have

$$x = 7 \quad \text{rate of the swimmer}$$
$$y = 1 \quad \text{rate of the current}$$

Thus, the rate of the swimmer is 7 kilometers per hour, and the rate of the current is 1 kilometer per hour.

Example 3   Applying Linear Systems

The sum of a two-digit number and its units digit is 64, and the sum of the number and its tens digit is 62. Find the number.

Solution

The basic idea in solving digit problems is to note that if we let

$$t = \text{tens digit}$$

and

$$u = \text{units digit}$$

then

$$10t + u = \text{the two-digit number}$$

Then "the sum of a two-digit number and its units digit is 64" translates into

$$(10t + u) + u = 64 \quad \text{or} \quad 10t + 2u = 64$$

Also, "the sum of the number and its tens digit is 62" becomes

$$(10t + u) + t = 62 \quad \text{or} \quad 11t + u = 62$$

Solving, we find that $t = 5$ and $u = 7$. Hence, the number is 57.

Applications in Business and Economics: Break-Even Analysis

An important problem faced by a manufacturer is that of determining the **level of production,** that is, the number of units of the product to be manufactured during a given time period—a day, a week or a month. Suppose that

$$C = 400 + 2x \tag{1}$$

is the total cost in thousands of dollars of producing x units of the product. Thus, after setting up production at a cost of \$400,000, the manufacturer has an additional cost of \$2000 to make each unit.

Furthermore, suppose that

$$R = 4x \tag{2}$$

is the total revenue in thousands of dollars when x units of the product are sold. In other words, a revenue of \$4000 is earned from the sale of each unit. If all units that are manufactured are sold, the total profit P is the difference between total revenue and total cost.

$$P = R - C$$
$$= 4x - (400 + 2x)$$
$$= 2x - 400$$

The value of x for which $R = C$, where the profit is zero, is called the **break-even point.** Therefore, at that level of production and sales, the manufacturer neither makes money nor loses money. To find the break-even point, we set $R = C$. Using Equations (1) and (2), we obtain

$$400 + 2x = 4x$$
$$x = 200$$

Thus, the break-even point is 200 units.

The break-even point can also be obtained graphically as follows. Observe that Equations (1) and (2) are linear equations. The break-even point is the x-coordinate of the point where the two lines intersect. Figure 6 shows the lines and their point of intersection (200, 800). When 200 units of the product are made, the cost ($800,000) is exactly equal to the revenue, and the profit is $0. If $x > 200$, then $R > C$, so the manufacturer is making a profit. If $x < 200$, $R < C$ and the manufacturer is losing money.

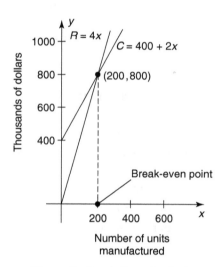

Figure 6   Break-Even Analysis

✔ Progress Check

A producer of photographic developer finds that the total weekly cost of producing x liters of developer is given in dollars by $C = 550 + 0.40x$. The manufacturer sells the product at $0.50 per liter.

a. What is the total revenue received when x liters of developer are sold?

b. Find the break-even point graphically.

c. What is the total revenue received at the break-even point?

Answers
a. $R = 0.50x$ b. 5500 liters   c. $2750

Applications in Business and Economics: Supply and Demand

A manufacturer of a product may set any price p (in dollars) for each unit of the product. If the price is too high, few people may buy the product. If the price is too low, so many people may want the product that the producer may not be able to satisfy demand. Thus, in setting price, the manufacturer must take into consideration the demand for the product as well as the supply.

Let S be the number of units that the manufacturer is willing to supply at the price p. Call S the **supply.** Generally, the value of S increases as p increases, that is, the manufacturer is willing to supply more of the product as the price p increases. Let D be the number of units of the product that consumers are willing to buy at the price p. Call D the **demand.** Generally, the value of D decreases as p increases, that is, consumers are willing to buy fewer units of the product as the price rises. For example, suppose that S and D are given by

$$S = 2p + 3 \tag{3}$$

$$D = -p + 12 \tag{4}$$

Equations (3) and (4) are linear equations, so they are equations of lines. (See Figure 7.) The price at which supply S and demand D are equal is called the **equilibrium price.** At this price, every unit that is supplied is purchased. Thus, there is neither a surplus nor a shortage. In Figure 7 the equilibrium price is $p = 3$. At this price, the number of units supplied equals the number of units demanded and is found by substituting into Equation (3): $S = 2(3) + 3 = 9$. This value can also be obtained by finding the ordinate at the point of intersection in Figure 7.

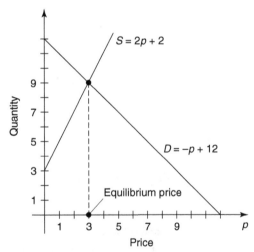

Figure 7   Break-Even Analysis

If we are in an economic system in which there is pure competition, the law of supply and demand states that the selling price of a product is its equilibrium price. That is, if the selling price was higher than the equilibrium price, consumers' reduced demand would leave the manufacturer with an unsold surplus. To sell this surplus, the manufacturer would be forced to reduce the selling price. If the selling price was below the equilibrium price, the increased demand would cause a shortage of the product, leading the manufacturer to raise the selling price.

In actual practice, the marketplace rarely operates under pure competition. Mathematical analysis of more realistic economic systems requires the use of more sophisticated equations.

Example 4   Applying Linear Systems

Suppose that supply and demand for ballpoint pens are given by

$$S = p + 5$$
$$D = -p + 7$$

a. Find the equilibrium price.

b. Find the number of pens sold at that price.

Solution

a. Figure 8 illustrates the graphical solution. The equilibrium price is $p = 1$. (Verify that algebraic methods yield the same solution.)

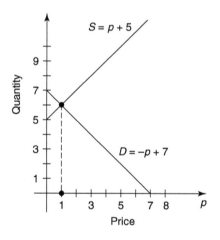

Figure 8   Figure for Example 4

b. When $p = 1$, the number of pens sold is $S = 1 + 5 = 6$, the value of the ordinate at the point of intersection.

✔ Progress Check

Suppose that supply and demand for radios are given by

$$S = 3p + 120$$
$$D = -p + 200$$

a. Find the equilibrium price.

b. Find the number of radios sold at that price.

Answers

a. 20   b. 180

Exercise Set 6.2

1. A pile of 40 coins consists of nickels and dimes. If the value of the coins is $2.75, how many of each type of coin are there?

2. An automatic vending machine in the post office sells a packet of 12 stamps for $3. There are 23-cent and 29-cent stamps in this packet. If there is no additional cost for using this machine, how many of each type of stamp are in the packet?

3. A photography store sells sampler A consisting of 6 rolls of color film and 4 rolls of black and white film for $21. It also sells sampler B, consisting of 4 rolls of color film and 6 rolls of black and white film for $19. What is the cost per roll of each type of film?

4. A hardware store sells power pack A, consisting of 4 D cells and 2 C cells for $1.70, and power pack B, consisting of 6 D cells and 4 C cells for $2.80. What is the price of each cell?

5. A fund manager invested $6000 in two types of bonds, A and B. Bond A, which is safer than bond B, pays annual interest of 8%, whereas bond B pays annual interest of 10%. If the total annual return on both investments is $520, how much was invested in each type of bond?

6. A trash removal company carries waste material in sealed containers weighing 4 kilograms and 3 kilograms. On a certain trip the company carries 30 containers weighing a total of 100 kilograms. How many of each type of container are there?

7. A paper firm makes rolls of paper 12 inches wide and 15 inches wide by cutting a sheet that is 180 inches wide. Suppose that a total of 14 rolls of paper are to be cut without any waste. How many of each type of roll will be made?

8. An animal-feed producer mixes two types of grain, A and B. Each unit of grain A contains 2 grams of fat and 80 calories, and each unit of grain B contains 3 grams of fat and 60 calories. If the producer wants the final product to provide 18 grams of fat and 480 calories, how much of each type of grain should be used?

9. A supermarket mixes coffee that sells for $1.20 per pound with coffee that sells for $1.80 per pound to

obtain 24 pounds of coffee selling for $1.60 per pound. How much of each type of coffee should be used?

10. An airplane flying against the wind covers a distance of 3000 kilometers in 6 hours. The return trip, with the aid of the wind, takes 5 hours. What is the speed of the airplane in still air, and what is the speed of the wind?

11. A cyclist traveling against the wind covers a distance of 45 miles in 4 hours. The return trip, with the aid of the wind, takes 3 hours. What is the speed of the cyclist in still air, and what is the speed of the wind?

12. The sum of a two-digit number and its units digit is 20, and the sum of the number and its tens digit is 16. Find the number.

13. The sum of the digits of a two-digit number is 7. If the digits are reversed, the resulting number exceeds the given number by 9. Find the number.

14. The sum of the units digit and 3 times the tens digit of a two-digit number is 14, and the sum of the tens digit and twice the units digit is 18. Find the number.

15. A health food shop mixes nuts and raisins into a snack pack. How many pounds of nuts, selling for $2.00 per pound, and how many pounds of raisins, selling for $1.50 per pound, must be mixed to produce a 50-pound mixture selling for $1.80 per pound?

16. A movie theater charges $3.00 admission for an adult and $1.50 for a child. On a particular day 600 tickets were sold and the total revenue received was $1350. How many tickets of each type were sold?

17. A moped dealer selling a model A and a model B moped has $18,000 in inventory. The profit on a model A moped is 12%, and the profit on a model B moped is 18%. If the profit on the entire stock is 16%, how much was invested in each model?

18. The cost of sending a telegram is determined as follows: there is a flat charge for the first 10 words and a uniform rate for each additional word. Suppose that an 18-word telegram costs $1.94 and a 22-word telegram costs $2.16. Find the cost of the first 10 words and the rate for each additional word.

19. A certain epidemic is treated by a combination of the drugs Epiline I and Epiline II. Suppose that each unit

of Epiline I contains 1 milligram of factor X and 2 milligrams of factor Y, whereas each unit of Epiline II contains 2 milligrams of factor X and 3 milligrams of factor Y. Successful treatment of the disease calls for 13 milligrams of factor X and 22 milligrams of factor Y. How many units of Epiline I and Epiline II should be administered to a patient?

20. (**Break-even analysis**) An animal-feed manufacturer finds that the weekly cost of making x kilograms of feed is given in dollars by $C = 2000 + 0.50x$ and that the revenue received from selling the feed is given by $R = 0.75x$.

   a. Find the break-even point graphically and algebraically.

   b. What is the total revenue at the break-even point?

21. (**Break-even analysis**) A small manufacturer of a new solar device finds that the annual cost of making x units is given in dollars by $C = 24,000 + 55x$. Each device sells for $95.

   a. What is the total revenue received when x devices are sold?

   b. Find the break-even point graphically and algebraically.

   c. What is the total revenue received at the break-even point?

22. (**Supply and demand**) A manufacturer of calculators finds that the supply and demand are given by

$$S = 0.5p + 0.5$$
$$D = -2p + 8$$

   a. Find the equilibrium price.

   b. What is the number of calculators sold at this price?

23. (**Supply and demand**) A manufacturer of mopeds finds that the supply and demand are given by

$$S = 2p + 10$$
$$D = -p + 22$$

   a. Find the equilibrium price.

   b. What is the number of mopeds sold at this price?

24. Find the dimensions of a rectangle with an area of 30 square feet and a perimeter of 22 feet.

25. Find two numbers whose product is 20 and whose sum is 9.

26. Find two numbers the sum of whose squares is 65 and whose sum is 11.

27. A pile of 34 coins worth $4.10 consists of nickels and quarters. Find the number of each type of coin.

28. Car A can travel 20 kilometers per hour faster than car B. If car A travels 240 kilometers in the same time that car B travels 200 kilometers, what is the speed of each car?

29. How many pounds of nuts worth $2.10 per pound and how many pounds of raisins worth $0.90 per pound must be mixed to obtain a mixture of 2 pounds that is worth $1.62 per pound?

30. A part of $8000 was invested at an annual interest of 7% and the remainder at 8%. If the total interest received at the end of 1 year is $590, how much was invested at each rate?

31. During World War II, the owner of a service station sold 1325 gallons of gasoline and collected 200 ration tickets. If type A ration tickets are used to purchase 10 gallons of gasoline and type B are used to purchase 1 gallon of gasoline, how many of each type of ration ticket did the station collect?

32. A bank is paying 12% annual interest on 1-year certificates, and treasury notes are paying 10% annual interest. An investor received $620 interest at the end of 1 year by investing a total of $6000. How much was invested at each rate?

33. The sum of the squares of the length and the width of a rectangle is 100 square meters. If the area of the rectangle is 48 square meters, find the length of each side of the rectangle.

Applications 6.2

1. A restaurant manager wants to purchase 300 sets of dishes. One design costs $15 per set, while another costs $25 per set. Her budget is $5500, how many of each design should be ordered?

2. One group of students purchased 10 hot dogs and 7 soft drinks at a cost of $34.30. A second group bought 9 hot dogs and 9 drinks at a cost of $36.00. What is the cost of a single hot dog? What is the cost of a single soft drink?

3. Tracy has $500,000 to invest for her retirement. As her financial planner, you recommend that she diversify into two investments: Treasury bills that yield 4% simple interest, and corporate bonds that yield 10% simple interest. Tracy wishes to earn $21,000 per year in income. How much money should Tracy place in each investment?

4. A movie theater charges $11.50 for adults and $8.00 for senior citizens. One day the theater sold 985 tickets and collected $9630.00 in receipts. How many adults and senior citizens went to the theater that day?

5. Boston Symphony Hall has 650 seats, divided into orchestra and balcony seating. Orchestra seats sell for $91 and balcony seats for $28. If all seats are sold, the gross revenue to Boston Symphony Hall is $30,800. How many are there of each kind of seat?

6. Three medium eggs and two cups of ice cream contain 700 milligrams of cholesterol. One medium egg and three cups of ice cream contain 700 milligrams of cholesterol. Determine the cholesterol content in each item.

7. One pan pizza and two beef burritos provide 2100 calories. Three pan pizzas and one beef burritos provide 3300 calories. Find the caloric content of each item.

8. When an airplane flies with the wind, it travels 900 miles in 4 hours. Against the wind, it takes 6 hours to cover the same distance. Find the plane's rate in still air and the rate of the wind.

6.3   Systems of Linear Equations in Three Unknowns

The method of substitution and the method of elimination can both be applied to systems of linear equations in three unknowns and, more generally, to systems of linear equations in any number of unknowns. There is yet another method, ideally suited for computers, which we will now apply to solving linear systems in three unknowns.

Gaussian Elimination and Triangular Form

In solving equations, we found it convenient to transform an equation into an equivalent equation having the same solution set. Similarly, we can attempt to transform a system of equations into another system, called an **equivalent system**, that has the same solution set. In particular, the objective of **Gaussian Elimination** is to transform a linear system into an equivalent system in triangular form, such as

$$3x - y + 3z = -11$$
$$2y + z = 2$$
$$2z = -4$$

A linear system is in **triangular form** when the only nonzero coefficient of x appears in the first equation, the only nonzero coefficients of y appear in the first and second equations, and so on.

Note that when a linear system is in triangular form, the last equation immediately yields the value of an unknown. In our example, we see that

$$2z = -4$$
$$z = -2$$

Substituting $z = -2$ into the second equation yields

$$2y + (-2) = 2$$
$$y = 2$$

Finally, substituting $z = -2$ and $y = 2$ into the first equation yields

$$3x - (2) + 3(-2) = -11$$
$$3x = -3$$
$$x = -1$$

Therefore, when a linear system is in triangular form, the process of **back-substitution** allows us to solve the system quickly. The challenge is to find a means of transforming a linear system into this form.

Operations that transform a system of linear equations into an equivalent system are:

1. Interchange any two equations.

2. Multiply an equation by a nonzero constant.

3. Replace an equation by the sum of itself plus a constant times another equation.

Using these operations we can demonstrate the method of Gaussian Elimination.

Example 1   Solving a Linear System by Gaussian Elimination

Solve the linear system

$$\begin{aligned} 2y - z &= -5 \\ x - 2y + 2z &= 9 \\ 2x - 3y + 3z &= 14 \end{aligned}$$

Solution

Gaussian Elimination

Step 1. If necessary, interchange equations to obtain a nonzero coefficient for x in the first equation.

Step 1. Interchanging the first two equations yields

$$\begin{aligned} x - 2y + 2z &= 9 \\ 2y - z &= -5 \\ 2x - 3y + 3z &= 14 \end{aligned}$$

Step 2. Replace the second equation with the sum of itself and an appropriate multiple of the first equation, so that the result has a zero coefficient for x.

Step 2. The coefficient of x in the second equation is already 0.

Step 3. Replace the third equation with the sum of itself and an appropriate multiple of the first equation, so that the result has a zero coefficient for x.

Step 4. Apply the procedures of *Steps 1–3* to the second and third equations and the coefficients of y and z, respectively.

Step 5. The system is now in triangular form. The solution is obtained by back-substitution.

Step 3. Replace the third equation with the sum of itself plus -2 times the first equation.

$$x - 2y + 2z = 9$$
$$2y - z = -5$$
$$y - z = -4$$

Step 4. Replace the third equation with the sum of itself and $-\frac{1}{2}$ times the second equation.

$$x - 2y + 2z = 9$$
$$2y - z = -5$$
$$-\frac{1}{2}z = -\frac{3}{2}$$

Step 5. From the third equation,

$$-\frac{1}{2}z = -\frac{3}{2}$$
$$z = 3$$

Substituting this value of z into the second equation, we have

$$2y - (3) = -5$$
$$y = -1$$

Substituting for y and for z into the first equation, we have

$$x - 2(-1) + 2(3) = 9$$
$$x + 8 = 9$$
$$x = 1$$

The solution is $x = 1$, $y = -1$, $z = 3$.

Warning

When solving a system of linear equations, we must be sure to align the unknowns. For example, to solve the system

$$-z + 2y = -5$$
$$-2y + x + 2z = 9$$
$$2x - 3y + 3z = 14$$

we rewrite it as

$$2y - z = -5$$
$$x - 2y + 2z = 9$$
$$2x - 3y + 3z = 14$$

Observe that this is the linear system in Example 1.

✔ **Progress Check**

Solve by Gaussian Elimination.

a. $2x - 4y + 2z = 1$ b. $-2x + 3y - 12z = -17$
   $3x + y + 3z = 5$ $3x - y - 15z = 11$
     $x - y - 2z = -8$ $-x + 5y + 3z = -9$

Answers

a. $x = -\dfrac{3}{2}, y = \dfrac{1}{2}, z = 3$ b. $x = 5, y = -1, z = \dfrac{1}{3}$

Consistent and Inconsistent Systems

The graph of a linear equation in three unknowns is a plane in three-dimensional space. A system of three linear equations in three unknowns corresponds to three planes. If the planes intersect in a point *P*, as shown in Figure 9(a), then the coordinates of the point *P* are the unique solution of the system, and this can be found by Gaussian Elimination. In Figure 9(b), the coordinates of *each* point of the line *L* is a solution of the system. One case where there is no solution is shown in Figure 9(c). (See the presentation in Figure 3.)

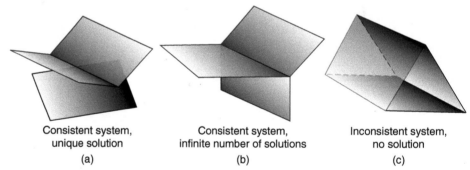

Consistent system,   Consistent system,   Inconsistent system,
unique solution   infinite number of solutions   no solution
(a)   (b)   (c)

Figure 9   Possible Situations with Three Linear Equations and Three Unknowns

---

Consistent and Inconsistent Systems

• A **consistent system** of equations has one or more solutions. (See Figures 3(a), 3(b), 9(a) and 9(b).) It has an infinite number of solutions if Gaussian Elimination yields an equation of the form

$$0x + 0y + 0z = 0$$

• An **inconsistent system** of equations has no solutions. (See Figures 3(c) and 9(c).) If Gaussian Elimination yields an equation of the form

$$0x + 0y + 0z = c, \quad c \neq 0$$

then the system is inconsistent.

Example 2   Consistent System

Solve the linear system.

$$x - 2y + 2z = -4$$
$$x + y - 7z = 8$$
$$-x - 4y + 16z = -20$$

Solution

Replacing the second equation by itself minus the first equation, and replacing the third equation by itself plus the first equation, we have

$$x - 2y + 2z = -4$$
$$3y - 9z = 12$$
$$-6y + 18z = -24$$

Replacing the third equation of the last system by itself plus 2 times the second equation results in the system

$$x - 2y + 2z = -4$$
$$3y - 9z = 12$$
$$0x + 0y + 0z = 0$$

The last equation indicates that the system is consistent. It has an infinite number of solutions. If we solve the second equation of the last system for y, we have

$$y = 3z + 4$$

Now solving the first equation for x, we have

$$x = 2y - 2z - 4$$

Substituting for y,

$$x = 2(3z + 4) - 2z - 4$$
$$x = 4z + 4$$

The equations

$$x = 4z + 4$$
$$y = 3z + 4$$

yield a solution of the original system for every real value of z. For example, if $z = 0$, then $x = 4$, $y = 4$, $z = 0$ satisfies the original system; if $z = -2$, then $x = -4$, $y = -2$, $z = -2$ is another solution.

✔ **Progress Check**

a. Verify that the linear system

$$x - 2y + z = 3$$
$$2x + y - 2z = -1$$
$$-x - 8y + 7z = 5$$

is inconsistent.

b. Verify that the linear system

$$2x + y + 2z = 1$$
$$x - 4y + 7z = -4$$
$$x - y + 3z = -1$$

has an infinite number of solutions.

Exercise Set 6.3

In Exercises 1–18, solve by Gaussian Elimination. Indicate if the system is inconsistent or has an infinite number of solutions.

1. $x + 2y + 3z = -6$
   $2x - 3y - 4z = 15$
   $3x + 4y + 5z = -8$

2. $2x + 3y + 4z = -12$
   $x - 2y + z = -5$
   $3x + y + 2z = 1$

3. $x + y + z = 1$
   $x + y - 2z = 3$
   $2x + y + z = 2$

4. $2x - y + z = 3$
   $x - 3y + z = 4$
   $-5x - 2z = -5$

5. $x + y + z = 2$
   $x - y + 2z = 3$
   $3x + 5y + 2z = 6$

6. $x + y + z = 0$
   $x + y = 3$
   $y + z = 1$

7. $x + 2y + z = 7$
   $x + 2y + 3z = 11$
   $2x + y + 4z = 12$

8. $4x + 2y - z = 5$
   $3x + 3y + 6z = 1$
   $5x + y - 8z = 8$

9. $x + y + z = 2$
   $x + 2y + z = 3$
   $x + y - z = 2$

10. $x + y - z = 2$
    $x + 2y + z = 3$
    $x + y + 4z = 3$

11. $2x + y + 3z = 8$
    $-x + y + z = 10$
    $x + y + z = 12$

12. $2x - 3z = 4$
    $x + 4y - 5z = -6$
    $3x + 4y - z = -2$

13. $x + 3y + 7z = 1$
    $3x - y - 5z = 9$
    $2x + y + z = 4$

14. $2x - y + z = 2$
    $3x + y + 2z = 3$
    $x + y - z = -1$

15. $x - 2y + 3z = -2$
    $x - 5y + 9z = 4$
    $2x - y = 6$

16. $x + 2y - 2z = 8$
    $5y - z = 6$
    $-2x + y + 3z = -2$

17. $z - 2y + x = -5$
    $z + 2x = -10$
    $y - z = 15$

18. $-3z + 2y = 4$
    $2z + x = -2$
    $-8y + x + 14z = -18$

19. A special low-calorie diet consists of dishes A, B and C. Each unit of A has 2 grams of fat, 1 gram of carbohydrate and 3 grams of protein. Each unit of B has 1 gram of fat, 2 grams of carbohydrate and 1 gram of protein. Each unit of C has 1 gram of fat, 2 grams of carbohydrate and 3 grams of protein. The diet must provide exactly 10 grams of fat, 14 grams of carbohydrate and 18 grams of protein. How much of each dish should be used?

20. A furniture manufacturer makes chairs, coffee tables and dining room tables. Each chair requires 2 minutes of sanding, 2 minutes of staining and 4 minutes of var-

nishing. Each coffee table requires 5 minutes of sanding, 4 minutes of staining and 3 minutes of varnishing. Each dining room table requires 5 minutes of sanding, 4 minutes of staining and 6 minutes of varnishing. The sanding bench is available 6 hours per day, the staining bench 5 hours per day and the varnishing bench 6 hours per day. How many of each type of furniture can be made if all facilities are used to capacity?

21. A manufacturer produces 12-inch, 16-inch and 19-inch television sets that require assembly, testing and packing. Each 12-inch set requires 45 minutes to assemble, 30 minutes to test and 10 minutes to package. Each 16-inch set requires 1 hour to assemble, 45 minutes to test and 15 minutes to package. Each 19-inch set requires 1.5 hours to assemble, 1 hour to test and 15 minutes to package. If the assembly line operates for 17.75 hours per day, the test facility is used for 12.5 hours per day and the packing equipment is used for 3.75 hours per day, how many of each type of set can be produced?

22. Recall that a second degree polynomial can be written as

$$y = a_2x^2 + a_1x + a_0$$

Suppose you want to model the following data by a quadratic function: $(0, 1)$, $(3, 16)$, and $(-1, 8)$. Proceed by substituting the given values for x and y into the standard form. This will give you three equations with three unknowns a_2, a_1, a_0. Solve this system, then use your solution to write the quadratic polynomial that fits this data.

23. Repeat Exercise 22 for the following data points: $(1, 11)$, $(2, 24)$, $(-2, -4)$.

24. Use your graphing calculator's MATRIX features to fit a quadratic polynomial to the data $(1, 0.8)$, $(2, 0.9)$, $(-1, 0.3)$.

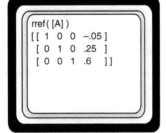

Applications 6.3

1. Boston Symphony Hall has 650 seats, divided into orchestra, main, and balcony seating. Orchestra seats sell for $91, main seats for $54, and balcony seats for $28. If all seats are sold, the gross revenue to Boston Symphony Hall is $32,850. If all the main and balcony seats are sold, but only half the orchestra seats are sold, the gross revenue is $26,025. How many are there of each kind of seat?

2. A movie theater charges $11.50 for adults, $5.50 for children, and $8.00 for senior citizens. One day the theater sold 1245 tickets and collected $10,400.00 in receipts. Twice as many adults' tickets were sold as senior citizens' tickets. How many adults, children, and senior citizens went to the theater that day?

3. Tracy has $500,000 to invest for her retirement. As her financial planner, you recommend that she diversify into three investments: Treasury bills that yield 4% simple interest, government bonds that yield 5% simple interest, and corporate bonds that yield 10% simple interest. Tracy wishes to earn $21,000 per year in income. Also, Tracy wants her investment in Treasury bills to be $9,000 more than her investment in corporate bonds. How much money should Tracy place in each investment?

4. One group of customers bought 10 deluxe hamburgers, 7 orders of small fries, and 6 large colas for $61.43. A second group ordered 10 deluxe hamburgers, 9 orders of small fries, and 6 large colas for $65.41. A third group ordered 5 deluxe hamburgers, 8 orders of small fries, and 5 large colas for $43.87. Determine the price of each food item.

5. A box the coins contains $112 in nickels, dimes, and quarters. If there are twice as many nickels as quarters and a total of 1000 coins together, how many of each type of coin are in the box?

6. A college algebra class of 20 students at Curry College was made up of people who were 18, 19, and 20 years of age. The average of their ages was 18.6 years. How many of each age were in the class if the number of 18-year-olds was 4 more than the combined number of 19- and 20-year-olds?

7. Jackie worked 50 hours one week and was paid at three different rates. She earned $29.50 per hour for her normal daytime work, $35.50 per hour for her night work, and $40.00 per hour for her holiday work. If her total gross wages for the week were $1587.50 and the number of regular daytime hours she worked exceeded the combined hours of night and holiday work by twenty hours, how many hours of each category of work did Jackie perform?

6.4   Applications: Partial Fractions

Students of algebra are taught how to add fractions, such as

$$\frac{2}{x-1} + \frac{3}{x+2} = \frac{5x+1}{(x-1)(x+2)}$$

Surprisingly, there is an important application of integral calculus that requires the *inverse* procedure. This procedure requires that we solve a system of linear equations.

Our objective in this section is to write a rational function $\frac{P(x)}{Q(x)}$ as a sum of fractions, each of which is called a **partial fraction**. Now we need only consider the situation where $\frac{P(x)}{Q(x)}$ is a **proper fraction**, that is, where the degree of $P(x)$ is less than the degree of $Q(x)$. If it is not a proper fraction, then it is called an **improper fraction**, and we divide through by $Q(x)$. For example,

$$\frac{2x^3 - x^2 - x + 1}{x^2 - 1}$$

is an improper fraction. We use long division to divide through by $x^2 - 1$ as follows:

$$
\begin{array}{r}
2x - 1 \qquad \text{quotient} \\
x^2 - 1 \overline{)\,2x^3 - x^2 - x + 1} \\
\underline{2x^3 \qquad\; - 2x} \\
-x^2 + x + 1 \\
\underline{-x^2 \qquad + 1} \\
x \qquad \text{remainder}
\end{array}
$$

Therefore

$$\frac{2x^3 - x^2 - x + 1}{x^2 - 1} = 2x - 1 + \frac{x}{x^2 - 1}$$

We can now work with the proper fraction $\frac{x}{x^2-1}$.

The procedure for partial-fraction decomposition of the rational function $\frac{P(x)}{Q(x)}$ begins with factoring the denominator $Q(x)$. As we showed in Chapter 4 (as a corollary to the Conjugate Zeros Theorem), every polynomial with real coefficients can be written as a product of linear and quadratic factors with real coefficients, such that the quadratic factors have no real zeros. Such quadratic factors are said to be *irreducible* over the reals. For example,

$$Q(x) = x^3 - x^2 + 2x - 2 = (x-1)(x^2+2)$$

where the quadratic factor $x^2 + 2$ cannot be decomposed into linear factors with real coefficients, since the polynomial $x^2 + 2$ has no real zeros.

Having factored $Q(x)$ in this manner, we collect the repeated factors so that $Q(x)$ is the product of distinct factors of the forms

$$(ax + b)^m \quad \text{and} \quad (ax^2 + bx + c)^n$$

The following rules tell us the format of the partial-fraction decomposition of $\frac{P(x)}{Q(x)}$.

Rules for Partial-Fraction Decomposition

Rule 1. Linear Factors

For each distinct factor of the form $(ax + b)^m$ in the denominator $Q(x)$, introduce the sum of m partial fractions

$$\frac{A_1}{ax + b} + \frac{A_2}{(ax + b)^2} + \cdots + \frac{A_m}{(ax + b)^m}$$

where $A_1, A_2, \ldots, A_m$ are constants.

Rule 2. Quadratic Factors

For each distinct factor of the form $(ax^2 + bx + c)^n$ in the denominator $Q(x)$, introduce the sum of n partial fractions

$$\frac{A_1 x + B_1}{ax^2 + bx + c} + \frac{A_2 x + B_2}{(ax^2 + bx + c)^2} + \cdots + \frac{A_n x + B_n}{(ax^2 + bx + c)^n}$$

where $A_1, A_2, \ldots, A_n$ and $B_1, B_2, \ldots, B_n$ are constants.

We must now find a method to determine the value of these constants. The constants used in *Rule 1* are different from the constants used in *Rule 2*.

Example 1 Partial-Fraction Decomposition: Linear Factors

Find the partial-fraction decomposition of

$$\frac{x + 5}{x^2 + x - 2}$$

Solution

Factoring the denominator gives us

$$\frac{x + 5}{x^2 + x - 2} = \frac{x + 5}{(x + 2)(x - 1)}$$

The denominator consists of linear factors. By *Rule 1*, each linear factor introduces one term.

factor	$x + 2$	$x - 1$
term	$\dfrac{A}{x + 2}$	$\dfrac{B}{x - 1}$

The partial-fraction decomposition is then

$$\frac{x + 5}{(x + 2)(x - 1)} = \frac{A}{x + 2} + \frac{B}{x - 1}$$

To solve for the constants A and B, we clear fractions by multiplying both sides by $(x + 2)(x - 1)$ to yield

$$x + 5 = A(x - 1) + B(x + 2)$$

This last equation may be solved for A and B by substituting different values for x. Sometimes, we may choose a value for x that will cause an unknown to "disappear." Setting $x = 1$ gives us

$$6 = 3B \quad \text{or} \quad B = 2$$

Setting $x = -2$ yields

$$3 = -3A \quad \text{or} \quad A = -1$$

Substituting these values for A and B, we arrive at the partial-fraction decomposition

$$\frac{x + 5}{(x + 2)(x - 1)} = \frac{-1}{x + 2} + \frac{2}{x - 1}$$

Verify that this is indeed an *identity*. Furthermore, verify that you obtain the same solution for A and B using different values of x. ▨

Example 2 Repeated Linear Factors

Find the partial-fraction decomposition of

$$\frac{x^2 - 2x - 9}{x(x + 3)^2}$$

Solution
The denominator is already in factored form and consists of the linear factor x and the repeated linear factor $x + 3$. By *Rule 1*, the factor x introduces one term

$$\frac{A}{x}$$

and the factor $x + 3$ introduces two terms ($m = 2$)

$$\frac{B}{x + 3} \quad \text{and} \quad \frac{C}{(x + 3)^2}$$

The partial-fraction decomposition is then

$$\frac{x^2 - 2x - 9}{x(x + 3)^2} = \frac{A}{x} + \frac{B}{x + 3} + \frac{C}{(x + 3)^2}$$

Clearing fractions by multiplying both sides by $x(x + 3)^2$ yields

$$x^2 - 2x - 9 = A(x + 3)^2 + Bx(x + 3) + Cx \qquad (1)$$

Setting $x = -3$ in Equation (1) allows us to solve for C.

$$6 = -3C \quad \text{or} \quad C = -2$$

Setting $x = 0$ in Equation (1) allows us to solve for A.

$$-9 = 9A \quad \text{or} \quad A = -1$$

Expanding the right-hand side of Equation (1) and collecting terms in the powers of x, we have

$$x^2 - 2x - 9 = (A + B)x^2 + (6A + 3B + C)x + 9A \qquad (2)$$

Substituting $A = -1$ and $C = -2$ in Equation (2) yields

$$x^2 - 2x - 9 = (B - 1)x^2 + (3B - 8)x - 9 \qquad (3)$$

Since the solution must be an identity, the coefficients of the same powers of x on both sides of Equation (3) must be equal. Equating the coefficients of the terms in x^2, we have

$$1 = B - 1 \quad \text{or} \quad B = 2$$

The same result is obtained by equating the coefficients of the terms in x. Alternatively, we may substitute another value for x in Equation (3) and obtain an equation in B yielding the same result, $B = 2$.

Therefore, the partial-fraction decomposition is

$$\frac{x^2 - 2x - 9}{x(x + 3)^2} = -\frac{1}{x} + \frac{2}{x + 3} - \frac{2}{(x + 3)^2}$$

Warning

For the rational function

$$\frac{2x - 1}{x^2(x^2 + 1)}$$

the factor x^2 in the denominator must be treated as the repeated *linear* factor $(x - 0)^2$. The partial-fraction decomposition has the structure

$$\frac{2x - 1}{x^2(x^2 + 1)} = \frac{A}{x} + \frac{B}{x^2} + \frac{Cx + D}{x^2 + 1}$$

Example 3   Linear and Quadratic Factors

Find the partial-fraction decomposition of

$$\frac{x^2 - 5x + 1}{2x^3 - x^2 + 2x - 1}$$

Solution

First we factor the denominator. By the factor theorem, $x - r$ is a factor of

$$Q(x) = 2x^3 - x^2 + 2x - 1$$

if and only if r is a zero of $Q(x)$. The Rational Zero Theorem tells us that the possible rational roots are 1, -1, $\frac{1}{2}$ and $-\frac{1}{2}$. Using the condensed form of synthetic division to test these possible roots

$$
\begin{array}{r|rrr|r}
 & 2 & -1 & 2 & -1 \\
\hline
1 & 2 & 1 & 3 & 2 \\
-1 & 2 & -3 & 5 & -6 \\
\frac{1}{2} & 2 & 0 & 2 & 0 \\
\end{array}
$$

$$\underbrace{\qquad\qquad\qquad}_{}$$

coefficients of quotient polynomial

we see that $Q(\frac{1}{2}) = 0$, so $x = \frac{1}{2}$ is a zero of $Q(x)$. Consequently $(x - \frac{1}{2})$ is a factor of $Q(x)$, and $2x^2 + 2 = 0$ is seen to be the deflated equation. Since $2x^2 + 2 = 2(x^2 + 1)$, we may write

$$Q(x) = \left(x - \frac{1}{2}\right)(2)(x^2 + 1)$$

To avoid fractions, multiply the first two factors to obtain

$$Q(x) = (2x - 1)(x^2 + 1)$$

By *Rule 1*, the factor $2x - 1$ introduces a term of the form

$$\frac{A}{2x - 1}$$

and by *Rule 2*, the factor $x^2 + 1$ introduces a term of the form

$$\frac{Bx + C}{x^2 + 1}$$

Then

$$\frac{x^2 - 5x + 1}{(2x - 1)(x^2 + 1)} = \frac{A}{2x - 1} + \frac{Bx + C}{x^2 + 1}$$

Multiplying by $(2x - 1)(x^2 + 1)$, we have

$$x^2 - 5x + 1 = A(x^2 + 1) + (Bx + C)(2x - 1)$$

Setting $x = \frac{1}{2}$, we obtain

$$-\frac{5}{4} = \frac{5}{4}A \quad \text{or} \quad A = -1$$

Setting $x = 0$ yields

$$1 = A - C$$

Since $A = -1$, we have

$$1 = -1 - C$$
$$C = -2$$

Setting $x = 1$, we obtain

$$-3 = 2A + B + C$$

Since $A = -1$ and $C = -2$,

$$-3 = -2 + B - 2$$
$$B = 1$$

Therefore, the partial-fraction decomposition is

$$\frac{x^2 - 5x + 1}{2x^3 - x^2 + 2x - 1} = \frac{-1}{2x - 1} + \frac{x - 2}{x^2 + 1}$$

Example 4   Linear and Repeated Quadratic Factors

Find the partial-fraction decomposition of

$$\frac{x^2 - 2x}{(x + 2)(x^2 + 4)^2}$$

Solution

The linear factor $x + 2$ introduces one term of the form

$$\frac{A}{x + 2}$$

The quadratic factor $x^2 + 4$ has no real roots. By *Rule 2*, this irreducible quadratic factor introduces two terms ($n = 2$) of the form

$$\frac{Bx + C}{x^2 + 4} \quad \text{and} \quad \frac{Dx + E}{(x^2 + 4)^2}$$

We then have to solve

$$\frac{x^2 - 2x}{(x + 2)(x^2 + 4)^2} = \frac{A}{x + 2} + \frac{Bx + C}{x^2 + 4} + \frac{Dx + E}{(x^2 + 4)^2}$$

for values of A, B, C, D and E that will produce an identity. Multiplying by $(x + 2)(x^2 + 4)^2$ yields

$$x^2 - 2x = A(x^2 + 4)^2 + (Bx + C)(x + 2)(x^2 + 4) + (Dx + E)(x + 2) \tag{4}$$

Setting $x = -2$ enables us to solve for A.

$$8 = 64A \quad \text{or} \quad A = \frac{1}{8}$$

A methodical way to solve for B, C, D and E is to successively equate the coefficients of the powers x^4, x^3 and x^2 in the left-hand and right-hand sides of Equation (4).

Coefficients of x^4: $0 = A + B$ or $B = -A = -\dfrac{1}{8}$

Coefficients of x^3: $0 = 2B + C$ or $C = -2B = \dfrac{1}{4}$

Coefficients of x^2: $1 = 8A + 4B + 2C + D$

$$1 = 1 - \frac{1}{2} + \frac{1}{2} + D$$

$$D = 0$$

To find E, we may equate the coefficients of x or the constant terms. Choosing the latter approach,

$$0 = 16A + 8C + 2E$$

$$0 = 2 + 2 + 2E$$

$$E = -2$$

Alternatively, we may substitute four other values for x in Equation (4) obtaining four linear equations in B, C, D and E. This also yields the same solution. (Verify this by letting $x = 0$, $x = 1$, $x = 2$ and $x = 3$.)

The partial-fraction decomposition is

$$\frac{x^2 - 2x}{(x + 2)(x^2 + 4)^2} = \frac{\dfrac{1}{8}}{x + 2} + \frac{-\dfrac{1}{8}x + \dfrac{1}{4}}{x^2 + 4} + \frac{-2}{(x^2 + 4)^2}$$

Exercise Set 6.4

Find the partial-fraction decomposition of each of the following.

1. $\dfrac{2x - 11}{(x + 2)(x - 3)}$

2. $\dfrac{1}{x^2 + 3x + 2}$

3. $\dfrac{3x - 2}{6x^2 - 5x + 1}$

4. $\dfrac{2x + 1}{x^2 - 1}$

5. $\dfrac{x^2 + x + 2}{x^3 - x}$

6. $\dfrac{3x - 14}{(x - 3)(x^2 - 4)}$

7. $\dfrac{3x - 2}{x^3 + 2x^2}$

8. $\dfrac{4x^2 - 5x + 2}{2x^3 - x^2}$

9. $\dfrac{x^2 - x + 2}{(x - 1)(x + 1)^2}$

10. $\dfrac{3x - 1}{x(x - 1)^3}$

11. $\dfrac{1 - 2x}{x^3 + 4x}$

12. $\dfrac{x^2 - 2x + 1}{x^3 + 2x^2 + 2x}$

13. $\dfrac{2x^3 - x^2 + x}{(x^2 + 3)^2}$

14. $\dfrac{x^2 + 2x + 10}{x^3 - 2x^2 + 2x - 4}$

15. $\dfrac{-x}{x^3 - 2x^2 - 4x - 1}$

16. $\dfrac{x^3 - 2x^2 + 1}{x^4 + 2x^2 + 1}$

17. $\dfrac{x^4 - x^2 - 9}{(x + 1)(x^2 + 2)^2}$

18. $\dfrac{-x^3 - x^2 + 5x + 1}{(2x - 1)(x^2 + 1)^2}$

19. $\dfrac{x^4 + x^3 + x^2 + 3x - 2}{(x + 1)(x^2 + 1)}$

20. $\dfrac{x^3 - 5x + 5}{(x - 1)^3}$

21. *Mathematics in Writing*: Suppose you are given a rational expression and asked to rewrite it as the sum of several other rational expressions, each one having a numerator which is constant. Is it always possible to do this? Under what circumstances would this task be easy? Difficult?

6.5   Systems of Linear Inequalities

Graphing Linear Inequalities

When we draw the graph of a linear equation, say

$$y = 2x - 1$$

we see that the graph of the line divides the plane into two regions, which we call **half-planes.** (See Figure 10.) If we replace the equal sign in $y = 2x - 1$ with any of the symbols, $<, >, \leq$ or $\geq$, we have a **linear inequality in two variables.** By the **graph of a linear inequality,** such as

$$y < 2x - 1$$

we mean the set of all points whose coordinates satisfy the inequality. Thus, the point $(4, 2)$ lies on the graph of $y < 2x - 1$, since

$$2 < (2)(4) - 1$$
$$2 < 7$$

is true. However, the point $(1, 5)$ does *not* lie on the graph of $y < 2x - 1$ since

$$5 < (2)(1) - 1$$
$$5 < 1$$

is not true. Since the coordinates of every point on the line L in Figure 10 satisfy the *equation* $y = 2x - 1$, we see that the coordinates of those points in the half-plane below the line must satisfy the *inequality* $y < 2x - 1$. Similarly, the coordinates of those points in the half-plane above the line satisfy the *inequality* $y > 2x - 1$. This suggests that the graph of a linear inequality in two variables is a half-plane, and it leads to a method for graphing inequalities.

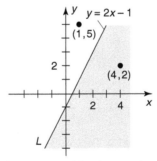

Figure 10   Half-planes Formed by the Graph of a Linear Equation

Example 1   Graphing a Linear Inequality

Sketch the graph of the inequality $x + y \geq 1$.

Solution

Graphing Linear Inequalities

Step 1. Replace the inequality sign with an equal sign and plot the line.

    a. If the inequality is ≤ or ≥, plot a solid line. (Points on the line satisfy the inequality.)

    b. If the inequality is < or >, plot a dashed line. (Points on the line do not satisfy the inequality.)

Step 1. $x + y = 1$

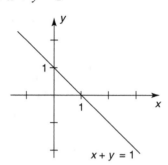

Step 2. Choose any point that is not on the line as a test point. If the origin is not on the line, it may be a convenient choice.

Step 2. Choose $(0, 0)$ as a test point.

Step 3. Substitute the coordinates of the test point into the inequality.

    a. If the test point satisfies the inequality, then the coordinates of every point in the half-plane that contains the test point satisfy the inequality.

    b. If the test point does not satisfy the inequality, then the half-plane that does not contain the test point will satisfy the inequality.

Step 3. Substituting $(0, 0)$ in

$$x + y \geq 1$$

gives

$$0 + 0 \geq 1 \quad (?)$$

$$0 \geq 1$$

which is false. Since $(0, 0)$ is in the half-plane below the line and does not satisfy the inequality, all points above the line satisfy the inequality. See Figure 11.

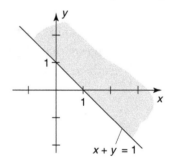

Figure 11 Diagram for Example 1

Example 2 Graphing a Linear Inequality

Sketch the graph of the inequality $2x - 3y > 6$.

Solution

We first graph the line $2x - 3y = 6$. We draw a dashed or broken line to indicate that $2x - 3y = 6$ is not part of the graph. (See Figure 12.) Since $(0, 0)$ is not on the line, we can use it as a test point.

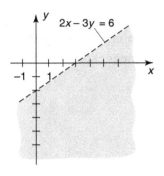

$$2x - 3y > 6$$
$$2(0) - 3(0) > 6 \quad (?)$$
$$0 - 0 > 6 \quad (?)$$
$$0 > 6$$

Figure 12 Diagram for Example 2

is false. Since $(0, 0)$ is in the half-plane above the line, the graph consists of the half-plane below the line.

✔ **Progress Check**

Graph the inequalities.

a. $y \le 2x + 1$ b. $y + 3x > -2$ c. $y > -x + 1$

Answers

a.

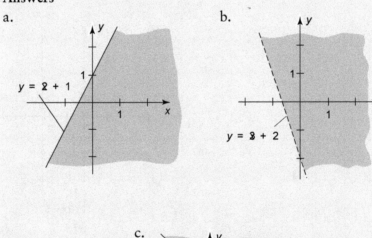

$y = 2 + 1$

b.

$y = 3 + 2$

c.

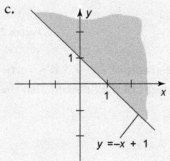

$y = -x + 1$

Example 3   **Graphing a Linear Inequality**

Graph the inequalities.

a. $y > x$ b. $2x \geq 5$

Solution

a. Since the origin lies on the line $y = x$, we choose another test point, say $(0, 1)$ above the line. Since $(0, 1)$ satisfies the inequality, the graph of the inequality is the half-plane above the line. See Figure 13(a).

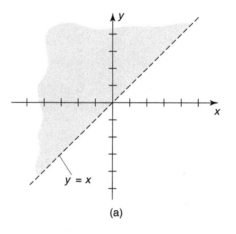

(a)

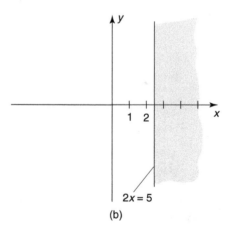

(b)

Figure 13   Diagram for Example 3

b. The graph of $2x = 5$ is a vertical line, and the graph of $2x \geq 5$ is the half-plane to the right of the line and also the line itself. See Figure 13(b).

✔ **Progress Check**

Graph the inequalities.

a. $2y \geq 7$ b. $x < -2$ c. $1 \leq y < 3$

Answers

a. 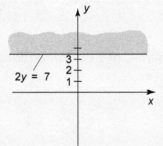 b.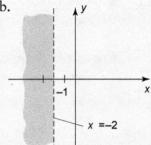

c.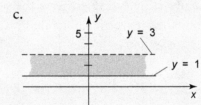

Systems of Linear Inequalities

We may also consider **systems of linear inequalities** in two variables x and y. Examples of such systems are

$$\begin{cases} 2x - 3y > 6 \\ x + 2y < 2 \end{cases} \quad \text{and} \quad \begin{cases} 2x - 5y \leq 12 \\ 2x + y \leq 18 \\ x \geq 0 \\ y \geq 0 \end{cases}$$

The **solution of a system of linear inequalities** consists of all ordered pairs (a, b) such that the substitution $x = a$, $y = b$ satisfies *all* the inequalities. Thus, the ordered pair $(0, -3)$ is a solution of the system

$$2x - 3y > 6$$

$$x + 2y < 2$$

since it satisfies both inequalities:

$$(2)(0) - 3(-3) = 9 > 6$$
$$0 + (2)(-3) = -6 < 2$$

We can graph the solution set of a system of linear inequalities by graphing the solution set of each inequality and marking that portion of the graph that satisfies *all* the inequalities.

Example 4   Graphing a System of Linear Inequalities

Graph the solution set of the system.

$$2x - 3y \le 2$$
$$x + y \le 6$$

Solution

In Figure 14, we have graphed the solution set of each of the inequalities. The purple region indicates those points that satisfy both inequalities and is therefore the solution set of the system of inequalities.

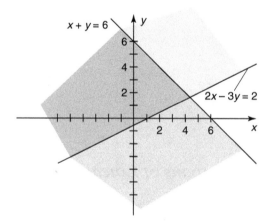

Figure 14   Diagram for Example 4

Example 5   Graphing a System of Linear Inequalities

Graph the solution set of the system.

$$x + y < 2$$
$$2x + 3y \ge 9$$
$$x \ge 1$$

Solution

See Figure 15. Since there are no points satisfying *all* the inequalities, we conclude that the system is inconsistent and has no solutions.

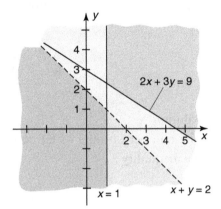

Figure 15   Diagram for Example 5

✔ Progress Check

Graph the solution set of the given system.

a. $x + y \geq 3$ b. $2x + y \leq 4$
   $x + 2y < 8$ $x + y \leq 3$
                             $x \geq 0$
                             $y \geq 0$

Answers

a.

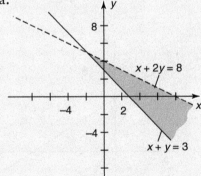

b.

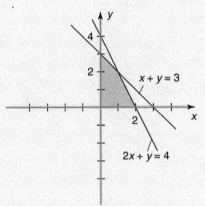

Example 6   Applying Systems of Linear Inequalities

A dietitian at a university is planning a menu that consists of two primary foods, A and B, whose nutritional contents are shown in the table. The dietitian insists that the meal provide at most 12 units of fat, at least 2 units of carbohydrate and at least 1 unit of protein. If x and y represent the number of grams of food types A and B, respectively, write a system of linear inequalities expressing the restrictions. Graph the solution set.

Nutritional Content in Units per Gram

	Fat	Carbohydrate	Protein
A	2	2	0
B	3	1	1

Solution

The number of units of fat contained in the meal is $2x + 3y$, so x and y must satisfy the inequality

$$2x + 3y \leq 12 \qquad \text{fat requirement}$$

Similarly, the requirements for carbohydrate and protein result in the inequalities

$$2x + y \geq 2 \qquad \text{carbohydrate requirement}$$

$$y \geq 1 \qquad \text{protein requirement}$$

We must also have $x \geq 0$, since negative quantities of food type A would make no sense. The system of linear inequalities is then

$$2x + 3y \leq 12$$

$$2x + y \geq 2$$

$$x \geq 0$$

$$y \geq 1$$

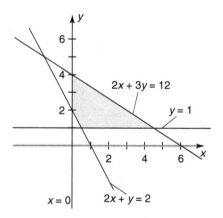

Figure 16 Diagram for Example 6

The graph is shown in Figure 16.

Graphing Calculator Power User's Corner

Solving Systems of Inequalities

Some graphing calculators draw inequality function graphs ($y \geq f(x)$, etc.), shading the appropriate portion of the plane. This capability differs for each model and you should consult your owner's manual for specific details. Some calculators automatically shade the intersection of the regions you have graphed. On some calculators, you need to shade each region with a different resolution to see the intersection of several regions. (Using resolutions that have no common factors leads to the best results.) Finally, if neither of these approaches works on your calculator, you can shade the other side of each inequality so that the solution set of the given system of equations is the portion of the plane that remains unshaded.

Exercise Set 6.5

In Exercises 1–8, graph the solution set of the given inequality.

1. $y \leq x + 2$ 2. $y \geq x + 3$

3. $y > x - 4$ 4. $y < x - 5$

5. $y \leq 4 - x$ 6. $y \geq 2 - x$

7. $y > x$ 8. $y \leq 2x$

9. $3x - 5y > 15$ 10. $2y - 3x < 12$

11. $x \leq 4$ 12. $3x > -2$

13. $y > -3$ 14. $5y \leq 25$

15. $x > 0$ 16. $y < 0$

17. $-2 \leq x \leq 3$ 18. $-6 < y < -2$

19. A steel producer makes two types of steel, regular and special. A ton of regular steel requires 2 hours in the open-hearth furnace and a ton of special steel requires 5 hours. Let x and y denote the number of tons of regular and special steel made per day, respectively. If the open-hearth furnace is available at most 15 hours per day, find the inequalities that must be satisfied by x and y, and graph the solution set.

20. A patient is placed on a diet that restricts caloric intake to 1500 calories per day. The patient plans to eat x ounces of cheese, y slices of bread and z apples on the first day of the diet. If cheese contains 100 calories per ounce, bread 110 calories per slice and apples 80 calories each, write an inequality that must be satisfied by x, y and z.

In Exercises 21–32, graph the solution set of the system of linear inequalities.

21. $2x - y \leq 3$
$2x + 3y \geq -3$

22. $x - y \leq 4$
$2x + y \geq 6$

23. $3x - y \geq -7$
$3x + y \leq -2$

24. $3x - 2y > 1$
$2x + 3y \leq 18$

25. $3x - 2y \geq -5$
$4x - y \leq 10$
$y \geq 2$

26. $2x - y \geq -3$
$x + y \leq 5$
$y \geq 1$

27. $2x - y \leq 5$
$x + 2y \geq 1$
$x \geq 0$
$y \geq 0$

28. $-x + 3y \leq 2$
$4x + 3y \leq 18$
$x \geq 0$
$y \geq 0$

29. $3x + y \leq 6$
$x - 2y \leq -1$
$x \geq 2$

30. $x - y \geq -2$
$x + y \geq -5$
$y \geq 0$

31. $3x - 2y \leq -6$
$8x + 3y \leq 24$
$5x + 4y \geq 20$
$x \geq 0$
$y \geq 0$

32. $2x + 3y \geq 18$
$x + 3y \geq 12$
$4x + 3y \geq 24$
$x \geq 0$
$y \geq 0$

33. A farmer has 10 quarts of milk and 15 quarts of cream that he will use to make ice cream and yogurt. Each quart of ice cream requires 0.4 quarts of milk and 0.2 quarts of cream, and each quart of yogurt requires 0.2 quarts of milk and 0.4 quarts of cream. Graph the set of points representing the possible production of ice cream and yogurt.

34. A coffee packer uses Jamaican and Colombian coffee to prepare a mild blend and a strong blend. Each pound of mild blend contains 0.5 pounds of Jamaican coffee and 0.5 pounds of Colombian coffee, and each pound of the strong blend requires 0.25 pounds of Jamaican coffee and 0.75 pounds of Colombian coffee. The packer has available 100 pounds of Jamaican coffee and 125 pounds of Colombian coffee. Graph the set of points representing the possible production of the two blends.

35. A trust fund of $100,000, established to provide university scholarships, must adhere to certain restrictions.

    a. No more than half of the fund may be invested in common stocks.

    b. No more than $35,000 may be invested in preferred stocks.

    c. No more than $60,000 may be invested in all types of stocks.

    d. The amount invested in common stock cannot be more than twice the amount invested in preferred stocks.

    Graph the solution set representing the possible investments in common and preferred stocks.

36. An institution serves a luncheon consisting of two dishes, A and B, whose nutritional content in grams per unit served is given in the accompanying table.

	Fat	Carbohydrate	Protein
A	1	1	2
B	2	1	6

The luncheon is to provide no more than 10 grams of fat, no more than 7 grams of carbohydrate and at least 6 grams of protein. Graph the solution set of possible quantities of dishes A and B.

In Exercises 37–40, write the inequality whose solution is graphed (all windows are set to the default setting).

37.
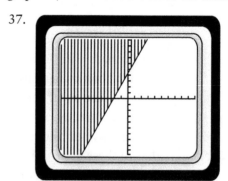

38.
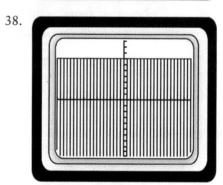

39.
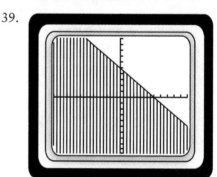

40.
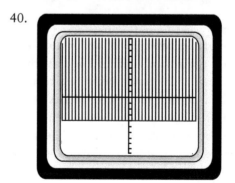

Applications 6.5

Write a system of inequalities for problems 1–2 and then graph the region of feasible solutions of the system. Please graph the feasible region as clearly as possible.

1. Tracy was given the following advice. She should supplement her daily diet with at least 5000 USP units of Vitamin A, at least 180 mg of Vitamin C, and at least 500 USP units of Vitamin D. She also finds that CVS Pharmacy carries Brand X and Brand Y vitamins. Each Brand X pill contains 3000 USP units of A, 45 mg of C, and 80 USP units of D, while the Brand Y pills contain 1000 USP units of A, 60 mg of C, and 200 USP units of D.

2. The Sony Company makes two products—ipods and DVD players. Each ipod gives a profit of $300, while each DVD player produces $40 profit. The company must manufacture at least 1000 ipods per day to satisfy one of its customers, but no more than 2000 because of production problems. The number of DVD players produced cannot exceed 1500 per day.

3. Sharon's local grocery store has shelf space for, at most 100 cases of Coke and Sprite. The grocer wants at least thirty cases of Coke and twenty cases of Sprite. Graph the possible stock arrangements.

4. Your budget requires you to earn at least $200 per week. You would like to work two part-time jobs for at most 30 hours per week. The first job pays $20 per hour and the second job pays $10 per hour. Let x represent the number of hours worked at the first job and let y represent the number of hours worked at the second job.

   a. Write an inequality that represents the number of hours worked at each job in order to meet your budget requirement.

   b. Write an inequality that represents the total number of hours you can work per week.

   c. Graph the equations in part (a) and part (b). Please label at least two ordered pairs (x, y) that identify the number of hours you must work at each job in order to meet your budget requirements.

6.6   Linear Programming

Consider the following problem.

A lot is zoned for an apartment building to consist of no more than 40 apartments, totaling no more than 45,000 square feet. A builder is planning to construct two types of apartments. A one-bedroom apartment will require 1000 square feet and will rent for $800 per month. A two-bedroom apartment will require 1500 square feet and will rent for $1120 per month. If all available apartments can be rented, how many apartments of each type should be built to maximize the builder's monthly rental revenue?

Let x denote the number of one-bedroom units and y the number of two-bedroom units. The accompanying table displays the information given in the problem.

	Number of Units	Square Feet	Rental ($)
one-bedroom	x	1,000	800
two-bedroom	y	1,500	1120
Total	40	45,000	z

Using the methods of the previous section, we can translate the **constraints,** or requirements, of the variables x and y into a system of inequalities. The total number of apartments is $x + y$, so we have

$$x + y \leq 40 \quad \text{number of units constraint}$$

Since each one-bedroom apartment occupies 1000 square feet of space, x apartments will occupy $1000x$ square feet of space. Similarly, the two-bedroom apartments will occupy $1500y$ square feet of space. The total amount of space is $1000x + 1500y$, so we must have

$$1000x + 1500y \leq 45{,}000 \quad \text{square footage constraint}$$

Moreover, since x and y denote the number of apartments to be built, we must have $x \geq 0$, $y \geq 0$. Thus, we have obtained the following system of inequalities:

$$
\begin{aligned}
x + \quad y &\leq \quad 40 &&\text{number of units constraint} \\
1000x + 1500y &\leq 45{,}000 &&\text{square footage constraint} \\
x &\geq \quad 0 &&\text{need for number of apartments} \\
y &\geq \quad 0 &&\text{to be nonnegative}
\end{aligned}
$$

We graph the solution set of this system of linear inequalities as shown in Figure 17.

However, the problem as stated asks that we *maximize* the monthly rental $z = 800x + 1120y$. It is this requirement to **optimize,** that is, to seek a maximum or a minimum value of a linear expression, that characterizes a linear programming problem.

Linear Programming Problem
A **linear programming problem** seeks the optimal (either the largest or the smallest) value of a linear expression called the **objective function** while satisfying constraints that can be formulated as a system of linear inequalities.

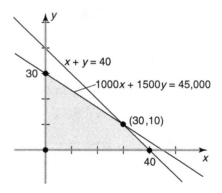

Figure 17 Graph of Linear Inequalities

Returning to our apartment builder, we can state the linear programming problem in this way:

$$\text{maximize} \quad z = 800x + 1120y$$

$$\text{subject to} \quad x + y \le 40$$

$$1000x + 1500y \le 45{,}000$$

$$x \ge 0$$

$$y \ge 0$$

The coordinates of each point of the solution set shown in Figure 17 are a **feasible solution,** that is, the coordinates give us ordered pairs (a, b) that satisfy the system of linear inequalities. But which points provide us with values of x and y that maximize the rental income z? For example, the points $(40, 0)$ and $(15, 20)$ are feasible solutions yielding these results for z:

x	y	$z = 800x + 1120y$
40	0	32,000
15	20	34,400

Building 15 one-bedroom and 20 two-bedroom units certainly yields a higher rental revenue than building 40 one-bedroom units. However, is there a solution that yields an even greater value for z?

Before providing the key to solving linear programming problems, we first note that the solution set is bounded by lines. We use the term **vertex** to denote an intersection point of any two boundary lines. We are then ready to state the following theorem.

Fundamental Theorem of Linear Programming

If a linear programming problem has an optimal solution, that solution occurs at a vertex of the set of feasible solutions.

With this result, the builder need only examine the vertices of the solution set of Figure 17, rather than considering each of the infinite number of feasible solutions available. We evaluate the objective function $z = 800x + 1120y$ for the coordinates of the vertices $(0, 0)$, $(0, 30)$, $(40, 0)$ and $(30, 10)$.

x	y	$z = 800x + 1120y$
0	0	0
0	30	33,600
40	0	32,000
30	10	35,200

Since the largest value of z is 35,200, and this corresponds to $x = 30$, $y = 10$, the builder finds that the optimal strategy is to build 30 one-bedroom units and 10 two-bedroom units.

Linear programming problems occur in real-life situations with great frequency. In certain industries these problems can involve thousands of variables and hundreds of constraints. Obviously, the method of graphical solution we presented for two variables cannot be used in those situations. A solution method known as the simplex algorithm was first devised by George Dantzig in 1947. Despite the sophistication of this approach, the number of calculations required becomes unmanageably large for hand computation even with a relatively small number of constraints. Fortunately, the discovery of the simplex algorithm occurred at the time electronic computers made their initial appearance. Since then, industries, such as oil refining and steel production, have used linear programming to determine the optimum use of their facilities.

We can now illustrate the steps in solving a linear programming problem.

Example 1

Solve the linear programming problem

$$\text{minimize} \quad z = x - 4y$$

$$\text{subject to} \quad x + 2y \leq 10$$

$$-x + 4y \leq \ 8$$

$$x \geq \ 0$$

$$y \geq \ 1$$

Solution

Linear Programming

Step 1. Sketch the solution set of the system of linear inequalities. (See Figure 18.)

Step 1.

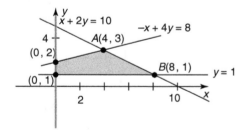

Figure 18   Graph of Linear Inequalities

Step 2. Determine all vertices of the solution set.

Step 2. The vertices $(0, 1)$ and $(0, 2)$ are the y-intercepts of the lines whose equations are $y = 1$ and $-x + 4y = 8$, respectively. The vertex B in Figure 18 is the intersection of the lines $y = 1$ and $x + 2y = 10$. The coordinates of B are $(8, 1)$. The vertex A in Figure 18 is the intersection of the lines

$$-x + 4y = 8$$

(continues)

Linear Programming *(continued)*

and

$$x + 2y = 10$$

Solving the system of equations yields the coordinates of A as $(4, 3)$.

Step 3. Evaluate the objective function for the coordinates of each vertex.

Step 3.

Vertex	x	y	$z = x - 4y$
$(0, 1)$	0	1	-4
$(0, 2)$	0	2	-8
$(8, 1)$	8	1	4
$(4, 3)$	4	3	-8

Step 4. The point or points providing the optimal value of the objective function are solutions of the linear programming problem.

Step 4. The minimum value of the objective function is -8, which occurs at the vertices $(0, 2)$ and $(4, 3)$. Thus, $x = 0, y = 2$ and $x = 4, y = 3$ are both solutions of the linear programming problem.

Exercise Set 6.6

In Exercises 1–8, find the minimum value and the maximum value of the linear expression, subject to the given constraints. Indicate coordinates of the vertices at which the minimum and maximum values occur.

1. $x - \dfrac{1}{2}y$ subject to
$$3x - y \geq 1$$
$$x \geq 0$$
$$x \leq 5$$
$$y \geq 0$$

2. $2x + y$ subject to
$$x + y \leq 4$$
$$x \geq 1$$
$$y \geq 2$$

3. $\dfrac{1}{2}x - 2y$ subject to
$$x + 2y \leq 6$$
$$3y - 2x \leq 2$$
$$x \geq 0$$
$$y \geq 0$$

4. $0.2x + 0.8y$ subject to
$$3y + x \leq 8$$
$$3x - 5y \geq 2$$
$$x \geq 0$$
$$y \geq 0$$

5. $2x - y$ subject to
$$y - x \leq 0$$
$$4y + 3x \geq 6$$
$$x \leq 4$$

6. $x + 3y$ subject to
$$2x + y \geq 2$$
$$4x + 5y \leq 40$$
$$x \geq 0$$
$$y \geq 1$$
$$y \leq 6$$

7. $2x - y$ subject to
$$2y - x \leq 8$$
$$x + 2y \geq 12$$
$$5x + 2y \leq 44$$
$$x \geq 3$$

8. $y - x$ subject to

$$2y - 5x \leq 10$$
$$5x + 6y \leq 50$$
$$5x + y \leq 20$$
$$x \geq 0$$
$$y \geq 1$$

9. A firm has budgeted $1500 for display space at a toy show. Two types of display booths are available: "preferred space" costs $18 per square foot, with a minimum rental of 60 square feet, and "regular space" costs $12 per square foot, with a minimum rental of 30 square feet. It is estimated that there will be 120 visitors for each square foot of "preferred space" and 60 visitors for each square foot of "regular space." How should the firm allot its budget to maximize the number of potential clients that will visit the booths?

10. A company manufactures an 8-bit computer and a 16-bit computer. To meet existing orders, it must schedule at least 50 8-bit computers for the next production cycle and can produce no more than 150 8-bit computers. The manufacturing facilities are adequate to produce no more than 300 16-bit computers, but the total number of computers that can be produced cannot exceed 400. The profit on each 8-bit computer is $310, and on each 16-bit computer, $275. Find the number of computers of each type that should be manufactured to maximize profit.

11. Swift Truckers is negotiating a contract with Better Spices, which uses two sizes of containers: large, 4-cubic foot containers weighing 10 pounds and small, 2-cubic foot containers weighing 8 pounds. Swift Truckers uses a vehicle that can handle a maximum load of 3280 pounds and a cargo size of up to 1000 cubic feet. The firms have agreed on a shipping rate of 50 cents for each large container and 30 cents for each small container. How many containers of each type should Swift place on a truck to maximize income?

12. A bakery makes both yellow cake and white cake. Each pound of yellow cake requires $\frac{1}{4}$ pound of flour and $\frac{1}{4}$ pound of sugar; each pound of white cake requires $\frac{1}{3}$ pound of flour and $\frac{1}{5}$ pound of sugar. The baker finds that 100 pounds of flour and 80 pounds of sugar are available. If yellow cake sells for $3 per pound and white cake sells for $2.50 per pound, how many pounds of each cake should the bakery produce

to maximize income, assuming that all cakes baked can be sold?

13. A shop sells a mixture of Java and Colombian coffee beans for $4 per pound. The shopkeeper has allocated $1000 for buying fresh beans and finds that she must pay $1.50 per pound for Java beans and $2 per pound for Colombian beans. In a satisfactory mixture the weight of Colombian beans is at least twice and no more than 4 times the weight of the Java beans. How many pounds of each type of coffee bean should be ordered to maximize the profit if all the mixture can be sold?

14. A pension fund plans to invest up to $50,000 in U.S. Treasury bonds yielding 12% interest per year and corporate bonds yielding 15% interest per year. The fund manager is told to invest a minimum of $25,000 in the Treasury bonds and a minimum of $10,000 in the corporate bonds, with no more than $\frac{1}{4}$ of the total investment to be in corporate bonds. How much should the manager invest in each type of bond to achieve a maximum amount of annual interest? What is the maximum interest?

15. A farmer intends to plant crops A and B on all or part of a 100-acre field. Seed for crop A costs $6 per acre, and labor and equipment costs $20 per acre. For crop B, seed costs $9 per acre, and labor and equipment costs $15 per acre. The farmer cannot spend more than $810 for seed and $1800 for labor and equipment. If the income per acre is $150 for crop A and $175 for crop B, how many acres of each crop should be planted to maximize total income?

16. The farmer in Exercise 15 finds that a worldwide surplus in crop B reduces the income to $140 per acre, but the income for crop A remains steady at $150 per acre. How many acres of each crop should be planted to maximize total income?

17. In preparing food for the college cafeteria, a dietitian combines volume pack A and volume pack B. Each pound of volume pack A costs $2.50 and contains 4 units of carbohydrate, 3 units of protein and 5 units of fat. Each pound of volume pack B costs $1.50 and contains 3 units of carbohydrate, 4 units of protein and 1 unit of fat. If minimum monthly requirements are 60 units of carbohydrates, 52 units of protein and 42 units of fat, how many pounds of each food pack does the dietitian use to minimize costs?

18. A lawn service uses a riding mower that cuts a 5000-square foot area per hour and a smaller mower that cuts a 3000-square foot area per hour. Surprisingly, each mower uses $\frac{1}{2}$ gallon of gasoline per hour. Near the end of the day, the supervisor finds that both mowers are empty and that there remains 0.6 gallons of gasoline in the storage cans. Suppose at least 4000 square feet of lawn must still be mowed. If the cost of operating the riding mower is $9 per hour and the cost of operating the smaller mower is $5 per hour, how much of the remaining gasoline should be allocated to each mower to do the job at the least possible cost?

Applications 6.6

1. Earthquake victims in Japan need medical supplies and bottled water. Each medical kit measures 1 ft^3 and weighs 10 lbs. Each container of water is also 1 ft^3 but weights 20 lbs. The plane can only carry 90,000 lb. with a total volume of 5000 ft^3. Each medical kit will aid 4 people, while each container of water will serve 10 people.

   a. How many of each should be sent to maximize the number of people helped?

   b. If each medical kit could aid 6 people instead of 4, how would the results from part (a) change?

2. The Sony Company makes two products—ipod and DVD players. Each ipod gives a profit of $300, which each DVD player produces $40 profit. The company must manufacture at least 1000 ipod per day to satisfy one of its customers, but no more than 2000 because of production problems. The number of DVD players produced cannot exceed 1500 per day, and the number of ipod cannot exceed the number of DVD players. How many of each should the company manufacture to obtain maximum profit?

3. Tracy takes vitamin pills each day. She wants at least 16 units of Vitamin A, at least 5 units of Vitamin B, and at least 20 units of Vitamin C. She can choose between red pills, costing $0.45 each, that contain 8 units of A, 1 of B, and 4 of C; and blue pills, costing $0.20 each, that contain 4 units of A, 2 of B, and 8 of C. How many of each pill should she buy to minimize her cost and yet fulfill her daily requirements?

4. Nancy wants to buy some filing cabinets for the Department of Natural Sciences and Mathematics at the Curry College. She knows that cabinet A costs $12 each, requires 6 ft^2 of floor space, and holds 8 ft^2 of files. Cabinet B costs $25 each, requires 8 ft^2 of floor space, and holds 15 ft^2 of files. Nancy cannot spend more than $200 due to budget limitations, and her office has room for no more than 72 ft^2 of cabinets. She wants to maximize storage capacity within the limits imposed by funds and space. How many of each type of cabinet should she buy?

5. Cannon Manufacturing has a division that produces two models of cameras, model G11 and model G12. To produce each model G11 camera requires $120 material cost and 30 minutes of labor. To produce each model of G12 camera requires $140 material cost and 40 minutes of labor. The profit for each model G11 is $90 and the profit for each model G12 is $130. If $1200 of material budget and 10 hours of labor are available for the production of cameras per day, how many cameras of each model should the division produce per day in order to maximize Cannon's profit?

6. Acadian Asset has a total of $50 billion earmarked for homeowner and auto loans. On the average, homeowner loans has an 8% annual rate of return, where auto loans yield a 10% annual rate of return. Management has also stipulated that the total amount of homeowner loans should be greater than or equal to four times the total amount of automobile loans. Determine the total amount of loans of each type Acadian should extend to each category in order to maximize its returns.

7. Tracy plans to invest up to $400,000 in two projects for her retirement. Project A yields a return of 5% on the investment, whereas project B yields a return of 8% on the investment. Because of the investment in project B is riskier than the investment in project A, she has decided that the investment in project B should not

exceed 50% of the total investment. How much should Tracy invest in each project in order to maximize the return on her retirement?

8. The manufacturing process requires that oil refineries manufacture at least 3 gallons of gasoline for each gallon of fuel oil. To meet the winter demand for fuel oil, at least 4 million gallons per day must be produced. The demand for gasoline is no more than 7.5 million gallons per day. If the price of gasoline is $3.98 per gallon and the price

of fuel oil is $3.50 per gallon, how much of each should be produced to maximize revenue?

9. A car maintenance shop must decide how many oil changes and how many tune-up can be scheduled in a typical week. One oil change takes 20 minutes and one tune-up requires 100 minutes. The maintenance shop makes a profit of $15 on an oil change and $65 on a tune-up. What mix of services should the shop schedule if the typical week has available 800 minutes for these two types of service?

Terms and Symbols

back-substitution	inconsistent system	proper fraction
break-even point	level of production	solution of a system of equations
consistent system	linear inequalities	solution of a system of linear
constraints	linear programming	inequalities
demand	linear programming problem	substitution
elimination	linear system	supply
equilibrium price	method of elimination	system of equations
equivalent system	method of graphing	system of linear equations
feasible solution	method of substitution	system of linear inequalities
Gaussian Elimination	objective function	triangular form
graphing linear inequalities	optimize	vertex
half-plane	partial fraction	
improper fraction	partial-fraction decomposition	

Key Ideas for Review

Topic	Key Idea
Solving Systems of Equations	To solve a system of equations, you must find a value for each unknown that satisfies all equations of the system.
Method of Substitution	The method of substitution involves solving an equation for one unknown and substituting the result into another equation.
Method of Elimination	The method of elimination involves multiplying an equation by a constant so that when it is added to a second equation, an unknown is eliminated.
Gaussian Elimination	Gaussian Elimination is a systematic way of transforming a linear system to triangular form. A linear system in triangular form may be solved by back-substitution.
Consistent Systems	A consistent system of equations has one or more solutions.
Inconsistent Systems	An inconsistent system has no solutions.

Topic	Key Idea
Applications	It is often more natural to set up word problems using two or more unknowns.
Partial Fractions	A proper fraction can always be written as a sum of partial fractions whose denominators are of the form $$(ax + b)^m \quad \text{and} \quad (ax^2 + bx + c)^n$$
Graphing Linear Systems	The graph of a pair of linear equations in two unknowns is two lines, not necessarily distinct. 1. If the lines intersect at a point, the system is consistent, and the coordinates of the point of intersection is the unique solution of the system of linear equations. 2. If the lines are the same, the system is consistent, and any point on the line is a solution of the system of linear equations. 3. If the lines are parallel and distinct, the system is inconsistent and the system of linear equations has no solution.
Solving a System of Linear Inequalities	The solution of a system of linear inequalities can be found graphically as the region that is the intersection of all regions satisfying each inequality.
Linear Programming Problems	To solve a linear programming problem, it is only necessary to consider the coordinates of the vertices of the region of feasible solutions.

Review Exercises

Solutions to exercises whose numbers are in **bold** are in the Solutions section in the back of the book.

In Exercises 1 and 2, solve the given system by graphing.

1. $2x + 3y = 2$
   $4x + 5y = 3$

2. $-y^2 + x = 1$
   $x + y = 7$

In Exercises 3–8, solve the given system by the method of substitution.

3. $-x + 6y = -11$
   $2x + 5y = 5$

4. $2x - 4y = -14$
   $-x - 6y = -5$

5. $2x + y = 0$
   $x - 3y = \frac{7}{4}$

6. $x^2 + y^2 = 25$
   $x + 3y = 5$

7. $x^2 - 4y^2 = 9$
   $y - 2x = 0$

8. $y^2 - 4x = 0$
   $y^2 + x - 2y = 12$

In Exercises 9–14, solve the given system by the method of elimination.

9. $x + 4y = 17$
   $2x - 3y = -21$

10. $5x - 2y = 14$
    $-x - 3y = 4$

11. $-3x + y = -13$
    $2x - 3y = 11$

12. $7x - 2y = -20$
    $3x - y = -9$

13. $y^2 = 2x - 1$
    $x - y = 2$

14. $x^2 + y^2 = 9$
    $-x^2 + y = 3$

15. The sum of a two-digit number and its tens digit is 49. If we reverse the digits of the number, the resulting number is 9 more than the original number. Find the number.

16. The sum of the digits of a two-digit number is 9. The sum of the number and its units digit is 74. Find the number.

17. Five pounds of hamburger and 4 pounds of steak cost $22, and 3 pounds of hamburger and 7 pounds of steak cost $28.15. Find the cost per pound of hamburger and of steak.

18. An airplane flying with a tail wind can complete a journey of 3500 kilometers in 5 hours. Flying the

reverse direction, the plane completes the same trip in 7 hours. What is the speed of the plane in still air?

19. A manufacturer of faucets finds that the supply S and demand D are related to price p as follows:

$$S = 3p + 2$$
$$D = -2p + 17$$

Find the equilibrium price and the number of faucets sold at that price.

20. An auto repair shop finds that its monthly expenditure in dollars is given by $C = 4025 + 9x$, where x is the total number of hours worked by all employees. If the revenue received in dollars is given by $R = 16x$, find the break-even point in number of work hours and the total revenue received at that point.

In Exercises 21–24, use Gaussian Elimination to solve the given linear system.

21. $-3x - y + z = 12$
    $2x + 5y - 2z = -9$
    $-x + 4y + 2z = 15$

22. $3x + 2y - z = -8$
    $2x + 3z = 5$
    $x - 4y = -4$

23. $5x - y + 2z = 10$
    $-2x + 3y - z = -7$
    $3x + 2z = 7$

24. $x + 4y = 4$
    $-x + 3z = -4$
    $2x + 2y - z = \frac{41}{6}$

In Exercises 25–28, solve by any method.

25. $2x + 3y = 6$
    $3x - y = -13$

26. $x + 2y = 0$
    $-x + 4y = 5$

27. $2x + 3y - z = -4$
    $x - 2y + 2z = -6$
    $2x - 3z = 5$

28. $2x + 2y - 3z = -4$
    $3y - z = -4$
    $4x - y + z = 4$

In Exercises 29–31, find the partial-fraction decomposition of the given rational function.

29. $\dfrac{8 - x}{2x^2 + 3x - 2}$

30. $\dfrac{3x^3 + 5x - 1}{(x^2 + 1)^2}$

31. $\dfrac{2x^3 - 3x^2 + 4x - 2}{(x - 1)^2}$

In Exercises 32–37, graph the solution set of the linear inequality or system of linear inequalities.

32. $x - 2y \le 5$

33. $2x + y > 4$

34. $2x + 3y \le 2$
    $x - y \ge 1$

35. $x - 2y \ge 4$
    $2x - y \le 2$

36. $2x + 3y \le 6$
    $x \ge 0$
    $y \ge 1$

37. $2x + y \le 42$
    $x - y \le 3$
    $x \ge 0$
    $y \ge 0$

In Exercises 38 and 39, solve the given linear programming problem.

38. maximize $z = 5y - x$
    subject to $8y - 3x \le 36$
                 $6x + y \le 30$
                 $y \ge 1$
                 $x \ge 0$

39. minimize $z = x + 4y$
    subject to $4x - y \ge 8$
                 $4x + y \le 24$
                 $5y + 4x \ge 32$

Review Test

1. Solve the linear system by graphing:

$$3x - y = -17$$
$$x + 2y = -1$$

In Exercises 2 and 3, solve the given system by the method of substitution.

2. $2x + y = 4$
   $3x - 2y = -15$

3. $y^2 - 5x = 0$
   $y^2 - x^2 = 6$

In Exercises 4 and 5, solve the given linear system by the method of elimination.

4. $x - 2y = 7$
   $3x + 4y = -9$

5. $x^2 + y^2 = 25$
   $4x^2 - y^2 = 20$

6. The sum of the digits of a two-digit number is 11. If the sum of the number and its tens digit is 41, find the number.

7. An elegant men's shop is having a post-Christmas sale. All shirts are reduced to one low price, and all ties are

reduced to an even lower price. A customer purchases 3 ties and 7 shirts, paying $135. Another customer selects 5 ties and 3 shirts and pays $95. What is the sale price of each tie and of each shirt?

8. A school cafeteria manager finds that the weekly cost of operation is $1375 plus $1.25 for every meal served. If the average meal produces a revenue of $2.50, find the number of meals served that results in zero profit.

9. Solve by Gaussian Elimination:

$$3x + 2y - z = {-4}$$
$$x - y + 3z = 12$$
$$2x - y - 2z = -20$$

Solve Exercises 10 and 11 by any method.

10. $-3x + 2y = -1$
$6x - y = -1$

11. $3x + y - 2z = 8$
$3y - 4z = 14$
$3x + \frac{1}{2}y + z = 1$

12. Find the partial-fraction decomposition of

$$\frac{x - 12}{x^2 + x - 6}$$

In Exercises 13 and 14, graph the solution set of the system of linear inequalities.

13. $2x - 3y \geq 6$
$3x + y \leq 3$

14. $2x + y \leq 4$
$2x - 5y \leq 5$
$y \geq 1$

15. Solve the linear programming problem.

maximize $\qquad z = x + 4y$
subject to $\qquad 4x - y \geq 8$
$\qquad\qquad\quad 4x + y \leq 24$
$\qquad\qquad\quad 4x + 5y \geq 32$

Writing Exercises

1. Write in complete sentences the procedure that you follow in solving the following problem using two unknowns: A stamp machine dispenses 29¢ stamps and 23¢ stamps. When you deposit a five dollar bill, you receive a packet containing 50% more 29¢ stamps than 23¢ stamps with 30¢ change.

2. Write a report on the origins of linear programming and its connection to World War II.

3. Describe an example of linear programming in everyday life.

4. Construct an example of a linear programming problem in two variables. Describe in words the geometric method used to solve it.

5. What are the limitations of solving linear programming problems geometrically?

6. Describe the method of elimination for solving a system of three linear equations in three unknowns.

Chapter 6 Project

In the chapter opener you read about polynomial curve fitting and how it can be used to model (that is, design equations for) data from the real world. Solving systems of equations, both "two-by-two" (two equations and two unknowns) and "three-by-three," was necessary to complete this task. Review Exercises 22–23 in Section 6.3.

Now use the method outlined in those exercises to model the following data with a quadratic polynomial:

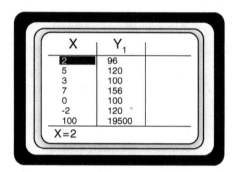

X	Y_1	
2	96	
5	120	
3	100	
7	156	
0	100	
-2	120	
100	19500	

X=2

(This table gives you many more data points than are needed. Use the "extra" data points to check your answer.)

Not all data perfectly matches a polynomial function. Your graphing calculator probably has regression capabilities. This means that you can enter your own data, select a type of function, and your calculator will give you the coefficients to complete the function. Try it!

Answers to Selected Odd-Numbered Exercises, Review Exercises, and Review Tests

Graphing Calculator Alert

In the answers that follow, the WINDOW values given will allow your graphing calculator to show important features of the functions examined in the various exercises. There are many other WINDOW values that will produce similar results. Note that viewing rectangles on some graphing calculators will not show all points. Furthermore, in some cases vertical lines will incorrectly appear on the graphing screen. (See Section 5.1 for additional information.) Therefore, because of differences in graphing calculators, the display on your calculator may vary from those shown here.

It is also important to note that the values you obtain when using TRACE on your graphing calculator are *approximate*. It is often necessary to ZOOM-IN to obtain more accurate results. Although the coordinates in the text are correct, they do not necessarily correspond to any values obtained when using the TRACE command.

Chapter 1

Exercise Set 1.1

1. $\{3, 4, 5, 6, 7\}$

3. $\{-9\}$

5. $\{1, 2\}$

7. $\{1, 3, 7\}$

9. F

11. F

13. T

15. T

17. T

19. F

21. F

23. commutative (addition)

25. distributive

27. associative (addition)

29. closure (multiplication)

31. commutative (multiplication)

33. commutative, associative (multiplication)

35. multiplicative inverse

41. symmetric

43. transitive or substitution

51. a. $\frac{1}{2} + \frac{1}{2} = 1, \frac{3}{2} + \left(-\frac{1}{2}\right) = 1, \frac{2}{3} + \frac{4}{3} = 2$

b. $\sqrt{2} + (-\sqrt{2}) = 0, (\pi + 2) + (-\pi) = 2,$ $(\sqrt{3} + 1) + (\sqrt{3} - 2) = -1$

53. a. 5   b. -21

  c. 21   d. -3

  e. $\dfrac{10}{3}$ f. $-\dfrac{10}{3}$

  g. $\dfrac{5}{4}$ h. $\dfrac{1}{2}$

  i. $\dfrac{111}{148}$ j. $\dfrac{28}{33}$

  k. $\dfrac{18}{175}$ l. $\dfrac{12}{35}$

55. a. 0.25   b. -0.6

  c. 0.769230769   d. 0.285714285

57. 35 miles   59. 4 feet and 6 feet

61. 1 pound 3 ounces   63. $256.10

Exercise Set 1.2

1.
  $-4\ -2\ \ 0\ \ 2\ \ 4$

3. $A:1, B:2.5, C:-2, D:4, O:0, E:-3.5$

5. 4   7. -2

9. -5

11.
  $0\ 1\ 2\ 3\ 4\ 5\ 6\ 7\ 8\ 9$

13.
  $2\ \ 3\ \ 4\ \ 5\ \ 6\ \ 7$

15. $10 > 9.99$ 17. $a \geq 0$

19. $x > 0$ 21. $\dfrac{1}{4} < a < \dfrac{1}{2}$

23. $b \geq 5$

25. multiplication by negative number

27. multiplication by negative number

29. multiplication by positive number

31. 2   33. 1.5

35. -2 37. 1

39. 4   41. 2

43. $\dfrac{1}{5}$ 45. 3

47. 2   49. $\dfrac{8}{5}$

51. when x and y have the same sign

53. $\{-2, -1, 0, 1, 2, 3, 4, 5, 6, 7, 8\}$

55. a. $1 < 7$ b. $-6 < 0$

  c. $-2 < 10$ d. $5 > -25$

  e. $1 > -5$ f. $-\dfrac{1}{2} < \dfrac{5}{2}$

  g. $1 < 25$

57. $\dfrac{7}{2}$ 59. -2

61. 0

63. a. $x \leq 3$ b. $x \leq \dfrac{2}{5}$

Exercise Set 1.3

1. 0   3. -8

5. $-\dfrac{1}{8}$ 7. 13

9. a. $2160   b. $2080   c. $2106.67

11. 9.37   13. -9

15. $\dfrac{3}{2}$ 17. 0

19. b^7 21. $-20y^9$

23. $-3x^4$

25. a. 1   b. 100,000,000

  c. 32   d. 7

27. c, d 29. 2; 3

31. $\dfrac{3}{5}; 4$ 33. 3

35. 4   37. 11

39. 176.20   41. $\dfrac{bh}{2}$

43. cost of all purchases   45. $5x + 3$

47. $2s^2t^3 - 3s^2t^2 + 2s^2t + 3st^2 + st - s + 2t - 3$

49. $-2a^2bc + ab^2c - 2ab^3 + 3$

51. $-2x^4 + 4x^3 - x^2 + 4x - 4$

53. $6s^3 - s^2 - 11s + 6$

55. $-4y^5 - 2y^4 + 2y^3 - 5y^2 - 3y$

57. $4a^5 - 16a^4 + 14a^3 - 3a^2 - 14a + 15$

59. $3b^4 + 3ab^3 + 2b^3 - 7ab^2 + 2b^2 - 4ab - 6a$

61. $-6x^2 + 22x - 12$

63. $-100x + 45y + 50z$

65. $x^2 + 2x - 3$

67. $4x^2 + 8x + 3$

69. $3x^2 - 5x + 2$

71. $x^2 + 2xy + y^2$

73. $9x^2 - 6x + 1$

75. $4x^2 - 1$

77. $x^4 + 2x^2y^2 + y^4$

79. a. 3^{11}
    b. 2^{n+2}

81. a. $\dfrac{4}{x^2} - 1$
    b. $\dfrac{w^2x^2}{y^2} - \dfrac{2wxz}{y} + z^2$
    c. $x^2 + y^2 - z^2 + 2xy$

83. Eric

85. a. 392
    b. 96
    c. 16,777,216
    d. 4,294,966,528

Exercise Set 1.4

1. $5(x - 3)$

3. $-2(x + 4y)$

5. $5b(c + 5)$

7. $-y^2(3 + 4y^3)$

9. $3x^2(1 + 2y - 3z)$

11. $(x + 1)(x + 3)$

13. $(y - 3)(y - 5)$

15. $(a - 3b)(a - 4b)$

17. $\left(y - \dfrac{1}{3}\right)\left(y + \dfrac{1}{3}\right)$

19. $(3 - x)(3 + x)$

21. $(x - 7)(x + 2)$

23. $\left(\dfrac{1}{4} + y\right)\left(\dfrac{1}{4} - y\right)$

25. $(x - 3)^2$

27. $(x - 10)(x - 2)$

29. $(x + 3)(x + 8)$

31. $(2x + 1)(x - 2)$

33. $(3a - 2)(a - 3)$

35. $(3x + 2)(2x + 3)$

37. $(4m + 3)(2m - 3)$

39. $(5x + 1)(2x - 3)$

41. $(3a + 2b)(2a - 3b)$

43. $(5rs + 2t)(2rs + t)$

45. $(4 + 3xy)(4 - 3xy)$

47. $(4n + 1)(2n - 5)$

49. $2(x + 2)(x - 3)$

51. $5(3x - 2)(2x - 1)$

53. $3m(2x + 3)(3x + 1)$

55. $2x^2(3 + 2x)(2 - 5x)$

57. $(x^2 + y^2)(x + y)(x - y)$

59. $(b^2 + 4)(b^2 - 2)$

61. $(x + 3y)(x^2 - 3xy + 9y^2)$

63. $(3x - y)(9x^2 + 3xy + y^2)$

65. $(a + 2)(a^2 - 2a + 4)$

67. $\left(\dfrac{1}{2}m - 2n\right)\left(\dfrac{1}{4}m^2 + mn + 4n^2\right)$

69. $(x + y - 2)(x^2 + 2xy + y^2 + 2x + 2y + 4)$

71. $(2x^2 - 5y^2)(4x^4 + 10x^2y^2 + 25y^4)$

73. $4(y + 2)(x - 1)$

75. $-(x + 2)^2(5x + 31)$

79. any integer

81. a. $h(3x^2 + 3xh + h^2)$
    b. $7 \cdot 2^n$
    c. $(4 + 9x^6)(2 - 3x^3)(2 + 3x^3)$
    d. $(z + x - y)(z - x + y)$

83. a. $C(R + 1 + r)(R + 1 - r)$
    b. $p(1 - p)(a - b)^2$
    c. $(X - L)(X - 2L)$
    d. $(R_1 + R_2)(R_1 + R_2 - 2r)$
    e. $-16(t - 7)(t + 3)$

Exercise Set 1.5

1. $\dfrac{1}{x - 4}, x \neq -4$

3. $x - 4, x \neq 4$

5. $\dfrac{3x + 1}{x + 2}, x \neq \dfrac{1}{2}$

7. $\dfrac{4}{9}$

9. $-2b(5 + a)$

11. $\dfrac{5y}{x - 4}, x \neq -2, y \neq 0$

13. $\dfrac{(2x + 1)(x - 2)}{(x - 1)(x + 1)}, x \neq \dfrac{2}{3}, x \neq \dfrac{3}{2}$

15. $\dfrac{(x + 2)(2x + 3)}{x + 4}, x \neq 2$

17. $\dfrac{(x + 3)(x^2 + 1)}{x - 2}, x \neq 5$

19. $\dfrac{x + 4}{(x - 5)(x + 1)}, x \neq 1, x \neq 2, x \neq -2, x \neq -3$

21. xy

23. $2a$

25. $(b - 1)^2$

27. $(x - 2)(x + 3)$

29. $x(x + 1)(x - 1)$

31. $\dfrac{4}{a - 2}$

33. $\dfrac{x + 5}{3}$

35. $\dfrac{4(a + 1)}{(a - 2)(a + 2)}$

37. $\dfrac{4y - 15}{3xy}$

39. $\dfrac{5 - 2x}{2(x + 3)}$

41. $\dfrac{23x + 24}{6(x + 3)(x - 3)}$

43. $\dfrac{3x^2 - 4x - 1}{(x - 1)(x - 2)(x + 1)}$

45. $\dfrac{5x - 3}{(x + 2)(x - 1)}$

47. $\dfrac{x^2 + x + 3}{(x + 1)(x + 2)(x + 3)}$

49. $\dfrac{3x^2 + 10x + 1}{(x + 4)(x - 1)(x + 1)}$

51. $\dfrac{x + 2}{x - 3}, x \neq 0$

53. $\dfrac{x(x + 1)}{x - 1}, x \neq 0$

55. $4x(x + 4), x \neq 0, x \neq 4$

57. $\dfrac{a + 2}{a + 1}, a \neq 0$

59. $a - b, a \neq -b, a \neq 0, b \neq 0$

61. $\dfrac{x - 2}{x}, x \neq -1$

63. $\dfrac{(y - 2)(y + 1)}{(y + 2)(y - 1)}, y \neq 0, y \neq -1$

65. $\dfrac{x + 1}{2x + 1}, x \neq -1, x \neq 0$

67. a. $\dfrac{\frac{1}{b}}{\frac{1}{a} + \frac{1}{b}} = \dfrac{a}{b + a}$

b. $\dfrac{\frac{1}{b}}{\frac{1}{a} + \frac{1}{b}} = \dfrac{a}{b + a}$

c. left-hand side cannot be simplified

d. left-hand side cannot be simplified

e. $(x^2 - y^2)^2 = x^4 - 2x^2y^2 + y^4$

f. left-hand side cannot be simplified

Exercise Set 1.6

1. x^6

3. b^4

5. $16x^4$

7. $-\dfrac{1}{128}$

9. y^{8n}

11. $-\dfrac{x^3}{y^3}$

13. x^{19}

15. $-32x^{10}$

17. x^{4n}

19. $\dfrac{1}{x^2}$

21. $30x^8$

23. 1

25. $\left(\dfrac{3}{2}\right)^n x^{2n} y^{3n}$

27. $(2x + 1)^{10}$

29. $2^{2n} a^{4n} b^{6n}$

31. $\dfrac{4}{3}$

33. 3

35. 81

37. $-x^3$

39. y^6

41. 25

43. $\dfrac{1}{3^6}$

45. x^9

47. 32

49. $2x^2y$

51. $\dfrac{a^4 b^6}{9}$

53. $-\dfrac{8y^{12}}{x^9}$

55. $\dfrac{a^9}{3b^4}$

57. $\dfrac{4a^{10}c^6}{b^8}$

59. $\dfrac{1}{a - 2b^2}$

61. $\dfrac{(a - b)^2}{a + b}$

63. $\dfrac{b + a}{b - a}$

67. 0.074

69. 0.0113

71. 9.1×10^{-3}

73. 2.3×10^1

75. 8.0×10^{-4}

77. 0.000893

79. $145,000$

81. 0.001253

83. 3.05×10^{-3}

85. 1.0833×10^4 persons per square mile

Exercise Set 1.7

1. 8

3. $\dfrac{1}{16}$

5. $2x^{13/12}$

7. $x^{5/36}$

9. $x^2 y^{12}$

11. $\dfrac{x^9}{y^6}$

13. $\sqrt[5]{\dfrac{1}{16}}$

15. $\sqrt[4]{a^3}$

17. $\sqrt[3]{\dfrac{144x^6}{y^4}}$

19. $8^{3/4}$

21. $(-8)^{-2/5}$

23. $\left(\dfrac{4a^3}{9}\right)^{-1/4}$

25. $\dfrac{2}{3}$

27. not real

29. 5

31. $\dfrac{5}{4}$

33. 54.82

35. 3, 4

37. $4\sqrt{3}$

39. $3\sqrt[3]{2}$

41. $y^2\sqrt[3]{y}$

43. $2x^2\sqrt[4]{6}\sqrt{x}$

45. $x^2y\sqrt{xy}$

47. $2x^2y\sqrt[4]{y}$

49. $\dfrac{\sqrt{5}}{5}$

51. $\dfrac{\sqrt{3y}}{3y}$

53. $2x\sqrt{2x}$

55. $y^2\sqrt[3]{x^2y}$

57. $7\sqrt{3}$

59. $7\sqrt{x}$

61. $4\sqrt{3}$

63. $11\sqrt{5} - \sqrt[3]{5}$

65. $-5\sqrt{5}$

67. $3 + 4\sqrt{3}$

69. $3xy$

71. $5 - 2\sqrt{6}$

73. $3x - 4y - \sqrt{6xy}$

75. $\dfrac{3(3 - \sqrt{2})}{7}$

77. $\dfrac{2(4 + \sqrt{3})}{13}$

79. $\dfrac{-3(3\sqrt{a} - 1)}{9a - 1}$

81. $\dfrac{-3(5 - \sqrt{5y})}{5(5 - y)}$

83. $3 + 2\sqrt{2}$

85. $2 + \sqrt{6} + 3\sqrt{2} + 2\sqrt{3}$

87. $\dfrac{2}{\sqrt{12} + \sqrt{10}}$

89. $\dfrac{-1}{\sqrt{x} + 4}$

Exercise Set 1.8

1. 1

3. $-i$

5. $-i$

7. 1

9. i

11. $-\dfrac{3}{4} + 0i$

13. $0 + 5i$

15. $0 - 6i$

17. $3 - 7i$

19. $0.3 - 7\sqrt{2}\,i$

21. $-2 - 4i$

23. $x = \dfrac{2}{3}, y = -8$

25. $x = -1, y = -\dfrac{9}{2}$

27. $3 + i$

29. $5 + i$

31. $-5 - 4i$

33. $2 - 6i$

35. $-1 - \dfrac{i}{2}$

37. $5 + 0i$

39. $2 + 14i$

41. $4 - 7i$

43. 5

45. 25

47. 20

49. $-\dfrac{13}{10} + \dfrac{11i}{10}$

51. $-\dfrac{7}{25} - \dfrac{24i}{25}$

53. $\dfrac{8}{5} - \dfrac{i}{5}$

55. $\dfrac{5}{3} - \dfrac{2i}{3}$

57. $\dfrac{4}{5} + \dfrac{8i}{5}$

59. $\dfrac{4}{25} - \dfrac{3i}{25}$

61. $\dfrac{9}{10} + \dfrac{3i}{10}$

63. $0 + \dfrac{i}{5}$

65. 0

67. 3

75. $y \geq 5$

Review Exercises

1. $\{1, 2, 3, 4\}$

2. $\{-3, -2, -1\}$

3. $\{2\}$

4. T

5. F

6. F

7. F

8. additive inverse

9. distributive

10. commutative (addition)

11. multiplicative identity

12.

13.

14.

15. -1

16. $\dfrac{3}{2}$

17. $\$51$

18. c

19. $-0.5, 7$

20. $-7, 5$

21. $a^2b^2 - 3a^2b + 4b$

22. $2x^3 + 3x^2 - 2x$

23. $12x^3 + 12x^2 + 3x$

24. $2(x + 1)(x - 1)$

25. $(x + 5y)(x - 5y)$

26. $(2a + 3b)(a + 3)$

27. $(4x - 1)(x + 5)$

28. $(x + 1)(x - 1)(x^2 + 1)(x^4 + 1)$

29. $(3r^2 + 2s^2)(9r^4 - 6r^2s^2 + 4s^4)$

30. $-\dfrac{6(y - 1)}{(x - y)xy^2}$

31. $-\dfrac{3(x + 2)}{2y}$

32. $\dfrac{3x(x + 1)}{2x - 1}, x \neq 0, x \neq 1, x \neq 3$

33. $\dfrac{a - 2b}{a - b}$

34. $2x^2(x + 2)(x - 2)$

35. $x(x - 1)^2$

36. $5y^2(x - 1)^2$

37. $4x^2(y + 1)^2(y - 1)$

38. $\dfrac{2(a^2 - 2)}{(a + 2)(a - 2)}$

39. $\dfrac{-2x - 5}{(x + 4)(x - 4)}$

40. $\dfrac{x - 7}{(x - 1)^2(x + 2)}$

41. $\dfrac{x^3 - x^2 + 1}{x - 1}$

42. $\dfrac{b^9}{8a^6}$

43. 2

44. $\dfrac{1}{x^4y^8}$

45. x^3

46. $4\sqrt{5}$

47. $\dfrac{\sqrt{3}}{3}$

48. $x^3y^2\sqrt{xy}$

49. $2x^2y\sqrt[4]{2y^2}$

50. $\dfrac{x - \sqrt{xy}}{x - y}$

51. 2.48×10^1

52. $\dfrac{1}{\sqrt{x} + \sqrt{y}}$

53. $3\sqrt{|xy|}$

54. $8 + 2\sqrt{15}$

55. a. 1.97   b. 15,689

c. 2.83   d. 9488.53

e. -1.93 f. -0.62

g. 1.94   h. 0.93

i. 0.20   j. 3.95

56. $x = -2, y = 4$

57. $-i$

58. $8 - i$

59. $3 + 4i$

60. $17 + 6i$

61. $-\dfrac{1}{13} - \dfrac{18i}{13}$

62. a. $\dfrac{bc + ac + ab}{abc}$ b. $\dfrac{(b + a)(cd)}{ab(d + c)}$

63. 1150 calories per day

64. a. 4

b. (president, vice-president, secretary), (president, vice-president, treasurer), (president, secretary, treasurer), (vice-president, secretary, treasurer)

65. 100 children   66. $100

67. $8x^2 - 2xy$

68. $(4 - 2s)(5 - 2s)s, 0 \leq s \leq 2$

69. a. $x^3 - y^3$

b. $x^4 - y^4$

c. $x^5 - y^5$

70. $x^n - y^n = (x - y)(x^{n-1} + x^{n-2}y + x^{n-3}y^2 + \cdots + xy^{n-2} + y^{n-1})$

71. $13 \times 17 = (20 - 7)(20 - 3)$

$= (20)(20) - 20(3) - (7)(20) + 21$

$= 400 - 60 - 140 + 21$

$= 221$

72. $a(c + d) - b(c + d); (a - b)c + (a - b)d; (a - b)(c + d)$

73. $F = 2, O = 9, R = 7, T = 8, Y = 6, E = 5, N = 0, S = 3, I = 1, X = 4$

74. 496; 8128; 33,550,336

75. a. 3.33×10^{17} seconds

b. 3.15×10^7 seconds

c. 1.06×10^{10} years

76. $[x + (x + x^{1/2})^{1/2}]^{1/2}$

77. yes

79. a. $\dfrac{h + 2}{h(\sqrt{x + h + 1} + \sqrt{x - 1})}$

b. $\dfrac{1}{\sqrt{3 + x} + \sqrt{3}}$

81. $18 - 14i$

Review Test

1. $\{2, 4, 6, 8, 10, 12\}$ 2. $\{3\}$

3. F   4. F

5. commutative (multiplication)

6. multiplicative inverse

7.

8.

9. -1 10. 2

11. 25   12. $-\dfrac{7}{3}$

13. b 14. $-2.2, 5$

15. $14, 6$

16. $4xy + 3x + 4y + 1$

17. $3a^3 + 5a^2 + 3a + 10$

18. $4a^2b(2ab^4 - 3a^3b + 4)$

19. $(2 - 3x)(2 + 3x)$

20. $\dfrac{6m^5}{n^2}$

21. $\dfrac{1 - x}{x + 1}$

22. $4x^2(x + 1)(x - 1)(x - 2)$

23. $\dfrac{11x - 15}{3(x^2 - 9)}$

24. $\dfrac{2}{x + 1}$

25. $\dfrac{1}{x^{17}}$

26. y^{n+1}

27. -1

28. $\dfrac{4a^4}{b^2}$

29. 0

30. $32 - 10\sqrt{7}$

31. $-\dfrac{11\sqrt{xy}}{4}$

32. $x \le 2$

33. $-1 + 0i$

34. $16 - 11i$

35. $\dfrac{8}{5} + \dfrac{9}{5}i$

Chapter 2

Exercise Set 2.1

1. T

3. T

5. -2

7. $-\dfrac{2}{3}$

9. 6

11. $-\dfrac{4}{3}$

13. $\dfrac{3}{2}$

15. $-\dfrac{10}{3}$

17. -2

19. 5

21. $-\dfrac{7}{2}$

23. 1

25. $\dfrac{8}{5 - k}$

27. $\dfrac{6 + k}{5}$

29. $\dfrac{10}{3}$

31. 1

33. 4

35. 4

37. 12

39. 2

41. $\dfrac{12}{7}$

43. none

45. I

47. C

49. T

51. F

53. T

55. a. $\dfrac{2}{9}$ b. $\dfrac{41}{333}$

c. $\dfrac{134}{99}$ d. 1

57. a. $w = \dfrac{cd}{c + d}$ b. $x = \dfrac{1}{a - c}$

c. $y = \dfrac{2c^2}{a - b - c}$

Exercise Set 2.2

1. $2n + 3$

3. $6n - 5 = 26$

5. $16, 28$

7. $6, 7, 8$

9. $68°$

11. 4 meters and 8 meters

13. 10 nickels, 25 dimes

15. 300 children, 400 adults

17. 61 three-dollar tickets, 40 five-dollar tickets, 20 six-dollar tickets

19. $11,636.36 on 10-speeds, $4363.64 on 3-speeds

21. $7000

23. 20 hours

25. 50 miles per hour and 54 miles per hour

27. 40 kilometers per hour, 80 kilometers per hour

29. Ceylon: 2.4 ounces, Formosa: 5.6 ounces

31. 13.5 gallons

33. $\dfrac{1}{12}, \dfrac{1}{4}; -\dfrac{1}{4}, -\dfrac{1}{12}$

35. 2.4 hours

37. $4\dfrac{1}{2}$ days, 9 days

39. 8 hours

41. 140 miles per hour

43. $\dfrac{C}{2\pi}$

45. $\dfrac{5(F - 32)}{9}$

47. $\dfrac{2A}{h} - b^1$

49. $\dfrac{ff_1}{f_1 - f}$

51. $\dfrac{a + Sr}{r + S}$

53. a. $2(r + s)$ b. $0.05|r - s|$

    c. $2s - 5$ d. $\dfrac{r}{s}$

    e. $r^2 + s^2$ f. $\dfrac{r + s}{2}$

    g. $6r - 4s$

55. 10, 12, 14

57. $\dfrac{30}{7}$ quarts

59. 80 miles

Exercise Set 2.3

1. $1, 2$

3. $1, -2$

5. $-2, -4$

7. $0, 4$

9. $\dfrac{1}{2}, 2$

11. ± 2

13. $\dfrac{1}{3}, \dfrac{1}{2}$

15. ± 3

17. $\pm\sqrt{5}$

19. $-\dfrac{5}{2} \pm \sqrt{2}$

21. $\dfrac{5 \pm 2\sqrt{2}}{3}$

23. $\pm\dfrac{8i}{3}$

25. $4, -2$

27. $-\dfrac{1}{2}, 4$

29. $\dfrac{1}{3}, -3$

31. $-\dfrac{1}{2} \pm \dfrac{i}{2}$

33. $1, -\dfrac{3}{4}$

35. $-\dfrac{1}{3} \pm \dfrac{\sqrt{2}i}{3}$

37. $0, -\dfrac{3}{2}$

39. $\dfrac{2}{5} \pm \dfrac{\sqrt{11}i}{5}$

41. $\dfrac{2}{5} \pm \dfrac{\sqrt{21}i}{5}$

43. $\dfrac{2}{3}, -1$

45. $\pm\dfrac{2\sqrt{3}}{3}$

47. $0, -\dfrac{3}{4}$

49. $-\dfrac{1}{2} \pm \dfrac{\sqrt{11}}{2}$

51. $-2, \dfrac{2}{3}$

53. $-\dfrac{5}{4} \pm \dfrac{\sqrt{7}i}{4}$

55. $\pm\dfrac{1}{2}$

57. $-\dfrac{1}{4} \pm \dfrac{\sqrt{11}i}{4}, 0$

59. $\pm\sqrt{c^2 - a^2}$

61. $\pm\sqrt{\dfrac{3V}{\pi h}}$

63. $\dfrac{-v \pm \sqrt{v^2 + 2gs}}{g}$

65. two complex roots

67. one real double root

69. two real roots

71. two real roots

73. two complex roots

75. two complex roots

77. two real roots

79. one real double root

81. 4

83. $0, -8$

85. 4

87. 3

89. $0, 4$

Exercise Set 2.4

1. A: 3 hours; B: 6 hours

3. roofer: 6 hours; assistant: 12 hours

5. $L = 12$ feet, $W = 4$ feet

7. $L = 8$ centimeters, $W = 6$ centimeters

9. 10 feet

11. 5 or $\dfrac{1}{5}$

13. $3, 7; -3, -7$

15. 6, 8

17. 150 shares

19. 8 days

21. 16 centimeters from the end

23. 4.5 seconds

25. 14%

27. $v = 0.99\,c$

29. a. $t = 2$ seconds

    b. $t = \dfrac{-w_0 \pm \sqrt{w_0^2 - 2\alpha_0(\theta_0 - \theta)}}{\alpha_0}$

Exercise Set 2.5

1. $[-5, 1)$

3. $(9, \infty)$

5. $[-12, -3]$

7. $(3, 7)$

9. $(-6, -4]$

11. $5 \leq x \leq 8$

13. $x > 3$

15. $x \leq 5$

17. $x \geq 0$

19. $x < 4$

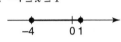

21. $x < -6$

23. $x \geq 5$

25. $a > -1$

27. $y < -\dfrac{1}{2}$

29. $x \geq 0$

31. $r < 2$

33. $x \geq 1$

35. $x > \dfrac{5}{3}$

37. $(-\infty, 2]$

39. $[2, \infty)$

41. $\left(-\infty, \dfrac{3}{2}\right)$

43. $(-12, \infty)$

45. $\left(-\infty, \dfrac{9}{2}\right)$

47. $(-\infty, -6]$

49. $\left(-\infty, \dfrac{3}{2}\right)$

51. $(-\infty, 7]$

53. $\left(-\dfrac{1}{2}, \dfrac{5}{4}\right]$

55. $[-3, -2]$

57. $(-3, -1]$

59. $[-1, 2)$

61. 98

63. 5

65. 2924

67. $L \leq 20$ meters

69. $-4 \leq x \leq 1$

71. $x \leq -\dfrac{2}{3}, x \geq 2$

73. $r \leq -4, r \geq 0$

75. $x < -4, x \geq 6$

77. $x \leq 1, x > \dfrac{3}{2}$

79. $x \leq -\dfrac{5}{4}$

81. $-\dfrac{5}{2} \leq x \leq 2, x \geq 4$

83. $x \leq -2, x \geq 5$

85. $-\dfrac{2}{3} \leq x \leq 2$

87. $x \leq -\dfrac{2}{3}, x > \dfrac{3}{2}$

89. $-2 < x \leq \dfrac{1}{2}$

91. $-2 \leq x \leq -\dfrac{1}{2}$

93. $x < -\dfrac{5}{2}, -1 < x < \dfrac{2}{3}$

95. $-\dfrac{1}{2} \leq x \leq \dfrac{1}{2}, x \geq 3$

97. $x \leq -\dfrac{1}{2}, x \geq 3$

99. $x \leq -1, x \geq -\dfrac{1}{2}$

101. $\dfrac{1}{2} \leq t \leq 2$

103. 40 centimeters

105. 12 feet

107. 5 amperes

109. 170

Exercise Set 2.6

1. $1, -5$

3. $3, 1$

5. $2, -\dfrac{4}{3}$

7. $\dfrac{3}{2}, -3$

9. $4, -2$

11. $x < -4$ or $x > 2$

13. $x < -\dfrac{1}{2}$ or $x > 1$

15. $-\dfrac{1}{3} < x < 1$

17. $(-\infty, -1], [7, \infty)$

19. $\left(-\dfrac{7}{2}, \dfrac{9}{2}\right)$

21. no solution

23. $(-\infty, -7), (17, \infty)$

25. $0, -1$

27. $2, 4$

31. $|x - 100| \leq 2; 98 \leq x \leq 102$

33. $|x| > 6$

35. $|x - 3| \geq 2$

37. $|x - 4| = 10; x = -6, x = 14$

39. $x = \dfrac{22}{7}, x = \dfrac{14}{5}$

Review Exercises

1. $\dfrac{8}{3}$

2. 0

3. $\dfrac{10}{3}$

4. $\dfrac{k}{2(2k+1)}$

5. $\dfrac{10}{3}$ centimeters $\times \dfrac{8}{3}$ centimeters

6. 5 quarters, 14 dimes

7. 240 miles

8. 6 hours

9. F

10. F

11. $5, -4$

12. $\dfrac{1}{2}, \dfrac{4}{3}$

13. $1 \pm \sqrt{5}i$

14. $\dfrac{2 \pm \sqrt{2}i}{2}$

15. $-1, \dfrac{1}{3}$

16. $\pm\dfrac{3}{7}$

17. $\pm\dfrac{\sqrt{3\pi k}}{k}$

18. $-4, 3$

19. two real roots

20. one real double root

21. two complex roots

22. 4

23. 6

24. $\pm1, \pm\sqrt{3}$

25. $-\dfrac{1}{2}, -1$

26. 60

27. $x \geq 1$

28. $-\dfrac{9}{2} \leq x < \dfrac{5}{2}$

29. $(-\infty, 8)$

30. $\left(\dfrac{5}{2}, \infty\right)$

31. $[-9, \infty)$

32. $\dfrac{5}{3}, -3$

33. $x = -1, x = \dfrac{3}{2}$

34. $x > 3$ or $x < -4$

35. $\left(\dfrac{1}{5}, \dfrac{3}{5}\right)$

36. $\left(-\infty, -\dfrac{4}{3}\right], \left[\dfrac{8}{3}, \infty\right)$

37. $x \leq -\dfrac{3}{2}, x \geq 2$

38. $[-5, 1]$

39. $(-\infty, -5), \left[-\dfrac{1}{2}, \infty\right)$

40. $\left(-2, -\dfrac{3}{2}\right), (3, \infty)$

41. 5 chairs

Review Test

1. $\dfrac{3}{4}$

2. $\dfrac{8}{13}$

3. $\dfrac{18}{5}$ meters, $\dfrac{28}{5}$ meters, $\dfrac{29}{5}$ meters

4. \$6000 at 6.5%, \$6200 at 7.5%, \$12,300 at 9%

5. T

6. $-2, 7$

7. $\dfrac{1 \pm \sqrt{79}i}{10}$

8. $-\dfrac{3}{4}, \dfrac{1}{3}$

9. $\dfrac{5 \pm 3i}{2}$

10. $1, -\dfrac{3}{2}$

11. two real roots

12. two complex numbers

13. -4

14. $\pm\sqrt{2}i, \pm\dfrac{\sqrt{3}}{3}$

15. 8 meters × 12 meters

16. $-2 \leq x < 1$

17.

$\left(-\infty, \dfrac{15}{2}\right]$

18. $[-4, 4]$

19. $\dfrac{5}{2}, -2$

20. $-2 \leq x \leq 3$

21. $\left(-\infty, -\dfrac{4}{3}\right), (2, \infty)$

22. $x \leq \dfrac{1}{3}, x \geq 1$

23. $\left(-\infty, \dfrac{1}{2}\right], [1, \infty)$

24. $\left[-2, \dfrac{2}{3}\right], [1, \infty)$

25. $(-\infty, -1), (2, \infty)$

Chapter 3

Exercise Set 3.1

1.

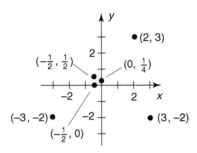

3. $3\sqrt{2}; \left(\frac{7}{2}, \frac{5}{2}\right)$

5. $4\sqrt{2}; (-3, -3)$

7. $\frac{\sqrt{1345}}{6}; \left(-\frac{2}{3}, -\frac{5}{4}\right)$

9. $\overline{BC} = \sqrt{37}$

11. $\overline{RS} = \frac{\sqrt{2}}{2}$

13. no

15. yes

21. $2\sqrt{10} + 7 + 5\sqrt{2} + \sqrt{37}$

25. $0, 5$

27. x-intercept: -2
    y-intercept: 4

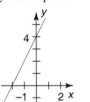

29. x-intercept: 0
    y-intercept: 0

31. x-intercept: -3
    y-intercept: 3

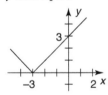

33. x-intercept: $\pm\sqrt{3}$
    y-intercept: 3

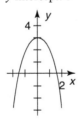

35. x-intercept: -1
    y-intercept: 1

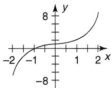

37. x-intercept: -1
    y-intercept: ± 1

XSCL = 5, YSCL = 5
x-intercept: 7
y-intercept: 7

39.

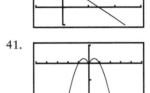

41.

XSCL = 1, YSCL = 1
x-intercepts: $-1, 0, 1$
y-intercept: 0

43.

XSCL = 1, YSCL = 1
x-intercepts: $-0.6, 0, 1.6$
y-intercept: 0

45. none

47. x-axis

49. x-axis

51. x-axis

53. none

55. y-axis

57. all

59. origin

63. $(1, 2)$

65. $x = -2, y = 4$

Exercise Set 3.2

1. domain: all reals
   range: all reals

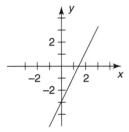

3. domain: all reals
   range: all reals

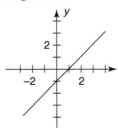

5. domain: $x \geq 1$
   range: $y \geq 0$

7. domain: $x \geq \dfrac{3}{2}$

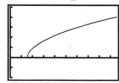

XMIN = 0, XMAX = 9.5, XSCL = 1
YMIN = −2, YMAX = 5, YSCL = 1

9. domain: $x > 2$

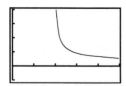

XMIN = 0, XMAX = 5, XSCL = 1
YMIN = −1, YMAX = 4, YSCL = 1

11. domain: $x \geq 1,\ x \neq 2$

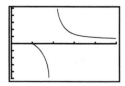

XMIN = 0, XMAX = 5, XSCL = 1
YMIN = −5, YMAX = 5, YSCL = 1

13. $\dfrac{7}{2}$

15. $\dfrac{3}{2}$

17. 5

19. $2a^2 + 5$

21. $6x^2 + 15$

23. $4a + 2h$

25. $\dfrac{1 + 2x}{x^2}$

27. $x^2 - 2x$

29. $2a + 2 + h$

31. $\dfrac{3x - 1}{x^2 + 1}$

33. $\dfrac{2(4x^2 + 1)}{6x - 1}$

35. -0.21

37. $\dfrac{2(a - 1)}{4a^2 + 4a - 3}$

39. $\dfrac{a - 1}{a(a + 4)}$

41. $I(x) = 0.28x$

43. $d(C) = \dfrac{C}{\pi}$

45. volume $= (10 - 2x)(12 - 2x)x$, where x is the height

47. a. $(400 + 10x)(300 - 5x)$, where x is the number of
    $5.00 decreases in price

    b. $125,000

Exercise Set 3.3

1. increasing: $(-\infty, \infty)$

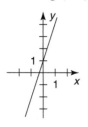

the default viewing window
XSCL = 1, YSCL = 1

3. increasing: $x \geq 0$
    decreasing: $x \leq 0$

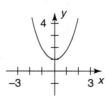

XMIN = −5, XMAX = 5, XSCL = 1
YMIN = −2, YMAX = 10, YSCL = 1

5. increasing: $x \leq 0$
   decreasing: $x \geq 0$

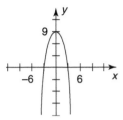

XMIN = -5, XMAX = 5, XSCL = 1
YMIN = -10, YMAX = 10, YSCL = 1

7. increasing $x \geq -\dfrac{1}{2}$

   decreasing: $x \leq -\dfrac{1}{2}$

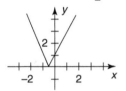

XMIN = -6, XMAX = 6, XSCL = 1
YMIN = -4, YMAX = 4, YSCL = 1

9. increasing: $x > -1$
   decreasing: $x \leq -1$

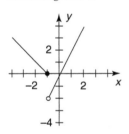

XMIN = -6, XMAX = 6, XSCL = 1
YMIN = -4, YMAX = 4, YSCL = 1

11. increasing: $x \leq 2$
    constant: $x \geq 2$

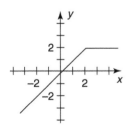

XMIN = -4, XMAX = 8, XSCL = 1
YMIN = -4, YMAX = 4, YSCL = 1

13. increasing: $-3 < x \leq 0$
    decreasing: $0 \leq x < 1$, $x > 2$
    constant: $1 \leq x \leq 2$

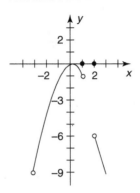

15. constant: $x < -2$, $-2 \leq x \leq -1$, $x > -1$

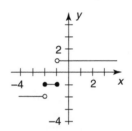

17.

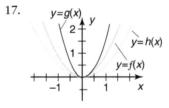

XMIN = -5, XMAX = 5, XSCL = 1
YMIN = -2, YMAX = 10, YSCL = 1

19.

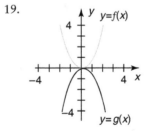

XMIN = -5, XMAX = 5, XSCL = 1
YMIN = -6, YMAX = 6, YSCL = 1

21.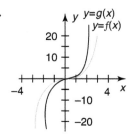

XMIN = −5, XMAX 5, XSCL = 1
YMIN = −6, YMAX = 6, YSCL = 1

23.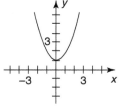

XMIN = −5, XMAX = 5, XSCL = 1
YMIN = −6, YMAX = 6, YSCL = 1

25.
$$C(u) = \begin{cases} 6.50 & \text{if } \ 0 \leq u \leq 100 \\ 6.50 + 0.06(u - 100) & \text{if } \ 100 < u \leq 200 \\ 12.50 + 0.05(u - 200) & \text{if } \ \ \ u > 200 \end{cases}$$

27.
$$R(x) = \begin{cases} 30{,}000 & \text{if } \ 0 \leq x \leq 100 \\ 400x - x^2 & \text{if } \ x > 100 \end{cases}$$

29. a. $C(m) = 14 + 0.08m$

b. $m \geq 0$

c. $22

31. a.
$$f(t) = \begin{cases} 2 & \text{if } 0 < t \leq \dfrac{1}{2} \\ 3.20 & \text{if } \dfrac{1}{2} < t \leq 1 \\ 4.40 & \text{if } 1 < t \leq \dfrac{3}{2} \\ 5.60 & \text{if } \dfrac{3}{2} < t \leq 2 \\ 6.80 & \text{if } 2 < t \leq \dfrac{5}{2} \\ 800 & \text{if } t > \dfrac{5}{2} \end{cases}$$

b. $5.60

c.

Graphs for Exercises 32–36

a.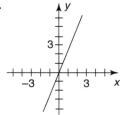

the default viewing window
XSCL = 1, YSCL = 1

b.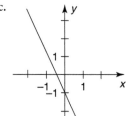

EQUAL viewing rectangle
XSCL = 1, YSCL = 1

c.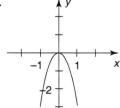

EQUAL viewing rectangle
XSCL = 1, YSCL = 1

d.

EQUAL viewing rectangle
XSCL = 1, YSCL = 1

e.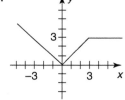

XMIN = −9, XMAX = 9, XSCL = 1
YMIN = −4, YMAX = 8, YSCL = 1

f.

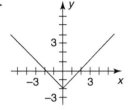

EQUAL viewing rectangle
XSCL = 1, YSCL = 1

g.

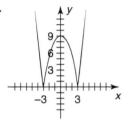

XMIN = −10, XMAX = 10, XSCL = 1
YMIN = −6, YMAX = 15, YSCL = 1

h.

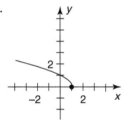

XMIN = −10, XMAX = 5, XSCL = 1
YMIN = −5, YMAX = 5, YSCL = 1

33. a. range : $y \geq 1$

b. range : all reals

c. range : all reals

d. range : $y \leq 0$

e. range : $y \geq 0$

f. range : $y \geq -2$

g. range : $y \geq 0$

h. range : $y \geq 0$

35. a. $(-\infty, 0]$

b. never

c. $(-\infty, \infty)$

d. $[0, \infty)$

e. $(-\infty, 0]$

f. $(-\infty, 0]$

g. $(-\infty, -3], [0, 3]$

h. $(-\infty, 1]$

37.

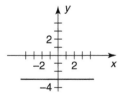

39.

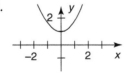

41.

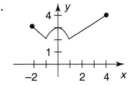

43.

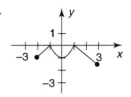

45.

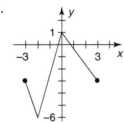

47.

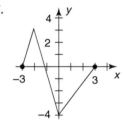

49.

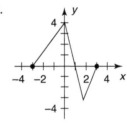

51.

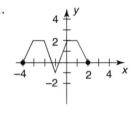

53.

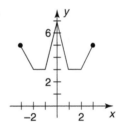

55.

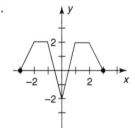

57.

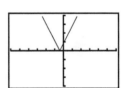

EQUAL viewing rectangle
XSCL = 1, YSCL = 1

59. a. Let x = the number of trees. Total number of bushels of apples = $(20 + x)(40 - x)$.

b.

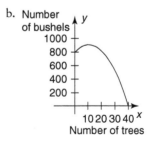

c. 10 trees

d. 900 bushels

Exercise Set 3.4

1. 2; increasing

3. $-\dfrac{3}{2}$, decreasing

5. -1; decreasing

9. $2x - y + 5 = 0$

11. $3x - y = 0$

13. $2x - y = 0$

15. $2x - 3y = 0$

17. $2x - y = 0$

19. $3x - y + 2 = 0$

21. $y - 2 = 0$

23. $x - 3y - 15 = 0$

25. $m = -\dfrac{3}{4}, b = \dfrac{5}{4}$

27. $m = 0, b = 4$

29. $m = -\dfrac{3}{4}, b = -\dfrac{1}{2}$

31. a. $y = 3$

    b. $x = -6$

33. a. $y = 0$

    b. $x = -7$

35. a. $y = -9$

    b. $x = 9$

37. a. -3

    b. $\dfrac{1}{3}$

39. a. $\dfrac{4}{3}$

    b. $-\dfrac{3}{4}$

41. a. $3x + y - 6 = 0$

    b. $x - 3y + 8 = 0$

43. a. $3x + 5y - 1 = 0$

    b. $5x - 3y + 21 = 0$

45. a. $F = \dfrac{9}{5}C + 32$

    b. $68°F$

47. $1,000,000

49. 5

51. $f(x) = 8x + 13$

61. a.

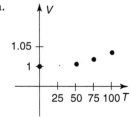

    b. not a line

63. a.

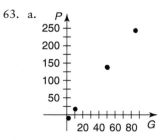

    b. $P = 3G - 10 \ or \ y = 3x - 10$

    c. XMIN = 0, XMAX = 100, XSCL = 10
       YMIN = -50, YMAX = 250, YSCL = 50

65. 356.35 miles per hour

67. no

69. a. 1

    b. 0

    c. 1

    d. $\dfrac{4}{7}$

    e. $\dfrac{1}{2}$

    f. $\dfrac{7}{10}$

    g. It is at rest during this time.

71. a. $p = \dfrac{4}{9}d + 15$

    b. 4815 pounds

    c. 189 feet

    d.

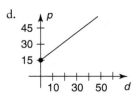

73. a. $V = \begin{cases} -2000t + 20{,}500 & \text{if } 0 < t \le 6 \\ 450t + 5800 & \text{if } t > 6 \end{cases}$

    b.

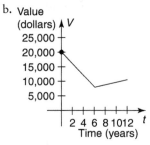

    c. $10,300

Exercise Set 3.5

1. $x^2 + x - 1$

3. $x^2 - x + 3$

5. $x^3 - 2x^2 + x - 2$

7. $\dfrac{x^2 + 1}{x - 2}$

9. domain of *f*: all reals
   domain of *g*: all reals

11. $4x^2 + 2x + 1$

13. 21

15. $4x^2 + 10x + 7$

17. $8x^2 - 6x + 1$

19. $x + 6, x \geq -2$

21. 29

23. all reals

25. $(f \circ g)(x) = x + 1; (g \circ f)(x) = x + 1$

27. $(f \circ g)(x) = \dfrac{x - 1}{x}, x \neq 1;$

   $(g \circ f)(x) = -\dfrac{x + 1}{x}, x \neq -1$

29. $f(x) = x + 3; g(x) = x^2$

31. $f(x) = x^8; g(x) = 3x + 2$

33. $f(x) = x^{1/3}; g(x) = x^3 - 2x^2$

35. $f(x) = |x|; g(x) = x^2 - 4$

37. $f(x) = \sqrt{x}; g(x) = 4 - x$

45. $f^{-1}(x) = \dfrac{x - 3}{2}$

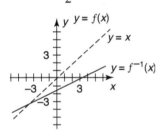

47. $f^{-1}(x) = \dfrac{3 - x}{2}$

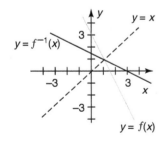

49. $f^{-1}(x) = 3x + 15$

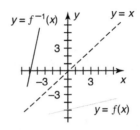

51. $f^{-1}(x) = (x - 1)^{1/3}$

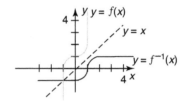

53. (b), (d), (e), (h), (i)

55. yes

57. no

59. yes

61. no

65. $\dfrac{x - b}{a}$

67. a. $C = \dfrac{5}{9}F - \dfrac{160}{9}$

   b. $F = \dfrac{9}{5}C + 32$

69. a. $(f \circ g)(p_m) = \dfrac{80{,}000}{p_m} - 5000$

   b. The expression gives the supply as a function of the price of a microchip.

71. a. $(g - f)(n) = 20n - 5500$

   b. The expression defines the profit function.

   c. $(g - f)(500) = 4500; (g - f)(250) = -500$

   If 500 items are sold, there is a \$4500 profit; if 250 items are sold, there is a \$500 loss.

   d. 275

   e. The result to part (d) is the break-even point, that is, if the Pirates Baseball Club Store sells 275 items, there is no profit and no loss.

Exercise Set 3.6

1. a. 4

    b. $y = 4x$

    c.

x	2	3	4	6	8	12	20	30
y	8	12	16	24	32	48	80	120

3. a. $-\dfrac{1}{32}$

    b. $-\dfrac{3}{8}$

7. a. -3

    b. $-\dfrac{1}{4}$

11. a. $M = \dfrac{r^2}{s^2}$

    b. $\dfrac{36}{25}$

15. a. 400 feet

    b. 7 seconds

5. a. $\dfrac{1}{10}$

    b. $\dfrac{5}{2}$

9. a. 512

    b. $\dfrac{512}{125}$

13. a. $T = \dfrac{16pv^3}{u^2}$

    b. $\dfrac{2}{3}$

17. $\dfrac{40}{3}$ ohms

19. a. $\dfrac{800}{9}$ candlepower

    b. 8 feet

21. 6

23. 120 candlepower per square foot

25. a. $I = \dfrac{k}{d^2}$

    b. 7.18 watts per square meter

27. 1456.88

29. a. 23.44 kilograms per cubic centimeter

    b. 111.54°F

31. a. $L = \dfrac{kwl^2}{d}$

    b. $\dfrac{32}{3}$ pounds per square foot

    c. 800 pounds

    d. The load is quadrupled.

    e. The load is quadrupled.

Review Exercises

1. $\sqrt{61}$

2. $\sqrt{65}$

3.

4.

5. x-axis

7. yes

9. $x \geq \dfrac{5}{3}$

11. 226

6. all

8. yes

10. $x \neq -1$

12. ±3

13.

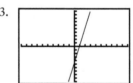

the default viewing window
XSCL = 1, YSCL = 1

14.

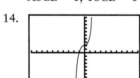

the default viewing window
XSCL = 1, YSCL = 1

15.

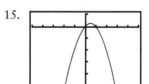

XMIN = −5, XMAX = 5, XSCL = 1
YMIN = −6, YMAX = 1, YSCL = 1

16.

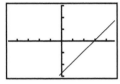

XMIN = −5, XMAX = 5, XSCL = 1
YMIN = −1, YMAX = 5, YSCL = 1

17.

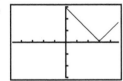

EQUAL viewing rectangle
XSCL = 1, YSCL = 1

18.

EQUAL viewing rectangle
XSCL = 1, YSCL = 1

19.

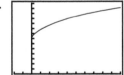

EQUAL viewing rectangle
XSCL = 1, YSCL = 1

20.

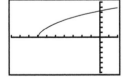

XMIN = −2, XMAX = 10, XSCL = 1
YMIN = 0, YMAX = 14, YSCL = 1

21.

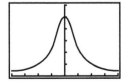

XMIN = −10, XMAX = 2, XSCL = 1
YMIN= −7, YMAX = 7, YSCL = 1

22.

XMIN = −4, XMAX = 4, XSCL = 1
YMIN = 0, YMAX = 6, YSCL = 1

23. 12

24. $y^2 - 3y + 2$

25. $3 + h$

26.

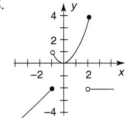

27. increasing: $x \le -1, 0 \le x \le 2$
decreasing: $-1 < x \le 0$
constant: $x > 2$

28. -5

29. -2

30.

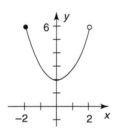

31.

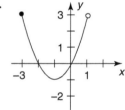

32.

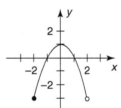

33.

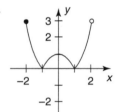

34.

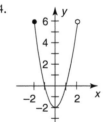

35.

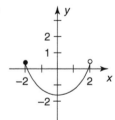

36. 3

37. $y - 3x - 6 = 0$

38. $x = -4$

39. $y = 3$

40. $y - 4x - 10 = 0$

41. $y - 2x - 5 = 0$

42. $x^2 + x$

43. 0

44. $\dfrac{1}{x - 1}$

45. $x \ne \pm 1$

46. $x^2 + 2x$

47. 4

48. $|x| - 2$

49. $x + 4 - 4\sqrt{x}$

50. 0

51. not defined

53.

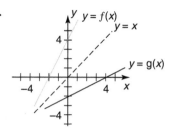

54. 160

55. 1

56. $-\dfrac{1}{4}$

57. a. $525 + 0.145x$

   b. $670

58. a. GPA = 0.004 SAT − 1.80

   b. SAT = 250 GPA + 450

   c. 1450

59. a. $\dfrac{1}{9}w$

   b. $\dfrac{8}{9}w$

   c. 35 grams of hydrogen and 280 grams of oxygen

60. a. $8\dfrac{1}{3}$ amperes, 14.4 ohms

   b. $4\dfrac{1}{6}$ amperes, 57.6 ohms

   c. $\dfrac{1}{2}$ ampere, 60 watts

Review Test

1. $3 + \sqrt{26} + \sqrt{41}$

2.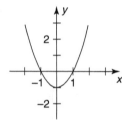

3. origin

4. $x \ge 0, x \ne 1$

5. 17

6. $8t^2 + 3$

7. increasing: $x \ge 0$
   decreasing: $-2 \le x \le 0$
   constant: $x < -2$

8. 0

9. 2

10.

11. $2y - 3x - 19 = 0$

12. $x = -3$

13. $m = \dfrac{1}{2}; b = 2$

14. $y = -1$

15. $3y + x - 7 = 0$

16. -3

17. $x^2(x - 1)$

18. $\dfrac{1}{4}$

20. -1024

21. 65,536

Cumulative Review Exercises

Chapters 1–3

1. yes

2. no

3. no

4. yes

5. yes

6. $a^2 b \sqrt{b}$

7. $\dfrac{3(7 + \sqrt{x})}{49 - x}$

8. $\dfrac{a^3}{b^{7/2}}$

9. $\dfrac{3 - x - x^3}{x(x^2 + 1)}$

10. $-\dfrac{x + 3}{x + 2}$

11. $u = -5, v = 1$

12. $5 - 12i$

13. $26 + 2i$

14. $88 + 234i$

15. $x^{11/6} - x^{5/2}$

16. $3\sqrt{3}$

17. $-\dfrac{2}{x}(1 + x)$

18. $\dfrac{1 + x^2}{x - 3x^2}$

19. $x(x + 1)(3x - 2)$

20. $(x - 1)^{2/3}(2x - 1)$

21. $\dfrac{2(\sqrt{x} + \sqrt{2})}{x - 2}$

22. $x \le \dfrac{5}{2}$

23. $h < -\dfrac{1}{2}, h > \dfrac{3}{2}$

24. $t \le -\dfrac{3}{2}, t \ge 4$

25. $-\sqrt{5} \le x \le -1, 1 \le x \le \sqrt{5}$

26. $x > \dfrac{1}{2}$

27. $\{x \mid x \ne \pm 1\}$

28. $\sqrt{61}$

29. a. $-4a^2 + 4a$

   b. $4, -4$

   c. $-2t - h$

30. a. 0

   b. $\dfrac{1}{2}$

   c.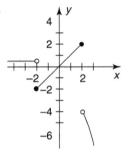

31. $0.05x + 0.07y + 0.035z$

32. $-1, \dfrac{3}{2}$

33. $\dfrac{1 \pm \sqrt{31}i}{4}$

34. 16

35. $-\dfrac{5}{9}$

36. $-\dfrac{4}{3}, \dfrac{1}{2}$

37. $7, -1$

38. -1

39. $-2 \le x \le \dfrac{3}{2}$

40. $x \le -17, x \ge 23$

41. $-2 \le x \le 5$

42. $2 < x \le 5$

43. $y = -1$

44. $y = -4x + 4$

45. a. -1

   b. $y = -x + 1$

   c. $x = -1$

   d. $y = x + 3$

46. $2\sqrt{10}$

47. x-intercepts: $-1, \dfrac{2}{3}$; y-intercepts: 2

48. $x + y = a$

49. $300, 40 months

50. Route 1

51. a. $[0, 1000]$

   b.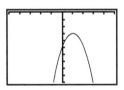

   c. i. $[-4000, 12{,}000]$

   ii. 600

   iii. $12,000

   d. 200

52. a. 0.6

   b. 45°F

Chapter 4

Exercise Set 4.1

1. $f(x) = (x - 3)^2 + 1$

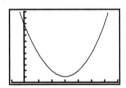

   XMIN = −1, XMAX = 7, XSCL = 1
   YMIN = 0, YMAX = 12, YSCL = 1

3. $f(x) = -2(x - 1)^2 - 3$

   XMIN = −5, XMAX = 5, XSCL = 1
   YMIN = −10, YMAX = 0, YSCL = 1

5. $f(x) = 2(x + \frac{3}{2})^2 + \frac{1}{2}$

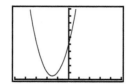

XMIN = −5, XMAX = 5, XSCL = 1
YMIN = 0, YMAX = 10, YSCL = 1

7. $f(x) = -(x + \frac{1}{2})^2 + \frac{1}{4}$

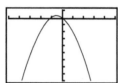

XMIN = −5, XMAX = 5, XSCL = 1
YMIN = −10, YMAX = 1, YSCL = 1

9. $f(x) = -2(x - 0)^2 + 5$

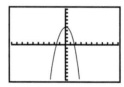

the default viewing window
XSCL = 1, YSCL = 1

11. vertex: $(1, -2)$
    x-intercepts: 0, 2
    y-intercept: 0

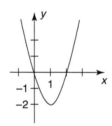

EQUAL viewing rectangle
XSCL = 1, YSCL = 1

13. vertex: $\left(\frac{1}{2}, 0\right)$

    x-intercept: $\frac{1}{2}$

    y-intercept: −1

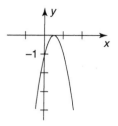

XMIN = −5, XMAX = 5, XSCL = 1
YMIN= −10, YMAX = 1, YSCL = 1

15. vertex: $(-2, 2)$
    y-intercept: 4

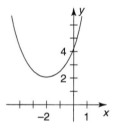

XMIN = −6, XMAX = 3, XSCL = 1
YMIN = −2, YMAX = 6, YSCL = 1

17. vertex: $\left(3, \frac{1}{2}\right)$

    x-intercept: 2, 4
    y-intercept: −4

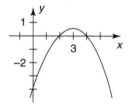

XMIN = −5, XMAX = 10, XSCL = 1
YMIN = −10, YMAX = 3, YSCL = 1

In Exercises 19–26, if $x - r$ is a factor of a quadratic function, then $(r, 0)$ is an x-intercept of the graph.

19.

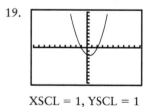

XSCL = 1, YSCL = 1

21.

XSCL = 1, YSCL = 1

23.

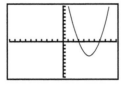

XSCL = 1, YSCL = 1

25.

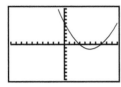

XSCL = 1, YSCL = 1

27. a. $r_1 = -4$
   $r_2 = 5$

   b. $f(x) = (x + 4)(x - 5) = x^2 - x - 20$

29. a. $r_1 = -8$
   $r_2 = -3$

   b. $f(x) = -(x + 8)(x + 3) = -x^2 - 11x - 24$

31. a. minimum

   b. $\dfrac{1}{3}$

   c. $\dfrac{11}{3}$

33. a. maximum

   b. 0

   c. -5

35. a. minimum

   b. $-\dfrac{5}{2}$

   c. $-\dfrac{25}{4}$

37. a. minimum

   b. $\dfrac{1}{8}$

   c. $-\dfrac{49}{32}$

39. 10, 10

41. 25, 25

43. $\left(\dfrac{1}{2}, \dfrac{\sqrt{2}}{2}\right)$

45. 250 feet × 500 feet

47. 10 feet × 10 feet

49. 2.5 seconds, 100 feet

51. $0.50

Exercise Set 4.2

9. leading term: x^7
   large values of $|x|, x > 0 : U$
   large values of $|x|, x < 0 : D$

   a.

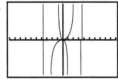

   XMIN = −10, XMAX = 10, XSCL = 1
   YMIN = −100, YMAX = 100, YSCL = 0

   b.

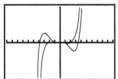

   XMIN = −10, XMAX = 10, XSCL = 1
   YMIN = −10,000, YMAX = 10,000, YSCL = 1

   c.

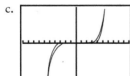

   XMIN = −10, XMAX = 10, XSCL = 1
   YMIN = −100,000, YMAX = 100,000, YSCL = 0

11. leading term: $-8x^3$
    large values of $|x|, x > 0 : D$
    large values of $|x|, x < 0 : U$

    a.

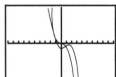

    XMIN = −10, XMAX = 10, XSCL = 1
    YMIN = −100, YMAX = 100, YSCL = 1

    b.

    XMIN = −10, XMAX = 10, XSCL = 1
    YMIN = −10,000, YMAX = 10,000, YSCL = 0

    c.

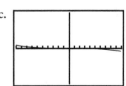

    XMIN = −10, XMAX = 10, XSCL = 1
    YMIN = −100,000, YMAX = 100,000, YSCL = 0

13. leading term: $-5x^{10}$

large values of $|x|$, $x > 0$: D

large values of $|x|$, $x < 0$: D

a.

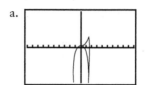

XMIN= -10, XMAX = 10, XSCL = 1
YMIN = -100, YMAX = 100, YSCL = 1

b.

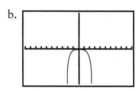

XMIN = -10, XMAX = 10, XSCL = 1
YMIN = $-10{,}000$, YMAX = 10,000, YSCL = 0

c.

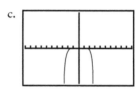

XMIN = -10, XMAX = 10, XSCL = 1
YMIN = $-100{,}000$, YMAX = 100,000, YSCL = 0

15. leading term: $4x^8$

large values of $|x|$, $x > 0$: U

large values of $|x|$, $x < 0$: U

a.

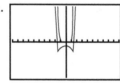

XMIN = -10, XMAX = 10, XSCL = 1
YMIN = -100, YMAX = 100, YSCL = 0

b.

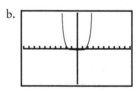

XMIN = -10, XMAX = 10, XSCL = 1
YMIN = $-10{,}000$, YMAX = 10,000, YSCL = 0

c.

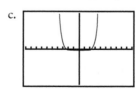

XMIN = -10, XMAX = 10, XSCL = 1
YMIN = $-100{,}000$, YMAX = 100,000, YSCL = 0

17. x-intercepts: $-2, \frac{1}{2}, 3$

$P(x) > 0$: $\left(-2, \frac{1}{2}\right)$, $(3, \infty)$

$P(x) < 0$: $(-\infty, -2)$, $\left(\frac{1}{2}, 3\right)$

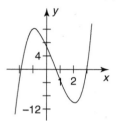

XMIN = -5, XMAX = 5, XSCL = 1
YMIN = -15, YMAX = 15, YSCL = 5

19. x-intercepts: $-\frac{5}{2}, 0, 1$

$P(x) > 0$: $\left(-\frac{5}{2}, 0\right)$, $(1, \infty)$

$P(x) < 0$: $\left(-\infty, -\frac{5}{2}\right)$, $(0, 1)$

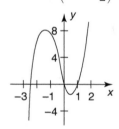

XMIN = -5, XMAX = 5, XSCL = 1
YMIN = -15, YMAX = 15, YSCL = 5

21. x-intercepts: $-2, 0, 3$

$P(x) > 0$: $(-\infty, -2)$, $(3, \infty)$

$P(x) < 0$: $(-2, 0)$, $(0, 3)$

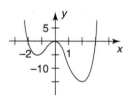

XMIN = -5, XMAX = 5, XSCL = 1
YMIN = -20, YMAX = 15, YSCL = 5

23. $x^3 - 2x^2 - 16x + 32$

25. $x^3 + 6x^2 + 11x + 6$

27. $x^3 - 6x^2 + 6x + 8$

29.

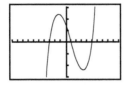

XSCL = 1, YSCL = 10
x-intercepts: $-3, 1, 5$
y-intercepts: 15

31.

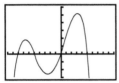

XSCL = 1, YSCL = 100
x-intercepts: $-8, -5, 0, 5$
y-intercept: 0

33.

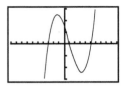

XSCL = 10, YSCL = 10,000
x-intercepts: $-30, 10, 50$
y-intercept: 15,000

35. a. $y = (x + 9)(x + 5)(x - 1)(x - 4)$

Exercise Set 4.3

1. $Q(x) = x - 2, R(x) = 2$

3. $Q(x) = 2x - 4, R(x) = 8x - 4$

5. $Q(x) = 3x^3 - 9x^2 + 25x - 75, R(x) = 226$

7. $Q(x) = 2x - 3, R(x) = -4x + 6$

9. $Q(x) = x^2 - x + 1, R(x) = 0$

11. $Q(x) = x^2 - 3x, R = 5$

13. $Q(x) = x^3 + 3x^2 + 9x + 27, R = 0$

15. $Q(x) = 3x^2 - 4x + 4, R = 4$

17. $Q(x) = x^4 - 2x^3 + 4x^2 - 8x + 16, R = 0$

19. $Q(x) = 6x^3 + 18x^2 + 53x + 159, R = 481$

Exercise Set 4.4

1. -7

3. -34

5. 0

7. -1

9. 0

11. -62

13. yes

15. no

17. yes

19. yes

21. yes

23. yes

25. no

27. $-1, 2$

29. $1, \dfrac{1}{2}$

31. $\dfrac{1}{2}, \dfrac{1}{2}, -\dfrac{1}{2}$

33. $r = 3, -1$

35. $\dfrac{5}{2}$

Exercise Set 4.5

1. 5

3. 25

5. 20

7. $-\dfrac{13}{10} + \dfrac{11}{10}i$

9. $-\dfrac{7}{25} - \dfrac{24}{25}i$

11. $\dfrac{8}{5} - \dfrac{1}{5}i$

13. $\dfrac{5}{3} - \dfrac{2}{3}i$

15. $\dfrac{4}{5} + \dfrac{8}{5}i$

17. $\dfrac{4}{25} - \dfrac{3}{25}i$

19. $\dfrac{9}{10} + \dfrac{3}{10}i$

21. $0 + \dfrac{1}{5}i$

25. $x^3 - 2x^2 - 16x + 32$

27. $x^3 + 6x^2 + 11x + 6$

29. $x^3 - 6x^2 + 6x + 8$

31. $\dfrac{x^3}{3} + \dfrac{x^2}{3} - \dfrac{7x}{12} + \dfrac{1}{6}$

33. $x^3 - 4x^2 - 2x + 8$

35. $3, -1, 2$

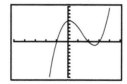

XMIN = -5, XMAX = 5, XSCL = 1
YMIN = -10, YMAX = 10, YSCL = 1

37. $-2, 4, -4$

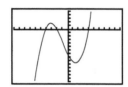

XMIN = -10, XMAX = 10, XSCL = 1
YMIN= -75, YMAX = 25 YSCL = 5

39. $-2, -1, 0, -\dfrac{1}{2}$

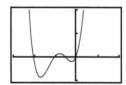

XMIN = -3, XMAX = 2, XSCL = 1
YMIN = -1, YMAX = 2, YSCL = 1

41. $5, 5, 5, -5, -5$

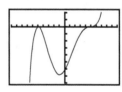

XMIN = -10, XMAX = 10, XSCL = 1
YMIN = -4000, YMAX = 1000, YSCL = 500

43. $x^3 + 6x^2 + 12x + 8$

45. $4x^4 + 4x^3 - 3x^2 - 2x + 1$

47. $2, -1$

49. $\dfrac{3}{2} \pm \dfrac{\sqrt{3}}{2}i$

51. $-1, 4$

53.

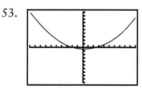

XSCL = 1, YSCL = 10

55.

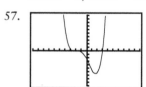

XSCL = 1, YSCL = 10

57.

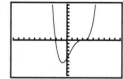

XSCL = 1, YSCL = 10

59.

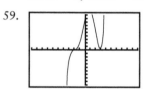

XSCL = 1, YSCL = 10

61.

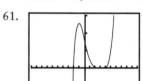

XSCL = 1
YMIN = -100, YMAX = 300, YSCL = 100

63.

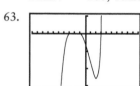

XSCL = 1
YMIN = -300, YMAX = 100, YSCL = 100

65.

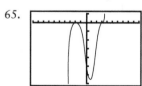

XSCL = 1
YMIN = -700, YMAX = 100, YSCL = 100

67.

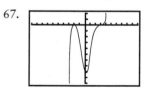

XSCL = 1
YMIN = -5000, YMAX = 1000, YSCL = 500

69. $x^2 + (1 - 3i)x - (2 + 6i)$

71. $x^2 - 3x + (3 + i)$

73. $x^3 + (1 + 2i)x^2 + (-8 + 8i)x + (-12 + 8i)$

75. $(x^2 - 6x + 10)(x - 1)$

77. $(x^2 + 2x + 5)(x^2 + 2x + 4)$

79. $(x - 2)(x + 2)(x - 3)(x^2 + 6x + 10)$

81. $x - (a + bi)$

Exercise Set 4.6

	POSITIVE ROOTS	NEGATIVE ROOTS	COMPLEX ROOTS
1.	3	1	0
	1	1	2
3.	0	0	6
5.	3	2	0
	1	2	2
	3	0	2
	1	0	4
7.	1	2	0
	1	0	2
9.	2	0	2
	0	0	4
11.	1	1	6

13. $1, -2, 3$

15. $2, -1, -\dfrac{1}{2}, \dfrac{2}{3}$

17. $1, -1, -1, \dfrac{1}{5}$

19. $1, -\dfrac{3}{4}$

21. $3, 3, \dfrac{1}{2}$

23. $-1, \dfrac{3}{4}, \pm i$

25. $\dfrac{3}{5}, \pm 2, \pm \sqrt{2}i$

27. $0, \dfrac{1}{2}, \dfrac{2}{3}, -1$

29. $\dfrac{1}{2}, -4, 2 \pm \sqrt{2}$

31. $3, 3, \pm i$

33. $2, -2, \pm \sqrt{2}$

35. $-\dfrac{1}{2}, -\dfrac{1}{2}, \pm 1$

37. $k = 3, r = -2; k = -\dfrac{3}{2}, r = 1; k = -\dfrac{5}{3}, r = 2$

39. $k = 7, r = 1; k = -7, r = -1$

Exercise Set 4.7

1. $[(3x - 2)x + 5]x - 1$

3. $(\{[(x + 2)x + 0]x + 0\}x - 2)x - 3$

5. $\{[(2x + 0)x - 1]x + 1\}x + 4$

7. -1.10

9. 1.73

11. 1.44

13. -1.87

15. 1.40

17. 1.10

Review Exercises

1. vertex: $(-2, 4)$; $x = 0, -4$; $y = 0$

2. vertex: $\left(\dfrac{5}{2}, \dfrac{3}{4}\right)$; no x-intercepts; $y = 7$

3. a. minimum

   b. $\dfrac{1}{4}$

   c. $\dfrac{7}{8}$

4. a. maximum

   b. $-\dfrac{3}{2}$

   c. $\dfrac{5}{4}$

5. large values of $|x|$, $x > 0$: down
   large values of $|x|$, $x < 0$: up

6. large values of $|x|$, $x > 0$: up
   large values of $|x|$, $x < 0$: down

7. $Q(x) = 2x^2 + 2x + 8, R = 4$

8. $Q(x) = x^3 - 5x^2 + 10x - 18, R = 31$

9. $46, -8$

10. $4, 1$

13. $\dfrac{6}{25} - \dfrac{17}{25}i$

14. $-\dfrac{1}{5} + \dfrac{2}{5}i$

15. $-\dfrac{5}{2} + \dfrac{5}{2}i$

16. $\dfrac{1}{10} - \dfrac{3}{10}i$

17. $0 + \dfrac{1}{4}i$

18. $\dfrac{2}{29} + \dfrac{5}{29}i$

19. $x^3 + 6x^2 + 11x + 6$

20. $x^3 - 3x^2 + 3x - 9$

21. $x^4 + x^3 - 5x^2 - 3x + 6$

22. $4x^4 + 4x^3 - 3x^2 - 2x + 1$

23. $x^4 + 2x^2 + 1$

24. $x^4 - 6x^2 - 8x - 3$

25. $-\dfrac{1}{2}, 3$

26. $-1 \pm \sqrt{2}$

27. $4, 2 + i, 2 - i$

28. 1 positive, 1 negative

29. 5 positive, 0 negative

30. 1 positive, 0 negative

31. 2 positive, 2 negative

32. $3, -\dfrac{2}{3}, -\dfrac{3}{2}$

33. $1, -2, \dfrac{2}{3}, \dfrac{3}{2}$

34. none

35. $-1, \dfrac{-9 \pm \sqrt{321}}{12}$

36. $2, \dfrac{3}{2}, -1 \pm \sqrt{2}$

Review Test

1. vertex: $(\frac{1}{3}, \frac{2}{3})$; x-intercept: none; y-intercept: 1; minimum value: $\frac{2}{3}$

2. extends indefinitely downward

3. extends indefinitely upward

4. $Q(x) = 2x^2 - 5$, $R(x) = 11$

5. $Q(x) = 3x^3 - 7x^2 + 14x - 28$, $R(x) = 54$

6. -25

7. -165

9. $x^3 - 2x^2 - 5x + 6$

10. $x^4 - 6x^3 - 6x^2 + 6x - 7$

11. $2, \pm i$

12. $-1, -1, \dfrac{3 \pm \sqrt{17}}{2}$

13. $x^5 + 3x^4 - 6x^3 - 10x^2 + 21x - 9$

14. $16x^5 - 8x^4 + 9x^3 - 9x^2 - 7x - 1$

15. $x^2 - (1 + 2i)x + (-1 + i)$

16. $\dfrac{1}{2}, \dfrac{1}{2}$

17. $1, -1 \pm i$

18. $(x^2 - 4x + 5)(x - 2)$

19. 2

20. 1

21. none

22. $1, 1, -1, -1, \dfrac{1}{2}$

23. $\dfrac{2}{3}, -3, \pm i$

Chapter 5

Exercise Set 5.1

1. domain: $\{x | x \neq 1\}$; intercepts: $(0, 0)$

3. domain: $\{x | x \neq 0, 2\}$; intercepts: none

5. domain: $\{x | x \text{ is real}\}$; intercepts: $(\pm\sqrt{3}, 0)$, $(0, -1)$

7. $x = 4, y = 0$

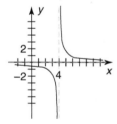

XMIN = -5, XMAX = 10, XSCL = 1
YMIN = -5, YMAX = 5, YSCL = 1

9. $x = -2, y = 0$

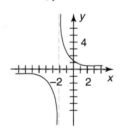

XMIN = -6, XMAX = 4, XSCL = 1
YMIN = -5, YMAX = 5, YSCL = 1

11. $x = -1, y = 0$

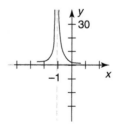

XMIN = -6, XMAX = 4, XSCL = 1
YMIN = -1, YMAX = 6, YSCL = 1

13. $x = 2, y = 1$

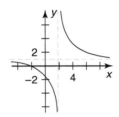

XMIN $= -10$, XMAX $= 10$, XSCL $= 1$
YMIN $= -5$, YMAX $= 5$, YSCL $= 1$

15. $x = 2, x = -2, y = 2$

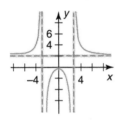

XMIN $= -10$; XMAX $= 10$, XSCL $= 1$
YMIN $= -5$, YMAX $= 5$, YSCL $= 1$

17. $x = 2, x = -\dfrac{3}{2}, y = \dfrac{1}{2}$

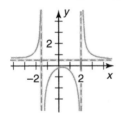

EQUAL viewing rectangle
XSCL $= 1$, YSCL $= 1$

19. $x = 1$

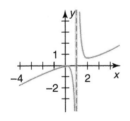

XMIN $= -5$, XMAX $= 5$, XSCL $= 1$
YMIN $= -3$, YMAX $= 3$, YSCL $= 1$

21. $x = 5, x = -5$

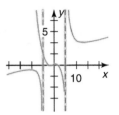

XMIN $= -10$, XMAX $= 15$, XSCL $= 5$
YMIN $= -15$, YMAX $= 25$, YSCL $= 5$

23. $x \neq -2$

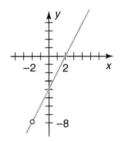

XMIN and XMAX are from the EQUAL viewing
rectangle. XSCL $= 1$
YMIN $= -10$, YMAX $= 5$, YSCL $= 1$

25. $x \neq 2$

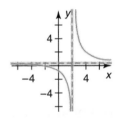

XMIN and XMAX are from the EQUAL viewing
rectangle. XSCL $= 5$
YMIN $= -5$, YMAX $= 5$, YSCL $= 1$

27. $x \neq 0, x \neq -1$

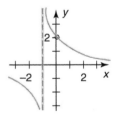

EQUAL viewing rectangle
XSCL $= 1$, YSCL $= 1$

Exercise Set 5.2

1. $(x - 2)^2 + (y - 3)^2 = 4$ 3. $(x + 2)^2 + (y + 3)^3 = 5$

5. $x^2 + y^2 = 9$ 7. $(x + 1)^2 + (y - 4)^2 = 8$

9. $(h, k) = (2, 3); r = 4$

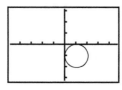

X and Y values are from 4 times the EQUAL viewing rectangle.
XSCL = 4, YSCL = 4

11. $(h, k) = (2, -2); r = 2$

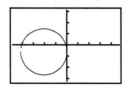

X and Y values are from 2 times the EQUAL viewing rectangle.
XSCL = 2, YSCL = 2

13. $(h, k) = \left(-4, -\dfrac{3}{2}\right); r = 3\sqrt{2}$

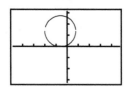

X and Y values are from 2 times the EQUAL viewing rectangle.
XSCL = 2, YSCL = 2

15. no graph

17. $(x + 2)^2 + (y - 4)^2 = 16; (h, k) = (-2, 4); r = 4$

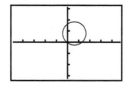

X and Y values are from 3 times the EQUAL viewing rectangle.
XSCL = 3, YSCL = 3

19. $\left(x - \dfrac{3}{2}\right)^2 + \left(y - \dfrac{5}{2}\right)^2 = \dfrac{11}{2}; (h, k) = \left(\dfrac{3}{2}, \dfrac{5}{2}\right); r = \dfrac{\sqrt{22}}{2}$

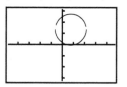

X and Y values are from 2 times the EQUAL viewing rectangle.
XSCL = 2, YSCL = 2

21. $(x - 1)^2 + y^2 = \dfrac{7}{2}; (h, k) = (1, 0); r = \dfrac{\sqrt{14}}{2}$

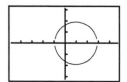

X and Y are from the EQUAL viewing rectangle.
XSCL = 1, YSCL = 1

23. $(x - 2)^2 + (y + 3)^2 = 8; (h, k) = (2, -3); r = 2\sqrt{2}$

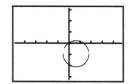

X and Y are from 3 times the EQUAL viewing rectangle.
XSCL = 3, YSCL = 3

25. $(x - 3)^2 + (y + 4)^2 = 0$; point at $(3, -4)$

27. $\left(x + \dfrac{3}{2}\right)^2 + \left(y - \dfrac{5}{2}\right)^2 = \dfrac{3}{2}; (h, k) = \left(-\dfrac{3}{2}, \dfrac{5}{2}\right); r = \dfrac{\sqrt{6}}{2}$

29. $(x - 3)^2 + y^2 = 11; (h, k) = (3, 0); r = \sqrt{11}$

31. $\left(x - \dfrac{3}{2}\right)^2 + (y - 1)^2 = \dfrac{17}{4}; (h, k) = \left(\dfrac{3}{2}, 1\right); r = \dfrac{\sqrt{17}}{2}$

33. $(x + 2)^2 + \left(y - \dfrac{2}{3}\right)^2 = \dfrac{100}{9}; (h, k) = \left(-2, \dfrac{2}{3}\right); r = \dfrac{10}{3}$

35. neither

37. 9π

41. $(x + 5)^2 + (y - 2)^2 = 8$

43. $(x - 5)^2 + (y - 1)^2 = 20$

45. The top and bottom "halves" of the circle do not necessarily form the entire circle when the "meeting points" are not plotted. In some cases, this can be avoided by choosing X values that are multiples of the EQUAL viewing rectangle. However, there is no way of defining the viewing rectangle to insure that the top and bottom halves will always meet. (Consider $x^2 + y^2 = 7$.)

47. $x^2 + (y - 2)^2 = 1$, center: $(0, 2)$; radius: 1

Exercise Set 5.3

1. focus: $(0, 1)$; directrix: $y = -1$

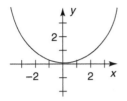

3.   focus: $\left(\frac{1}{2}, 0\right)$; directrix: $x = -\frac{1}{2}$

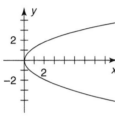

5.   focus: $\left(0, -\frac{5}{4}\right)$; directrix: $y = \frac{5}{4}$

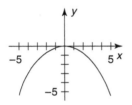

7. focus: $(3, 0)$; directrix: $x = -3$

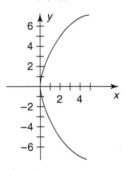

9. $y^2 = 4x$ 11. $y^2 = 6x$

13. $x^2 = -8y$ 15. $y^2 = -5x$

17. $y^2 = -4x$ 19. $y^2 = x$

21. downward   23. to the left

25. $(x - 1)^2 = 3(y - 2)$; vertex: $(1, 2)$; axis: $x = 1$; direction: up

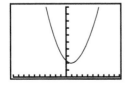

XMIN $= -10$, XMAX $= 10$, XSCL $= 1$
YMIN $= 0$, YMAX $= 10$, YSCL $= 1$

27. $(y - 4)^2 = -2(x - 2)$; vertex: $(2, 4)$; axis: $y = 4$; direction: left

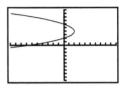

the default viewing window
XSCL $= 1$, YSCL $= 1$

29. $\left(x - \frac{1}{2}\right)^2 = -3\left(y + \frac{1}{4}\right)$; vertex: $\left(\frac{1}{2}, -\frac{1}{4}\right)$; axis: $x = \frac{1}{2}$; direction: down

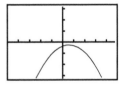

EQUAL viewing rectangle
XSCL $= 1$, YSCL $= 1$

31. $(y - 5)^2 = 3\left(x + \frac{1}{3}\right)$; vertex: $\left(-\frac{1}{3}, 5\right)$; axis: $y = 5$; direction: right

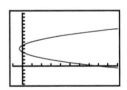

XMIN $= -1$, XMAX $= 10$, XSCL $= 1$
YMIN $= -5$, YMAX $= 15$, YSCL $= 1$

33. $\left(x - \frac{3}{2}\right)^2 = 3\left(y + \frac{5}{12}\right)$; vertex: $\left(\frac{3}{2}, -\frac{5}{12}\right)$; axis: $x = \frac{3}{2}$; direction: up

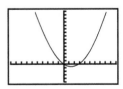

XMIN $= -10$, XMAX $= 10$, XSCL $= 1$
YMIN $= -5$, YMAX $= 15$, YSCL $= 1$

35. $(y + 3)^2 = -\frac{1}{2}(x - 4)$; vertex: $(4, -3)$; axis: $y = -3$; direction: left

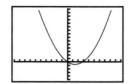

XMIN = −30, XMAX = 5, XSCL = 5
YMIN = −10, YMAX = 5, YSCL = 1

37. $(x + 1)^2 = -2(y + 1)$; vertex: $(-1, -1)$; axis: $x = -1$; direction: down

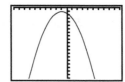

XMIN = −10, XMAX = 10, XSCL = 1
YMIN = −20, YMAX = 0, YSCL = 1

39. vertex: $(2, -1)$; axis: $x = 2$; direction: up

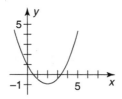

the default viewing window
XSCL = 1, YSCL = 1

41. vertex: $(-4, -2)$; axis: $x = -4$; direction: down

XMIN = −15, XMAX = 5, XSCL = 1
YMIN = −50, YMAX = 0, YSCL = 10

43. vertex: $(-1, 0)$; axis: $y = 0$; direction: left

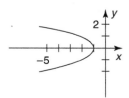

XMIN = −10, XMAX = 10, XSCL = 1
YMIN = −20, YMAX = 0, YSCL = 1

45. a.

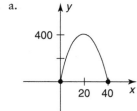

b. no

47. a. $20\sqrt{6}$ inches

b. 31 inches

Exercise Set 5.4

1. $(1, -4)$

3. $(5, -1)$

5. $(-3, 4)$

7. $(1, 7)$

9.

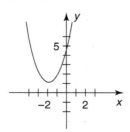

X and Y values are from 3 times the EQUAL viewing rectangle.
XSCL = 3, YSCL = 3

11.

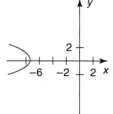

XMIN = −20, XMAX = 0, XSCL = 1
YMIN = −10, YMAX = 10, YSCL = 1

Exercise Set 5.5

1. a. 4

   b. −5

   c. $y + 1$

   d.
   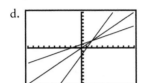

   the default viewing window
   XSCL = 1, YSCL = 1

3. yes, $f^{-1}(x) = x^2$, $x \geq 0$

   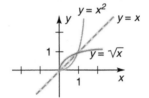

5. yes, $f^{-1}(x) = \frac{1}{x}$

   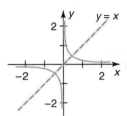

7. 0

9. a. yes

   b. 5

   c. 0

   d.

x	17	20	−4	3	10
$G^{-1}(x)$	−10	−5	0	5	10

11. $x \geq 0$ and $x \leq 0$

13.

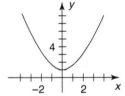

Exercise Set 5.6

1.
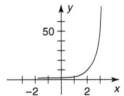

3.
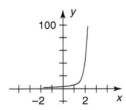

5.
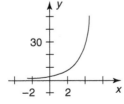

7.
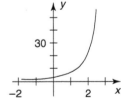

9.
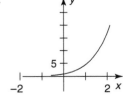

11.
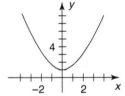

13.

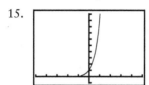

XMIN = −5, XMAX = 5, XSCL = 1
YMIN = −1, YMAX = 10, YSCL = 1

15.

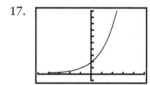

XMIN = −5, XMAX = 5, XSCL = 1
YMIN = −1, YMAX = 10, YSCL = 1

17.

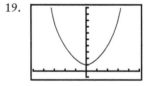

XMIN = −5, XMAX = 5, XSCL = 1
YMIN = −1, YMAX = 10, YSCL = 1

19.

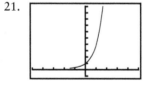

XMIN = −5, XMAX = 5, XSCL = 1
YMIN = −1, YMAX = 10, YSCL = 1

21.

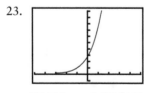

XMIN = −5, XMAX = 5, XSCL = 1
YMIN = −1, YMAX = 10, YSCL = 1

23.

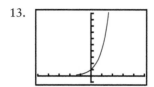

XMIN = −5, XMAX = 5, XSCL = 1
YMIN = −1, YMAX = 10, YSCL = 1

25. 3

27. 4

29. 2

31. 4

33. 2

35. 1

37. 7.39

39. 10.07

41. 0.83

43. 3^{π}

45. a. 717.81   b. 722.52

c. 724.97   d. 726.65

e. 727.47   f. 727.49

g. 727.50

h. (a) is equivalent to $500 compounded annually at 7.5% interest for 5 years; (g) is equivalent to $500 compounded continuously at 7.5% interest for 5 years.

47. a. 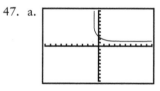   b.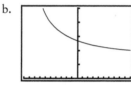

XSCL = 1, YSCL = 1   XSCL = 0.1, YSCL = 1

c. 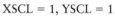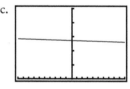   d.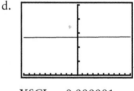

XSCL = 0.01, YSCL = 1   XSCL = 0.000001, YSCL = 1

49. symmetry with respect to the y-axis

51. $2,840.25

53. $q_0 = 2500$, $Q(7) = 320,000$

55. a. 200

b. 29,683

c. $Q(1) = 257$, $Q(4) = 544$, $Q(8) = 1478$, $Q(10) = 2436$

57. 17.93 billion   59. 670.32 grams

61. $41,611.40   63. $45,417.42

65. $173.33   67. $2489.35

69. $2054.43   71. a. $3.11

b. $1.96

Exercise Set 5.7

1. $2^2 = 4$

3. $9^{-2} = \dfrac{1}{81}$

5. $e^3 \approx 20.09$

7. $10^3 = 1000$

9. $e^0 = 1$

11. $3^{-3} = \dfrac{1}{27}$

13. $\log_5 25 = 2$

15. $\log_{10} 10{,}000 = 4$

17. $\log_2 \dfrac{1}{8} = -3$

19. $\log_2 1 = 0$

21. $\log_{36} 6 = \dfrac{1}{2}$

23. $\log_{16} 64 = \dfrac{3}{2}$

25. $\log_{27} \dfrac{1}{3} = -\dfrac{1}{3}$

27. 25

29. $\dfrac{1}{5}$

31. e^2

33. $e^{-1/2}$

35. -2

37. 512

39. 124

41. 2

43. 3

45. 6

47. 2

49. 3

51. $\dfrac{1}{2}$

53. 2

55. 1

57. 0

59. -2

61. 4

63. 2

65. 0.2041

67. 1.2920

69. 501.72

71.
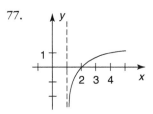

73.
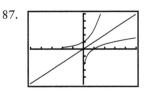

75.

77.

In Exercises 79–86, your graphs should clearly indicate the limited domains of these logarithmic functions. Be careful to choose RANGE values that indicate the vertical asymptotic behavior of these functions.

79. $\{x \mid x < 1\}$

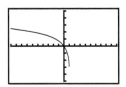

XMIN = −10, XMAX = 10, XSCL = 1
YMIN = −5, YMAX = 5, YSCL = 1

81. $\{x \mid x < 0, x > 1\}$

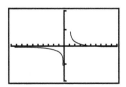

XMIN = −10, XMAX = 10, XSCL = 1
YMIN = −2, YMAX = 2, YSCL = 1

83. $\{x \mid x \text{ is real}\}$

EQUAL viewing rectangle
XSCL = 1, YSCL = 1

85. Since the domain has no elements, there is no graph.

87.
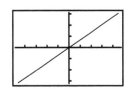

XSCL = 1, YSCL = 1

89. 18.45 years

91. 5.49%

93.

94. $y = 2(3^x)$

Exercise Set 5.8

1. $1 + 4 \log_{10} 2 + 3 \log_{10} 3$

3. 4

5. $\log_a 2 + \log_a x + \log_a y$

7. $\log_a x - \log_a y - \log_a z$

9. $5 \ln x$

11. $2 \log_a x + 3 \log_a y$

13. $\frac{1}{2}(\log_a x + 3 \log_a y)$

15. $2 \ln x + 3 \ln y + 4 \ln z$

17. $\frac{1}{2} \ln x + \frac{1}{3} \ln y$

19. $2 \log_a x + 3 \log_a y - 4 \log_a z$

21. 0.77

23. 0.94

25. 1.07

27. 0.87

29. 0.435

31. $\log x^2 \sqrt{y}$

33. $\ln \sqrt[3]{xy}$

35. $\log_a \dfrac{x^{1/3} y^2}{z^{3/2}}$

37. $\log_a \sqrt{xy}$

39. $\ln \dfrac{\sqrt[3]{x^2 y^4}}{z^3}$

41. $\log_a \dfrac{\sqrt{x-1}}{(x+1)^2}$

43. $\log_a \dfrac{x^3 (x+1)^{1/6}}{(x-1)^2}$

45. 1.2304

47. 4.5046

49. 2.3892

51. a. 1.255

 b. -0.342

 c. 0.699

53. 1.4307

55. 1.4037

57.

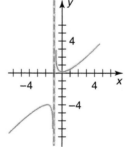

XSCL = 1, YSCL = 1

Exercise Set 5.9

1. $\dfrac{\log 18}{\log 5}$

3. $1 + \dfrac{\log 7}{\log 2}$

5. $\dfrac{\log 46}{2 \log 3}$

7. $\dfrac{1}{2}\left(5 + \dfrac{\log 564}{\log 5}\right)$

9. $\dfrac{\log 3 - \log 2}{\log 3 - 2 \log 2}$

11. $-\dfrac{\log 15}{\log 2}$

13. $\dfrac{1}{2}\left(1 - \dfrac{\log 12}{\log 4}\right)$

15. $\ln 18$

17. $\dfrac{-3 + \ln 30}{2}$

19. 500

21. $\dfrac{1}{2}$

23. 5

25. 3

27. 8

29. $-1 + \sqrt{17}$

31. $\ln(y + \sqrt{y^2 + 1})$

33. 36.62 years

35. 12.6 hours

37. 8.84 years

39. 27.47 years

41. 1.39 days

Review Exercises

1.

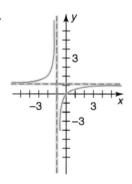

XMIN = −5, XMAX = 5, XSCL = 1
YMIN = −5, YMAX = 5, YSCL = 1

2.

XMIN = −5, XMAX = 5, XSCL = 1
YMIN = −10, YMAX = 5, YSCL = 1

3.

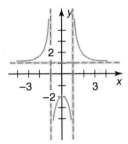

XMIN = −5, XMAX = 5, XSCL = 1
YMIN = −10, YMAX = 10, YSCL = 1

4. $(x + 5)^2 + (y − 2)^2 = 16$

5. $(x + 3)^2 + (y − 3)^2 = 4$

6. $(h, k) = (2, −3); r = 3$

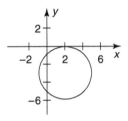

7. $(h, k) = (−\frac{1}{2}, 4); r = \frac{1}{3}$

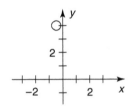

8. $(h, k) = (−2, 3); r = \sqrt{3}$

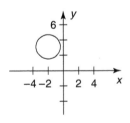

9. $(h, k) = (1, −1); r = \frac{\sqrt{2}}{2}$

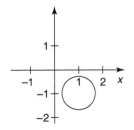

10. $(h, k) = (0, 3); r = \sqrt{6}$

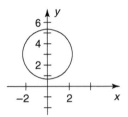

11. $(h, k) = (1, 1); r = \sqrt{10}$

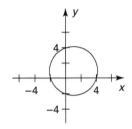

12. vertex: $(\frac{3}{2}, −5)$; axis: $y = −5$

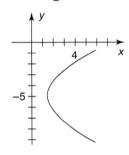

13. vertex: $(1, 2)$; axis: $x = 1$

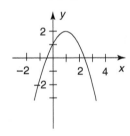

	VERTEX	AXIS	DIRECTION
14.	$(−3, 0)$	$y = 0$	left
15.	$(2, −2)$	$y = −2$	left
16.	$(3, −2)$	$x = 3$	up
17.	$(−2, −\frac{1}{2})$	$x = −2$	down
18.	$(0, 1)$	$y = 1$	right
19.	$(−3, 0)$	$x = −3$	down

20. focus: $\left(0, -\dfrac{1}{6}\right)$; directrix: $y = \dfrac{1}{6}$

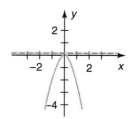

21. focus: $\left(-\dfrac{1}{6}, 0\right)$; directrix: $x = \dfrac{1}{6}$

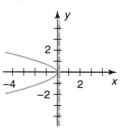

22. $x^2 = -7y$

23. $x^2 = \dfrac{2}{5}y$

24. $\dfrac{x^2}{4} - \dfrac{y^2}{9} = 1$; $(\pm 2, 0)$

25. $\dfrac{x^2}{1} + \dfrac{y^2}{9} = 1$; $(\pm 1, 0), (0, \pm 3)$

26. $\dfrac{x^2}{7} + \dfrac{y^2}{5} = 1$; $(\pm\sqrt{7}, 0), (0, \pm\sqrt{5})$

27. $\dfrac{x^2}{16} - \dfrac{y^2}{9} = 1$; $(\pm 4, 0)$

28. $\dfrac{x^2}{3} + \dfrac{y^2}{\frac{9}{4}} = 1$; $(\pm\sqrt{3}, 0), \left(0, \pm\dfrac{3}{2}\right)$

29. $\dfrac{y^2}{\frac{20}{3}} - \dfrac{x^2}{4} = 1$; $\left(0, \dfrac{\pm 2\sqrt{15}}{3}\right)$

30.

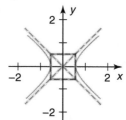

31.

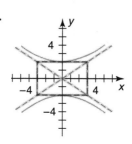

32. $x^2 + y^2 = 10$

33. ellipse

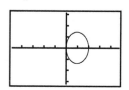

EQUAL viewing rectangle
XSCL = 1, YSCL = 1

34. parabola

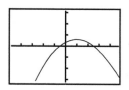

EQUAL viewing rectangle
XSCL = 1, YSCL = 1

35. no graph

36. hyperbola

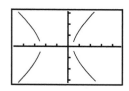

X and Y values are from 2 times the EQUAL viewing rectangle.
XSCL = 2, YSCL = 2

37. two intersecting lines

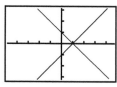

X and Y values are from 2 times the EQUAL viewing rectangle.
XSCL = 2, YSCL = 2

38. hyperbola

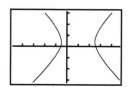

X and Y values are from 2 times the EQUAL viewing rectangle.
XSCL = 2, YSCL = 2

39. parabola

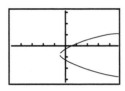

X and Y values are from 2 times the EQUAL viewing rectangle.
XSCL = 2, YSCL = 2

40. hyperbola

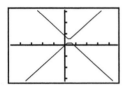

EQUAL viewing rectangle
XSCL = 1, YSCL = 1

41. ellipse

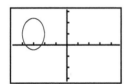

EQUAL viewing rectangle
XSCL = 1, YSCL = 1

42. no graph

43. $f^{-1}(x) = 3x + 6$

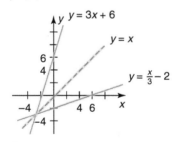

44. $f(x)$ is not one-to-one.

45.

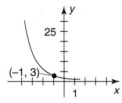

46. 3

47. 2

48. $12,750.78

49. $\log_9 27 = \dfrac{3}{2}$

50. $8 = 64^{1/2}$

51. $\dfrac{1}{8} = 2^{-3}$

52. $\log_6 1 = 0$

53. 2

54. -2

55. e^{-4}

56. 26

57. 5

58. $-\dfrac{1}{3}$

59. -1

60. 3

61.

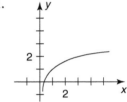

62. $\dfrac{1}{2}\log_a(x-1) - \log_a 2 - \log_a x$

63. $\log_a x + 2\log_a(2-x) - \dfrac{1}{2}\log_a(y+1)$

64. $4\ln(x+1) + 2\ln(y-1)$

65. $\dfrac{2}{5}\log y + \dfrac{1}{5}\log z - \dfrac{1}{5}\log(z+3)$

66. 0.0067

67. 0.3466

68. -2.4709

69. 12,188.60

70. 12,382.58

71. 2.3219

72. 1.2619

73. 32

74. 6.5809

75. 0.2691

76. Joe, by $527.73

77. 3.71 days

78. 2,560,000

79. 1,139,062.5

80. bank A

81. a. 1.15

b.

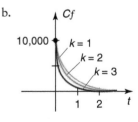

82. 40 decibels

83. 30 decibels

Review Test

1.

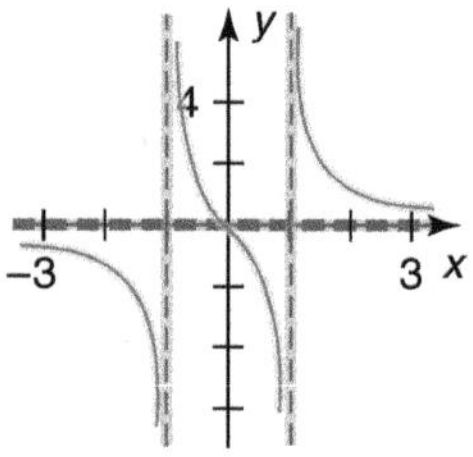

2. $(x - 2)^2 + (y + 3)^2 = 36$

3. $(h, k) = (1, -2)$; $r = 2$

4. $(h, k) = (2, 0)$; $r = \sqrt{5}$

5. vertex: $(-3, 1)$; axis: $x = -3$

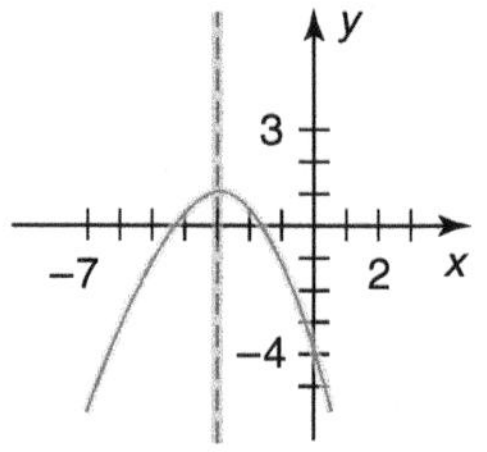

6. vertex: $(1, 2)$; axis: $y = 2$

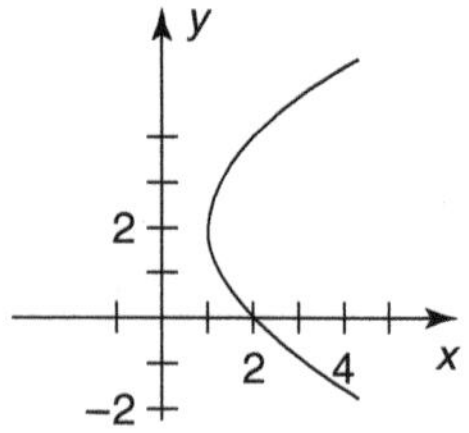

7. vertex: $(3, 2)$; axis: $x = 3$; direction: down

8. vertex: $(-2, -4)$; axis: $y = -4$; direction: right

9. $f^{-1}(x) = \dfrac{2 - x}{4}$

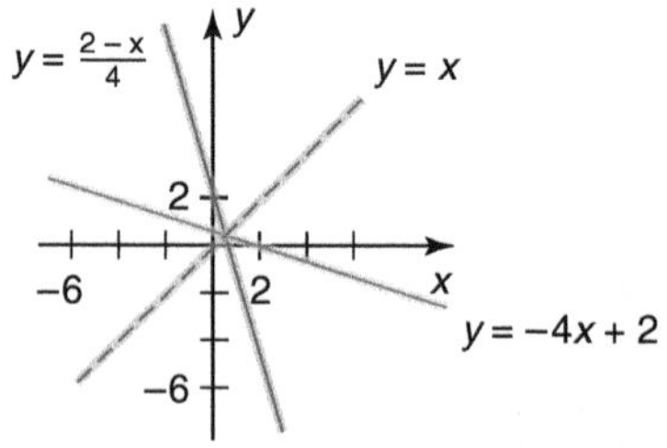

10. $f^{-1}(x) = -\dfrac{1}{x}$

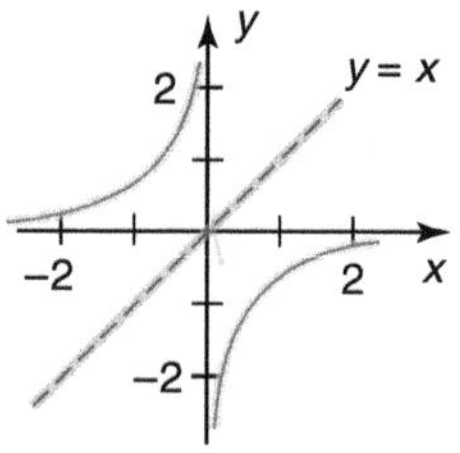

11.

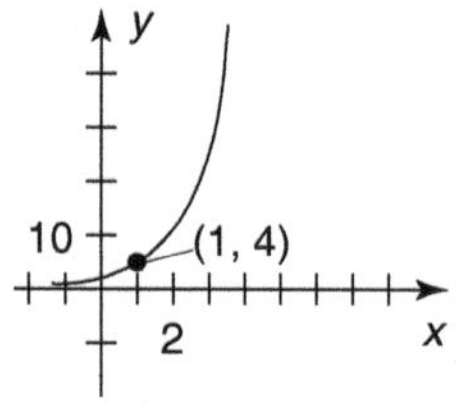

12. $-\dfrac{2}{3}$

13. $\dfrac{1}{9} = 3^{-2}$

14. $\log_{16} 64 = \dfrac{3}{2}$

15. 3

16. −1

17. $\dfrac{5}{2}$

18. $\dfrac{1}{2}$

19. $3 \log_a x - 2 \log_a y - \log_a z$

20. $2 \log x + \dfrac{1}{2} \log (2y - 1) - 3 \log y$

21. 0.7

22. 0.45

23. $\log \dfrac{x^2}{(y + 1)^3}$

24. $\log_a \left(\dfrac{x + 3}{x - 3}\right)^{2/3}$

25. 34.66 hours

26. \$530.76

27. 200

28. 4

29. 1.15

30. 0.55

31. 0.39

32. −0.15

33. $\log_a \left(\dfrac{\sqrt[3]{x}}{\sqrt{y}}\right)$

34. $\log (x^2 - x)^{4/3}$

35. $\ln \dfrac{3xy^2}{z}$

36. $\log_a \left[\dfrac{(x + 2)^2}{(x + 1)^{3/2}}\right]$

37. $\dfrac{5}{3}$

38. $\dfrac{15}{7}$

39. 11.55 hours

40. $\dfrac{1}{3}\left(1 + \dfrac{\log 14}{\log 2}\right)$

41. $50\sqrt{2}$

42. $\dfrac{199}{98}$

Cumulative Review Exercises

Chapters 4–5

1. a. 7

   b. $2x^2 + 3x - 3, 6$

2. $\dfrac{1}{5}$

3. $(\sqrt{3}, 0), (-\sqrt{3}, 0)$

4. a. $\{x \mid x \neq \pm 3\}$

   b. vertical asymptote: $x = 3$
   horizontal asymptote: $y = 2$

   c.

   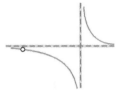

   d.

   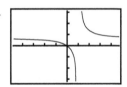

   X and Y values are from 3 times the EQUAL viewing
   rectangle.
   XSCL = 3, YSCL = 3

5. $\}95\}$

6. 3

7. 9

8. 7.92 years

9.

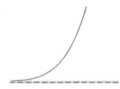

10. a. $2t + s$

    b. $u - 2s$

    c. $t - s$

    d. $\dfrac{u + t - s}{2}$

11. $960.79

12. $2 \ln x + \dfrac{1}{2} \ln(x + 1) - \ln(x - 1)$

13. 9.24%

14. $7919.58, $1919.58

15. $7970.38

16. 17.33 years

17. bond B

18. 0.9730

Chapter 6

Exercise Set 6.1

1. $x = 2, y = -1$

3. no solution

5. $x = 1, y = -4$

7. $x = 3, y = 2; x = 3, y = -2$

9. no solution

11. $x = 2, y = -1$

13. $x = 3, y = 2; x = \dfrac{1}{5}, y = -\dfrac{18}{5}$

15. $x = 1, y = 1; x = \dfrac{9}{16}, y = -\dfrac{3}{4}$

17. $x = 1, y = 2; x = \dfrac{13}{5}, y = -\dfrac{6}{5}$

19. $x = \dfrac{-1 + \sqrt{5}}{2}, y = \dfrac{1 + \sqrt{5}}{2}; x = \dfrac{-1 - \sqrt{5}}{2}, y = \dfrac{1 - \sqrt{5}}{2}$

21. $x = 3, y = -1$

23. no solution

25. $x = 3, y = 2; x = 3, y = -2$

27. no solution

29. $x = 3, y = 2; x = -3, y = 2; x = 3, y = -2; x = -3, y = -2$

31. I

33. I

35. I

37. C; all points on the line $3x - y = 18$

39. C; $x = 1, y = -1; x = \dfrac{5}{2}, y = \dfrac{1}{2}$

41. I

Exercise Set 6.2

1. 25 nickels, 15 dimes

3. color: \$2.50; black and white: \$1.50

5. \$4000 in bond A, \$2000 in bond B

7. 10 rolls of 12 inches, 4 rolls of 15 inches

9. 8 pounds of \$1.20 coffee, 16 pounds of \$1.80 coffee

11. speed of bicycle: $\dfrac{105}{8}$ miles per hour; wind speed: $\dfrac{15}{8}$ miles per hour

13. 34

15. 30 pounds of nuts, 20 pounds of raisins

17. \$6000 in type A, \$12,000 in type B

19. 5 units Epiline I, 4 units Epiline II

21. a. $R = 95x$

b.
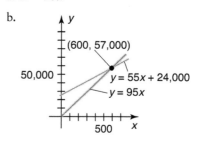

c. \$57,000

23. a. $p = 4$

b. 18

24. 4, 5

27. 22 nickels, 12 quarters

29. $\dfrac{6}{5}$ pound nuts, $\dfrac{4}{5}$ pound raisins

31. 125 type-A, 75 type-B

33. 6 meters and 8 meters

Exercise Set 6.3

1. $x = 2, y = -1, z = -2$

3. $x = 1, y = \dfrac{2}{3}, z = -\dfrac{2}{3}$

5. inconsistent

7. $x = 1, y = 2, z = 2$

9. $x = 1, y = 1, z = 0$

11. $x = 1, y = \dfrac{27}{2}, z = -\dfrac{5}{2}$

13. inconsistent

15. inconsistent

17. $x = 5, y = -5, z = -20$

19. 2 units of A, 3 units of B, 3 units of C

21. three 12-inch sets, eight 16-inch sets, five 19-inch sets

Exercise Set 6.4

1. $\dfrac{3}{x + 2} - \dfrac{1}{x - 3}$

3. $\dfrac{3}{3x - 1} - \dfrac{1}{2x - 1}$

5. $-\dfrac{2}{x} + \dfrac{2}{x - 1} + \dfrac{1}{x + 1}$

7. $\dfrac{2}{x} - \dfrac{1}{x^2} - \dfrac{2}{x + 2}$

9. $\dfrac{\frac{1}{2}}{x - 1} + \dfrac{\frac{1}{2}}{x + 1} - \dfrac{2}{(x + 1)^2}$

11. $\dfrac{\frac{1}{4}}{x} - \dfrac{\frac{1}{4}x + 2}{x^2 + 4}$

13. $\dfrac{2x - 1}{x^2 + 3} + \dfrac{3 - 5x}{(x^2 + 3)^2}$

15. $\dfrac{\frac{1}{3}}{x + 1} + \dfrac{\frac{1}{3} - \frac{1}{3}x}{x^2 - 3x - 1}$

17. $\dfrac{-1}{x + 1} + \dfrac{2x - 2}{x^2 + 2} + \dfrac{x - 1}{(x^2 + 2)^2}$

19. $x + \dfrac{2x}{x^2 + 1} - \dfrac{2}{x + 1}$

Exercise Set 6.5

1.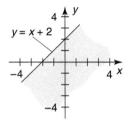

3.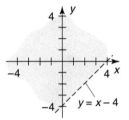

5.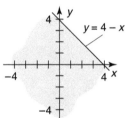

7.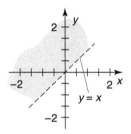

9.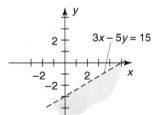

11.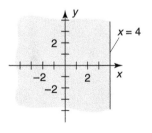

13.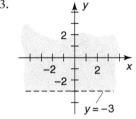

15.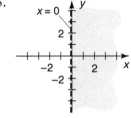

17.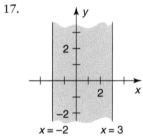

19. $2x + 5y \le 15; x \ge 0; y \ge 0$

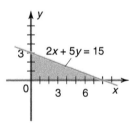

21.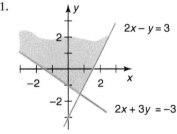

23.

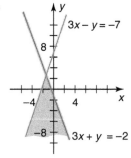

$3x - y = -7$
$3x + y = -2$

29. no solution

31.

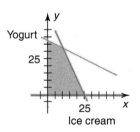

$8x + 3y = 24$ $3x - 2y = -6$
$5x + 4y = 20$

25.

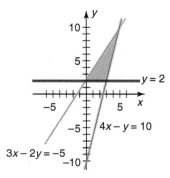

$y = 2$
$4x - y = 10$
$3x - 2y = -5$

33.

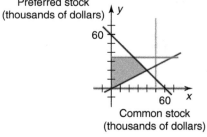

Yogurt
Ice cream

27.

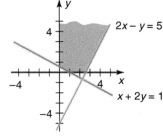

$2x - y = 5$
$x + 2y = 1$

35.   Preferred stock
(thousands of dollars)

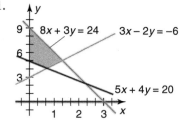

Common stock
(thousands of dollars)

Exercise Set 6.6

	MINIMUM	MAXIMUM
1.	-2; $(5, 14)$	5; $(5, 0)$
3.	-3; $(2, 2)$	3; $(6, 0)$
5.	$\dfrac{6}{7}$; $\left(\dfrac{6}{7}, \dfrac{6}{7}\right)$	$\dfrac{19}{2}$; $\left(4, -\dfrac{3}{2}\right)$
7.	$\dfrac{1}{2}$; $\left(3, \dfrac{11}{2}\right)$	14; $(8, 2)$

9. preferred: $\dfrac{190}{3}$ square feet
regular: 30 square feet

11. large: 120
small: 260

13. Java: $\dfrac{2000}{11}$ pounds
Colombian: $\dfrac{4000}{11}$ pounds

15. crop A: 30 acres
crop B: 70 acres

17. pack A: 6 pounds
pack B: 12 pounds

Review Exercises

1. $x = -\frac{1}{2}, y = 1$

2. $x = 5, y = 2; x = 10, y = -3$

3. $x = 5, y = -1$

4. $x = -4, y = \frac{3}{2}$

5. $x = \frac{1}{4}, y = -\frac{1}{2}$

6. $x = 5, y = 0; x = -4, y = 3$

7. none

8. $x = 4, y = 4; x = \frac{36}{25}, y = -\frac{12}{5}$

9. $x = -3, y = 5$

10. $x = 2, y = -2$

11. $x = 4, y = -1$

12. $x = -2, y = 3$

13. $x = 1, y = -1; x = 5, y = 3$

14. $x = 0, y = 3$

15. 45

16. 72

17. steak: $3.25 per pound; hamburger: $1.80 per pound

18. 600 kilometers per hour

19. 3, 11

20. 474, $9200

21. $x = -3, y = 1, z = 4$

22. $x = -2, y = \frac{1}{2}, z = 3$

23. $x = 1, y = -1, z = 2$

24. $x = 3, y = \frac{1}{4}, z = -\frac{1}{3}$

25. $x = -3, y = 4$

26. $x = -\frac{5}{3}, y = \frac{5}{6}$

27. $x = -2, y = -1, z = -3$

28. $x = \frac{1}{2}, y = -1, z = 1$

29. $\dfrac{3}{2x - 1} - \dfrac{2}{x + 2}$

30. $\dfrac{3x}{x^2 + 1} + \dfrac{2x - 1}{(x^2 + 1)^2}$

31. $2x + 1 + \dfrac{4}{x - 1} + \dfrac{1}{(x - 1)^2}$

32.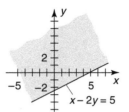

33.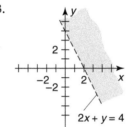

34.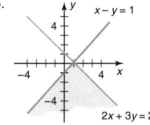

35.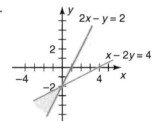

36.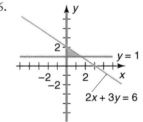

37.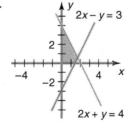

38. $x = 4, y = 6, z = 26$ 39. $x = \frac{11}{2}, y = 2, z = \frac{27}{2}$

Review Test

1. $x = -5, y = 2$

2. $x = -1, y = 6$

3. $x = 2, y = \pm\sqrt{10}; x = 3, y = \pm\sqrt{15}$

4. $x = 1, y = -3$

5. $x = 3, y = \pm4; x = -3, y = \pm4$

6. 38

7. shirts: $15; ties: $10

8. 1100

9. $x = -2, y = 4, z = 6$

10. $x = -\dfrac{1}{3}, y = -1$

11. $x = \dfrac{2}{3}, y = 2, z = -2$

12. $\dfrac{3}{x+3} - \dfrac{2}{x-2}$

13.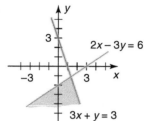

14.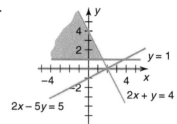

15. $x = 4, y = 8, z = 36$

Solutions to Selected Review Exercises

Chapter 1

1. $\{1, 2, 3, 4\}$. (The negative integers and zero are not natural numbers.)

4. T. (Irrational numbers are a subset of the real numbers.)

6. F. (The negative integers and zero are a subset of the integers.)

15. $\begin{aligned}|-3| - |1 - 5| &= |-3| - |-4| \\ &= 3 - 4 \\ &= -1\end{aligned}$

16. $\overline{PQ} = \left|\dfrac{9}{2} - 6\right| = \left|-\dfrac{3}{2}\right| = \dfrac{3}{2}$

18. c. (Every exponent of a polynomial must be a non-negative integer.)

22. $\begin{aligned}x(2x - 1)(x + 2) &= (2x^2 - x)(x + 2) \\ &= 2x^3 + 3x^2 - 2x\end{aligned}$

26. $\begin{aligned}&2a^2 + 3ab + 6a + 9b \\ &= (2a^2 + 6a) + (3ab + 9b) \quad \text{Grouping} \\ &= 2a(a + 3) + 3b\,(a + 3) \quad \text{Common factors } 2a, 3b \\ &= (a + 3)(2a + 3b) \quad\quad \text{Common factor } a + 3\end{aligned}$

28. $\begin{aligned}x^8 - 1 &= (x^4)^2 - (1)^2 \\ &= (x^4 + 1)(x^4 - 1) \\ &= (x^4 + 1)(x^2 + 1)(x^2 - 1) \\ &= (x^4 + 1)(x^2 + 1)(x + 1)(x - 1)\end{aligned}$

32. $\begin{aligned}&\dfrac{x^2 - 2x - 3}{2x^2 - x} \div \dfrac{x^2 - 4x + 3}{3x^3 - 3x^2} \\[2mm] &= \dfrac{x^2 - 2x - 3}{2x^2 - x} \cdot \dfrac{3x^3 - 3x^2}{x^2 - 4x + 3} \\[2mm] &= \dfrac{(x + 1)(x - 3)}{x(2x - 1)} \cdot \dfrac{3x^2(x - 1)}{(x - 1)(x - 3)} \\[2mm] &= \dfrac{3x(x + 1)}{2x - 1}, \quad x \neq 0, 1, 3\end{aligned}$

34. Factor each denominator:
$$\dfrac{-1}{2x^2} \qquad \dfrac{2}{(x + 2)(x - 2)} \qquad \dfrac{3}{x - 2}$$
Product of all factors each to its highest power:
$$2x^2(x + 2)(x - 2)$$

39. LCD $= (x + 4)(x - 4)$
$$\begin{aligned}\dfrac{3}{x^2 - 16} - \dfrac{2}{x - 4} &= \dfrac{3}{(x + 4)(x - 4)} - \dfrac{2(x + 4)}{(x + 4)(x - 4)} \\[2mm] &= \dfrac{3 - 2(x + 4)}{(x + 4)(x - 4)} = \dfrac{-2x - 5}{(x + 4)(x - 4)}\end{aligned}$$

40. Multiply numerator and denominator by
$$\text{LCD} = (x + 2)(x - 1)$$
$$\begin{aligned}\dfrac{\dfrac{3}{x + 2} - \dfrac{2}{x - 1}}{x - 1} &= \dfrac{3(x - 1) - 2(x + 2)}{(x + 2)(x - 1)^2} \\[2mm] &= \dfrac{x - 7}{(x + 2)(x - 1)^2}\end{aligned}$$

42. $\begin{aligned}(2a^2b^{-3})^{-3} &= (2)^{-3}(a^2)^{-3}(b^{-3})^{-3} \\[2mm] &= \dfrac{1}{8}a^{-6}b^9 = \dfrac{b^9}{8a^6}\end{aligned}$

46. $\sqrt{80} = \sqrt{16 \cdot 5} = \sqrt{16} \cdot \sqrt{5} = 4\sqrt{5}$

48. $\sqrt{x^7 y^5} = (x^7 y^5)^{1/2} = x^{7/2} y^{5/2} = x^3 x^{1/2} y^2 y^{1/2} = x^3 y^2 \sqrt{xy}$

or

$\sqrt{x^7 y^5} = \sqrt{x^6 x y^4 y} = x^3 y^2 \sqrt{xy}$

50. $\dfrac{\sqrt{x}}{\sqrt{x} + \sqrt{y}} = \dfrac{\sqrt{x}}{\sqrt{x} + \sqrt{y}} \cdot \dfrac{\sqrt{x} - \sqrt{y}}{\sqrt{x} - \sqrt{y}} = \dfrac{x - \sqrt{xy}}{x - y}$

53. $\sqrt[4]{x^2 y^2} + 2\sqrt[4]{x^2 y^2} = 3\sqrt[4]{x^2 y^2} = 3\,|x|^{1/2}|y|^{1/2} = 3\sqrt{\,|xy|\,}$

56. Equate the real and the imaginary parts.

$$\begin{array}{ll} x - 2 = -4 & 2y - 1 = 7 \\ x = -2 & y = 4 \end{array}$$

57. $i^{47} = i^{44} \cdot i^3 = i^3 = -i$

59. $\begin{aligned} (2 + i)(2 + i) &= 4 + 2i + 2i + i^2 \\ &= 4 + 4i - 1 \\ &= 3 + 4i \end{aligned}$

61. $\dfrac{4 - 3i}{2 + 3i} \cdot \dfrac{2 - 3i}{2 - 3i} = \dfrac{8 - 12i - 6i + 9i^2}{4 - 9i^2} = -\dfrac{1}{13} - \dfrac{18}{13}i$

67.

$$\begin{aligned} 4x + 4x - z &= 2y \\ z &= 8x - 2y \end{aligned}$$

Area of shaded rectangle $= (8x - 2y)x$
$$\qquad\qquad\qquad\quad = 8x^2 - 2xy$$

72. $ac + ad - bc - bd = a(c + d) - b(c + d) = (c + d)(a - b)$

and

$ac + ad - bc - bd = (a - b)c + (a - b)d = (a - b)(c + d)$

77. $\left(\sqrt{5 - \sqrt{24}}\right)^2 = 5 - \sqrt{24} = 5 - 2\sqrt{6} = 5 - 2\sqrt{2}\sqrt{3}$

$(\sqrt{2} - \sqrt{3})^2 = 2 - 2\sqrt{2}\sqrt{3} + 3 = 5 - 2\sqrt{2}\sqrt{3}$

Yes, they are equal.

78. $$\begin{aligned} T &= 1 + \frac{1}{T} \\ T^2 &= T + 1 \\ T^2 - T - 1 &= 0 \\ T &= \frac{1 \pm \sqrt{1 - 4(-1)}}{2} = \frac{1 \pm \sqrt{5}}{2} \end{aligned}$$

Chapter 2

4. $\begin{aligned} k - 2x &= 4kx \\ k &= 4kx + 2x \\ k &= x(4k + 2) \\ x &= \frac{k}{4k + 2} = \frac{k}{2(2k + 1)} \end{aligned}$

6. Let n be the number of quarters.

	Number of Coins	×	Cents per coin	=	Value
Quarters	n		25		$25n$
Dimes	$2n + 4$		10		$10(2n + 4)$

$$\text{Total value} = \left(\begin{array}{c}\text{Value of}\\\text{quarters}\end{array}\right) + \left(\begin{array}{c}\text{Value of}\\\text{dimes}\end{array}\right)$$

$$\begin{aligned} 265 &= 25n + 10(2n + 4) \\ 265 &= 25n + 20n + 40 \\ 225 &= 45n \\ n &= 5 = \text{Number of quarters} \\ 2n + 4 &= 14 = \text{Number of dimes} \end{aligned}$$

8. Let x be the number of hours for machine B.

	Rate	×	Time	=	Work done
A	$\frac{1}{3}$		2		$\frac{2}{3}$
B	$\frac{1}{x}$		2		$\frac{2}{x}$

(Work done by A) + (Work done by B) = 1

$$\begin{aligned} \frac{2}{3} + \frac{2}{x} &= 1 \\ 2x + 6 &= 3x \\ x &= 6 \text{ hours} \end{aligned}$$

9. F. The equation does not hold for $x = 0$, and therefore it does not hold for all real values of x.

12. $\begin{aligned} 6x^2 - 11x + 4 &= (2x - 1)(3x - 4) = 0 \\ 2x - 1 &= 0 \qquad 3x - 4 = 0 \\ x &= \frac{1}{2} \qquad\quad\ x = \frac{4}{3} \end{aligned}$

13. $\begin{aligned} x^2 - 2x &= -6 \\ x^2 - 2x + 1 &= -6 + 1 \\ (x - 1)^2 &= -5 \\ x - 1 &= \pm\sqrt{-5} \\ x &= 1 \pm \sqrt{5}\,i \end{aligned}$

17. $\begin{aligned} kx^2 - 3\pi &= 0 \\ kx^2 &= 3\pi \\ x^2 &= \frac{3\pi}{k} \\ x &= \pm\sqrt{\frac{3\pi}{k}} = \pm\frac{\sqrt{3\pi k}}{k} \end{aligned}$

19. $3r^2 - 2r - 5 = 0$

$a = 3, b = -2, c = -5$

$b^2 - 4ac = 64$

Since $b^2 - 4ac$ is positive and a square, the roots are real.

23. $\sqrt{x + 3} + \sqrt{2x - 3} = 6$

$\sqrt{x + 3} = 6 - \sqrt{2x - 3}$

$x + 3 = 36 - 12\sqrt{2x - 3} + 2x - 3$

$12\sqrt{2x - 3} = x + 30$

$144(2x - 3) = x^2 + 60x + 900$

$x^2 - 228x + 1332 = 0$

$(x - 6)(x - 222) = 0$

$x = 6 \quad x = 222$

Check:

$$x = 6 \qquad\qquad x = 222$$

$$\sqrt{6 + 3} + \sqrt{12 - 3} \stackrel{?}{=} 6 \qquad \sqrt{225} + \sqrt{441} \stackrel{?}{=} 6$$

$$3 + 3 \stackrel{?}{=} 6 \qquad\qquad 15 + 21 \stackrel{?}{=} 6$$

$$6 \stackrel{\checkmark}{=} 6 \qquad\qquad 36 \neq 6$$

The solution is 6.

25. Let $u = 1 - \dfrac{2}{x}$.

$$u^2 - 8u + 15 = 0$$

$$(u - 3)(u - 5) = 0$$

$$u = 3 \quad u = 5$$

Substituting, we have

$$3 = 1 - \frac{2}{x} \qquad 5 = 1 - \frac{2}{x}$$

$$2 = -\frac{2}{x} \qquad 4 = -\frac{2}{x}$$

$$x = -1 \qquad x = -\frac{1}{2}$$

26. Let n = number of actual attendees.

	Number of attendees	Cost per attendee
Actual group	n	$\dfrac{420}{n}$
Enlarged group	$n + 10$	$\dfrac{420}{n + 10}$

Since the large group would have paid \$1 less per attendee,

$$\frac{420}{n + 10} + 1 = \frac{420}{n}$$

$$420n + n(n + 10) = 420(n + 10)$$

$$n^2 + 10n - 4200 = 0$$

$$(n - 60)(n + 70) = 0$$

$$n = 60$$

28. Using the Critical Value Method to solve

$$-4 < -2x + 1 \leq 10$$

consider

$$-4 = -2x + 1 \quad \text{and} \quad -2x + 1 = 10$$

$$x = \frac{5}{2} \qquad \text{and} \qquad x = -\frac{9}{2}$$

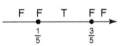

The solution is $[-\frac{9}{2}, \frac{5}{2})$ or

30. The inequality $-\frac{1}{2x - 5} \leq 0$ is not defined when $2x - 5 = 0$, that is, where $x = \frac{5}{2}$.

So $(\frac{5}{2}, \infty)$ is the solution.

32. $|3x + 2| = 7$

$$3x + 2 = 7 \quad \text{or} \quad -(3x + 2) = 7$$

$$3x = 5 \qquad\qquad -3x = 9$$

$$x = \frac{5}{3} \qquad\qquad x = -3$$

35. To solve $|2 - 5x| < 1$, consider $|2 - 5x| = 1$. Then $2 - 5x = 1$ or $2 - 5x = -1$, in which case $x = \frac{3}{5}$ or $x = \frac{1}{5}$, respectively.

The solution is $(\frac{1}{5}, \frac{3}{5})$ or

37. The quantity under the radical sign must be nonnegative.

$$2x^2 - x - 6 \geq 0$$

If $2x^2 - x - 6 = 0$, then $x = 2$ or $x = -\frac{3}{2}$.

The solution is

$$\left\{ x \mid x \leq -\frac{3}{2} \text{ or } x \geq 2 \right\}$$

or

$$\left(-\infty, -\frac{3}{2} \right], [2, \infty)$$

39. The inequality $\frac{2x+1}{x+5} \geq 0$ is not defined when $x + 5 = 0$, that is, where $x = -5$. If $\frac{2x+1}{x+5} = 0$ then $2x + 1 = 0$ in which case $x = -\frac{1}{2}$.

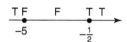

The solution is $(-\infty, -5)$, $[-\frac{1}{2}, \infty)$

42. Let x denote a side of the square. Then $x = \frac{P}{4}$, so the area of the square is $\left(\frac{P}{4}\right)^2 = \frac{P^2}{16}$. If the perimeter of the circle is P, then

$$2\pi r = P$$

so $r = \frac{P}{2\pi}$ and the area of the circle is

$$\pi r^2 = \pi \left(\frac{P}{2\pi}\right)^2 = \frac{\pi P^2}{4\pi^2} = \frac{P^2}{4\pi}$$

since $\pi \approx 3.14$, $4\pi < 16$, so

$$\frac{P^2}{16} < \frac{P^2}{4\pi}$$

That is, the area of the circle is greater than the area of the square.

46.

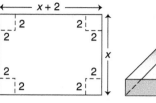
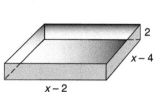

Volume = Length · Width · Height

$$= (x - 4)(x - 2) \cdot 2$$
$$= 2x^2 - 12x + 16$$
$$2x^2 - 12x + 16 = 96$$
$$2x^2 - 12x - 80 = 0$$
$$x^2 - 6x - 40 = 0$$
$$(x - 10)(x + 4) = 0$$
$$x = 10 \quad x = -4$$

Then $x - 2 = 8$ and $x - 4 = 6$, so the dimensions of the box are 8 inches × 6 inches × 2 inches.

Chapter 3

1. $d = \sqrt{(x_2 - x_1)^2 + (y_2 - y_1)^2}$
$= \sqrt{(2 + 4)^2 + (-1 + 6)^2}$
$= \sqrt{36 + 25} = \sqrt{61}$

5.

y-axis test	**x-axis test**
Replace x with $-x$:	Replace y with $-y$:
$y^2 = 1 - (-x)^3$	$(-y)^2 = 1 - x^3$
$y^2 = 1 + x^3$	$y^2 = 1 - x^3$
no	yes

origin test
Replace both:
$(-y)^2 = 1 - (-x)^3$
$y^2 = 1 + x^3$
no

7. Yes. No vertical line meets the graph in more than one point.

9. The quantity under the radical cannot be negative.

$$3x - 5 \geq 0$$
$$x \geq \frac{5}{3}$$

11. Solve the equation:

$$f(x) = 15 = \sqrt{x - 1}$$
$$225 = x - 1$$
$$x = 226$$

16. On your graphing calculator, set

$$\text{XMIN} = -5, \text{XMAX} = 5, \text{XSCL} = 1$$
$$\text{YMIN} = -1, \text{YMAX} = 5, \text{YSCL} = 1$$

This will produce the following output on your viewing rectangle.

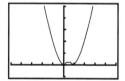

20. On you graphing calculator, set

$$\text{XMIN} = -2, \text{XMAX} = 10, \text{XSCL} = 1$$
$$\text{YMIN} = 0, \quad \text{YMAX} = 14, \text{YSCL} = 1$$

This will produce the following output on your viewing rectangle.

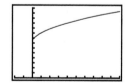

21. On your graphing calculator, set

$$\text{XMIN} = -10, \quad \text{XMAX} = 2, \quad \text{XSCL} = 1$$
$$\text{YMIN} = -7, \quad \text{YMAX} = 7, \quad \text{YSCL} = 1$$

This will produce the following output on your viewing rectangle.

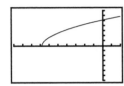

24. Replace x with $y - 1$:

$$\begin{aligned}
f(x) = x^2 - x &= (y-1)^2 - (y-1)\\
&= y^2 - 2y + 1 - y + 1\\
&= y^2 - 3y + 2
\end{aligned}$$

28. $f(x) = x - 1$ when $x \le -1$
$f(-4) = -4 - 1 = -5$

29. $f(x) = -2$ when $x > 2$
$f(4) = -2$

36. $m = \dfrac{y_2 - y_1}{x_2 - x_1} = \dfrac{3 - (-6)}{-1 - (-4)} = \dfrac{9}{3} = 3$

37. $y - y_1 = m(x - x_1)$
$y - (-6) = 3[x - (-4)]$
$y + 6 = 3x + 12$
$y = 3x + 6$

41. $2y + x - 5 = 0$
$y = -\dfrac{1}{2}x + \dfrac{5}{2}$

The slope of the given line is $m_1 = -\frac{1}{2}$. The slope m of any line perpendicular to the given line is

$$m = -\frac{1}{m_1} = 2$$

Then, with $m = 2$ and $(x_1, y_1) = (-1, 3)$,

$$\begin{aligned}
y - y_1 &= m(x - x_1)\\
y - 3 &= 2(x + 1)\\
y &= 2x + 5
\end{aligned}$$

43. $(f \circ g)(x) = (x + 1)(x^2 - 1)$
$ = x^3 + x^2 - x - 1$
$(f \circ g)(-1) = (-1)^3 + (-1)^2 - (-1) - 1 = 0$

46. $(g \circ f)(x) = g(x + 1) = (x + 1)^2 - 1 = x^2 + 2x$

47. $g(x) = x^2 - 1$
$g(2) = 2^2 - 1 = 3$
$(f \circ g)(2) = f(3) = 3 + 1 = 4$

48. $(f \circ g)(x) = f(x^2) = \sqrt{x^2} - 2 = |x| - 2$

50. $(f \circ g)(-2) = |-2| - 2 = 0$

52. $(f \circ g)(x) = f\left(\dfrac{x}{2} - 2\right) = 2\left(\dfrac{x}{2} - 2\right) + 4 = x$
$(g \circ f)(x) = g(2x + 4) = \dfrac{2x + 4}{2} - 2 = x$

56. $P = k\dfrac{qr}{t^2}$
$-3 = k\dfrac{(2)(-3)}{4^2}$
$k = 8$
$P = 8\dfrac{qr}{t^2}$
$P = -\dfrac{1}{4}$

57. a. Let

$$x = \text{Amount invested in tax-free municipal bonds}$$

Then

$$3x = \text{Amount invested in certificates of deposit}$$

$$10{,}000 - 4x = \text{Amount invested in savings account}$$

$$\begin{aligned}
\text{Interest earned} &= 0.085x + 0.09(3x) +\\
&\quad 0.0525(10{,}000 - 4x)\\
&= 525 + 0.145x
\end{aligned}$$

b. $3x = 3000$ so $x = 1000$

From the answer to (a)

$$\begin{aligned}
\text{Interest earned} &= 525 + 0.145(1000)\\
&= 525 + 145 = \$670
\end{aligned}$$

58. a. Slope $= \dfrac{2.40 - 2.10}{1050 - 975} = \dfrac{0.30}{75} = 0.004$

$\text{GPA} - 2.40 = 0.004(\text{SAT} - 1050)$
$\text{GPA} = 0.004\,\text{SAT} - 1.80$

b. Solving for SAT,

$$\begin{aligned}
0.004\,\text{SAT} &= \text{GPA} + 1.8\\
\text{SAT} &= 250\,\text{GPA} + 450
\end{aligned}$$

c. Substituting 4.00 in the answer to (b), we obtain

$$\text{SAT} = 250(4.00) + 450 = 1450$$

Chapter 4

1. $f(x) = -x^2 - 4x$
$= -(x^2 + 4 \qquad)$
$= -(x^2 + 4x + 4) + 4$
$= -(x + 2)^2 + 4$

vertex: $(-2, 4)$

x-intercepts
Let $y = f(x) = 0$.

$0 = -x^2 - 4x$
$0 = -x(x + 4)$

$x = 0 \quad x = -4$

y-intercept
Let $x = 0$.

Then $y = f(0) = 0$.

3. $a = 2, b = -1$

a. Since $a > 0$, it is a minimum.

b. The minimum occurs at

$$x = -\frac{b}{2a} = -\frac{-1}{4} = \frac{1}{4}$$

c. The minimum value is

$$f\left(\frac{1}{4}\right) = 2\left(\frac{1}{4}\right)^2 - \frac{1}{4} + 1$$
$$= \frac{7}{8}$$

7. $\begin{array}{r|rrrr} 1 & 2 & 0 & 6 & -4 \\ & & 2 & 2 & 8 \\ \hline & 2 & 2 & 8 & 4 \\ & & Q(x) & & R \end{array}$

$Q(x) = 2x^2 + 2x + 8, R = 4$

9. $\begin{array}{r|rrrr} 2 & 7 & -3 & 0 & 2 \\ & & 14 & 22 & 44 \\ \hline & 7 & 11 & 22 & 44 \end{array}$

$P(2) = 46$

$\begin{array}{r|rrrr} -1 & 7 & -3 & 0 & 2 \\ & & -7 & 10 & -10 \\ \hline & 7 & -10 & 10 & -8 \end{array}$

$P(-1) = -8$

11. $\begin{array}{r|rrrrr} -2 & 2 & 4 & 3 & 5 & -2 \\ & & -4 & 0 & -6 & 2 \\ \hline & 2 & 0 & 3 & -1 & 0 \end{array}$

Since $P(-2) = 0$, $x + 2$ is a factor.

$$\frac{10i + 5i^2}{-25i^2} = \frac{-5 + 10i}{25} = -\frac{1}{5} + \frac{2}{5}i$$

14. $\dfrac{2 + i}{0 - 5i}\left(\dfrac{0 + 5i}{0 + 5i}\right) =$

20. With $\sqrt{-3} = \sqrt{3}i$, form the product:

$(x - 3)(x - \sqrt{3}i)(x + \sqrt{3}i) = (x - 3)(x^2 + 3)$
$= x^3 - 3x^2 + 3x - 9$

22. The number $\frac{1}{2}$ is a zero for the linear factor $(2x - 1)$, and -1 is a zero of the linear factor $(x + 1)$. Form the product:

$(2x - 1)^2(x + 1)^2 = 4x^4 + 4x^3 - 3x^2 - 2x + 1$

25. Divide by $x + 2$ to find the depressed equation:

$\begin{array}{r|rrrr} -2 & 2 & -1 & -13 & -6 \\ & & -4 & 10 & 6 \\ \hline & \underbrace{2 \quad -5 \quad -3}_{\substack{\text{deflated} \\ \text{polynomial}}} & & & 0 \end{array}$

Solving $2x^2 - 5x - 3 = 0$, we have

$(2x + 1)(x - 3) = 0$

$x = -\frac{1}{2} \qquad x = 3$

29. The polynomial

$$P(x) = x^5 - x^4 + 3x^3 - 4x^2 + x - 5$$

has five variations in sign and therefore has a maximum of five positive zeros.

The polynomial

$$P(-x) = -x^5 - x^4 - 3x^3 - 4x^2 - x - 5$$

has no variations in sign, and therefore there are no negative zeros.

31. The polynomial

$$P(x) = 3x^4 - 2x^2 + 1$$

has two variations in sign, so there can be at most two positive zeros, $P(-x) = P(x)$, so there can be at most two negative zeros.

34. The only possible rational roots are ± 1. Using condensed synthetic division, we find

$\begin{array}{r|rrrrr} & 1 & 3 & 2 & 1 & -1 \\ 1 & 1 & 4 & 6 & 7 & \boxed{6} \\ -1 & 1 & 2 & 0 & 1 & \boxed{-2} \end{array}$

Since neither remainder is zero, there are no rational roots.

35. Since the coefficients are all integers, the Rational Zero Theorem restricts the possible rational roots to

$$\pm 1, \pm\frac{1}{2}, \pm\frac{1}{3}, \pm\frac{1}{6}, \pm 2, \pm\frac{2}{3}, \pm 5, \pm\frac{5}{2}, \pm\frac{5}{3}, \pm\frac{5}{6}, \pm 10, \pm\frac{10}{3}$$

Testing by synthetic division,

$\begin{array}{r|rrrr} -1 & 6 & 15 & -1 & -10 \\ & & -6 & -9 & 10 \\ \hline & 6 & 9 & -10 & 0 \end{array}$

we show that -1 is a root. The remaining roots are those of the deflated equation

$$6x^2 + 9x - 10 = 0$$

and are found by the quadratic formula:

$$x = \frac{-9 \pm \sqrt{81 + 240}}{12} = \frac{-9 \pm \sqrt{321}}{12}$$

Chapter 5

4. $h = -5, k = 2, r = 4$
$(x - h)^2 + (y - k)^2 = r^2$
$(x + 5)^2 + (y - 2)^2 = 16$

6. $x - h = x - 2 \quad y - k = y + 3 \quad r^2 = 9$
$\qquad h = 2 \qquad\qquad k = -3 \qquad r = 3$
center: $(2, -3); r = 3$

8. $\qquad\qquad x^2 + 4x + y^2 - 6y = -10$
$(x^2 + 4x + 4) + (y^2 - 6y + 9) = -10 + 4 + 9$
$\qquad\qquad (x + 2)^2 + (y - 3)^2 = 3$
center: $(-2, 3); r = \sqrt{3}$

15. $\qquad y^2 + 4y = -x - 2$
$y^2 + 4y + 4 = -x - 2 + 4$
$\qquad (y + 2)^2 = -x + 2 = -(x - 2)$
Since $(y - k)^2 = 4p(x - h)$,
vertex: $(h, k) = (2, -2)$;
axis: $y + 2 = 0 \quad$ or $\quad y = -2$;
direction: opens left, since $p < 0$.

16. $\qquad 2x^2 - 12x = y - 16$
$2(x^2 - 6x + 9) = y - 16 + 18$
$\qquad 2(x - 3)^2 = y + 2$
$\qquad\qquad (x - 3)^2 = \frac{1}{2}(y + 2)$
Since $(x - h)^2 = 4p(y - k)$,
vertex: $(3, -2)$;
axis: $x - 3 = 0 \quad$ or $\quad x = 3$;
direction: opens up, since $p > 0$.

20. We have $4p = -\frac{2}{3}$, so $p = -\frac{1}{6}$. Thus, the focus is at $(0, -\frac{1}{6})$, and the directrix is $y = \frac{1}{6}$.

22. Since the directrix is $y = \frac{7}{4}$, $p = -\frac{7}{4}$ and $4p = -7$. The equation of the parabola is then
$$x^2 = 4py = -7y$$

24. Dividing by 36, we have
$$\frac{x^2}{4} - \frac{y^2}{9} = 1$$
Setting $y = 0$, we have
$$x^2 = 4 \quad \text{or} \quad x = \pm 2$$
Setting $x = 0$, we see that there are no y-intercepts.

28. Dividing by 9, we have
$$\frac{x^2}{3} + \frac{y^2}{\frac{9}{4}} = 1$$
If $y = 0, x = \pm\sqrt{3}$. If $x = 0, y = \pm\frac{3}{2}$.

41. $2x^2 + 12x + y^2 - 2y = -17$

Completing the square, we have
$$2(x^2 + 6x + 9) + (y^2 - 2y + 1) = -17 + 18 + 1$$
$$2(x + 3)^2 + (y - 1)^2 = 2$$

Since the right-hand side is positive, $A \neq C$, and $AC > 0$, the graph is an ellipse.

On your graphing calculator set the X and Y values for your EQUAL viewing rectangle, with XSCL = 1 and YSCL = 1. This will produce the following output on your viewing rectangle.

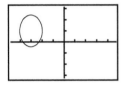

46. $2^{2x} = 8^{x-1} = (2^3)^{x-1}$ — Write in terms of same base.
$\qquad 2^{2x} = 2^{3x-3}$ — $(a^m)^n = a^{mn}$
$\qquad 2x = 3x - 3$ — If $a^u = a^v$, then $u = v$.
$\qquad\quad x = 3$ — Solve for x.

48. $S = P(1 + i)^n$ — Compound interest formula
$\quad i = \dfrac{r}{k} = \dfrac{0.12}{2} = 0.06$ — Interest rate i per conversion period
$\quad n = 4 \cdot 2 = 8$ — Number of conversion periods
$\quad S = 8000(1 + 0.06)^8$ — Substitute for P, i and n.
$\qquad \approx \$12,750.78$

54. $\log_5 \dfrac{1}{125} = x - 1$

$\quad 5^{x-1} = \dfrac{1}{125}$ — Equivalent exponential form

$\quad 5^{x-1} = 5^{-3}$ — Write in terms of same base.

$\quad x - 1 = -3$ — If $a^u = a^v$, then $u = v$.

$\qquad x = -2$ — Solve for x.

56. $\log_3(x + 1) = \log_3 27$
$\qquad x + 1 = 27$ — If $\log_a u = \log_a v$, then $u = v$.
$\qquad\quad x = 26$ — Solve for x.

57. $\log_3 3^5 = 5$ — Since $\log_a a^x = x$.
or
$\log_3 3^5 = x$ — Introduce unknown x.
$\qquad 3^x = 3^5$ — Equivalent exponential form
$\qquad\; x = 5$ — If $a^u = a^v$, then $u = v$.

60. $e^{\ln 3} = 3$ Since $a^{\log_a x} = x$.
    or
    $e^{\ln 3} = x$ Introduce unknown x.
    $\ln x = \ln 3$ Equivalent logarithmic form
    $x = 3$ If $\log_a u = \log_a v$, then $u = v$.

62. $\log_a \dfrac{\sqrt{x-1}}{2x} = \log_a \dfrac{(x-1)^{1/2}}{2x}$ Exponent form of radical

    $= \log_a(x-1)^{1/2} - \log_a 2x$ *Property 2*
    $= \log_a(x-1)^{1/2} - [\log_a 2 + \log_a x]$ *Property 1*
    $= \frac{1}{2}\log_a(x-1) - \log_a 2 - \log_a x$ *Property 3*

77. We have 3×10^6 RBC/cm³ and require 5×10^6 RBC/cm³. If it takes t days to manufacture 2×10^6 RBC/cm³ then
$$2{,}000{,}000 = 50^t$$
$$t = \frac{\ln(2{,}000{,}000)}{\ln(50)} \approx 3.71 \text{ days}$$

80. Bank A: $A = Pe^{rt}$
$$A = 1000e^{(.05)5} \approx \$1284.03$$
    Bank B: $A = P\left(1 + \dfrac{r}{k}\right)^{kt}$
$$A = 1000\left(1 + \frac{0.0505}{2}\right)^{2(5)} \approx \$1283.21$$
    Bank A is better than Bank B.

Chapter 6

3. Substituting $x = 6y + 11$, we have
$$2(6y + 11) + 5y = 5$$
$$17y = -17$$
$$y = -1$$
$$x = 6y + 11 = 6(-1) + 11 = 5$$
Solution: $x = 5, y = -1$.

6. Substituting $x = 5 - 3y$, we have
$$(5 - 3y)^2 + y^2 = 25$$
$$25 - 30y + 9y^2 + y^2 = 25$$
$$10y^2 - 30y = 0$$
$$10y(y - 3) = 0$$

$y = 0$ or $y = 3$
$x = 5 - 3y$ $x = 5 - 3y$
$x = 5 - 0 = 5$ $x = 5 - 9 = -4$

9. To eliminate x, multiply the first equation by -2 and the second equation by 1. Then add the two equations:
$$-2x - 8y = -34$$
$$\underline{2x - 3y = -21}$$
$$-11y = -55$$
$$y = 5$$
$$x + 4(5) = 17$$
$$x = -3$$
Solution: $x = -3, y = 5$.

14. Rewriting the equations and adding, we have
$$x^2 + y^2 \qquad - 9 = 0$$
$$\underline{-x^2 \qquad + y - 3 = 0}$$
$$y^2 + y - 12 = 0$$
$$(y - 3)(y + 4) = 0$$

$y = 3$ or $y = -4$
$x^2 = y - 3 = 0$ $x^2 = y - 3 = -7$
$x = 0$ no real solutions

The circle and parabola are tangent at $(0, 3)$.

15. t = tens digit, u = units digit
              $10t + u$ = original number

Then
$$(10t + u) + t = 49$$
or
$$11t + u = 49 \qquad (1)$$

Also,
$$10u + t = \text{number with digits reversed}$$

Then
$$10u + t = (10t + u) + 9$$
or
$$-9t + 9u = 9 \qquad (2)$$

Solving Equations (1) and (2) simultaneously, we find
$$t = 4, \quad u = 5$$

The original number is 45.

17. x = cost per pound of hamburger
    y = cost per pound of steak

Then
$$5x + 4y = 22.00$$
$$3x + 7y = 28.15$$

Solving, we find
$$x = \$1.80, \quad y = \$3.25$$

21. Interchange Equations (1) and (3):

$$-x + 4y + 2z = 15$$
$$2x + 5y - 2z = -9$$
$$-3x - y + z = 12$$

Add 2 times Equation (1) to Equation (2); add -3 times Equation (1) to Equation (3):

$$-x + 4y + 2z = 15$$
$$13y + 2z = 21$$
$$-13y - 5z = -33$$

Add Equation (2) to Equation (3):

$$-x + 4y + 2z = 15$$
$$13y + 2z = 21$$
$$-3z = -12$$

Use back-substitution

$$-3z = -12 \quad \text{or} \quad z = 4$$
$$13y + 2(4) = 21 \quad \text{or} \quad y = 1$$
$$-x + 4(1) + 2(4) = 15 \quad \text{or} \quad x = -3$$
$$x = -3 \quad y = 1 \quad z = 4$$

29. $$\frac{8 - x}{2x^2 + 3x - 2} = \frac{8 - x}{(2x - 1)(x + 2)} = \frac{A}{2x - 1} + \frac{B}{x + 2}$$

$$8 - x = A(x + 2) + B(2x - 1)$$
$$x = -2: \quad 10 = -5B \quad \text{or} \quad B = -2$$
$$x = \frac{1}{2}: \quad \frac{15}{2} = \frac{5}{2}A \quad \text{or} \quad A = 3$$
$$\frac{8 - x}{2x^2 + 3x - 2} = \frac{3}{2x - 1} - \frac{2}{x + 2}$$

30. $$\frac{3x^3 + 5x - 1}{(x^2 + 1)^2} = \frac{Ax + B}{x^2 + 1} + \frac{Cx + D}{(x^2 + 1)^2}$$

$$3x^3 + 5x - 1 = (Ax + B)(x^2 + 1) + Cx + D$$
$$3x^3 + 5x - 1 = Ax^3 + Bx^2 + (A + C)x + (B + D)$$

coefficient of x^3: $A = 3$

coefficient of x^2: $B = 0$

coefficient of X: $A + C = 5$
$$3 + C = 5$$
$$C = 2$$

coefficient of x^0: $B + D = -1$
$$D = -1$$

$$\frac{3x^3 + 5x - 1}{(x^2 + 1)^2} = \frac{3x}{x^2 + 1} + \frac{2x - 1}{(x^2 + 1)^2}$$

38. The figure shows the set of feasible solutions and the coordinates of the vertices.

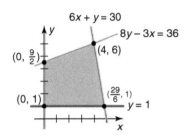

Evaluating the objective function at these points gives us the following information:

x	y	$z = 5y - x$
0	1	5
0	$\frac{9}{2}$	$\frac{45}{2}$
4	6	26
$\frac{29}{6}$	1	$\frac{1}{6}$

The maximum value, $z = 26$, occurs at $x = 4$, $y = 6$.

Index

CPSIA information can be obtained
at www.ICGtesting.com
Printed in the USA
JSHW051358081222
34213JS00005B/1

9 781596 026117